FORMULAS FOR STRESS AND STRAIN

FORMULAS FOR STRESS AND STRAIN

RAYMOND J. ROARK

Emeritus Professor of Mechanics, The University of Wisconsin

FOURTH EDITION

McGRAW-HILL BOOK COMPANY

New York St. Louis San Francisco Düsseldorf Johannesburg
Kuala Lumpur London Mexico Montreal New Delhi
Panama Rio de Janeiro Singapore Sydney Toronto

FORMULAS FOR STRESS AND STRAIN

Printed in the United States of America.

Library of Congress Catalog Card Number 64-66027

ISBN 07-053030-0

9 10 11 12 13 14 15 16 - MAMM - 7 6 5 4 3 2

PREFACE TO THE FOURTH EDITION

As in former revisions, new data have been added, tables of formulas and coefficients have been amplified, and several new topics have been introduced. Some of the more important additions are as follows:

In Chapter 3 (Behavior of Bodies under Stress) the three forms of the modified Goodman diagram are described, the discussion of fatigue has been extended, and many new references on fatigue and brittle fracture have been supplied.

In Chapter 8 (Beams; Flexure of Straight and Curved Bars) a brief discussion of plastic analysis (with an illustrative example) has been introduced. Very short and very wide beams have been discussed more fully with new data. Table VI (combined axial and transverse loading) and Table VIII (rings and arches) have been extended and; in the latter, several cases of parabolic arches and of rigid frames have been added.

In Chapter 10 (Flat Plates) several new cases of loading and support have been added in Table X and some approximate formulas have been replaced by the tabulated coefficients on which they were based. In Chapter 11 (Columns and Other Compression Members) new material has been added on simultaneous axial and transverse loading, and Table XI has been revised to bring it up to date. In Chapter 12 (Pressure Vessels; Pipes) Table XIII has been extended to include the results of recent work on conical shells and on the influence of localized loading on thin cylinders, and several formulas for bursting pressure have been added. In Chapter 15 (Dynamic and Temperature Stresses) a very brief discussion of mechanical vibrations and a table of frequencies for a number of simple structural elements have been introduced. Table XVII (stress concentration factors) has again been amplified, and Table XIX (properties of materials) has been revised and a list of references appended. A new Table XX (allowable stresses and factors of safety) with references has been added to the group of miscellaneous tables.

The literature pertaining to applied mechanics and elasticity has grown to such proportions, and continues to grow at such an explosive rate, that it is manifestly impossible to include more than a very small fraction of it in a single volume, even by reference. In choosing that fraction, the author has been guided mainly by his own conception—derived through consulting work and correspondence—of the needs of the designing engineer and stress analyst. For additional information, use should be made of references given herein and in such compilations as *Applied Mechanics Reviews*, published monthly by the American Society of Mechanical Engineers, *Scientific and Technical Aerospace Reports* (semimonthly) and *Technical Publications Announcements* (biweekly), both published by the National Aeronautics and Space Administration, Office of Scientific and Technical Information, and special publications of the several engineering societies, such as the *References on Fatigue* of the American Society for Testing Materials.

Again the author wishes to acknowledge gratefully his indebtedness to the many individuals, publishers, institutions, and corporations whose generosity in permitting the use of material made the writing of this book possible. Thanks are also again extended to the readers who have helpfully drawn attention to errors and omissions.

Raymond J. Roark

PREFACE TO THE FIRST EDITION

This book was written for the purpose of making available a compact, adequate summary of the formulas, facts, and principles pertaining to strength of materials. It is intended primarily as a reference book and represents an attempt to meet what is believed to be a present need of the designing engineer.

This need results from the necessity for more accurate methods of stress analysis imposed by the trend of engineering practice. That trend is toward greater speed and complexity of machinery, greater size and diversity of structures, and greater economy and refinement of design. In consequence of such developments, familiar problems, for which approximate solutions were formerly considered adequate, are now frequently found to require more precise treatment, and many less familiar problems, once of academic interest only, have become of great practical importance. The solutions and data desired are often to be found only in advanced treatises or scattered through an extensive literature, and the results are not always presented in such form as to be suited to the requirements of the engineer. To bring together as much of this material as is likely to prove generally useful and to present it in convenient form have been the author's aim.

The scope and arrangement of the book are indicated by the Contents. In Part I are defined all terms whose exact meaning might otherwise not be clear. In Part II certain useful general principles are stated; analytical and experimental methods of stress analysis are briefly described, and information concerning the behavior of material under stress is given. In Part III the behavior of structural elements under various conditions of loading is discussed, and extensive tables of formulas for the calculation of stress, strain, and strength are given.

Because they are not believed to serve the purpose of this book, derivations of formulas and detailed explanations, such as are appropriate in a textbook, are omitted, but a sufficient number of examples are included to illustrate the application of the various formulas and methods. Numerous references to more detailed discussions are given, but for the most part these are limited to sources that are generally available and no attempt has been made to compile an exhaustive bibliography.

That such a book as this derives almost wholly from the work of others is self-evident, and it is the author's hope that due acknowledgment has been made of the immediate sources of all material here presented. To the publishers and others who have generously permitted the use of material, he wishes to express his thanks. The helpful criticisms and suggestions of his colleagues, Professors E. R. Maurer, M. O. Withey, J. B. Kommers, and K. F. Wendt, are gratefully acknowledged. A considerable number of the tables of formulas have been published from time to time in *Product Engineering*, and the opportunity thus afforded for criticism and study of arrangement has been of great advantage.

Finally, it should be said that, although every care has been taken to avoid errors, it would be over-sanguine to hope that none had escaped detection; for any suggestions that readers may make concerning needed corrections the author will be grateful.

Raymond J. Roark

CONTENTS

PART I

Definitions and Symbols

PART II

Facts; Principles; Methods

PART III

Formulas and Examples

LIST OF TABLES

PART I

DEFINITIONS AND SYMBOLS

CHAPTER 1

DEFINITIONS

The definitions here given apply to the terms in question as they are used in this book. Some of these terms are differently defined by other authors; when this is the case, the fact is noted. When two or more terms with identical meaning are in general acceptance, they are given in the order of the present writer's preference. The references referred to by number are listed at the end of this section.

Allowable Stress (Working Stress).—If a member is so designed that the maximum stress as calculated for the expected conditions of service is less than some certain value, the member will have a proper margin of security against damage or failure. This certain value is the *allowable stress*, of the kind, and for the material and condition of service in question. The allowable stress is less than the damaging stress because of uncertainty as to the conditions of service, nonuniformity of material, and inaccuracy of stress analysis. The margin between the allowable stress and the damaging stress may be reduced in proportion to the certainty with which the conditions of service are known, the intrinsic reliability of the material, the accuracy with which the stress produced by the loading can be calculated, and the degree to which failure is unattended by danger or loss. (Compare *Damaging Stress; Factor of Safety; Factor of Utilization; Margin of Safety*. See Refs. 1, 2, and Table XX.)

Apparent Elastic Limit (Useful Limit Point).—The stress at which the rate of change of strain with respect to stress is 50 per cent greater than at zero stress. It is more definitely determinable from the stress-strain diagram than is the proportional limit, and is useful for comparing materials of the same general class. (Compare *Elastic Limit; Proportional Limit; Yield Point; Yield Strength.*)

Apparent Stress.—The stress corresponding to a given unit strain on the assumption of uniaxial elastic stress. It is calculated by multiplying the unit strain by the modulus of elasticity, and may differ from the true stress because the effect of transverse stresses is not taken into account.

Bending Moment.—Reference is to a beam, assumed for convenience to be horizontal and to be loaded and supported by forces, all of which lie in a vertical plane. The *bending moment* at any section of the beam is the moment of all forces that act on the beam to the left of that section, taken about the horizontal axis of the section. The bending moment is positive when clockwise and negative when counterclockwise; a positive bending moment therefore bends the beam so that it is concave upward, a negative bending moment bends it so that it is concave downward. The *moment equation* is an expression for the bending moment at any section in terms of x, the distance to that section measured from a chosen origin, usually taken at the left end of the beam.

Boundary Conditions.—As used in strength of materials, the term usually refers to the condition of stress, displacement or slope at the ends or edges of a member, where these conditions are apparent from the circumstances of the problem. Thus for a beam with fixed ends the zero slope at each end is a boundary condition; for a pierced circular plate with freely supported edges, the zero radial stress at each edge is a boundary condition.

Brittle Fracture.—The tensile failure with negligible plastic deformation of an ordinarily ductile metal. (See Art. 7.)

Bulk Modulus of Elasticity.—The ratio of a tensile or compressive stress, triaxial and equal in all directions (*e.g.*, hydrostatic pressure), to the relative change it produces in volume.

Central Axis (Centroidal Axis).—A central axis of an area is one that passes through the centroid; it is understood to lie in the plane of the area unless the contrary is stated. When taken normal to the plane of the area, it is called the *central polar axis.*

Centroid of an Area (Center of Gravity of an Area).—That point in the plane of the area about any axis through which the moment of the area is zero; it coincides with the center of gravity of the area materialized as an infinitely thin homogeneous and uniform plate.

Chafing Fatigue (Fretting Fatigue).—Fatigue aggravated by surface rubbing, as in shafts with press-fitted collars.

Corrosion Fatigue.—Fatigue aggravated by corrosion, as in parts repeatedly stressed while exposed to salt water.

Creep.—Continuous increase in deformation under constant or decreasing stress. The term is usually used with reference to the behavior of metals under tension at elevated temperatures. The similar yielding of a material under compressive stress is usually called *plastic flow* or *flow.* Creep at atmospheric temperature due to sustained elastic stress is sometimes called *drift* or *elastic drift.* Another manifestation of creep—the diminution in *stress* when the deformation is maintained constant—is called *relaxation.*

Damaging Stress.—The least unit stress, of a given kind and for a given material and condition of service, that will render a member unfit for service before the end of its normal life. It may do this by producing excessive set, or by causing creep to occur at an excessive rate, or by causing fatigue cracking, excessive strain hardening, or rupture.

Damping Capacity.—The amount of work dissipated into heat by a unit volume of material during a completely reversed cycle of unit stress (see Ref. 3).

Deformation (Strain).—Change in the form or in the dimensions of a body produced by stress. *Elongation* is often used for tensile strain, *compression* or *shortening* for compressive strain, and *detrusion* for shear strain. *Elastic deformation* is such deformation as disappears on removal of stress; *permanent deformation* is such deformation as remains on removal of stress. (Compare *Set.*)

Eccentricity.—A load or component of a load normal to a given cross section of a member is eccentric with respect to that section if it does not act through the centroid. The perpendicular distance from the line of action of the load to either principal central axis is the *eccentricity* with respect to that axis.

Elastic.—Capable of sustaining stress without permanent deformation; the term is also used to denote conformity to the law of stress-strain proportionality. An elastic stress or elastic strain is a stress or strain within the elastic limit.

Elastic Axis.—The elastic axis of a beam is the line, lengthwise of the beam, along which transverse loads must be applied in order to produce bending only, with no torsion of the beam at any section. Strictly speaking, no such line exists except for a few conditions of loading. Usually the elastic axis is assumed to be the line that passes through the elastic center of every section. The term is most often used with reference to an airplane wing of either the shell or multiple-spar type. (Compare *Torsional Center*, *Flexural Center*, *Elastic Center*. See Ref. 4.)

Elastic Center.—The elastic center of a given section of a beam is that point in the plane of the section lying midway between the flexural center and center of twist of that section. The three points may be identical and are usually assumed to be so. (Compare *Flexural Center, Torsional Center, Elastic Axis.* See Refs. 4, 5.)

Elastic Curve.—The curve assumed by the axis of a normally straight beam or column when bent by loads that do not stress it beyond the proportional limit.

Elastic Limit.—The least stress that will cause permanent set. (Compare *Proportional Limit, Apparent Elastic Limit, Yield Point, Yield Strength.* See Art. 2 and Ref. 6.)

Elastic Ratio.—The ratio of the elastic limit to the ultimate strength.

Ellipsoid of Strain.—An ellipsoid that represents the state of strain at any given point in a body; it has the form assumed under stress by a sphere centered at the point in question (Ref. 7).

Ellipsoid of Stress.—An ellipsoid that represents the state of stress at a given point in a body; its semiaxes are vectors representing the principal stresses at the point, and any radius vector represents the resultant stress on a particular plane through the point. For a condition of plane stress (one principal stress zero) the ellipsoid becomes the *ellipse of stress* (see Ref. 8).

Endurance Limit (Fatigue Strength).—By endurance limit of a material is usually meant the maximum stress which can be reversed an indefinitely large number of times without producing fracture (see Art. 10).

Endurance Ratio.—Ratio of the endurance limit to the ultimate static tensile strength.

Endurance Strength.—The highest stress repeated application or reversal of which a material can withstand without rupture for a given number of cycles is the endurance strength of that material for that number of cycles. Unless otherwise specified, reversed stressing is usually implied. (Compare *Endurance Limit.*)

Energy of Rupture.—The work done per unit volume in producing fracture. It is not practicable to establish a definite energy of rupture value for a given material, because the result obtained depends upon the form and proportions of the test specimen and the manner of loading. As determined by similar tests on similar specimens, the energy of rupture affords a criterion for comparing the toughness of different materials.

Equivalent Bending Moment.—A bending moment which, acting alone, would produce in a circular shaft a normal (tensile or compressive) stress of the same magnitude as the maximum normal stress produced by a given bending moment and a given twisting moment acting simultaneously.

Equivalent Twisting Moment.—A twisting moment which, acting alone, would produce in a circular shaft a shear stress of the same magnitude as the shear stress produced by a given twisting moment and a given bending moment acting simultaneously.

Factor of Safety.—The ratio of the load that would cause failure of a member or structure, to the load that is imposed upon it in service. The term usually has this meaning; it may also be used to represent the ratio of breaking to service value of speed, deflection, temperature variation, or other stress-producing factor against possible increase in which the factor of safety is provided as a safeguard. (Compare *Allowable Stress, Margin of Safety*. See Table XX.)

Factor of Stress Concentration.—Irregularities of form such as holes, screw threads, notches, sharp shoulders, etc., when present in a beam, shaft or other member subject to loading, may produce high localized stresses. This phenomenon is called *stress concentration*, and the form irregularities that cause it are called *stress raisers*. The ratio of the true maximum stress to the stress calculated by the ordinary formulas of mechanics (flexure formula, torsion formula, etc.), using the net section but ignoring the changed distribution of stress, is the factor of stress concentration for the particular type of stress raiser in question (see Art. 8).

Factor of Utilization.—The ratio of the allowable stress to the ultimate strength. For cases in which stress is proportional to load, the factor of utilization is the reciprocal of the factor of safety (see Ref. 1).

Fatigue.—Tendency of materials to fracture under many repetitions of a stress considerably less than the ultimate static strength.

Fatigue Strength Reduction Factor.—Alternative term for *factor of stress concentration in fatigue*.

Fiber Stress.—A term used for convenience to denote the longitudinal tensile or compressive stress in a beam or other member subject to bending. It is sometimes used to denote this stress at the point or points most remote from the neutral axis, but the term *stress in extreme fiber* is preferable for this pupose. Also, for convenience, the longitudinal elements or filaments of which a beam may be imagined as composed are called *fibers.*

Fixed (Clamped, Built-in, Encastré).—A condition of support at the ends of a beam or column, or at the edges of a plate, which prevents the ends or edges from rotating in the plane of bending. It does not imply longitudinal constraint. (Compare *Held, Supported.*)

Flexural Center (Shear Center).—With reference to a beam, the flexural center of any section is that point in the plane of the section through which a transverse load, applied at that section, must act if bending deflection only is to be produced, with no twist of the section. (Compare *Torsional Center Elastic Center, Elastic Axis.* See Refs. 4, 9.)

Form Factor.—The term pertains to a beam section of given shape, and means the ratio of the modulus of rupture of a beam having that particular section to the modulus of rupture of a beam otherwise similar but having a section adopted as standard. This standard section is usually taken as rectangular or square; for wood it is a 2- by 2-in. square, with edges horizontal and vertical (see Arts. 9 and 33). The term is also used to mean the ratio, for a given maximum fiber stress within the elastic limit, of the actual resisting moment of a wide-flanged beam to the resisting moment the beam would develop if the fiber stress were uniformly distributed across the entire width of the flanges. So used, the term expresses the strength-reducing effect of shear lag.

Held.—A condition of support at the ends of a beam or edges of a plate which prevents displacement of the edge of the neutral surface, but permits rotation in the plane of bending. (Compare *Fixed; Supported.*)

Influence Line.—An influence line usually pertains to a particular section of a beam, and is a curve so drawn that its ordinate at any point represents the value of the reaction, vertical shear, bending moment or deflection produced at the particular section by a unit load applied at the point where the ordinate is measured. An influence line may be used to show the effect of load position on any quantity dependent thereon, such as the stress in a given truss member, the deflection of a truss, the twisting moment in a shaft, etc.

Isoclinic.—A line (in a stressed body) at all points on which the corresponding principal stresses have the same direction.

Isotropic.—Having the same properties in all directions. In discussions pertaining to strength of materials, isotropic usually means having the same strength and elastic properties (modulus of elasticity, modulus of rigidity, Poisson's ratio) in all directions.

Kern (Kernel).—Reference is to some particular section of a member. The kern is that area in the plane of the section through which the line of action of a force must pass if that force is to produce, at all points in the given section, the same kind of normal stress, *i.e.*, tension throughout or compression throughout.

Lüders Lines.—See *Slip Lines.*

Margin of Safety.—As used in aeronautical design, the term means the percentage by which the ultimate strength of a member exceeds the *design load.* The *design load* is the applied load, or maximum probable load, multiplied by a specified factor of safety. The use of the terms margin of safety and design load in the above sense is practically restricted to aeronautical engineering (see Ref. 10).

Mechanical Hysteresis.—The dissipation of energy as heat during a stress cycle. It is revealed graphically by failure of the descending and ascending branches of the stress-strain diagram to coincide.

Member.—Any part or element of a machine or structure such as a beam, column, shaft, etc.

Modulus of Elasticity (Young's Modulus).—The rate of change of unit tensile or compressive stress with respect to unit tensile or compressive strain for the condition of uniaxial stress within the proportional limit. For most, but not all materials, the modulus of elasticity is the same for tension and compression. For nonisotropic materials such as wood, it is necessary to distinguish between the moduli of elasticity in different directions.

Modulus of Rigidity (Modulus of Elasticity in Shear).—The rate of change of unit shear stress with respect to unit shear strain, for the condition of pure shear within the proportional limit. For nonisotropic materials such as wood, it is necessary to distinguish between the moduli of rigidity in different directions.

Modulus of Resilience.—The strain energy per unit volume absorbed up to the elastic limit under the condition of uniform uniaxial stress.

Modulus of Rupture in Bending (Computed Ultimate Bending Strength).—The fictitious tensile or compressive stress in the extreme fiber of a beam computed by the flexure equation $s = Mc/I$, where M is the bending moment that causes rupture.

Modulus of Rupture in Torsion (Computed Ultimate Twisting Strength).—The fictitious shear stress at the surface of a circular shaft computed by the torsion formula $s_s = Tr/J$, where T is the twisting moment that causes rupture.

Moment of an Area (First Moment of an Area, Statical Moment of an Area).—The moment of an area with respect to an axis is the sum of the products obtained by multiplying each element of the area dA by its distance from the axis y; it is therefore the quantity $\int dA \cdot y$. An axis in the plane of the area is implied.

Moment of Inertia of an Area (Second Moment of an Area).—The moment of inertia of an area with respect to an axis is the sum of the products obtained by multiplying each element of the area dA by the square of its distance from the axis y; it is therefore the quantity $\int dA \cdot y^2$. An axis in the plane of the area is implied; if the axis is normal to that plane the term *polar moment of inertia is used* (see Chap. 6).

Neutral Axis.—The line of zero fiber stress in any given section of a member subject to bending; it is the line formed by the intersection of the neutral surface and the section.

Neutral Surface.—The longitudinal surface of zero fiber stress in a member subject to bending; it contains the neutral axis of every section.

Notch-sensitivity Ratio.—Alternative term for *factor of stress concentration in fatigue* or *fatigue strength reduction factor.*

Plastic Moment; Plastic Hinge; Plastic Section Modulus.—These terms are explained in Art. 48.

Plasticity.—The property of sustaining appreciable (visible to the eye) permanent deformation without rupture. The term is also used to denote the property of yielding or flowing under steady load (Ref. 11).

Poisson's Ratio.—The ratio of lateral unit strain to longitudinal unit strain, under the condition of uniform and uniaxial longitudinal stress within the proportional limit.

Polar Moment of Inertia.—See *Moment of Inertia of an Area.*

Principal Axes.—The principal axes of an area for a given point in its plane are the two mutually perpendicular axes, passing through the point and lying in the plane of the area, for one of which the moment of inertia is greater, and for the other less, than for any other coplanar axis passing through that point. If the point in question is the centroid of the area, these axes are called *principal central axes* (see Chap. 6).

Principal Moment of Inertia.—The moment of inertia of an area about either principal axis (see Chap. 6).

Principal Planes; Principal Stresses.—Through any point in a stressed body there pass three mutually perpendicular planes the stress on each of which is purely normal, tension or compression; these are the *principal planes* for that point. The stresses on these planes are the *principal stresses;* one of them is the maximum stress at the point, and one of them is the minimum stress at the point. When one of the principal stresses is zero, the condition is one of *plane stress;* when two of them are zero, the condition is one of *uniaxial stress.*

Product of Inertia of an Area.—The product of inertia of an area with respect to a pair of rectangular axes in its plane is the sum of the products obtained by multiplying each element of the area dA by its coordinates with respect to those axes, x and y; it is therefore the quantity $\int dA \cdot xy$ (see Chap. 6).

Proof Stress.—The term pertains to acceptance tests of metals and means a specified tensile stress which must be sustained without deformation in excess of a specified amount.

Proportional Limit.—The greatest stress which a material can sustain without deviating from the law of stress-strain proportionality. (Compare *Elastic Limit, Apparent Elastic Limit, Yield Point, Yield Strength.* See Art. 2 and Ref. 6.)

Radius of Gyration.—The radius of gyration of an area with respect to a given axis is the square root of the quantity obtained by dividing the moment of inertia of the area with respect to that axis by the area (see Chap. 6).

Reduction of Area.—The difference between the cross-sectional area of a tension specimen at the section of rupture before loading and after rupture, usually expressed as a percentage of the original area.

Rupture Factor.—The term is used with reference to brittle materials, *i.e.*, materials in which failure occurs through tensile rupture rather than through excessive deformation. For a member of given form, size, and material, loaded and supported in a given manner, the *rupture factor* is the ratio of the fictitious maximum tensile stress at failure, as calculated by the appropriate formula for elastic stress, to the ultimate tensile strength of the material as determined by a conventional tension test (Art. 9).

Section Modulus (Section Factor).—The term pertains to the cross section of a beam. The *section modulus* with respect to either principal central axis is the moment of inertia with respect to that axis divided by the distance from that axis to the most remote point of the section. The section modulus largely determines the flexural strength of a beam of given material.

Set (Permanent Set, Permanent Deformation, Plastic Strain, Plastic Deformation).—Strain remaining after removal of stress.

Shakedown Load (Stabilizing Load).—The maximum load that can be applied to a beam or rigid frame and, on removal, leave such residual moments that subsequent applications of the same or a smaller load will cause only elastic stresses.

Shape Factor.—The ratio of the plastic section modulus to the elastic section modulus.

Shear Center.—See *Flexural Center.*

Shear Lag.—On account of shear strain, the longitudinal tensile or compressive bending stress in wide beam flanges diminishes with the distance from the web or webs; this stress diminution is called *shear lag.*

Slenderness Ratio.—The ratio of the length of a uniform column to the least radius of gyration of the cross section.

Slip Lines (Lüders Lines).—Lines which appear on the polished surface of a crystal or crystalline body which has been stressed beyond the elastic limit. They represent the intersection of the surface by planes on which shear stress has produced plastic slip or gliding (see Art. 5 and Ref. 11).

Strain.—Any forced change in the dimensions of a body. A stretch is a *tensile strain;* a shortening is a *compressive strain;* an angular distortion is a *shear strain.* The word *strain* is commonly used to connote *unit strain* (which see); this usage is followed in this book.

Strain Energy (Elastic Energy, Potential Energy of Deformation).—Mechanical energy stored up in stressed material. Stress within the elastic limit is implied; therefore the strain energy is equal to the work done by the external forces in producing the stress, and is recoverable.

Strain Rosette.—At any point on the surface of a stressed body, strains measured on each of three properly chosen intersecting gauge lines make possible the calculation of the principal stresses at that point. Such gauge lines, and the corresponding strains, are called a *strain rosette.*

Stress.—Internal force exerted by either of two adjacent parts of a body upon the other across an imagined plane of separation. When the forces are parallel to the plane, the stress is called *shear stress;* when the forces are normal to the plane the stress is called *normal stress;* when the normal stress is directed toward the part on which it acts it is called *compressive stress;* when it is directed away from the part on which it acts it is called *tensile stress.* Shear, compressive and tensile stresses, respectively, resist the tendency of the parts to mutually slide, approach, or separate under the action of applied forces. For brevity, the word stress is often used to connote *unit stress* (which see); this usage is followed in this book.

Stress-strain Diagram (Stress Diagram).—The curve obtained by plotting unit stresses as ordinates against corresponding unit strains as abscissas.

Stress Solid.—The solid figure formed by surfaces bounding vectors drawn at all points of the cross section of a member and representing the unit normal stress at each such point. The stress solid gives a picture of the stress distribution on a section.

Stress Trajectory (Isostatic).—A line (in a stressed body) tangent to the direction of one of the principal stresses at every point through which it passes.

System.—The term is used to denote any member or any assemblage of members such as a composite column, a coupling, a truss, or other structure.

Torsional Center (Center of Twist, Center of Torsion, Center of Shear).—If a twisting couple is applied at a given section of a straight member, that section rotates about some point in its plane. This point, which does not move when the member twists, is the *torsional center* of that section. It is sometimes defined as though identical with the flexural center, but the two points do not always coincide. (Compare *Flexural Center; Elastic Center, Elastic Axis.* See Refs. 4, 5.)

True Strain (Natural Strain, Logarithmic Strain).—The integral, over the whole of a finite extension, of each infinitesimal elongation divided by the corresponding momentary length.

It is equal to $\log_e (1 + \epsilon)$, where ϵ is the strain as ordinarily defined (Ref. 12).

True Stress.—For an axially loaded bar, the load divided by the corresponding actual cross section area. It differs from the stress as ordinarily defined because of the change in area due to loading.

Twisting Moment (Torque).—The twisting moment at any section of a member is the moment of all forces that act on the member to the left (or right) of that section, taken about a polar axis through the flexural center of that section. For sections that are symmetrical about each principal central axis, the flexural center coincides with the centroid (see Refs. 5, 9).

Ultimate Elongation.—The percentage of permanent deformation remaining after tensile rupture, measured over an arbitrary length including the section of rupture.

Ultimate Strength.—The ultimate strength of a material in tension, compression, or shear respectively, is the maximum tensile, compressive, or shear stress that the material can sustain, calculated on the basis of the ultimate load and the original or unstrained dimensions. It is implied that the condition of stress represents uniaxial tension, uniaxial compression, or pure shear, as the case may be.

Unit Strain.—Unit tensile strain is the elongation per unit length; unit compressive strain is the shortening per unit length; unit shear strain is the change in angle (radians) between two lines originally at right angles to each other.

Unit Stress.—The amount of stress per unit of area. The unit stress (tensile, compressive, or shear) at any point on a plane is the limit, as ΔA approaches 0, of $\Delta P/\Delta A$, where ΔP is the total tension, compression, or shear on an area ΔA which lies in the plane and includes the point. In this book, *stress* connotes *unit stress*, in general.

Vertical Shear.—Reference is to a beam, assumed for convenience to be horizontal and to be loaded and supported by forces all of which lie in a vertical plane. The vertical shear at any section of the beam is the vertical component of all forces that act on the beam to the left of the section. The vertical shear is positive when upward and negative when downward. The *shear equation* is an expression for the vertical shear at any section in terms of x, the distance to that section measured from a chosen origin, usually taken at the left end of the beam.

Yield Point.—The lowest stress at which strain increases without increase in stress. For some purposes it is important to distinguish between the *upper* yield point, which is the stress at which the stress-strain diagram first becomes horizontal, and the *lower* yield point, which is the somewhat lower and almost constant stress under which the metal continues to deform. Only a few materials exhibit a true yield point; for other materials the term is sometimes used as synonymous with yield strength. (Compare *Yield Strength, Elastic Limit, Apparent Elastic Limit, Proportional Limit.* See Ref. 6.)

References

1. SODERBERG, C. R.: Working Stresses, *Am. Soc. Mech. Eng., Paper* A-106, *Jour. Appl. Mech.*, Vol. 2, No. 3, 1935.
2. Unit Stress in Structural Materials (Symposium), *Trans. Am. Soc. Civil Eng.*, Vol. 91, p. 388, 1927.
3. VON HEYDENKAMPF, G. S.: Damping Capacity of Materials, *Proc. Am. Soc. Testing Materials*, Vol. 21, Part II, p. 157, 1931.
4. KUHN, P.: Remarks on the Elastic Axis of Shell Wings, *Nat. Adv. Comm. Aeron., Tech. Note* 562, 1936.
5. SCHWALBE, W. L.: The Center of Torsion for Angle and Channel Sections, *Trans. Am. Soc. Mech. Eng., Paper* APM-54-11, Vol. 54, No. 1, 1932.
6. Tentative Definitions of Terms Relating to Methods of Testing, *Proc. Am. Soc. Testing Materials*, Vol. 35, Part I, p. 1315, 1935.
7. MORLEY, A.: "Strength of Materials," 5th ed., Longmans, Green & Company, 1919.
8. TIMOSHENKO, S.: "Theory of Elasticity," Engineering Societies Monograph, McGraw-Hill Book Company, 1934.
9. GRIFFITH, A. A., and G. I. TAYLOR: The Problem of Flexure and Its Solution by the Soap Film Method, *Tech. Report Adv. Comm. Aeron.* (British), *Reports and Memoranda* No. 399, p. 950, 1917.
10. Airworthiness Requirements for Aircraft, *Aeron. Bull.* No. 7-A, U.S. Dept. of Commerce, 1934.
11. NADAI, A.: "Plasticity," Engineering Societies Monograph, McGraw-Hill Book Company, 1931.
12. FREUDENTHAL, A. M.: "The Inelastic Behavior of Engineering Materials and Structures," John Wiley & Sons, Inc., 1950.

CHAPTER 2

SYMBOLS AND UNITS

Throughout this book, in each discussion and at the head of each table of formulas, the notation and units there employed are indicated. For this reason, complete consistency was not felt to be necessary. Furthermore, to facilitate comparison, it was sometimes considered advantageous to adopt a notation identical with that used in some article to which reference was made, even though such notation might differ from that used elsewhere in this book. The symbols listed below, however, have been employed in all cases.

E Modulus of elasticity (pounds per square inch).
G Modulus of rigidity (pounds per square inch).
g Acceleration of gravity (feet per second per second).
H Product of inertia of an area, with subscript indicating the axes of reference (inches^4).
I Moment of inertia of an area, with subscript indicating the axis of reference (inches^4).
J Polar moment of inertia of an area, with subscript indicating the axis of reference (inches^4).
K Bulk modulus of elasticity (pounds per square inch).
M Bending moment (inch-pounds).
s Unit stress, with subscript indicating kind or direction (pounds per square inch).
T Twisting moment (inch-pounds).
U Strain energy (inch-pounds).
V Vertical shear (pounds).
ν (nu) or $\frac{1}{m}$ Poisson's ratio (number).

PART II

FACTS; PRINCIPLES; METHODS

CHAPTER 3

THE BEHAVIOR OF BODIES UNDER STRESS

This discussion pertains to what are commonly designated as structural materials, by which is meant materials suitable for structures and members that must sustain loads without suffering damage. In this category are included most of the metals, concrete, wood, brick and tile, stone, glass, some plastics, etc. It is beyond the scope of this book to give more than a mere statement of a few important facts concerning the behavior of material under stress; there is available an extensive literature on every phase of the subject, to which the articles referred to will serve as introduction.

(For numerical values of quantities discussed in this section, the reader is referred to Table XIX.)

1. Methods of Loading.—The mechanical properties of a material are usually determined by laboratory tests, and the commonly accepted values of ultimate strength, elastic limit, etc., are those found by testing a specimen of a certain form in a certain manner. To apply results so obtained in engineering design requires an understanding of the effects of many different variables, such as form and scale, temperature and other conditions of service, and method of loading.

The method of loading in particular affects the behavior of bodies under stress. There are an infinite number of ways in which stress may be applied to a body, but for most purposes it is sufficient to distinguish the types of loading now to be defined.

1. *Short-time Static Loading.*—The load is applied so gradually that all parts are at any instant essentially in equilibrium. In testing, the load is increased progressively until failure occurs, and the total time required to produce failure is not more than a few minutes. In service, the load is increased progressively up to its maximum value, is maintained at that maximum value for but a limited time, and is not reapplied often enough to make fatigue a consideration. The ultimate strength, elastic limit, yield point, yield strength, and modulus of elasticity of a material

are usually determined by short-time static testing at room temperature.

2. *Long-time Static Loading.*—The maximum load is applied gradually and maintained; in testing, it is maintained for a sufficient time to enable its probable final effect to be predicted; in service, it is maintained continuously or intermittently during the life of the structure. The creep or flow characteristics of a material and its probable permanent strength are determined by long-time static testing at the temperatures prevailing under service conditions (see Art. 6).

3. *Repeated Loading.*—Typically, a load or stress is applied and wholly or partially removed or reversed many times in rapid succession. Generally, the term implies a great number of repetitions such as will occur in the life of rapidly moving machine parts. This type of loading is discussed under Fatigue (Art. 10).

4. *Dynamic Loading.*—The circumstances are such that the rate of change of momentum of the parts must be taken into account. The conditions may be such that the parts are given a definite acceleration corresponding to a controlled motion (rotating disk, piston rod), or such that the parts are accelerated by *impact.* In the first case the loading, so far as stress effects are concerned, is virtually static; the "inertia forces" (Art. 84) are treated exactly as though they were ordinary static loads. In impact, the stress conditions are complex, and depend upon the properties of the material as well as upon the nature of the blow (see Art. 85).

It is important to distinguish between impact and very quick static loading. In impact, the loaded member is usually required to absorb a definite amount of *energy;* in static loading, the member is usually required to resist a definite *force.* Impact loading occurs when a rigid weight is dropped upon a beam; during the period of impact and for some time afterward both weight and beam are in a state of vibration, and static equilibrium does not supervene until all the kinetic energy possessed by the weight at the instant of impact has been absorbed by the beam and stored up as strain energy or dissipated as heat. Quick static loading occurs when a charge of powder explodes in a gun barrel; neither the powder gas nor any part of the barrel acquires appreciable radial momentum, therefore equilibrium may be considered to exist at any instant, and the maximum stress produced in the gun barrel is the same as though the powder pressure had been developed gradually.

A special case of dynamic loading, generally called *sudden loading,* occurs when a weight or "dead load," not in motion, is suddenly placed upon a member or structure. A beam would be thus loaded if a weight were suspended by a cord which allowed the weight just to touch the beam, and the cord were then cut. The stress and deflection so produced would be approximately twice as great as if the weight were "eased" onto the beam, as in static loading (see Art. 85). Any force will cause approximately twice as much stress and deformation when applied suddenly as when applied progressively, but it should be noted that truly sudden loading is very hard to secure. Most instances of apparently sudden loading are really instances of very quick progressive loading, like that produced by the powder pressure discussed above.

It is obvious, on consideration, that methods of loading really differ only in degree. As the time required for the load to be applied increases, short-time static loading merges imperceptibly into long-time static loading; impact may be produced by a body moving so slowly that the resulting stress conditions are practically the same as though equal deflection had been produced by static loading; the number of stress repetitions at which fatigue becomes involved is not altogether definite. Furthermore, all these methods of loading may be combined or superimposed in various ways. None the less, the above classification is convenient, because most structural and machine parts function under loading that may be definitely classed as one or another of the types described.

2. Elasticity; Proportionality of Stress and Strain.—In determining stress by mathematical analysis, it is customary to assume that material is elastic, isotropic, homogeneous, infinitely divisible without change in properties, and that it conforms to Hooke's law, which states that strain is proportional to stress. Actually, none of these assumptions is strictly true. A structural material is usually an aggregate of crystals, fibers, or cemented particles, the arrangement of which may be either random or systematic. When the arrangement is random the material is essentially isotropic if the part considered is large in comparison with the constituent units; when the arrangement is systematic the elastic properties and strength are usually different in different directions and the material is anistropic. Again, when subdivision is carried to the point where the part under consideration comprises but a portion of a single crystal, fiber or other unit, its properties will in all probability differ from those of a larger part which is an aggregate of such units. Finally, very careful experiments show that for all materials there is probably some set, and some deviation from Hooke's law, for any stress, however small.

These facts impose certain limitations upon the conventional methods of stress analysis and must often be taken into account, but formulas for stress and strain, mathematically derived and based on the assumptions stated, give satisfactory results for nearly all problems of engineering design. In particular, Hooke's law may be regarded as practically true up to a proportional limit which, though often not sharply defined, can for most materials be established with sufficient definiteness. So, too, a fairly definite elastic limit is determinable, which in most cases is so nearly equal to the proportional limit that no distinction need be made between the two.

3. Factors Affecting Elastic Properties.—For ordinary purposes it may be assumed that the elastic properties of most metals (lead, zinc, tin, and some alloys of these metals are exceptions), when stressed below a nominal proportional limit, are constant with respect to stress, unaffected by ordinary atmospheric variations of temperature, unaffected by prior applications of moderate stress, and independent of the rate of loading. When precise relations between stress and strain are important, as in the design or calibration of instruments, these assumptions cannot always be made.

Careful experiments (Ref. 1.) on wires of steel, iron, brass, copper, phosphor bronze, nickel, and aluminum alloys show that: (1) for tension, the modulus of elasticity E and the bulk modulus of elasticity K decrease very slightly as the stress increases, the relation being a linear one; (2) for compression, E and K increase very slightly as the stress increases, the relation being a linear one; (3) under a condition of pure shear the modulus of rigidity G does not vary consistently with stress, but shows considerable irregular variation at very low stresses; (4) application of shear stress beyond the proportional limit causes a reduction of G under subsequent moderate stress; (5) application of tensile or compressive stress beyond the proportional limit sometimes, but not always, causes a reduction of E under subsequent moderate stress of the same kind; (6) for a condition of combined shear and tensile stress G is less than for pure shear; (7) E, G, and K all decrease with increase in temperature; (8) because there is some creep, partly thermal, partly plastic, even at nominally elastic stresses, tensile or compressive deformation is less for a quickly applied stress than for a gradually applied stress, and hence a higher value of E is obtained from a rapid (adiabatic) than from a slow (isothermal) test; (9) because of the absence of the thermal effect that accompanies change in volume, G as determined by a torsion test is more nearly independent of time than E as determined by a tension or compression test.

All steels have approximately the same E, K, and G, these quantities being but little affected by composition or heat treatment. Overstressing, however, in addition to slightly lowering E (or G) for the same kind of stress, greatly lowers the proportional limit for the opposite kind of stress. Repeated stressing through a moderate range enables steel to exhibit perfect elasticity within that range, the slight set observable as a result of the primitive loading not being increased by the later loadings. Under very sudden application of stress (impact) the modulus of elasticity of steel is approximately the same as under static loading, but the elastic limit appears to be higher (see Refs. 2, 3). There is some reason for believing that under extremely high speed impact the capacity of steel to absorb energy without *rupture* is considerably less than under impact at moderate speed (Ref. 4).

The various strong alloys of aluminum, cast and wrought alike, have practically the same moduli of elasticity, and E is equal for tension and compression (Ref. 5). The moduli of elasticity of copper, brass, and bronze, unlike that of steel, are appreciably affected by annealing (Ref. 6).

Wood exhibits a higher modulus of elasticity and much higher proportional limit when tested rapidly than when tested slowly. The standard impact test on a beam indicates a fiber stress at the proportional limit approximately twice as great as that found by the standard static bending test. Absorption of moisture, up to the fiber saturation point, greatly lowers both the modulus of elasticity and proportional limit (Ref. 7).

Both concrete and cast iron have stress-strain curves more or less curved throughout, and neither has a definite proportional limit. For these materials it is customary to define E as the ratio of some definite stress (for example, the allowable stress, or one-fourth the ultimate strength) to the corresponding unit strain; the quantity so determined is called the *secant* modulus, since it represents the slope of the secant of the stress-strain diagram drawn from the origin to the point representing the stress chosen. The moduli of elasticity of cast iron are much more variable than those of steel, and the stronger grades are stiffer than the weaker ones. Cast iron suffers a distinct set from the first application of even a moderate stress, but after several repetitions of that stress the material exhibits perfect elasticity up to, but not beyond, that stress. The modulus of elasticity is slightly less in tension than in compression (Ref. 8).

Concrete also shows considerable variation in modulus of elasticity, and in general its stiffness increases with its strength. Like cast iron, concrete can be made to exhibit perfect elasticity up to a moderate stress by repeated loading up to that stress. Because of its tendency to yield under continued load, the modulus of elasticity indicated by long-time loading is much less than that obtained by progressive loading at ordinary speeds (Refs. 2, 17).

4. Load-deformation Relation for a Body.—If Hooke's law holds for the material of which a member or structure is composed, the member or structure will usually conform to a similar law of load-deformation proportionality, and the deflection of a beam or truss, the twisting of a shaft, the dilation of a pressure container, etc., may in most instances be assumed proportional to the magnitude of the applied load or loads.

There are two important exceptions to this rule. One is to be found in any case where the stresses due to the loading are appreciably affected by the deformation. Examples of this are: A beam subjected to axial and transverse loads; a flexible wire or cable held at the ends and loaded transversely; a thin diaphragm held at the edges and loaded normal to its plane; a ball pressed against a plate or against another ball; a helical spring under severe extension.

The other type of exception is represented by any case in which failure occurs through elastic instability, as in a slender (Euler) column. Here, for loads less than the critical, elastic instability plays no part and the load deformation is linear. At the critical load the type of deformation changes, the column bending instead of merely shortening axially, and the deformation becomes indeterminate. For any load beyond the critical failure occurs through excessive deflection (see Art. 12).

5. Plasticity.—Elastic deformation represents an actual change in the distance between atoms or molecules; plastic deformation represents a permanent change in their relative positions. In crystalline material this permanent rearrangement consists largely of group displacements of the atoms in the crystal lattice brought about by slip on planes of least resistance, parts of a crystal sliding past one another and in some instances suffering angular displacement. In amorphous material the rearrangement appears to take place through the individual shifting from positions of equilibrium of many atoms or molecules, the cause being thermal agitation due to external work and the result appearing as a more or less uniform flow like that of a viscous liquid. It should be noted that plastic deformation before rupture is much less for biaxial or triaxial tension than for one-way stress and that for this reason metals that are ordinarily ductile may prove brittle when thus stressed.

The laws governing plastic deformation are less amenable to mathematical statement than those assumed to govern elastic behavior, but a mathematical theory of plastic action is being developed. Important applications are to the prediction of the ultimate strength and postbuckling behavior of structures, and in the study of metal working, creep, and flow (see Refs. 9, 10, 37, 67).

6. Creep and Rupture under Long-time Loading.—Most materials will creep or flow to some extent, and eventually fail, under a sustained stress less than the short-time ultimate strength. In the case of most metals, this tendency is greatly increased by high temperatures, and is an important consideration in the design of high-pressure steam and distillation equipment. It makes necessary the selection of a working stress which will cause, during the normal life of the machine or structure, neither excessive deformation nor rupture. Creep, elastic drift, and long-time strength at atmospheric temperatures must sometimes be taken into account in designing members made of nonferrous metals (copper and aluminum transmission lines, springs and diaphragms in precision instruments, lead sheathing for cables, etc.) and in selecting allowable stresses for wood and concrete.

The problem of making proper allowance in design for creep and strength diminution under long-time loading, especially at high temperatures, has not yet been satisfactorily solved, and many questions concerning testing technic, interpretation of tests, and design procedure must be regarded as controversial. A summary of theory and knowledge concerning creep in metals as of 1951 is given in Ref. 38, and a great deal of more recent information (1963) can be found in Ref. 44. One concerned with a specific problem should consult the relevant literature. In general, the following statements appear to be warranted by the evidence available.

Steel.—At atmospheric temperatures, steel can sustain for a very long time a tensile stress only slightly below the short-time ultimate strength, but not without a gradually increasing deformation. An apparent exception is to be noted in some very high strength steels (s_u = 250,000 lb. per sq. in.); in some instances such steels have been known to fail under a continuously applied tensile stress only 82 per cent of the short-time ultimate strength (Ref. 45). At any given temperature, steel can probably sustain for a very long time and without appreciably increasing deformation a tensile stress approximately equal to its proportional limit as determined at that temperature by a short-time test (Ref. 11).

Creep tests provide the data necessary for determining a working stress which, at a given temperature, will produce a creep rate not higher than is permissible, but such tests require careful study and interpretation (see Refs. 12, 13). Steel pressure vessels have been successfully designed on the basis of a working stress determined by the following procedure: Specimens are tested at the temperature in question and at different rates of loading. The yield point and ultimate strength are found to diminish with the time of loading, but at a decreasing rate, so that at a certain time of loading (perhaps a few hundred hours) the strength-time curve appears to become horizontal or nearly so. The strength indicated by this horizontal portion of the strength-time curve reduced by a suitable factor of safety is taken as the allowable stress.

Cast Iron.—At atmospheric temperature cast iron has been

made to sustain, for a very long time and without appreciably increasing deformation, a tensile stress up to about 80 per cent of its ultimate strength. Ordinary cast iron retains its strength up to about 850°F., but castings may become unserviceable because of growth at temperatures that are above 650°F. (see Ref. 8).

Copper.—Hard-drawn copper wire will creep at room temperature for many days under a tensile stress of only half its ultimate strength. The creep characteristics of different copper wires are similar under stresses that are proportional to their respective ultimate strengths, and these characteristics are the same under continuous and intermittent loading for tensile loads up to about 78 per cent of the ultimate strength (Ref. 6).

Aluminum.—At room temperature certain wrought-aluminum alloys have been found capable of sustaining a tensile stress equal to nearly 90 per cent of the tensile strength for three years without fracture and with a very slow creep rate at the end of that period (Ref. 14). On the other hand, one low-strength non-heat-treated alloy exhibited gradual but appreciable and continuing creep at normal temperature for 73 days at a stress only one-sixth the tensile strength (Ref. 27). The mechanical properties of the various aluminum alloys as determined by short-time tests at room temperatures afford no index to their creep properties at high temperatures (Ref. 15).

Lead.—Tests indicate that lead and lead alloys creep persistently and eventually fracture under any sustained tensile stress, even at room temperature (Ref. 16).

Concrete.—Under sustained compressive stress concrete suffers considerable plastic deformation, and may flow for a very long time at stresses less than the ordinary working stress. Continuous flow has been observed over a period of ten years, though ordinarily it ceases or becomes imperceptible within one or two years. The rate of flow is greater for air than for water storage, greater for small than for large specimens, and for moderate stresses increases approximately as the applied stress. On removal of stress, some elastic recovery occurs. Concrete also shows creep under tensile stress, the early creep rate being greater than the flow rate under compression (Ref. 17).

Under very gradually applied loading concrete exhibits an ultimate strength considerably less than that found by short-time loading; in certain compression tests it was found that increasing the time of testing from one second to four hours decreased the unit stress at failure about 30 per cent, most of this decrease occurring as between the extremely quick (one or two seconds) and the conventional (several minutes) testing. This indicates that the compressive stress that concrete can sustain indefinitely may be considerably less than the ultimate strength as determined by a conventional test. On the other hand the long-time imposition of a moderate loading appears to have no harmful effect; certain tests showed that, after ten years of constant loading equal to one-fourth the ultimate strength, the compressive strength of concrete cylinders was practically the same, and the modulus of elasticity was considerably greater than for similar cylinders that had not been kept under load (Ref. 39).

The modulus of rupture of plain concrete also decreases with the rate of loading, and some tests indicate that the long-time strength in cross-breaking may be only 55 to 75 per cent of the short-time strength (Ref. 18).

Wood.—Wood also yields under sustained stress; the long-time (several years) strength is about 55 per cent of the short-time (several minutes) strength in bending; for direct compression parallel to the grain the corresponding ratio is about 75 per cent (Ref. 7).

7. Criteria of Elastic Failure and of Rupture.—For the purpose of this discussion it is convenient to divide metals into two classes: (1) *ductile* metals, in which marked plastic deformation commences at a fairly definite stress (yield point, yield strength, possibly elastic limit) and which exhibit considerable ultimate elongation, and (2) *brittle* metals, for which the beginning of plastic deformation is not clearly defined and which exhibit but little ultimate elongation. Mild steel is typical of the first class, cast iron of the second, and an ultimate elongation of 5 per cent has been suggested as the arbitrary dividing line between the two classes of metals (Ref. 19). Under certain circumstances not yet fully understood, an ordinarily ductile steel may suffer *brittle fracture,* breaking with very little plastic deformation and at an abnormally low stress. The circumstances that seem to conduce to such behavior are low temperature, high strain rate, biaxial or triaxial stress conditions, residual stress, large size, the presence of stress raisers, and hydrogen absorption. Aluminum and certain alloy steels seem to be relatively immune to brittle fracture (Refs. 40, 47, 48, 68, 72).

A ductile metal is usually considered to have failed when it has suffered *elastic failure, i.e.*, when marked plastic deformation has begun. Under simple uniaxial tension this occurs when the stress reaches a value we will denote by s_y, which represents the yield strength, yield point, or elastic limit, according to which one of these is the most satisfactory indication of elastic failure for the material in question. The question arises, When does elastic failure occur under other conditions of stress, such as compression, or shear, or a combination of tension, compression, and shear?

The four theories of elastic failure that have received, at various times, the widest acceptance are: (1) the *maximum stress* theory, which states that elastic failure occurs when the maximum tensile stress becomes equal to s_y; (2) the *maximum strain* theory, which states that elastic failure occurs when the maximum tensile strain becomes equal to s_y/E; (3) the maximum shear theory, which states that elastic failure occurs when the maximum shear stress becomes equal to $\frac{1}{2}s_y$; (4) the theory of constant energy of distortion, which states that elastic failure occurs when the principal stresses s_1, s_2, s_3 satisfy the equation:

$$(s_1 - s_2)^2 + (s_2 - s_3)^2 + (s_3 - s_1)^2 = 2s_y^2$$

Of these four theories, (4) is the one that agrees best with experimental evidence, but (3) leads to results so nearly the same and is so much simpler in application that it is much more widely used as a basis for design (Refs. 19, 20).

The criteria discussed above have to do with the elastic failure of *material.* Such failure may occur locally in a *member* and do no real damage if the volume of material affected is so small or so located as to have but negligible influence on the form and strength of the member as a whole. Whether or not such local overstressing is significant depends upon the properties of the material and the conditions of service. Fatigue properties, resistance to impact, and mechanical functioning are much more likely to be affected than static strength, and a degree of local overstressing that would constitute failure in a high-speed machine part might be of no consequence whatever in a bridge member.

A brittle material cannot be considered to have definitely failed until it has broken, and this takes place either through a tensile fracture when the maximum tensile stress reaches the ultimate strength, or through what appears to be a shear fracture when the maximum compressive stress reaches a certain value. The fracture occurs on a plane oblique to the maximum compressive stress, but not, as a rule, on the plane of maximum shear stress, and so cannot be considered as purely a shear failure (see Ref. 20). The results of some tests on glass and Bakelite (Ref. 28) indicate that for these brittle materials either the maximum tensile stress or the maximum tensile strain theory affords a satisfactory criterion of rupture, while neither the maximum shear stress (3) nor maximum shear strain energy (4) theory does. These tests also indicated that strength increases with rate of stress application and that the increase is more marked when the location of the most stressed zone changes during loading (pressure of a sphere on a flat surface) than when this zone is fixed (axial tension).

The accurate prediction of the breaking strength of a member composed of brittle metal requires a knowledge of the effect of form and scale, and these effects are expressed by the *rupture factor* (see Art. 9).

What has been said here of a brittle metal applies also to any essentially isotropic brittle material.

All that has been said above concerning failure applies to *isotropic* materials. For wood, which is distinctly anisotropic, the possibility of failure in each of several ways and directions must be taken into account, *viz.:* (1) by tension parallel to the grain which causes fracture; (2) by tension transverse to the grain which causes fracture; (3) by shear parallel to the grain which causes fracture; (4) by compression parallel to the grain which causes gradual buckling of the fibers, usually accompanied by a shear displacement on an oblique plane; (5) by compression transverse to the grain which causes sufficient deformation to unfit the part for service. The unit stress which produces each of these types of failure must be ascertained by suitable tests (Ref. 7).

8. Stress Concentration.—The distribution of elastic stress across the section of a member may be nominally uniform or may vary in some regular manner, as illustrated by the linear distribution of stress in flexure. When the variation is abrupt, so that within a very short distance the intensity of stress increases greatly, the condition is described as *stress concentration.* It is usually due to local irregularities of form such as small holes, screw threads, scratches and similar "stress raisers." There is obviously no hard and fast line of demarcation between the rapid variation of stress brought about by a stress raiser and the variation that occurs in such members as sharply curved beams, but in general the term stress concentration implies some form irregularity not inherent in the member as such, but accidental (tool marks) or introduced for some special purpose (screw thread).

The maximum intensity of elastic stress produced by many of the common kinds of stress raisers can be ascertained by mathematical analysis, photoelastic analysis, or direct strain measurement, and is usually expressed by the *factor of stress concentration.* This term has been defined (Chap. 1), but its meaning may be made clearer by an example. Consider a straight rectangular beam, originally of uniform breadth b and depth d, which has had cut across the lower face a fairly sharp transverse V-notch of uniform depth D, making the net depth of the beam section at that point $d - D$. If now the beam is subjected to a uniform bending moment M, the *nominal* fiber stress s at the root of the notch may be calculated by the ordinary flexure formula $s = Mc/I$, which here reduces to $s = M/\frac{1}{6}b(d - D)^2$. But the actual stress s' is very much greater than this, because of the stress concentration that occurs at the point of the notch. The ratio s'/s, actual stress divided by nominal stress, is the factor of stress concentration, k, for this particular case. Values of k (or k_t, to use the more common current notation) for a number of common stress raisers are given in Table XVII. The most successful determination of k by the theory of elasticity is perhaps that due to Neuber (Ref. 40), who presents the results of solutions for a number of cases in the form of nomographic charts. The values of k given for Cases 1, 2, 3, 4, 12, 13, and 21, near the end of Table XVII, were taken from these charts.

The abrupt variation and high local intensity of stress produced by stress raisers are characteristics of *elastic behavior.* The plastic yielding that occurs on overstressing greatly mitigates stress concentration even in relatively brittle materials, and causes it to have much less influence on breaking strength than might be expected from a consideration of the elastic stresses only. The practical significance of stress concentration therefore depends on circumstances. For ductile metal under static loading it is usually (though not always) of little or no importance; for example, the high stresses that occur at the edges of rivet holes in structural steel members are safely ignored, the stress due to a tensile load being assumed uniform on the net section. (In the case of eyebars and other pin-connected members, however, a reduction of 25 per cent in allowable stress on the net section is recommended.) For brittle material under static loading, stress concentration is often a serious consideration, but its effect varies widely and cannot be predicted either from k or from the brittleness of the material (see Ref. 21). What may be termed the factor of stress concentration at rupture, or factor of strength reduction, represents the significance of stress concentration for static loading. This factor, which will be denoted by k_r, is the ratio of the computed stress at rupture for a plain specimen to the computed stress at rupture for the specimen containing the stress raiser. For the case described above, it would be the ratio of the modulus of rupture of the plain beam to that of the notched beam, the latter being calculated for the net section. k_r is therefore a ratio of stresses, one or both of which may be fictitious, but is none the less a measure of the strength-reducing effect of stress concentration. Some values of k_r are given in Table XVII.

It is for conditions involving fatigue that stress concentration is most important. Even the most highly localized stresses, such as are produced by small surface scratches, may greatly lower the apparent endurance limit, but materials vary greatly in "notch sensitivity," as susceptibility to this effect is sometimes called. Contrary to what might be expected, ductility (as ordinarily determined by axial testing) is not a measure of immunity to stress concentration in fatigue, steel, for instance, being much more susceptible than cast iron. What may be termed the factor of stress concentration for fatigue k_f is the practical measure of notch sensitivity. It is the ratio of the endurance limit of a plain specimen to the nominal stress at the endurance limit of a specimen containing the stress raiser. A study of available experimental data shows that k_f is almost always less, and often significantly less, than k, and various methods for estimating k_f from k have been proposed. Neuber (Ref. 40) proposes the formula

$$k_f = 1 + \frac{k - 1}{1 + \dfrac{\pi}{\pi - \omega}\sqrt{\dfrac{\rho'}{\rho}}}$$

where ω is the flank angle of the notch (called θ in Table XVII); ρ is the radius of curvature in inches at the root of the notch (called r in Table XVII); and ρ' is a dimension related to the grain size, or size of some type of basic building block, of the material, and may be taken as 0.0189 in. for steel. Moore (Ref. 41) states that for steel both the size effect and ductility can be taken into account by taking

$$\rho' = 0.2\left(1 - \frac{s_y}{s_u}\right)^3\left(1 - \frac{0.05}{d}\right)$$

where s_y = yield strength, s_u = ultimate tensile strength, and d = minimum diameter or depth of specimen in inches. This formula yields results in good agreement with tests over a limited range of sizes.

Heywood (Ref. 49) suggests a relationship that can be expressed by the formula

$$k_f = \frac{k}{1 + 2\left(\dfrac{k - 1}{k}\right)\sqrt{\dfrac{a}{R}}}$$

where R is the root radius of the notch and $\sqrt{a} = 5000/s_u$, s_u again being the ultimate tensile strength. This formula also shows good agreement with a large number of test results.

It has been suggested (Ref. 29) that the relationship between k and k_f can be expressed by the equation: $(k_f - 1)/(k - 1) = q$, a constant called the *notch sensitivity index*. For a given *material* q does seem to be approximately constant for all ordinary types of stress raisers except those that are very sharp (*e.g.*, V notch with root radius nominally zero), and so by ascertaining the value of q for a case where both k and k_f are known, the value of k_f can be estimated for a different case where k only is known. But a common value of q cannot be used for different materials.

All the methods described above are valuable and applicable within certain limitations, but none can be applied with confidence to all situations (Ref. 50). Probably none of them gives sufficient weight to scale effect in the larger size range. There is abundant evidence to show that the significance of stress concentration increases with size for both static and repeated loading, especially the latter. Of geometrically similar specimens, the larger indicate higher values for both k_r and k_f (Refs. 21, 22, 41, 51). For this reason it is important, when giving values of these factors that have been experimentally determined, to state the dimensions of the specimens tested, and this has been done in Table XVII. On the whole, it seems doubtful that any completely reliable criterion of notch sensitivity is available except tests on specimens of the material, shape, and approximate size of the part under consideration, and for this reason it is growing practice to make fatigue tests on the actual part or assembly of parts with which the design problem is concerned.

An important fact concerning stress concentration is that a single isolated notch or hole has a worse effect than have a number of similar stress raisers placed close together; thus, a single V groove reduces the strength of a part more than does a continuous screw thread of almost identical form. The deleterious effect of an unavoidable stress raiser can, therefore, be mitigated sometimes by juxtaposing additional form irregularities of like nature, but the actual superposition of stress raisers, such as the introduction of a small notch in a fillet, may result in a stress concentration factor equal to or even exceeding the product of the factors for the individual stress raisers (Ref. 52).

It should be clear from the above discussion that the presence of a stress raiser of any kind in a part subject to cyclic stress should be avoided, if possible, and if not avoidable, its effect should be minimized by one or more of the several expedients that have proved effective and that are described in the literature. An extended and authoritative discussion of design against fatigue failure and of fatigue in general, together with an extensive bibliography, is to be found in each of a number of books, such as Refs. 33, 49, 53, and 73. A large number of informative papers is to be found in Ref. 54, and Ref. 55 gives a very extensive list of published material covering the years 1951 to 1956.

9. Effect of Form and Scale on Strength; Rupture Factor.—It has been pointed out (Art. 7) that a member composed of brittle material breaks in tension when the maximum tensile stress reaches the ultimate strength, or in shear when the maximum compressive stress reaches a certain value. In calculating the stress at rupture in such a member it is customary to employ an elastic-stress formula; thus the ultimate fiber stress in a beam is usually calculated by the ordinary flexure formula. It is known that the result (modulus of rupture) is not a true stress, but it can be used to predict the strength of a similar beam of the same material. However, if another beam of the same material but of different cross section, or of different span-depth ratio, or of different size, or having a different manner of loading and support, is tested, the modulus of rupture will be found to be different. (The effect of shape of section is often taken into account by the *form factor*, and the effect of span-depth ratio and of manner of loading is recognized in testing procedure.) Similarly, the *calculated* maximum stress at rupture in a curved beam, or flat plate, or torsion member is not equal to the ultimate strength of the material, and the magnitude of the disparity will vary greatly with the material, the form of the member, the manner of loading, and the absolute scale. In order to predict accurately the breaking load for such a member, it is necessary to take into account this variation, and the *rupture factor* (defined in Chap. 1) provides a convenient means of doing this. Values of the rupture factor for a number of materials and types of member are given in Table XVIII.

On the basis of many experimental determinations of rupture factor (Ref. 21) the following generalizations may be made:

1. The smaller the proportional part of the member subjected to high stress, the larger the rupture factor. This is exemplified by the facts that a beam of circular section exhibits a higher modulus of rupture than a rectangular beam, and that a flat plate under a concentrated center load fails at a higher computed stress than one uniformly loaded. The extremes in this respect are, on the one hand, a uniform bar under axial tension, for which the rupture factor is unity, and on the other, a case of severe

stress concentration such as a sharply notched bar, for which the rupture factor may be indefinitely large.

2. In the flexure of statically indeterminate members, the redistribution of bending moments that occurs when plastic yielding starts at the most highly stressed section increases the rupture factor. For this reason a flat plate gives a higher value than a simple beam, and a circular ring gives a higher value than does a portion of it tested as a statically determinate curved beam.

3. The rupture factor seems to vary inversely with the absolute scale for conditions involving abrupt stress variation, which is consistent with the fact, already noted, that for cases of stress concentration, both k_r and k_f diminish with the absolute scale.

4. As a rule, the more brittle the material, the more nearly all rupture factors approach unity. There are, however, many exceptions to this rule. It has been pointed out (Art. 8) that immunity to notch effect even under static loading is not always proportional to ductility, and a study of the strength-reduction factors k_r in Table XVII and of the rupture factors in Table XVIII will emphasize the truth of this.

The practical significance of these facts is that for a given material and given factor of safety, some members may be designed with a much higher allowable stress than others. This fact is often recognized in design; for example, the allowable stress for wooden airplane spars varies according to the form factor and the proportion of the stress that is flexural.

What has been said here pertains especially to comparatively brittle materials, *i.e.*, materials for which failure consists in fracture rather than in the beginning of plastic deformation. The effect of form on the ultimate strength of ductile members is less important, though even for steel the allowable unit stress is often chosen with regard to circumstances such as those discussed above. For instance, in gun design the maximum stress is allowed to approach, and even exceed, the nominal elastic limit, the volume of material affected being very small, and in structural design extreme fiber stresses in bending are permitted to exceed the value allowed for axial loading. In testing, account must be taken of the fact that some ductile metals exhibit a higher ultimate strength when fracture occurs at a reduced section such as would be formed in a tensile specimen by a concentric groove or notch. Whatever effect of stress concentration may remain during plastic deformation is more than offset by the supporting action of the shoulders, which tends to prevent the normal "necking down."

10. Fatigue.—Practically all materials will break under numerous repetitions of a stress less than that required to produce immediate rupture. This phenomenon is known as *fatigue*, and was formerly attributed to a supposed alteration in structure brought about by recurrent stressing. Metals, for instance, were said to crystallize, a belief probably due to the facts that fatigue fractures often occur at points of weakness where the grain structure is abnormally coarse, and are, even in ductile material, square and crystalline in appearance because of the absence of plastic flow. It is now known that repeated stressing does not produce a change in the crystalline structure of a metal,[1] but that in some way as yet obscure it causes a crack to develop and spread, first gradually, then rapidly, until fracture occurs.

The tendency of metals to fracture under repeated stressing increases with the maximum stress applied and with the *range* of stress; stressing from zero up to s is more destructive than stressing, say, from $\frac{1}{2}s$ up to s, and completely reversed or alternating stress, from s in compression to s in tension, is the most drastic of all. For this reason, and also because alternating stress represents a condition common in service and easily realized in experiments, fatigue tests are often made by rotating a small circular beam under constant bending moment, so that the outer fibers are subjected to alternate tension and compression of equal intensity. For any given stress thus produced, above a certain critical value, a specimen will fracture after a sufficient number of cycles. As the applied stress is decreased, the number of cycles required to produce failure increases, and when the stress becomes equal to or less than the critical value mentioned, the material appears to be able to withstand an indefinitely large number of cycles. This critical stress is the *endurance limit* (strictly speaking, the endurance limit in reversed bending). It may be greater or less than the elastic limit; for ferrous metals

[1] That is, does not produce an interatomic rearrangement. Investigations have shown that the grains appear to be progressively broken up so that there is, in effect, a change in grain structure. See A New Attack upon the Problem of Fatigue of Metals, Using X-ray Methods of Precision, by H. G. Gough and W. A. Wood, *Proc. Royal Soc. London,* Series *A*, Vol. 154, 1936.

it is usually about one-half, and for nonferrous metals about one-third, of the ultimate tensile strength, though it may vary considerably above or below these approximate values.

The behavior of a material under repeated stress is well represented by the so-called s-N diagram, which is a graph plotted with s, the unit stress, as ordinates and N, the number or cycles producing fracture, as abscissas. Such a graph starts at the stress corresponding to the static ultimate strength (or modulus of rupture) and slopes downward, until at the endurance limit it becomes horizontal. The transition may be abrupt, in which case the endurance limit is sharply defined, or it may be gradual, in which case the endurance limit may be vaguely defined or even nonexistent. The number of stress cycles necessary to establish the endurance limit varies according to the material. For wrought ferrous metals it is usually less than 5,000,000; for cast iron and cast steel it is 10,000,000 or more; for nonferrous metals it varies widely, being less than 1,000,000 for some magnesium alloys and as much as 400,000,000 or 500,000,000 for some grades of aluminum (Refs. 23, 24). For very hard steels, notably ball bearings, fatigue tests have been carried to a billion cycles without establishing a definitive endurance limit.

Some metals, notably certain light alloys, have no true endurance limit; their s-N diagrams never become quite horizontal. For such materials, and for structural and machine parts which are expected to sustain only a finite number of stress cycles during their service life, the *endurance strength* (see Definitions) is important. The endurance strength for any number of cycles can be ascertained from the s-N diagram, if available. If the endurance strength s_1 for a number of stress cycles N_1 is known, then the endurance strength s_2 for N_2 cycles can be estimated by using an assumed equation for the s-N diagram. For several kinds of steel the empirical equation $s_1/s_2 = (N_2/N_1)^{0.1}$ has been found to give closely approximate results (Ref. 30). This equation is correct in form for any material whose s-N diagram, logarithmically plotted, is approximately a straight line, but the exponent would differ somewhat for different materials. Failure at a very small number of cycles (low-cycle fatigue) seems to depend more on plastic strain than on stress, and for a large variety of metals the relationship $N^{\frac{1}{2}} \Delta\epsilon_p = \frac{1}{2} \log_e (A/A_u)$ has been shown to hold (Ref. 56). Here N is the number of cycles to failure, $\Delta\epsilon_p$ is the plastic strain range, A is the original cross-section area and A_u is the cross-section area after rupture of a conventional tension specimen.

The interpretation of fatigue test data and their use in determining allowable stresses require a knowledge of the effects of various influencing factors, together with recognition of the facts that even laboratory tests reveal considerable "scatter," and that actual machine parts rarely show either the strength or degree of uniformity of conventional polished specimens. Available test results are not altogether consistent, but it is believed that the following statements are in line with generally accepted findings.

Method of Loading.—Fatigue limits determined by vibratory bending run slightly higher than those determined by the rotating beam test; the ratio for two alloy steels was found to be 1.008 and 1.072. Somewhat higher values of the ratio have been found for aluminum alloy (Ref. 31). Fatigue limits determined by reversed axial loading run lower than those determined by the rotating beam test. The ratio was found to be 0.950 and 0.884 for the alloy steels mentioned above, and 0.933 for the aluminum alloy 17S-T (Ref. 31). For a large group of carbon steels the ratio was found to lie between 0.74 and 0.996 (Ref. 32). In some tests ratios as low as 0.6 have been found, possibly because of eccentric loading, and in a few instances ratios above unity have been reported (Ref. 33). For service conditions the ratio should be assumed lower than the value indicated by laboratory tests on the same material, because of the greater probability of eccentric loading. The ratio of the endurance limit in reversed torsion to the endurance limit in reversed bending is about 0.6 for steel, about 0.55 for wrought aluminum alloys, and about 0.9 for cast iron. Although in most fatigue failures the critical stress is tensile, repeated compression can also produce failure, but the endurance limit in compression is higher than in tension (Ref. 57).

Range of Stress.—Various empirical formulas for the endurance limit corresponding to any given range of stress variation have been suggested, of which the most generally accepted is that expressed by the *Goodman diagram*, or some modification thereof. Figure 1 shows one method of constructing this diagram. In each cycle the stress varies from a maximum value s_{max} to a minimum value s_{min}, either of which is plus or minus according to whether it is tensile or compressive. The *mean* stress is $s_m = \frac{1}{2}(s_{\max} + s_{\min})$, and the *alternating* stress is

$$s_a = \tfrac{1}{2}(s_{\max} - s_{\min})$$

the addition and subtraction being algebraic. With reference to rectangular axes, s_m is measured horizontally and s_a vertically. Obviously when $s_m = 0$, the limiting value of s_a is the endurance limit for fully reversed stress, here denoted by s_e. When $s_a = 0$, the limiting value of s_m is the ultimate tensile strength, here denoted by s_u. Points A and B on the axes are thus located. According to the Goodman theory, the ordinate to a point on the straight line AB represents the maximum alternating stress s_a that

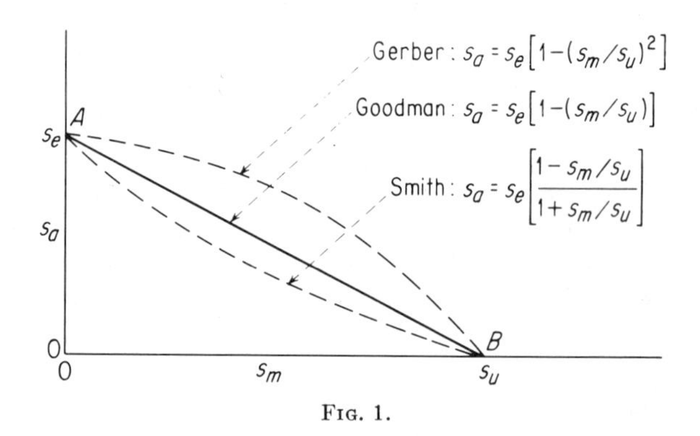

FIG. 1.

can be imposed in conjunction with the corresponding mean stress s_m. Any point above AB represents a stress condition that would eventually cause failure; any point below AB represents a stress condition with more or less margin of safety. A more conservative construction, suggested by Soderberg (Ref. 19), is to move B back to s_y, the yield strength. A less conservative but sometimes preferred construction (proposed by Gerber) is to replace the straight line by the parabola.

The Goodman diagrams described can be used for steel, and for aluminum and titanium alloys, but for cast iron many test results fall below the straight line AB, and the lower curved line, suggested by Smith (Ref. 58), is preferred. Test results for magnesium alloys also sometimes fall below the straight line.

Figure 1 represents conditions where s_m is tensile; if s_m is compressive, s_a is increased, and for values of s_m less than the compression yield strength, the relationship is represented approximately by the straight line AB extended to the left with the same slope. When the mean stress and alternating stress are both torsional, s_a is practically constant until s_m exceeds the yield strength in shear, and for alternating bending combined with mean torsion, the same thing is true. But when s_m is tensile and s_a is torsional, s_a diminishes as s_m increases, about as represented by the Goodman line.

When stress concentration is to be taken into account, accepted practice is to apply k_f (or k, if k_f is not known) to s_a only, not to s_m.

Shape of Specimen or Part.—The endurance limit determined by reversed bending is lower for rectangular specimens than for round ones. For the two alloy steels mentioned above (Ref. 31) the ratio was found to be 0.876 and 0.944. Somewhat lower ratios have been found for aluminum alloy. The lower strength of rectangular specimens is due in part to the corners, which, if sharp, act as stress raisers (Cazaud, in Ref. 54). The effect of notches, holes, etc., is shown in Table XVII.

Surface Conditions.—Surface roughness constitutes a kind of stress raiser, and its effect is indicated in Table XVII. Discussion of the effect of surface coatings and platings is beyond the scope of this book (see Refs. 33, 49).

Rate of Loading.—Up to a frequency of 10,000 cycles per minute, the rate of stress repetition does not appear to affect the endurance limit of steel; for higher frequencies the endurance limit increases somewhat, reaching a maximum value at from 1200 to 1800 cycles per second, beyond which point there is a decrease (Ref. 59).

Combined Stress.—The stress condition under combined loading (e.g., bending and torsion) will probably not produce fatigue failure, provided for steel $(f/f_1)^2 + (q/q_1)^2 \leqq 1$, and for cast iron $(q/q_1)^2 + (f/f_1)^2(f/q - 1) + (f/f_1)(2 - f_1/q_1) \leqq 1$. Here f is the tensile-compressive stress due to bending only, q is the shear stress due to torsion only, f_1 is the endurance strength in pure bending, and q_1 is the endurance strength in pure torsion (Ref. 34). Biaxial stress may lower the fatigue strength of a metal materially. Tests on an aluminum alloy, reported in Ref. 42, showed that under biaxial tension the fatigue strength may be as low as 50 per cent of the fatigue strength under uniaxial tension. Some reported tests on steel show no such effect (Refs.

60, 71), and this was also true of a very limited number of tests made by the author on cast iron. A more extensive discussion of fatigue under combined stress is to be found in Refs. 53 and 73.

Stress History.—A very important question and one that has been given much attention is the influence on fatigue strength of previous stressing. One theory that has had considerable acceptance is the linear damage law (Miner in Ref. 73); here the assumption is made that the damage produced by repeated stressing at any level is directly proportional to the number of cycles. Thus, if the number of cycles producing failure (100 per cent damage) at a stress range s_1 is N_1, then the proportional damage produced by N cycles of the stress is N/N_1, and stressing at various stress levels for various numbers of cycles causes cumulative damage equal to the summation of such fractional values. Failure, therefore, occurs when $\Sigma N/N_1 = 1$. The formula implies that the effect of a given number of cycles is the same, whether they are applied continuously or intermittently, and does not take into the account the fact that for some metals understressing (stressing below the endurance limit) raises the endurance limit. The linear damage law is not reliable for all stress conditions, and various modifications have been proposed, such as replacing 1 in the formula by a quantity x whose numerical value, either more or less than unity, must be determined experimentally. Attempts have been made to develop a better theory (*e.g.*, Corten and Dolan, Freudenthal and Gumbel, in Ref. 54). Though the several theories are all of value when used knowledgeably, it does not appear that as yet any generally reliable method is available for predicting the life of a stressed part under variable or random loading.

Size of Specimen or Part.—Results of reversed bending tests on unnotched steel specimens indicate a decrease in the endurance limit with increasing size; this scale effect seems to be absent in reversed axial loading. Several empirical formulas have been proposed to represent the influence of size. Moore (Ref. 41) suggested the equation

$$s_e'\left(1 - \frac{0.016}{d'}\right) = s_e''\left(1 - \frac{0.016}{d''}\right)$$

where s_e' is the endurance limit for a specimen of diameter d', and s_e'' is the endurance limit for a specimen of diameter d''.

This formula was based on test results obtained with specimens from 0.125 to 1.875 in. in diameter, and shows good agreement within that size range. Obviously it cannot be used for predicting the endurance limit of very small specimens.

Heywood (Ref. 49) suggests an equation equivalent to $s_d = \left(1 + \frac{0.014}{0.1 + d^2}\right) s_D$, where s_d is the predicted endurance limit for a specimen of diameter d, and s_D is the experimentally determined endurance limit for a specimen of diameter $D > d$. In this reference $D = 2$ in. This formula also shows reasonably good agreement with test results up to a diameter of 2 in. The few relevant test results available indicate a considerable decrease in endurance limit for very large diameters (Refs. 61, 62, 63). There are not enough experimental data to establish any formula for these large sizes, but for d from 2 up to 9 in., the equation $s_d = s_{0.3}[1 - \frac{1}{15}(d - 0.3)]$ provides, in a very rough way, a lower limit that appears conservative. Here $s_{0.3}$ represents the endurance limit for a diameter of 0.3 in.

Corrosion Fatigue.—Under the simultaneous action of corrosion and repeated stress the fatigue strength of most metals is drastically reduced, sometimes to a small fraction of the strength in air, and a true endurance limit can no longer be said to exist. Liquids and gases not ordinarily thought of as especially conducive to corrosion will often be found to have a very deleterious effect on fatigue properties, and resistance to corrosion is more important than normal fatigue strength in determining the relative rating of different metals (Refs. 25, 26, 53, 63, 64, 74).

Wood and Concrete.—The fatigue properties of wood and concrete have been less thoroughly investigated than those of metals. Neither material can be said to have a true endurance limit. Tests in reversed bending on both solid wood and plywood have indicated an endurance strength at 30,000,000 cycles of about 30 per cent of the static modulus of rupture. The weakening influence of sloping grain, knots, and drilled holes is greater for repeated than for static loading (Ref. 7).

For concrete, the endurance strength for 1,000,000 to 2,000,000 cycles of compression from zero to a maximum is 50 to 55 per cent of the ultimate compressive strength, and the endurance strength determined by either one-way or reversed bending of plain beams is about 50 per cent of the static modulus of rupture. The endurance strength of concrete, like that of steel, can be slightly raised by understressing (Ref. 2).

Structural Joints.—The fatigue properties of riveted and welded structural joints have been studied extensively. Here it is the endurance strength for the expected number of stress cycles—often taken as 2,000,000—that is usually important. The tests reported in Ref. 30 gave as the endurance strength (2,000,000 cycles from 0 to s in tension) of plates in riveted joints almost the same value—about 26,000 lb. per sq. in.—for carbon steel of 62,000 lb. per sq. in. tensile strength, silicon steel of 81,000 lb. per sq. in. tensile strength, and nickel steel of 99,000 lb. per sq. in. tensile strength. For the same method of testing, the endurance strength of carbon steel rivets (ultimate shearing strength about 46,000 lb. per sq. in.) was found to be 30,000 lb. per sq. in. Under completely reversed loading the results for the rivets were inconsistent, the endurance strength varying from 15,000 to 30,000 lb. per sq. in. Joints in which the plate ends were milled and closely fitted, so that compression could be carried largely by direct bearing, showed notably higher strength than joints in which the rivets had to take all or most of the compression. For electrically welded butt joints in mild steel the endurance limit is about 30,000 lb. per sq. in. when covered electrodes are used and about 16,000 lb. per sq. in. when bare electrodes are used. For transverse fillet welds the corresponding values are about 16,000 and 9600 lb. per sq. in., and for longitudinal fillet welds about 13,500 and 8200 lb. per sq. in. For gas welds the endurance limit for any type of joint is somewhere between the covered and bare electrode values indicated for electric welds (values from Ref. 35).

The fatigue strength of bolted joints with the bolts in tension depends upon many factors. It can be extremely low, and proper design and assembling are of the greatest importance. The problem has received much attention, and a great deal of relevant information can be found in Refs. 49, 65, and 66. See also Chap. 13. Bolted joints with the bolts in shear have been shown to be superior to riveted joints under repeated loading (Ref. 66).

11. Prestressing.—Parts of an elastic system may, by accident or design, have introduced into them stresses which cause and are balanced by opposing stresses in other parts, so that the system reaches a state of stress without the imposition of any external load. Examples of such initial or locked-up stresses are the temperature stresses in welded members, the stresses in a statically indeterminate truss due to tightening or "rigging" some of the members by turnbuckles, and the stresses in the flange couplings of a pipe line caused by screwing down the nuts. The effects of such prestressing upon the rigidity and strength of a system will now be considered, the assumption being made that the prestressing is not so severe as to affect the properties of the *material*.

In discussing this question it is necessary to distinguish two types of systems, *viz.*, (1) one in which the component parts can sustain reversal of stress, and (2) one in which at least some of the component parts cannot sustain reversal of stress. Examples of the first type are furnished by a solid bar, and by a truss all members of which can sustain either tension or compression. Examples of the second type are furnished by the bolt-flange combination mentioned, and by a truss with wire diagonals that can take tension only.

For the first type of system, prestressing has no effect on initial rigidity. Thus a plain bar with locked-up temperature stresses will exhibit the same modulus of elasticity as a similar bar from which these stresses have been removed by annealing; two prestressed helical springs arranged in parallel, the tension in one balancing the compression in the other, will deflect neither more nor less under load than the same two springs similarly placed without prestressing.

Prestressing will lower the elastic limit (or allowable load, or ultimate strength) provided that in the absence of prestressing all parts of the system would reach their respective elastic limits (or allowable loads, or ultimate strengths) simultaneously. But if this relation between the parts does not exist, then prestressing may raise any or all of these quantities. One or two examples illustrating each condition may serve to make this clear.

Consider first a plain bar which is to be loaded in axial tension. If there are no locked-up stresses, then (practically speaking) all parts of the bar reach their allowable stress, elastic limit, and ultimate strength simultaneously. But if there are locked-up stresses present, then the parts in which the initial tension is highest reach the elastic limit before other parts, and the elastic limit of the bar as a whole is thus lowered. The load at which the allowable unit stress is first reached is similarly lowered, and the ultimate strength may also be reduced, although if the material is ductile the equalization of stress that occurs during elongation will largely prevent this.

As an example of the second condition (all parts do not simultaneously reach the elastic limit or allowable stress) consider a thick cylinder under internal pressure. If the cylinder is not prestressed, the stress at the interior surface reaches the elastic limit first, and so governs the pressure that may be applied. But if the cylinder is prestressed by shrinking on a jacket, or wrapping with wire under tension, as is done in gun construction, then the walls are put into an initial state of compression. This compressive stress also is greatest at the inner surface, and the pressure required to reverse it and produce a tensile stress equal to the elastic limit is much greater than before. As another example, consider a composite member comprising two rods of equal length, one aluminum, the other steel, which are placed side by side to jointly carry a tensile load. For simplicity, it will be assumed that the allowable unit stresses for the materials are the same. Because the modulus of elasticity of the steel is about three times that of the aluminum, it will reach the allowable stress first, and at a total load less than the sum of the allowable loads for the bars acting separately. But if the composite bar is properly prestressed, the steel being put into initial compression and the aluminum into initial tension (the ends being in some way rigidly connected to permit this), then on the application of a tensile load the two bars will reach the allowable stress simultaneously and the load-carrying capacity of the combination is thus greater than before. The elastic limit and, sometimes, the ultimate strength of a composite member similarly may be raised by prestressing.

In a system of the second type (one all parts of which *cannot* sustain stress reversal) prestressing increases the rigidity for any load less than that required to produce stress reversal. The effect of prestressing, up to that point, is to make the rigidity of the system the same as though all parts were effective. Thus in the case of the truss with wire diagonals it is as though the counterwires were taking compression; in the case of the flange-bolt combination it is as though the flanges were taking tension. (If the flanges are practically rigid in comparison with the bolts, there is no deformation until the applied load exceeds the bolt tension, and so the system is rigid.) When the applied load becomes large enough to cause stress reversal (to make the counterwires go slack, or to separate the flanges) the effect of prestressing disappears and the system is neither more nor less rigid than a similar one not prestressed, provided, of course, none of the parts has been overstressed.

The elastic limit (or allowable load, or ultimate strength) of a system of this type is not affected by prestressing unless the elastic limit (or allowable load, or ultimate strength) of one or more of the parts is reached before stress reversal occurs. In effect, a system of this type is exactly like a system of type (1) until stress reversal occurs, after which all effects of prestressing vanish.

The effects of prestressing are often taken advantage of, notably in bolted joints (flanges, cylinder heads, etc.) where high initial tension in the bolts prevents stress fluctuation and consequent fatigue, and in prestressed reinforced-concrete members, where the initially compressed concrete is enabled, in effect, to act in tension without cracking up to the point of stress reversal. The example of the prestressed thick cylinder has already been mentioned.

12. Elastic Stability.—Under certain circumstances the maximum load a member will sustain is determined, not by the strength of the material, but by the stiffness of the member. This condition arises when the load produces a bending or a twisting moment which is proportional to the corresponding deformation. The most familiar example is an Euler column. When a straight slender column is loaded axially, it remains straight and suffers only axial compressive deformation under small loads. If while thus loaded it is slightly deflected by a transverse force, it will straighten after removal of that force. But there is obviously some axial load that will just hold the column in the deflected position, and since both the bending moment due to the load and the resisting moment due to the stresses are directly proportional to the deflection, the load required thus to hold the column is independent of the amount of the deflection. If this condition of balance obtains at stresses less than the elastic limit, the condition is called *elastic stability*, and the load which produces this condition is called the *critical* load. Any increase of the load beyond this critical value is usually attended by immediate collapse of the member.

Other examples of elastic stability are afforded by a thin cylinder under external pressure, a thin plate under edge compression or edge shear, and a deep thin cantilever beam under a transverse end load applied at the top surface. Some such elements, unlike the simple column described above, do not fail under the load that initiates elastic buckling, but demonstrate increasing resistance as the buckling progresses. Such "post-buckling" behavior is important in many problems of shell design.

Elastic stability is discussed further in Chap. 14, and formulas for the critical loads for various members and types of loading are given in Tables XV and XVI.

References

1. SAYRE, M. F.: Laws of Elastic Behavior in Metals, *Trans. Am. Soc. Mech. Eng., Paper* RP-56-7, Vol. 56, p. 555, 1934.
2. WITHEY, M. O., and J. ASTON: "Johnson's Materials of Construction," 7th ed., John Wiley & Sons, Inc., 1930.
3. SEARS, J. E.: Some Experiments on Impact, *Engineering* (London), April 30 and May 7, 1909.
4. MANN, H. C.: High Velocity Tension-impact Tests, *Proc. Am. Soc. Testing Materials,* Vol. 36, Part II, p. 85, 1936.
5. "Alcoa Aluminum and Its Alloys," Aluminum Company of America.
6. PHILLIPS, A. G., and A. A. SMITH: Effect of Time on the Tensile Properties of Hard-drawn Copper Wire, *Am. Soc. Testing Materials,* Vol. 36, Part II, p. 263, 1936.
7. "Wood Handbook," Forest Products Laboratory, U.S. Dept. Agr.
8. Symposium on Cast Iron, *Am. Soc. Testing Materials,* Vol. 33, Part II, p. 115, 1933.
9. NÁDAI, A.: "Theory of Flow and Fracture of Solids," 2d ed., Vol. I, Engineering Societies Monograph, McGraw-Hill Book Company, 1950.
10. HENCKY, H.: The New Theory of Plasticity, Strain Hardening and Creep and the Testing of the Inelastic Behavior of Metals, *Am. Soc. Mech. Eng., Paper* APM-55-18; *Jour. Appl. Mech.,* Vol. 1, No. 4, 1933.
11. FRENCH, H. J.: Flow of Steels at Various Temperatures, *Proc. Am. Soc. Testing Materials,* Vol. 26, Part II, p. 7, 1926.
12. BAILEY, R. W.: Design Aspects of Creep, *Am. Soc. Mech. Eng. Jour. Appl. Mech.,* Vol. 3, No. 1, March, 1936.
13. MCVETTY, P. G.: The Interpretation of Creep Tests, *Proc. Am. Soc. Testing Materials,* Vol. 34, Part II, p. 105, 1934.
14. EDWARDS, FRARY and JEFFRIES: "The Aluminum Industry," McGraw-Hill Book Company, 1930.

15. KENNEDY, R. R.: Creep Characteristics of Aluminum Alloys, *Proc. Am. Soc. Testing Materials*, Vol. 35, Part II, p. 218, 1935.
16. MOORE, H. F., B. B. BETTY, and C. W. DOLLIS: The Creep and Fracture of Lead and Lead Alloys, *Univ. Ill. Exp. Sta. Bull.* 272, 1935.
17. DAVIS, R. E., H. E. DAVIS, and J. S. HAMILTON: Plastic Flow of Concrete under Sustained Stress, *Proc. Am. Soc. Testing Materials*, Vol. 34, Part II, p. 354, 1934.
18. Report of Committee on Materials of Construction, *Bull. Assoc. State Eng. Soc.*, July, 1934.
19. SODERBERG, R.: Working Stresses, *Am. Soc. Mech. Eng., Paper* A-106, *Jour. Appl. Mech.*, Vol. 2, No. 3, 1935.
20. NÁDAI, A.: Theories of Strength, *Am. Soc. Mech. Eng., Paper* APM 55-15, *Jour. Appl. Mech.*, Vol. 1, No. 3, 1933.
21. ROARK, R. J., R. S. HARTENBERG, and F. Z. WILLIAMS: The Influence of Form and Scale on Strength, *Univ. Wis. Exp. Sta. Bull.* 84, 1938.
22. PETERSON, R. E.: Model Testing as Applied to Strength of Materials, *Am. Soc. Mech. Eng., Paper* APM-55-11, *Jour. Appl. Mech.*, Vol. 1, No. 2, p. 79, 1933.
23. MOORE, H. F., and J. B. KOMMERS: "The Fatigue of Metals," 1st ed. McGraw-Hill Book Company, 1927.
24. TEMPLIN, R. L.: The Fatigue Properties of Light Metals and Alloys, *Proc. Am. Soc. Testing Materials*, Vol. 33, Part II, p. 364, 1933.
25. MCADAM, D. J.: Stress-Strain-Cycle Relationship and Corrosion-Fatigue of Metals, *Proc. Am. Soc. Testing Materials*, Vol. 26, Part II, p. 224, 1926.
26. Present-Day Knowledge of Fatigue, Report of Research Committee on Fatigue of Metals, *Proc. Am. Soc. Testing Materials*, Vol. 30, Part I, p. 250, 1930.
27. MARIN, J., and L. E. ZWISSLER: Creep of Aluminum Subjected to Bending at Normal Temperature, *Proc. Am. Soc. Testing Materials*, Vol. 40, p. 937, 1940.
28. WEIBULL, W.: Investigations into Strength Properties of Brittle Materials, *Proc. Royal Swedish Inst. Eng. Research*, No. 149, 1938.
29. WILSON, W. K.: "Practical Solution of Torsional Vibration Problems," 2d ed., Vol. II, John Wiley & Sons, Inc., 1941.
30. WILSON, W. M., and F. P. THOMAS: Fatigue Tests of Riveted Joints, *Eng. Exp. Sta., Univ. Ill., Bull.* 302, 1938.
31. Report of the Research Committee on Fatigue of Metals, *Proc. Am. Soc. Testing Materials*, Vol. 41, p. 133, 1941.
32. FRANCE, R. D.: Endurance Testing of Steel: Comparison of Results Obtained with Rotating Beam vs. Axially Loaded Specimens, *Proc. Am. Soc. Testing Materials*, Vol. 31, Part II, p. 176, 1931.
33. Battelle Memorial Institute, "Prevention of Fatigue of Metals," John Wiley & Sons, Inc., 1941.
34. GOUGH, H. J., and H. V. POLLARD: The Strength of Metals under Combined Alternating Stresses, *Proc. Inst. Mech. Eng.*, Vol. 131, p. 3, 1935.
35. "Welding Handbook," The American Welding Society, 1938.
36. SMITH, J. O.: The Effect of Range of Stress on the Torsional Fatigue Strength of Steel, *Eng. Exp. Sta., Univ. Ill., Bull.* 316, 1939.

37. FREUDENTHAL, A. M.: "The Inelastic Behavior of Engineering Materials and Structures," John Wiley & Sons, Inc., 1950.
38. SCHWONE, A. D., and L. R. JACKSON: A Survey of Creep in Metals, *Nat. Adv. Comm. Aeron., Tech. Note* 2516, 1951.
39. WASHA, G. W., and P. G. FLUCK: Effect of Sustained Loading on Compressive Strength and Modulus of Elasticity of Concrete, *Jour. Am. Concrete Inst.*, Vol. 46, May, 1950.
40. NEUBER, H.: "Theory of Notch Stresses," J. W. Edwards, 1946.
41. MOORE, H. F.: A Study of Size Effect and Notch Sensitivity in Fatigue Tests of Steel, *Proc. Am. Soc. Testing Materials*, Vol. 45, p. 507, 1945.
42. MARIN, J., and W. SHELSON: Biaxial Fatigue Strength of 24S-T Aluminum Alloy, *Nat. Adv. Comm. Aeron., Tech. Note* 1889, 1949.
43. "Fatigue and Fracture of Metals" (symposium) Technology Press of The Massachusetts Institute of Technology and John Wiley & Sons, Inc., 1950.
44. *Proceedings of the Joint International Conference on Creep*, American Society of Mechanical Engineers, New York; Institution of Mechanical Engineers, London, 1963.
45. RARING, R. H., and J. A. RINEBOLT: Static Fatigue of High Strength Steel, *Proc. Soc. Metals*, Vol. 48, 1956.
46. PARKER, E. W.: "Brittle Fracture of Engineering Materials," John Wiley & Sons, Inc., 1957.
47. WELLS, A. A.: "Brittle Fracture Mechanics: a Survey of Published Work," British Welding Association, 1959.
48. BOYD, G. M.: "Some Observations on the Brittle Fracture Problem," Report SSC-125, Ship Structure Committee, National Research Council, 1959.
49. HEYWOOD, R. B.: "Designing against Fatigue of Metals," Reinhold Publishing Corporation, 1962.
50. YEN, C. S., and T. J. DOLAN: A Critical Review of the Criteria for Notch Sensitivity in Fatigue of Metals, *Univ. Ill., Exp. Sta. Bull.* 398, 1952.
51. PHILLIPS, C. E., and R. B. HEYWOOD: Size Effect in Fatigue of Steel Specimens under Reversed Direct Stress, *Proc. Inst. Mech. Eng., London*, Vol. 165, 1951.
52. MOWBRAY, A. Q., JR.: The Effect of Superposition of Stress Raisers on Members Subjected to Static or Repeated Loads, *Proc. Soc. Exp. Stress Anal.*, Vol. 10, No. 2, 1953.
53. FORREST, P. G.: "Fatigue of Metals," Pergamon Press, Addison-Wesley Publishing Company, Inc., 1962.
54. International Conference on Fatigue of Metals, Institution of Mechanical Engineers, London; American Society of Mechanical Engineers, New York, 1956.
55. References on Fatigue, American Society for Testing Materials, 1950–1958.
56. TAVERNELLI, J. F., and L. F. COFFIN, JR.: A Compilation and Interpretation of Cyclic Strain Fatigue Tests on Metals, *Trans. Am. Soc. Metals*, Vol. 51, 1959.
57. NEWMARK, N. M., R. J. MOSBORG, W. M. MENSE, and R. E. ELLING:

Fatigue Tests in Axial Compression, *Proc. Am. Soc. Testing Materials*, Vol. 51, 1951.
58. SMITH, J. O.: The Effect of Range of Stress on Fatigue Strength, *Univ. Ill., Eng. Exp. Sta. Bull.* 334, 1942.
59. LOMAS, T. W., J. O. WARDT, J. R. RAIT, and E. W. COLBECK: The Influence of Frequency of Vibration on the Endurance Limit of Ferrous Alloys at Speeds up to 150,000 Cycles per Minute, (in Ref. 54).
60. BOWMAN, C. E., and T. J. DOLAN: Biaxial Fatigue Properties of Pressure Vessel Steels, *Welding Jour. Research Supplement*, November, 1953, and January, 1955.
61. HORGER, O. J., and H. R. NEIFERT: Fatigue Strength of Machined Forgings 6 to 7 Inches in Diameter, *Proc. Am. Soc. Testing Materials*, Vol. 39, 1939.
62. EATON, F. C.: Fatigue Tests of Large Alloy Steel Shafts; Symposium on Large Fatigue Testing Machines and their Results, *Am. Soc. Testing Materials, Spec. Tech. Pub.* 216, 1957.
63. JIRO, H., and A. JUNICH: Studies on Rotating Beam Fatigue of Large Mild Steel Specimens, *Proc. 9th Japanese Nat. Congr. Appl. Mech.*, 1959.
64. GOULD, A. J.: Corrosion Fatigue (in Ref. 54).
65. NORDFIN, L.: Some Problems of Fatigue of Bolts and Bolted Joints in Aircraft Applications, *Nat. Bur. Standards, Tech. Note* 136, 1962.
66. MUNSE, W. H., D. T. WRIGHT, and N. M. NEWMARK: *Am. Soc. Civil Eng. Proc. Separate* 441, 1954.
67. LUBAHN, J. D., and R. P. FELGAR: "Plasticity and Creep of Metals," John Wiley & Sons, Inc., 1961.
68. SHANK, M. E.: A Critical Survey of Brittle Fracture in Carbon Plate Steel Structures Other than Ships, *Am. Soc. Testing Materials, Spec. Tech. Pub.*, 158, 1954.
69. BUTLER, R. H., and T. L. CARTER: Stress-Life Relationship of the Rolling-contact Fatigue Spin Rig, *Nat. Adv. Comm. Aeron., Tech. Note* 3930, 1957.
70. WEISMAN, M. H., and M. H. KAPLAN: Fatigue Strength of Steel through the Range $\frac{1}{2}$ to 30,000 Cycles of Stress, *Proc. Am. Soc. Testing Materials*, Vol. 50, 1950.
71. MARIN, J.: Biaxial Tension–Tension Fatigue Strengths of Metals, *Am. Soc. Mech. Eng., Jour. Appl. Mech.*, Vol. 17, No. 2, June, 1950.
72. TIPPER, C. F.: "The Brittle Fracture Story," Cambridge University Press, 1962.
73. SINES, GEORGE, and J. L. WAISMAN (eds.): "Metal Fatigue," McGraw-Hill Book Company, 1959.
74. GOUGH, H. J.: Corrosion Fatigue of Metals, *Jour. Inst. Metals*, Vol. 49 No. 2, 1932.

CHAPTER 4

PRINCIPLES AND ANALYTICAL METHODS

Most of the formulas of strength of materials express the relations between the form and dimensions of a member, the loads applied thereto, and the resulting stress or deformation. Any such formula is valid only within certain limitations and is applicable only to certain problems. An understanding of these limitations, and of the way in which formulas may be combined and extended for the solution of problems to which they do not immediately apply, requires a knowledge of certain principles and methods which are briefly stated in the following articles. The significance and use of these principles and methods are illustrated in Part III by examples that accompany the discussion of specific problems.

13. Equations of Motion and of Equilibrium.—The relations that exist at any instant between the motion of a body and the forces acting on it may be expressed by these two equations: (1) F_x (the component along any line x of all forces acting on a body) $= m\bar{a}_x$ (the product of the mass of the body and the x component of the acceleration of its mass center); (2) T_x (the torque about any line x of all forces acting on the body) $= dh_x/dt$ (the time rate at which its angular momentum about that line is changing).

If the body in question is in equilibrium, these equations reduce to: (1) $F_x = 0$; (2) $T_x = 0$.

These equations, Hooke's law, and experimentally determined values of the elastic constants E, G, and ν constitute the basis for the mathematical analysis of most problems of strength of materials. The majority of the common formulas for stress are derived by considering a portion of the loaded member as a body in equilibrium under the action of forces that include the stresses sought, and then solving for these stresses by applying the equations of equilibrium.

14. Principle of Superposition.—With certain exceptions, the effect (stress, strain, deflection) produced on an elastic system by any final state of loading is the same whether the forces that constitute that loading are applied simultaneously or in any given sequence, and is the resultant of the effects that the several forces would produce if each acted singly.

An exception to this principle is afforded by any case in which some of the forces cause a deformation that enables other forces to produce an effect they would not otherwise have. A beam subjected to transverse and axial loading is an example of this; the transverse loads cause a deflection which enables the longitudinal load to produce a bending effect it would not produce if acting alone. In no case does the principle apply if the deformations are so large as to appreciably alter the geometrical relations of the parts of the system.

The principle of superposition is important and has many applications. It often makes it possible to resolve or break down a complex problem into a number of simple ones, each of which can be solved separately for stresses, deformations, etc., that are then algebraically added to yield the solution of the original problem.

15. Principle of Reciprocal Deflections.—Let A and B be any two points of an elastic system. Let the displacement of B in any direction U due to a force P acting in any direction V at A be u; and let the displacement of A in the direction V due to a force Q acting in the direction U at B be v. Then $Pv = Qu$.

This is the general statement of the principle. If P and Q are equal and parallel, and u and v are parallel, the statement can be greatly simplified. Thus, for a horizontal beam with vertical loading and deflection understood, the principle expresses the following relation: A load applied at any point A produces the same deflection at any other point B as it would produce at A if applied at B.

The principle of reciprocal deflections is a corollary of the principle of superposition and so can be applied only to cases for which that principle is valid. It can be used to advantage in many problems involving deformation, and is the basis of certain mechanical methods of structural analysis (see Refs. 1, 2). Examples of the application of the principle are given in Chaps. 8 and 10.

16. Method of Consistent Deformations (Strain Compatibility).—Many statically indeterminate problems are easily solved by utilizing the obvious relations between the deformations of the several parts, or between the deformations produced by the several loads. Thus the division of load between the parts of a composite member is readily ascertained by expressing the deformation or deflection of each part in terms of the load it carries, and then equating these deformations or deflections. Or the reaction at the supported end of a beam with one end fixed and the other supported can be found by regarding the beam as a cantilever, acted on by the downward loads and an upward end load (the reaction), and setting the resultant deflection at the end equal to zero.

The method of consistent deformations is based on the principle of superposition; it can be applied only to cases for which that principle is valid.

17. Principles and Methods Involving Strain Energy.—Strain energy has been defined (Chap. 1) as the mechanical energy stored up in an elastically stressed system; formulas for the amount of strain energy developed in members under various conditions of loading are given in Part III. It is the purpose of this article to state certain relations between strain energy and external forces that are useful in the analysis of stress and deformation. For convenience, external forces whose points of application do not move will here be called reactions, and external forces whose points of application do move will be called loads.

External Work Equal to Strain Energy.—When an elastic system is subjected to static loading, the external work done by the loads as they increase from zero to their maximum value is equal to the strain energy acquired by the system.

This relation may be used directly to determine the deflection of a system under a single load; for such a case it shows that the deflection at the point of loading in the direction of the load is equal to twice the strain energy divided by the load. The relationship also furnishes a means of determining the critical load that produces elastic instability in a member. A reasonable form of curvature, compatible with the boundary conditions, is assumed, and the corresponding critical load found by equating the work of the load to the strain energy developed, both quantities being calculated for the curvature assumed. For each such assumed curvature, a corresponding approximate critical load will be found, and the least load so found represents the closest approximation to the true critical load (see Ref. 3).

Method of Unit Loads.—During the static loading of an elastic system the external work done by a *constant* force acting thereon is equal to the internal work done by the stresses due to that constant force. This relationship is the basis of the following method for finding the deflection of any given point of an elastic system: A unit force is imagined to act at the point in question and in the direction of the deflection that is to be found. The stresses produced by such a unit force would do a certain amount of internal work during the application of the actual loads. This work, which can be readily found, is equal to the work done by the unit force. But this work, since the unit force is constant, is equal to the deflection sought.

If the direction of the deflection cannot be ascertained in advance, its horizontal and vertical components can be determined separately in the way described, and the resultant deflection found therefrom (see Refs. 4, 5). Examples of application of the method are given in Art. 28.

Deflection the Partial Derivative of Strain Energy.—When an elastic system is statically loaded, the partial derivative of the strain energy with respect to any one of the applied forces is equal to the movement of the point of application of that force in the direction of that force. This relationship (known as Castigliano's first theorem) provides a means of finding the deflection of a beam or truss under several loads (see Ref. 4).

Theorem of Least Work.[1]—When an elastic system is statically loaded, the distribution of stress is such as to make the strain energy a minimum consistent with equilibrium and the imposed boundary conditions.

[1] By theorem of least work is usually meant only so much of the theorem as is embodied in the first application here described, and so understood, it is often referred to as Castigliano's second theorem. But, as originally stated by Castigliano, it had a somewhat different significance. (See his "Théorème de l'équilibre des systèmes élastiques et ses applications," Paris, 1879, or the English translation "Elastic Stresses in Structures," by E. S. Andrews, Scott, Greenwood, London. See also R. V. Southwell, Castigliano's Principle of Minimum Strain-energy, *Proc. Royal Soc. London*, Series *A*, Vol. 154, 1936.) The more general theory stated is called *theorem of minimum energy,* by Love ("Mathematical Theory of Elasticity") and *theorem of minimum resilience* by Morley ("Theory of Structures").

This principle is extensively used in the solution of statically indeterminate problems. In the simpler type of problem (beams with redundant supports, trusses with redundant members) the first step in the solution consists in arbitrarily selecting certain reactions or members to be considered redundant, the number and identity of these being such that the remaining system is just determinate. The strain energy of the entire system is then expressed in terms of the unknown redundant reactions or stresses. The partial derivative of the strain energy with respect to each of the redundant reactions or stresses is then set equal to zero and the resulting equations solved for the redundant reactions or stresses. The remaining reactions or stresses are then found by the equations of equilibrium. An example of the application of this method is given in Art. 28.

As defined by this procedure, the theorem of least work is implicit in Castigliano's first theorem: it furnishes a method of solution identical with the method of consistent deflections, the deflection used being zero and being expressed as a partial derivative of the strain energy. In a more general type of problem, it is necessary to determine which of an infinite number of possible stress distributions or configurations satisfies the condition of minimum strain energy. The electronic computer has made practicable the solution of many problems of this kind—shell analysis, elastic and plastic buckling, etc.—which formerly were relatively intractable (Refs. 6, 9, 10, 11).

18. Dimensional Analysis.—Most physical quantities can be expressed in terms of mass, length, and time, conveniently represented by the symbols M, L, and T, respectively. Thus velocity $= LT^{-1}$; acceleration $= LT^{-2}$; force $= MLT^{-2}$; unit stress $= ML^{-1}T^{-2}$; etc. A formula in which the several quantities are thus expressed is a dimensional formula, and the various applications of this system of representation constitute dimensional analysis.

Dimensional analysis may be used to check formulas for homogeneity, to check or change units, to derive formulas, and to establish the relationships between similar physical systems which differ in scale (*e.g.*, a model and its prototype). In strength of materials, dimensional analysis is especially useful in checking formulas for homogeneity. To do this, it is not always necessary to express *all* quantities dimensionally, since it may be possible to cancel some terms. Thus it is often convenient to express force by some symbol, as F, until it is ascertained whether or not all terms representing force can be canceled.

For example, consider the formula for the deflection y at the free end of a cantilever beam of length l carrying a uniform load W. This formula (Table III) is: $y = \frac{1}{8}\frac{Wl^3}{EI}$. To test for homogeneity, omit the coefficient $\frac{1}{8}$ (which is dimensionless) and write the formula: $L = \frac{FL^3}{\left(\frac{F}{L^2}\right)L^4}$. It is seen that F cancels and the equation reduces at once to $L = L$, showing that the original equation was homogeneous.

Instead of the symbols M, L, T, and F, one can use the names of the *units* in which the quantities are to be expressed. Thus the above equation may be written:

$$\text{Inches} = \frac{(\text{pounds})(\text{inches}^3)}{(\text{pounds/inches}^2)(\text{inches}^4)} = \text{inches}$$

This practice is especially convenient if it is desired to change units. Thus it might be desired to write the above formula so that y is given in inches when l is expressed in feet. It is only necessary to write:

$$\text{Inches} = \frac{1}{8}\,\frac{\text{pounds (feet} \times 12)^3}{(\text{pounds/inches}^2)\ \text{inches}^4}$$

the coefficient is thus found to be 216 instead of $\frac{1}{8}$.

By what amounts to a reversal of the checking process described, it is often possible to determine the way in which a certain term or terms should appear in a formula, provided the other terms involved are known. For example, consider the formula for the critical load on an Euler column. Familiarity with the theory of flexure suggests that this load will be directly proportional to E and I. It is evident that the length l will be involved in some way as yet unknown. It is also reasonable to assume that the load is independent of the deflection, since both the bending moment and the resisting moment would be expected to vary in direct proportion to the deflection. One can then write: $P = kEIl^a$, where k is a dimensionless constant that must be found in some other way, and the exponent a shows how l

enters the expression. Writing the equation dimensionally and omitting k, we have $F = (F/L^2)L^4L^a$ or $L^2 = L^{4+a}$. Equating the exponents of L (as required for homogeneity) we find $a = -2$, showing that the original formula should be $P = kEI/l^2$. Note that the derivation of a formula in this way requires at least a partial knowledge of the relationship that is to be expressed.

The use of dimensional analysis in planning and interpreting model tests is of greater importance in aerodynamics and hydrodynamics than in strength of materials, although it has important applications in problems involving dynamic loading and vibrations (Refs. 7, 8).

19. Remarks on the Use of Formulas.—No calculated value of stress, strength, or deformation can be regarded as exact. The formulas used are based on certain assumptions as to properties of materials, regularity of form, and boundary conditions that are only approximately true, and they are derived by mathematical procedures that often involve further approximations. In general, therefore, great precision in numerical work is not justified. Each individual problem requires the exercise of judgment, and it is impossible to lay down rigid rules of procedure, but the following suggestions concerning the use of formulas may be of value.

1. For most cases, slide rule calculations giving results to three significant figures are sufficiently precise. An exception is afforded by any calculation that involves the algebraic addition of quantities which are large in comparison with the final result (*e.g.*, some of the formulas for beams under axial and transverse loading, some of the formulas for circular rings, and any case of superposition in which the effects of several loads tend to counteract each other). For such cases a desk calculator should be used.

2. In view of uncertainties as to actual conditions, many of the formulas may appear to be unnecessarily elaborate and to include constants given to more significant figures than is warranted. For this reason, one may often be inclined to simplify a formula by dropping unimportant terms, "rounding off" constants, etc. It is sometimes advantageous to do this, but it is usually better to use the formula as it stands, bearing in mind that the result is at best only a close approximation. The only disadvantage of using an allegedly "precise" formula

is the possibility of being misled into thinking that the result it yields corresponds exactly to a real condition. So far as the time required for calculation is concerned, little is saved by simplification and it is as easy to operate with large numbers as with small ones when a slide rule is used. If a complicated formula is to be used frequently, it is of course advantageous to represent it by charts or graphs.

3. When using an unfamiliar formula, one may be uncertain as to the correctness of the numerical substitutions made and mistrustful of the result. It is nearly always possible to effect some sort of check by analogy, superposition, reciprocal deflections, comparison, or merely by judgment and common sense. Thus the membrane analogy (Art. 23) shows that the torsional stiffness of any irregular section is greater than that of the largest inscribed circular section and less than that of the smallest circumscribed section. Superposition shows that the deflection and bending moment at the center of a beam under triangular loading (Case 15, Table III) is the same as under an equal load uniformly distributed (Case 13). The principle of reciprocal deflections shows that the stress and deflection at the center of a circular flat plate under eccentric concentrated load (Case 4, Table X) is the same as for an equal load uniformly distributed along a concentric circle with radius equal to the eccentricity (Case 3). Comparison shows that the critical unit compressive stress is greater for a thin plate under edge loading than for a strip of that plate regarded as an Euler column. Common sense and judgment should generally serve to prevent the acceptance of grossly erroneous calculations.

4. A difficulty frequently encountered is uncertainty as to boundary conditions—whether a beam or flat plate should be calculated as freely supported or fixed, whether a load should be assumed uniformly or otherwise distributed, etc. In any such case it is a good plan to make "bracketing assumptions," *i.e.*, to calculate the desired quantity on the basis of each of two assumptions representing limits between which the actual conditions must lie. Thus for a beam whose ends have an unknown degree of fixity the bending moment at the center cannot be more than if the ends were freely supported, and the bending moments at the ends cannot be more than if the ends were truly fixed. If so

designed as to be safe for either extreme condition, the beam will be safe for any intermediate degree of fixity.

5. Formulas concerning the validity of which there is reason for doubt, especially empirical formulas, should be checked dimensionally. If such a formula expresses the results of some intermediate condition, it should be checked for extreme or terminal conditions; thus an expression for the deflection of a beam carrying a uniform load over a portion of its length should agree with the corresponding expression for a fully loaded beam when the loaded portion becomes equal to the full length, and should vanish when the loaded portion becomes zero.

References

1. TIMOSHENKO, S., and J. M. LESSELLS: "Applied Elasticity," Westinghouse Technical Night School Press, 1925.
2. BEGGS, G. E.: The Use of Models in the Solution of Indeterminate Structures, *Jour. Franklin Inst.*, March, 1927.
3. TIMOSHENKO, S.: "Theory of Elastic Stability," Engineering Societies Monograph, McGraw-Hill Book Company, 1936.
4. SPOFFORD, C. M.: "Theory of Structures," McGraw-Hill Book Company, 1928.
5. NILES, A. S., and J. S. NEWELL: "Airplane Structures," 3d ed., John Wiley & Sons, Inc., 1943.
6. JAKOBSEN, B. F.: Stresses in Gravity Dams by Principle of Least Work, *Trans. Am. Soc. Civil Eng.*, Vol. 96, p. 489, 1932.
7. ROBERTSON, B. L.: Dimensional Analysis, *Gen. Elec. Rev.*, April, 1930.
8. BRIDGMAN, P. W.: "Dimensional Analysis," Yale University Press, 1922.
9. LANGHAAR, H. L.: "Energy Methods in Applied Mechanics," John Wiley & Sons, Inc., 1962.
10. SOUTHWELL, R. V.: "Relaxation Methods in Engineering Science," Oxford University Press, 1940.
11. BERG, G. V.: "Computer Analysis of Structures," College of Engineering, University of Michigan, 1963.

CHAPTER 5

EXPERIMENTAL METHODS

A structural member or part may be of such form, or may be loaded in such a way, that calculation of the stresses and strains produced in it is impracticable. When this is the case, resort may be had to experimental methods, which can be applied to the actual member, or to a model thereof, or to a conventionalized specimen. Some of the more important methods used for this purpose are briefly described in this chapter. There is available an extensive literature on experimental stress determination (see Refs. 1, 2, 3, 4) to which the interested reader is referred.

20. Measurement of Strain.—The most direct way of determining the stress produced under given circumstances is to measure the accompanying strain. This is comparatively easy when the stress is fairly uniform over a considerable length of the part in question, but becomes difficult when the stress is localized or varies abruptly, since measurement must then be made over a very short gauge length and with great precision. When localized stress occurs at the edge of a plate or similar member, its value can sometimes best be determined by measuring the *lateral* strain across the thickness of the plate and computing the corresponding longitudinal strain from Poisson's ratio. Under conditions of uniaxial tension or compression, it is sufficient to measure strains in one direction; under conditions of combined stress it is necessary to measure strains in each of two or three directions, preferably in the directions of the principal stresses. When a strain rosette (see Definitions) is to be analyzed, use may be made of either graphical or mathematical methods. A graphical method is described in Ref. 5; a mathematical method is described in Ref. 6; charts for rapid analysis are given in Ref. 7.

Extensometers and strain gauges commonly used in the laboratory testing of materials, where the form of specimen facilitates attachment and permits the use of almost any desired gauge length, are often not suitable for field use or even for laboratory tests on parts of irregular form.

Of the many instruments and technics that have been successfully used for the measurement of strain, the following, listed in the general order of mechanical, optical, and electrical, are among the more important and are commercially available.

1. *Olsen and Olsen-DeShazer Strain Gauges.*—Several different models of mechanical strain gauges, in general comprising a multiplying lever system in conjunction with an indicating dial. In some models contact with the strained part is through knife-edges, in some through points set in center-punch marks or in small drilled holes. In the Olsen-DeShazer gauge the measurements may be made by manually applying the points to drilled holes, so that readings on any number of gauge lines can be taken with a single instrument (Ref. 8).

2. *Whittemore Strain Gauge.*—Another manually applied gauge used with drilled holes; like the foregoing, of rugged construction and well suited to field work on structures (Ref. 9).

3. *Huggenberger Tensometer.*—A small, light instrument adapted to measurement of surface strains on members of almost any form. Instrument is attached to member, and no drilling or notching of the latter is necessary. Strains measured by a multiplying lever are read directly by eye from a scale. The instrument is adapted to static loading and is easily operated (Refs. 3, 12).

4. *Porter-Lipp Tensometer.*—Similiar to the Huggenberger tensometer but smaller and lighter (Ref. 10).

5. *The Mikrotator.*—Measures change in length of a twisted strip held under tension, by measuring the twisting or untwisting that occurs at mid-length when the strip elongates or shortens. Represented as being extremely sensitive (Ref. 11).

6. *deForest Scratch-recording Strain Gauge.*—A very small, light instrument which is attached to the member and which records actual deformations by means of a scratch on a polished metal surface. Record must be measured or photographed at suitable magnification. Adapted especially to use on parts subject to impact, vibration, or highly accelerated motion (Ref. 12).

7. *Stresscoat.*—A specially designed lacquer which, used as a brittle coating, reveals by the pattern in which it cracks, the zone and direction of the surface stresses in the part to which it is applied. By comparison with a calibration strip, quantitative results can be obtained (Ref. 13).

8. *Dials.*—There are several types of indicating dials which measure displacements directly, the motion of a plunger being multiplied by a ratchet and indicated by a pointer on a circular scale. Such dials are used in conjunction with a multiplying lever mechanism in the Olsen and Whittemore strain gauges, but can be used to measure strains and deflections directly, since some of them read to 1/10,000 in. (Ref. 14).

9. *Tuckerman Optical Strain Gauge.*—Light, sensitive, and very accurate gauge operating on the optical lever principle (Ref. 15).

10. *Electrical Resistance Gauge.*—Measures deformation by variation in electrical resistance of a strained element, which may be a wire or wire grid, a strip of metallic foil, or—for maximum sensitivity—a filament of silicon. Very light and suitable for use with either static or dynamic loading. Available in models for measurement of either one-way strain or strain rosettes. The most versatile and widely used of all strain measuring devices (Ref. 16).

11. *The Differential Transformer.*—Linear relationship between core motion and output voltage makes possible accurate measurement of displacement under a wide variety of conditions (Ref. 17).

In addition to those listed above, other devices and methods have been found advantageous for use under various special conditions. Among these may be mentioned the moiré method, which has been used to study thermal stress fields (Ref. 4), and the vibrating wire strain gauge, which is well adapted to field use over a considerable period of time (Ref. 18).

21. Photoelastic Analysis.—When a beam of circularly polarized light passes through an elastically stressed plate of transparent isotropic material, the beam is decomposed into two rays polarized in the planes of the principal stresses, and these rays have a phase difference which is proportional to the difference between the principal stresses.

This phenomenon provides a valuable means of studying the distribution and intensity of two-dimensional stress, especially in members subject to stress concentration at the boundaries. A model of the member made of celluloid or Bakelite is loaded, a beam of circularly polarized monochromatic light is passed through it, and the emerging plane-polarized rays then are passed through an analyzer which brings them into a common plane so that interference due to phase difference is registered on a screen image. At any point or zone of the model where the stress conditions cause a relative retardation equal to a certain value or some multiple of that value, complete interference results in a corresponding dark spot or fringe on the screen, and as the load is increased, each successive appearance of such a fringe indicates a definite increment in the difference between principal stresses. The value of this increment is determined by observation of a specimen under pure tension, and the stress difference produced at any point in the model by a given loading can then be ascertained by counting the number of fringes that pass over that point as the load is applied. At any point on the boundary, one of the principal stresses must be zero, and so the other principal stress there must be equal to the stress difference. At points away from the boundary it is often possible to calculate one of the two principal stresses, or to determine their sum by measuring the lateral strain, and then the value of each principal stress can be determined from the stress difference found as above. The general distribution and relative intensity of stresses throughout the member are indicated by the shape and spacing of the fringes. If, instead of monochromatic light, white light is used, the specimen and screen image appear colored, and each tint corresponds to a certain difference in principal stresses (Ref. 19).

Although the photoelastic method of stress analysis is best adapted to the study of plane stress, it has been successfully employed in investigating certain cases of three-dimensional stress (Refs. 19, 20).

Large (plastic) surface strains in metal parts have been successfully measured by using photoelastic material bonded to the part with an adhesive, or cast or brushed directly on the surface (Refs. 4, 41).

X-rays.—X-ray diffraction makes possible the determination of changes in interatomic distance, and thus the measurement of elastic strain. The method has the particular advantages that it can be used at points of high stress concentration and can be used to determine residual stresses without cutting the object of investigation (Ref. 21).

22. Detection of Plastic Yielding.—In parts made of ductile metal, much may sometimes be learned concerning the location of the most highly stressed region and the load that produces elastic failure by noting the first signs of plastic yielding. Such yielding may be detected in the following ways:

Observation of Slip Lines.—If yielding first occurs at some point on the surface, it can be detected by the appearance of slip lines if the surface is suitably polished. If yielding occurs first at some interior point, it can sometimes be discovered by cutting a section that includes the zone of high stress, and then etching the cut surfaces with a solution of cupric chloride in hydrochloric acid and water to make the slip lines visible. This method, however, is applicable only to certain low-carbon steels, and there appears to be no way to ascertain, except by trial, whether or not a given steel can thus be made to reveal overstrain (Ref. 22).

Brittle Coating.—If a member is coated with some material which will flake off easily, this flaking will indicate local yielding of the member. A coating of resin, or a wash of lime or white portland cement, applied and allowed to dry, is best for this purpose, but chalk or mill scale will often serve. By this method zones of high stress such as occur in pressure vessels around openings and projections can be located and the load required to produce local yielding can be approximately determined.

23. Analogies.—Certain problems in elasticity involve equations that cannot be solved but that happen to be mathematically identical with the equations that describe some other physical phenomenon which can be investigated experimentally. Among the more useful of such analogies are the following:

Membrane Analogy.—This is especially useful in determining the torsion properties of bars having noncircular sections. If in a thin flat plate holes are cut having the outlines of various sections, and over each of these holes a soap film (or other membrane) is stretched and slightly distended by pressure from one side, the volumes of the bubbles thus formed are proportional to the torsional rigidities of the corresponding sections, and the slope of a bubble surface at any point is proportional to the stress caused at that point of the corresponding section by a given twist per unit length of bar. By cutting in the plate one hole the shape of the section to be studied and another hole that is circular, the torsional properties of the irregular section can be determined by comparing the bubble formed on the hole of that shape with the bubble formed on the circular hole, since the torsional properties of the circular section are known. This method has been used successfully to determine the torsional stiffness of various members used in airplane construction (Refs. 23, 24, 25).

A similar membrane analogy may be used to determine the distribution of shear stress and the position of the center of flexure in a beam having any given section. Here, however, the procedure is much less simple than that described above. The soap film, instead of being inflated, is stretched over a hole cut in a curved sheet of metal. The shape of the hole and the curvature of the sheet must be such that a projection of the hole, on a fixed reference plane, has the form of the section being studied, while distances of points along the edge of the hole from that reference plane represent a given function of the shape of the section (see Ref. 26).

Hydrodynamic Analogy for Torsion.—If a prismatic vessel or tube having a cross section like that of a twisted member is filled with fluid, set with its axis vertical and rotated by a horizontal couple, the velocity of the fluid at any point, relative to the vessel, will be proportional to and have the same direction as the shear stress at a corresponding point in the twisted member.

This and other hydrodynamic analogies are not well adapted to quantitative investigation of torsion problems, but they may be used to give a good representation of the shear distribution and the warping of sections (see Refs. 27, 28).

Electrical Analogy for Torsion.—This is especially applicable to the study of stresses in a circular shaft having circumferential grooves or other somewhat abrupt changes in section. Consider a plate having the outline of a longitudinal half-section of the shaft, and a thickness at any point proportional to the cube of the distance from that edge which represents the axis of the shaft. If the ends of this plate, which correspond to the ends of the shaft, are maintained at a constant difference of electrical potential, the rate of drop of potential at any point along the thick edge of the plate is proportional to the shear stress at the corresponding point on the surface of the shaft.

This analogy has been used to determine the factor of torsional-stress concentration at fillets, etc. (Refs. 25, 28, 29).

24. Models.—In addition to the use of models in photoelastic analysis, they may be employed in other ways to investigate stress in members of peculiar form and to predict strength.

Rubber Models.—By ruling a grid or lattice of fine lines on the surface of a model and studying the distortion of this grid under load, it is possible to ascertain something concerning the distribution and magnitude of the stresses in a member or structure. The material used must be one that can sustain very large deformations without ceasing to be approximately elastic. Models of rubber and of gelatin have been used to study the stresses in dams (Ref. 30), in flat slabs (Ref. 31), and in members subject to stress concentration (Ref. 32).

Plastic Models.—The above procedure may be followed using, instead of an elastic material like rubber, a soft metal which will sustain large *plastic* deformations without rupture, and in which such deformations are approximately proportional to the applied stress (Ref. 33).

Brittle Models.—If a brittle material were available for which the proportional limit and ultimate strength were identical, then for members made thereof all stresses would be proportional to the applied load, and formulas for elastic stress would be valid clear up to rupture. It would therefore be possible, by testing to failure models made of such material, to determine the relation between load and maximum stress in a member of any form, simply by the relation between the breaking load and the ultimate tensile strength.

There is probably no material available for which Hooke's law applies clear up to fracture, but there are materials which almost conform to this requirement. Models made of pottery plaster, plaster of Paris, and Bakelite have been used to check formulas for the maximum stress in torsion members, curved beams, flat plates, etc., and to determine factors of stress concentration (Refs. 34, 35, 36, 37).

This method has the advantages of being cheap, quick, and applicable to any form of member and any condition of stress. It has the disadvantages of yielding information concerning the maximum stress only, and of being only fairly dependable because of the fact that there is some plastic action, even in the most brittle of available materials.

Proportionate-strength Models.—The breaking strength of members, and even of structures of some complexity, can be predicted with fair accuracy from tests of plaster models, provided allowance is made for all factors involved. In principle, this method comprises the following steps: (1) determination by test of the load P_m carried by a scale model $1/n$ times as large as the structure; (2) determination, by tests of suitable coupons, of R, the ratio of the ultimate strength of the structural material to the ultimate strength of the model material; (3) calculation of the predicted load P that the structure will carry by the relation $P = P_m \times n^2 \times R$. To secure satisfactory results from so simple a procedure would require certain relationships between the structural and model materials; in particular, the strength ratio R should be the same for all kinds of stress likely to prove critical, and the materials should respond similarly to the influence of form on strength. Differences in this latter respect can be taken into account if values of k_r, rupture factors, form factors, etc., are known for each material. This method has been used to predict the strength of castings of irregular form and of reinforced concrete structures with reasonable accuracy (Ref. 36).

Models for Investigation of Elastic Stability.—The critical loading for thin-walled structures—submarine hulls, pipes, monocoque fuselages, etc.—is sometimes determined by tests on small models. Since elastic stability is influenced greatly by small departures from geometrical regularity of form, the models so used must be constructed with great care, and of material similar to that of which the prototype is made. Paper models have been used to check basic theories and to secure information as to the general behavior of thin-walled cylinders, but it is generally agreed that for reliable quantitative results the model material should be identical with that used in the actual structure (Refs. 38, 39).

References

1. *Proceedings of the Society for Experimental Stress Analysis*, 1943–1960, and Experimental Mechanics, *Jour. Soc. Exp. Mech.*, after Jan. 1, 1961.
2. HETENYI, M.: "Handbook of Experimental Stress Analysis," John Wiley & Sons, Inc., 1950.
3. LEE, G. H.: "Introduction to Experimental Stress Analysis," John Wiley & Sons, Inc., 1950.
4. DOVE, R. C., and P. H. ADAMS: "Experimental Stress Analysis and Motion Measurement," Charles E. Merrill Books, Inc., 1955.
5. HILL, H. N.: A Semi-graphical Method for Analyzing Strains Measured on Three or Four Gauge Lines Intersecting at 45°, *Nat. Adv. Comm. Aeron., Tech. Note* 709, 1939.
6. BEGGS, G. E., and E. K. TIMBY: Interpreting Data from Strain Rosettes, *Eng. News-Record,* Mar. 10, 1938.

7. Manson, S. S.: Charts for Rapid Analysis of 45° Strain Rosette Data, *Nat. Adv. Comm. Aeron., Tech. Note* 940, 1944.
8. Descriptive literature, Tinius Olsen Testing Machine Co., Willow Grove, Pa.
9. Descriptive literature, Wiedemann Machine Co., King of Prussia, Pa.
10. Descriptive literature, P. L. Porter, Los Angeles, Calif.
11. Descriptive literature, Swedish Gauge Co. of America.
12. Descriptive literature, Baldwin Southwark Corp.
13. Descriptive literature, Stresscoat Division, Magnaflux Corp., Chicago, Ill.
14. Descriptive literature, Federal Products Corp.; Standard Gage Co.; B. C. Ames Co.; L. S. Starrett Co.
15. Descriptive literature, American Instrument Co., Inc.
16. Perry, C. C., and H. R. Lissner: "The Strain Gage Primer," 2d ed., McGraw-Hill Book Company, 1962.
17. Descriptive literature, Schaevitz Engineering, Pennsauken, N.J.
18. Shepherd, R.: Strain Measurements Using Vibrating Wire Gauges, *Exp. Mech.*, Vol. 4, No. 8, August, 1964.
19. Frocht, M. M.: "Photoelasticity," Vols. 1 and 2, John Wiley & Sons, Inc., 1941, 1948.
20. Oppel, G.: The Photoelastic Investigation of Three-dimensional Stress and Strain Conditions, *Nat. Adv. Comm. Aeron., Tech. Memo.* 824.
21. Norton, J. T., and D. Rosenthal: Stress Measurement by X-ray Diffraction, and Applications of the X-ray Diffraction Method of Stress Measurement to Problems Involving Residual Stresses in Metals, *Proc. Soc. Exp. Stress Anal.*, Vol. 1, No. 2, 1944.
22. Frye, A.: *Stahl und Eisen*, Aug. 11, 1921, also *Iron Age*, Dec. 1, 1921.
23. Trayer, G. W., and H. W. March: The Torsion of Members Having Sections Common in Aircraft Construction, *Adv. Comm. Aeron., Report* 334, 1930.
24. Taylor, G. I., and A. A. Griffith: The Use of Soap Films in Solving Torsion Problems, *Tech. Report Adv. Comm. Aeron.* (British), *Reports and Memoranda*, No. 333, p. 920, 1917.
25. Higgins, T. J.: Analogic Experimental Methods in Stress Analysis as Exemplified by Saint-Venant's Torsion Problem, *Proc. Soc. Exp. Stress Anal.*, Vol. 2, No. 2, p. 17, 1945.
26. Griffith, A. A., and G. I. Taylor: The Problem of Flexure and Its Solution by the Soap Film Method, *Tech. Report Adv. Comm. Aeron.* (British), *Reports and Memoranda*, No. 399, p. 950, 1917.
27. DenHartog, J. P.: On the Hydrodynamic Analogy of Torsion, *Am. Soc. Mech. Eng., Paper* A-46, *Jour. Appl. Mech.*, Vol. 2, No. 2, 1935.
28. Timoshenko, S.: "Theory of Elasticity," Engineering Societies Monograph, McGraw-Hill Book Company, 1934.
29. Jacobsen, L. S.: Torsional-Stress Concentrations in Shafts of Circular Cross-section and Variable Diameter, *Trans. Am. Soc. Mech. Eng.*, Vol. 47, p. 619, 1925.
30. "An Experimental Study of the Stresses in Masonry Dams," Research Memoirs, Technical Series V, Cambridge University Press. (See also *Trans. Am. Soc. Civil Eng.*, Vol. 98, p. 1022, 1933.)

31. TRELEASE, F. J.: "The Design of Concrete Flat Slabs," *Proc. Nat. Assoc. Cement Users*, Vol. 8, p. 218, 1912.
32. CHILES, G. S., and R. G. KELLEY: The Resistance of Materials; the Effect of Sudden or Abrupt Changes in the Section on the Distribution of Unit-stress, *Railway Mech. Eng.*, March, April, and May, 1919.
33. BACH, C.: "Elastizität und Festigkeit," 8th ed., p. 342, Berlin.
34. PETERSEN, R. E.: An Investigation of Stress Concentration by Means of Plaster of Paris Specimens, *Mech. Eng.*, p. 1449, December, 1926.
35. SEELY, F. B., and R. V. JAMES: The Plaster-model Method of Determining Stresses Applied to Curved Beams, *Univ. Ill. Eng. Exp. Sta., Bull.* 195, 1928.
36. ROARK, R. J., and R. S. HARTENBERG: Predicting the Strength of Structures from Tests of Plaster Models, *Univ. Wis. Eng. Exp. Sta., Bull.* 81, 1935.
37. FROCHT, M. M.: The Behavior of Brittle Materials at Failure, *Am. Soc. Mech. Eng., Paper* A-99, *Jour. Appl. Mech.*, Vol. 3, No. 3, 1931.
38. RHODE, R. V., and E. E. LUNDQUIST: Strength Tests of Paper Cylinders in Compression, Bending and Shear, *Nat. Adv. Comm. Aeron., Tech. Note* 370.
39. SAUNDERS, H. E., and D. F. WINDENBURG: The Use of Models in Determining the Strength of Thin-walled Structures, *Trans. Am. Soc. Mech. Eng.*, Vol. 54, No. 23, p. 263, 1932.
40. Descriptive literature, Instrument Division, Budd Co.

CHAPTER 6

PROPERTIES OF A PLANE AREA

Because of their importance in connection with the analysis of bending and torsion, certain relations between the moments of inertia and product of inertia of a plane area (here called *section*) are indicated below. The equations are given with reference to Fig. 2, and the notation is as follows: A is the area of the section; X and Y are rectangular axes in the plane of the section intersecting at any point 0; Z is a polar axis through 0; U and V are rectangular axes through 0, inclined at an angle θ to X and Y; U' and V' are the *principal axes* at the point 0; L and M are rectangular axes parallel respectively to X and Y and intersecting at G, the centroid of the area; $\bar{x}$ and $\bar{y}$ are the distances of X and Y from L and M, respectively; r is the distance from 0 to dA.

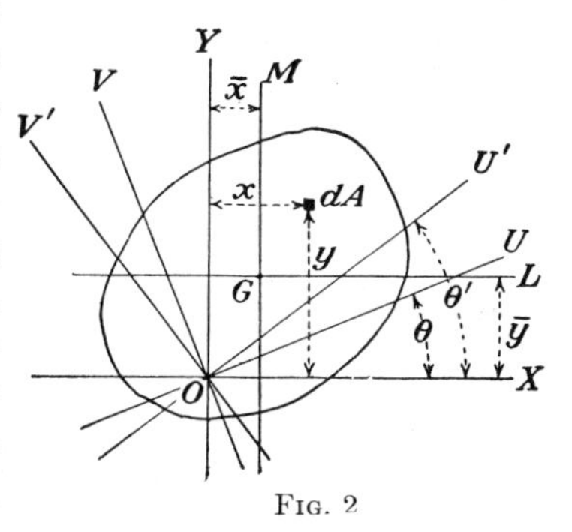

FIG. 2

By definition (see Chap. 1):

$$I_x = \int dA \cdot y^2$$
$$I_y = \int dA \cdot x^2$$
$$J_z = \int dA \cdot r^2$$
$$H_{xy} = \int dA \cdot xy$$
$$k_x = \sqrt{\frac{I_x}{A}}$$
$$k_y = \sqrt{\frac{I_y}{A}}$$

The following equations and statements hold true:

$$J_z = I_x + I_y = I_u + I_v = I_{u'} + I_{v'}$$
$$I_x = I_l + A\bar{y}^2$$
$$I_u = I_x \cos^2\theta + I_y \sin^2\theta - H_{xy}\sin 2\theta$$

$$\theta' = \frac{1}{2} \text{ arc tan } \frac{2H_{xy}}{I_y - I_x}$$

$$I_{u'} = \tfrac{1}{2}(I_x + I_y) \pm \sqrt{\tfrac{1}{4}(I_y - I_x)^2 + H_{xy}^2} \begin{cases} (+ \text{ if } I_{u'} \text{ is max } I) \\ (- \text{ if } I_{u'} \text{ is min } I) \end{cases}$$

$$H_{xy} = H_{lm} + A\bar{x}\bar{y}$$

$$H_{uv} = H_{xy} \cos 2\theta - \tfrac{1}{2}(I_y - I_x) \sin 2\theta$$

$$H_{u'v'} = 0$$

Which of the axes, U' or V', is the axis of maximum moment of inertia and which the axis of minimum moment of inertia must be ascertained by calculation, unless the shape of the section is such as to make this obvious.

Any axis of symmetry is one of the principal axes for every point thereon.

The product of inertia is zero for any pair of axes one of which is an axis of symmetry.

If the moment of inertia for one of the principal axes through a point is equal to that for any other axis through that point, it follows that the moments of inertia for all axes through that point are equal. (This refers to axes in the plane of the section.) Thus the moment of inertia of a square, or of an equilateral triangle, or of any section having two or more axes of identical symmetry, is the same for any central axis.

The moment of inertia and radius of gyration of a section with respect to a central axis are less than for any other axis parallel thereto.

The moment of inertia of a composite section (one regarded as made up of rectangles, triangles, etc.) is equal to the sum of the moments of inertia of its components parts. Voids are taken into account by subtracting the moment of inertia of the corresponding area.

Expressions for the area, distance of centroid from edges, moment of inertia, radius of gyration, and section modulus are given in Table I for each of a number of representative sections. I and H for composite areas can be found by addition; the centroid of composite areas can be found by using the relation that the statical moment, about any line, of the entire area is equal to the sum of the statical moments of its component parts. Properties of structural sections—I-beams, channels, angles, etc.—are given in the structural-steel handbooks.

A closely approximate formula (due to Steinitz, *Aero. Digest*, November, 1939) for the section modulus I/c of any solid section of compact form (*e.g.*, approximately square, circular, triangular, or trapezoidal) is $I/c = A^2/6.15b$, where A is the area and b is the maximum width of the section. The formula gives the least I/c for nonsymmetrical sections, and makes it unnecessary to locate the position of the neutral axis. The formula applies, though with less accuracy, to closed hollow sections, of uniform wall thickness, for which b should be taken as the net width, equal to twice the wall thickness. It cannot be used for flanged or otherwise "spread" sections.

TABLE I.—PROPERTIES OF SECTIONS

Form of section	Area A	Distance from centroid to extremities of section y_1, y_2	Moments of inertia I_1 and I_2 about principal central axes 1 and 2	Radii of gyration, r_1 and r_2, about principal central axes
1. Square 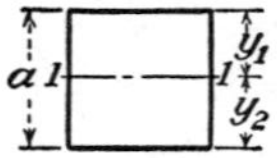	$A = a^2$	$y_1 = y_2 = \frac{1}{2}a$	$I_1 = I_2 = I_3 = \frac{1}{12}a^4$	$r_1 = r_2 = r_3 = 0.289a$
2. Rectangle 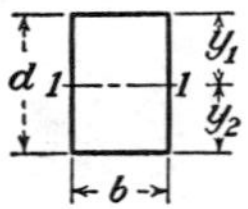	$A = bd$	$y_1 = y_2 = \frac{1}{2}d$	$I_1 = \frac{1}{12}bd^3$	$r_1 = 0.289d$
3. Triangle 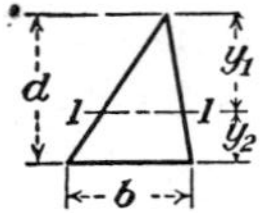	$A = \frac{1}{2}bd$	$y_1 = \frac{2}{3}d$ $y_2 = \frac{1}{3}d$	$I_1 = \frac{1}{36}bd^3$	$r_1 = 0.2358d$
4. Trapezoid 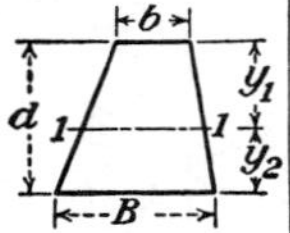	$A = \frac{1}{2}(B + b)d$	$y_1 = d\frac{2B + b}{3(B + b)}$ $y_2 = d\frac{B + 2b}{3(B + b)}$	$I_1 = \frac{d^3(B^2 + 4Bb + b^2)}{36(B + b)}$	$r_1 = \frac{d}{6(B + b)}\sqrt{2(B^2 + 4Bb + b^2)}$
5. Regular polygon with n sides 	$A = \frac{1}{4}na^2 \cot \alpha$	$y_1 = \frac{a}{2 \sin \alpha}$ $y_2 = \frac{a}{2 \tan \alpha}$	$I_1 = \frac{A(6y_1^2 - a^2)}{24}$ $I_2 = \frac{A(12y_2^2 + a^2)}{48}$	$r_1 = \sqrt{\frac{6y_1^2 - a^2}{24}}$ $r_2 = \sqrt{\frac{12y_2^2 + a^2}{48}}$

6. Solid circle	$A = \pi R^2$	$y_1 = y_2 = R$	$I = \frac{1}{4}\pi R^4$ [illegible]	[illegible]
7. Hollow circle	$A = \pi(R^2 - R_0^2)$	$y_1 = y_2 = R$	$I = \frac{1}{4}\pi(R^4 - R_0^4)$	$r = \sqrt{\frac{1}{4}(R^2 + R_0^2)}$
8. Solid semicircle	$A = \frac{1}{2}\pi R^2$	$y_1 = 0.5756R$ $y_2 = 0.4244R$	$I_1 = 0.1098R^4$ $I_2 = \frac{1}{8}\pi R^4$	$r_1 = 0.2643R$ $r_2 = \frac{1}{2}R$
9. Circular sector	$A = \alpha R^2$	$y_1 = R\left(1 - \frac{2\sin\alpha}{3\alpha}\right)$ $y_2 = 2R\frac{\sin\alpha}{3\alpha}$	$I_1 = \frac{1}{4}R^4\left[\alpha + \sin\alpha\cos\alpha - \frac{16\sin^2\alpha}{9\alpha}\right]$ $I_2 = \frac{1}{4}R^4[\alpha - \sin\alpha\cos\alpha]$	$r_1 = \frac{1}{2}R\sqrt{1 + \frac{\sin\alpha\cos\alpha}{\alpha} - \frac{16\sin^2\alpha}{9\alpha^2}}$ $r_2 = \frac{1}{2}R\sqrt{1 - \frac{\sin\alpha\cos\alpha}{\alpha}}$
10. Circular segment	$A = \frac{1}{2}R^2(2\alpha - \sin 2\alpha)$	$y_1 = R\left(1 - \frac{4\sin^3\alpha}{6\alpha - 3\sin 2\alpha}\right)$ $y_2 = R\left(\frac{4\sin^3\alpha}{6\alpha - 3\sin 2\alpha} - \cos\alpha\right)$	$I_1 = R^4\left[\frac{1}{8}(2\alpha - \sin 2\alpha)\left(1 + \frac{2\sin^3\alpha\cos\alpha}{\alpha - \sin\alpha\cos\alpha}\right) - \frac{8}{9}\frac{\sin^6\alpha}{2\alpha - \sin 2\alpha}\right]$ $I_2 = R^4\left[\frac{1}{8}(2\alpha - \sin 2\alpha) - \frac{1}{12}\frac{(2\alpha - \sin 2\alpha)\sin^3\alpha\cos\alpha}{\alpha - \sin\alpha\cos\alpha}\right]$	$r_1 = \frac{1}{2}R\sqrt{1 + \frac{2\sin^3\alpha\cos\alpha}{\alpha - \sin\alpha\cos\alpha} - \frac{64}{9}\frac{\sin^6\alpha}{(2\alpha - \sin 2\alpha)^2}}$ $r_2 = \frac{1}{2}R\sqrt{1 - \frac{2\sin^3\alpha\cos\alpha}{3(\alpha - \sin\alpha\cos\alpha)}}$

TABLE I.—PROPERTIES OF SECTIONS.—(*Continued*)

Form of section	Area A	Distance from centroid to extremities of section y_1, y_2	Moments of inertia I_1 and I_2 about principal central axes 1 and 2	Radii of gyration, r_1 and r_2, about principal central axes
11. Very thin annulus	$A = 2\pi Rt$	$y_1 = y_2 = R$	$I = \pi R^3 t$	$r = 0.707R$
12. Sector of thin annulus	$A = 2\alpha Rt$	$y_1 = R\left(1 - \frac{\sin \alpha}{\alpha}\right)$ $y_2 = R\left(\frac{\sin \alpha}{\alpha} - \cos \alpha\right)$	$I_1 = R^3 t\left(\alpha + \sin \alpha \cos \alpha - \frac{2 \sin^2 \alpha}{\alpha}\right)$ $I_2 = R^3 t(\alpha - \sin \alpha \cos \alpha)$	$r_1 = R\sqrt{\frac{\alpha + \sin \alpha \cos \alpha - 2 \sin^2 \alpha/\alpha}{2\alpha}}$ $r_2 = R\sqrt{\frac{\alpha - \sin \alpha \cos \alpha}{2\alpha}}$
13. Solid ellipse	$A = \frac{1}{4}\pi bd$	$y_1 = y_2 = \frac{1}{2}d$	$I_1 = \frac{1}{64}\pi bd^3$	$r_1 = \frac{1}{4}d$
14. Hollow ellipse	$A = \frac{1}{4}\pi(bd - b_1d_1)$	$y_1 = y_2 = \frac{1}{2}d$	$I_1 = \frac{1}{64}\pi(bd^3 - b_1d_1^3)$	$r_1 = \frac{1}{4}\sqrt{\frac{bd^3 - b_1d_1^3}{bd - b_1d_1}}$

PART III

FORMULAS AND EXAMPLES

Each of the following chapters deals with a certain type of structural member or with a certain condition of stress. What may be called the common or typical case is usually discussed first; special cases, representing peculiarities of form, proportions, or circumstances of loading, are considered subsequently. In the discussion of each case the underlying assumptions are stated, the general behavior of the loaded member is described, and formulas for the stress and deformation are given. The more important of the general equations are numbered consecutively throughout each section to facilitate reference but, wherever possible, formulas applying to specific cases are tabulated for convenience and for economy of space.

In all formulas, unless other units are specified, the unit of distance is the inch and the unit of force is the pound. Therefore all areas are in square inches, all moments of inertia are in inches fourth, all distributed loads are in pounds per linear inch or pounds per square inch, all moments are in inch-pounds, and all stresses are in pounds per square inch.

CHAPTER 7

TENSION, COMPRESSION, SHEAR, AND COMBINED STRESS

25. Bar under Axial Tension (or Compression); Common Case. The bar is straight, of any uniform cross section, of homogeneous material, and (if under compression) short or constrained against lateral buckling. The loads are applied at the ends, centrally, and in such a manner as to avoid nonuniform stress distribution at any section of the part under consideration. The stress does not exceed the proportional limit.

Behavior.—The bar elongates (under tension) or shortens (under compression), the unit longitudinal strain being ϵ, the total longitudinal strain in the length l being e. The bar contracts (under

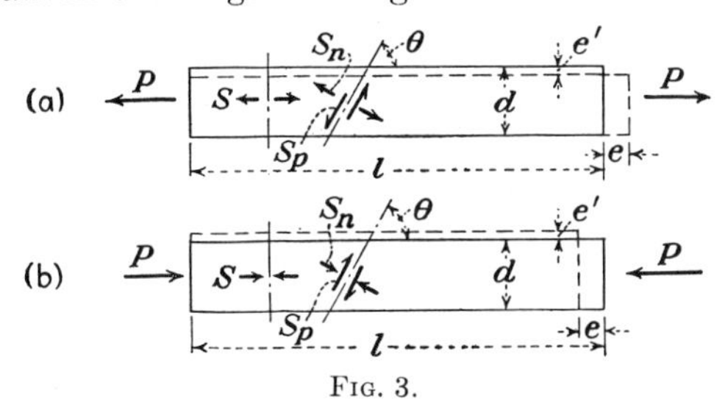

FIG. 3.

tension) or expands (under compression); the unit lateral strain ϵ' is the same in all transverse directions; the total lateral strain e' in any direction is proportional to the lateral dimension d measured in that direction. Both longitudinal and lateral strains are proportional to the applied load. On any right section there is a uniform tensile (or compressive) stress s; on any oblique section there is a uniform tensile (or compressive) normal stress s_n and a uniform shear stress s_p. In Fig. 3, the conditions under tension are represented in (*a*), the conditions under compression in (*b*).

Formulas.—Let P = applied load.

A = cross-sectional area (before loading).

l = length (before loading).

E = modulus of elasticity.

ν = Poisson's ratio.

Then:

$$s = \frac{P}{A} \tag{1}$$

$$s_n = \frac{P}{A} \sin^2 \theta; \qquad \max s_n = s \text{ (when } \theta = 90°)$$

$$s_p = \frac{P}{2A} \sin 2\theta; \qquad \max s_p = \frac{1}{2}s \text{ (when } \theta = 45°)$$

$$\epsilon = \frac{s}{E} \tag{2}$$

$$e = l\epsilon = \frac{Pl}{AE} \tag{3}$$

$$\epsilon' = \nu\epsilon \tag{4}$$

$$e' = d\epsilon' \tag{5}$$

$$\text{Strain energy per unit volume} = \frac{1}{2}\frac{s^2}{E} \text{ (in.-lb. per cu. in.)} \tag{6}$$

$$\text{Total strain energy} = \frac{1}{2}\frac{s^2}{E}lA = \frac{1}{2}Pe \text{ (in.-lb.)} \tag{7}$$

Each square inch of cross section diminishes to $(1 - 2\nu\epsilon)$ sq. in. under tension, and increases to $(1 + 2\nu\epsilon)$ sq. in. under compression. Each cubic inch of volume increases to $(1 - 2\nu\epsilon + \epsilon)$ cu. in. under tension, and decreases to $(1 + 2\nu\epsilon - \epsilon)$ cu. in. under compression.

In some discussions it is convenient to refer to the *stiffness* of a member, which is a measure of the resistance it offers to being deformed. The stiffness of a uniform bar under axial load is shown by Eq. 3 to be proportional to A and E directly and to l inversely, *i.e.*, proportional to $\frac{AE}{l}$.

Example

A cylindrical specimen of cast iron 4 in. long and $1\frac{1}{2}$ in. in diameter has applied to it a compressive load of 20,000 lb. For this cast iron, $\nu = 0.25$ and E (secant modulus) = 15,000,000. It is required to find (*a*) the unit compressive stress s; (*b*) the total longitudinal deformation e; (*c*) the total transverse deformation e'; (*d*) the change in volume ΔV; (*e*) the total energy, or work done in applying the load.

(*a*) $s = \frac{P}{A} = \frac{20{,}000}{1.77} = 11{,}300$ lb. per sq. in.

(*b*) $\epsilon = \frac{s}{E} = \frac{11{,}300}{15{,}000{,}000} = 0.000754; e = l\epsilon = 4 \times 0.000754 = 0.00302$ in. (shortening)

(c) $\epsilon' = \nu\epsilon = 0.25 \times 0.000754 = 0.000189$; $e' = d\epsilon' = 1.5 \times 0.000189 =$ 0.000283 in. (expansion)

(d) Change in volume per cu. in. $= 1 - (1 + 2\nu\epsilon - \epsilon) = 0.000377$ cu. in.
Total change in volume $\Delta V = 4 \times 1.77 \times 0.000377 = 0.00267$ cu. in. (decrease)

(e) Strain energy $= \frac{1}{2}Pe = \frac{1}{2}(20{,}000)(0.00302) = 30.2$ in.-lb.

26. Bar under Tension (or Compression); Special Cases.—If the bar is not straight, it is subject to bending; formulas for this case are given in Art. 67.

If the load is applied eccentrically, the bar is subject to bending; formulas for this case are given in Arts. 40, and 67.

If the load is compressive and the bar is long and not laterally constrained, it must be analyzed as a column by the methods of Chap. 11.

If the stress exceeds the proportional limit, the formulas for stress given in Art. 25 still hold, but the deformation and the work done in producing it can be determined only from experimental data.

If the section is not uniform but changes *gradually*, the stress at any section can be found by dividing the load by the area of that section; the total longitudinal deformation over a length l is given by $\int_0^l \frac{P}{AE}dl$; the strain energy is given by $\int_0^l \frac{1}{2}\frac{P^2}{AE}dl$. If the change in section is *abrupt*, stress concentration may have to be taken into account, values of k being used to find elastic stresses and values of k_r being used to predict the breaking load. Stress concentration may also have to be considered if the end attachments for loading involve pinholes, screw threads, or other stress raisers (see Art. 8 and Table XVII).

If instead of being applied at the ends of a uniform bar the load is applied at an intermediate point, both ends being held, the *method of consistent deformations* shows that the load is apportioned to the two parts of the bar in inverse proportion to their respective lengths.

If a uniform bar is supported at one end in a vertical position and loaded only by its own weight, the maximum stress occurs at the supported end, and is equal to the weight divided by the cross-sectional area. The total elongation is *half* as great, and the total strain energy *one-third* as great, as if a load equal to the weight were applied at the unsupported end. A bar supported at one end and loaded only by its own weight will have the same unit stress s (pounds per square inch) at all sections if tapered so that all sections are similar in form but vary in scale according to the formula: $y = (s/w) \log_e A$, where y is the distance (inches) from the free end of the bar to any section, A is the area (square inches) of that section, and w is the density of the material (pounds per cubic inch). If in addition to its own weight the bar is loaded by an axial downward force P (pounds) applied at the unsupported end, the stress will be the same at all sections if the bar tapers in conformity with the equation $y = (s/w)\ (\log_e A - \log_e (P/s))$.

If a bar is stressed by having both ends rigidly held while a change in temperature is imposed, the resulting stress is found by calculating the longitudinal expansion (or contraction) that the change in temperature would produce if the bar were not held, and then calculating the load necessary to shorten (or lengthen) it by that amount (principle of superposition). If the bar is uniform, the unit stress produced is independent of the length of the bar.

If a bar is stressed by being struck an axial blow at one end, the case is one of *impact* loading, discussed in Art. 85.

Examples

1. Figure 4 represents a uniform bar rigidly held at the ends A and D, and axially loaded at the intermediate points B and C. It is required to determine the (total) stress in each portion of the bar AB, BC, CD.

Solution.—Each load is divided between the portions of the bar to right and left in inverse proportion to the lengths of these parts (consistent deformations), and the total stress sustained by each part is the algebraic sum of the stresses imposed by the individual loads (superposition). Of the 9000-lb. load, therefore, $\frac{7}{9}$, or 7000 lb., is carried in tension by the part AB, and $\frac{2}{9}$, or 2000 lb., is carried in compression by the part BD. Of the 18,000-lb. load, $\frac{4}{9}$, or 8000 lb., is carried in compression by the part AC, and $\frac{5}{9}$, or 10,000 lb., is carried in tension by the part CD. Denoting tension by the $+$ sign and compression by the $-$ sign, and adding algebraically, the actual stresses in the parts are found to be:

FIG. 4.

(In AB) $+7000 - 8000 = -1000$ lb.
(In BC) $-2000 - 8000 = -10{,}000$ lb.
(In CD) $-2000 + 10{,}000 = +8000$ lb.

The results are quite independent of the diameter of the bar and of E.

If instead of being *held* at the ends, the bar were prestressed by wedging it between rigid walls under an initial compression of, say, 10,000 lb., and the loads at B and C then applied, the results secured above would represent the *changes* in stress the several parts would undergo. The final stresses in the bar would therefore be 11,000 lb. compression in AB; 20,000 lb. compression in BC; 2000 lb. compression in CD. But if the initial compression were less than 8000 lb., the bar would break contact with the wall at D (no tension possible); there would be no stress at all in CD, and the stresses in AB and BC, now statically determinate, would be 9000 and 18,000 lb. compression, respectively.

2. A steel bar 24 in. long has the form of a truncated cone, being circular in section with a diameter at one end of 1 in. and at the other of 3 in. For this steel, $E = 30{,}000{,}000$ and the coefficient of thermal expansion is 0.0000065 per degree Fahrenheit. This bar is rigidly held at both ends and subjected to a drop in temperature of 50°F. It is required to determine the maximum tensile stress thus caused.

Using the principle of superposition, solution is effected in three steps: (*a*) the shortening e due to the drop in temperature is found, assuming the bar free to contract; (*b*) the force P required to produce an elongation equal to e, that is, to stretch the bar back to its original length, is calculated; (*c*) the maximum tensile stress produced by this force P is calculated.

(*a*) $e = 50 \times 0.0000065 \times 24 = 0.00780$ in.

(*b*) Let d denote the diameter and A the area of any section distant x in. from the small end of the bar. Then $d = 1 + \frac{1}{12}x$, $A = \frac{\pi}{4}\left(1 + \frac{1}{12}x\right)^2$,

and $e = \displaystyle\int_0^{24} \frac{P}{E \cdot \frac{\pi}{4}\left(1 + \frac{1}{12}x\right)^2} dx = 0.00000034P = 0.00780$, or $P =$ 22,900 lb.

(*c*) The maximum stress occurs at the smallest section and is

$$s = \frac{22{,}900}{0.785} = 29{,}200 \text{ lb. per sq. in.}$$

The result can be accepted as correct only if the proportional limit of the steel is known to be as great as or greater than the maximum stress.

27. Composite Members.—A tension or compression member may be made up of parallel elements or parts which jointly carry the applied load. The essential problem is to determine how the load is apportioned among the several parts, and this is easily done by the method of consistent deformations. If the parts are so arranged that all undergo the same total elongation or shortening, then each will carry a portion of the load proportional to its stiffness, *i.e.*, proportional to $\frac{AE}{l}$ if each is a uniform bar, and proportional to AE if these uniform bars are all of equal length. It follows that if there are n bars, with section areas $A_1, A_2, \ldots A_n$ lengths $l_1, l_2, \ldots l_n$, and moduli $E_1, E_2, \ldots E_n$, then the loads on the several bars, $P_1, P_2, \ldots P_n$ are given by

$$P_1 = P\frac{\dfrac{A_1E_1}{l_1}}{\dfrac{A_1E_1}{l_1} + \dfrac{A_2E_2}{l_2} + \cdots + \dfrac{A_nE_n}{l_n}} \tag{8}$$

$$P_2 = P\frac{\dfrac{A_2E_2}{l_2}}{\dfrac{A_1E_1}{l_1} + \dfrac{A_2E_2}{l_2} + \cdots + \dfrac{A_nE_n}{l_n}}$$

etc. If the lengths are all the same, then

$$P_1 = P\frac{A_1E_1}{A_1E_1 + A_2E_2 + \cdots + A_nE_n} \tag{9}$$

$$P_2 = P\frac{A_2E_2}{A_1E_1 + A_2E_2 + \cdots + A_nE_n}$$

etc.

A composite member of this kind can be *prestressed*, P_1, P_2, etc., then represent the *increments* of total stress in each member due to the applied load, and can be found by Eqs. 8 and 9, provided all bars can sustain reversal of stress, or provided the applied load is not great enough to cause such reversal in any bar which cannot sustain it. As explained in Art. 11, all parts of a composite member can, by proper prestressing, be made to reach their allowable loads, or elastic limits, or ultimate strengths simultaneously (Example 2).

Examples

1. A ring is suspended by three vertical bars, A, B, and C, of unequal length. The upper ends of the bars are held at different levels, so that as assembled none of the bars is stressed. A is 4 ft. long, has a section area of 0.3 sq. in., and is of steel for which $E = 30{,}000{,}000$; B is 3 ft. long, has a section area of 0.2 sq. in., and is of copper for which $E = 17{,}000{,}000$; C is 2 ft. long, has a section area of 0.4 sq. in., and is of aluminum for which $E = 10{,}000{,}000$. A load of 10,000 lb. is hung on the ring. It is required to determine how much of this load is carried by each bar.

Solution.—Denoting by P_A, P_B, P_C the loads carried by A, B, and C, respectively, and expressing the moduli of elasticity in millions of pounds per square inch and the lengths in feet, we substitute in Eq. 8 and find:

$$P_A = 10{,}000\left[\frac{\dfrac{(0.3)(30)}{4}}{\dfrac{(0.3)(30)}{4} + \dfrac{(0.2)(17)}{3} + \dfrac{(0.4)(10)}{2}}\right] = 4180 \text{ lb.}$$

$$P_B = 10{,}000\left[\frac{\dfrac{(0.2)(17)}{3}}{\dfrac{(0.3)(30)}{4} + \dfrac{(0.2)(17)}{3} + \dfrac{(0.4)(10)}{2}}\right] = 2100 \text{ lb.}$$

$$P_C = 10{,}000\left[\frac{\dfrac{(0.4)(10)}{2}}{\dfrac{(0.3)(30)}{4} + \dfrac{(0.2)(17)}{3} + \dfrac{(0.4)(10)}{2}}\right] = 3720 \text{ lb.}$$

2. A composite member is formed by passing a steel rod through an aluminum tube of the same length and fastening the two parts together at both ends. The fastening is accomplished by adjustable nuts which make it possible to assemble the rod and tube so that one is under initial tension, the other under an equal initial compression. For the steel rod the section area is 1.5 sq. in., the modulus of elasticity 30,000,000, and the allowable stress 15,000 lb. per sq. in. For the aluminum tube the section area is 2 sq. in., the modulus of elasticity 10,000,000, and the allowable stress 10,000 lb. per sq. in. It is desired so to prestress the composite member that under a tensile load both parts will reach their allowable stresses simultaneously.

Solution.—When the allowable stresses are reached, the total stress in the steel rod will be $1.5 \times 15{,}000 = 22{,}500$ lb.; the total stress in the aluminum tube will be $2 \times 10{,}000 = 20{,}000$ lb.; the total load on the member will be $22{,}500 + 20{,}000 = 42{,}500$ lb. Let P_i denote the initial tension or compression in the members, and as before let tension be considered positive and compression negative. Then, since Eq. 9 gives the *increment* in total stress, we have (for the aluminum tube)

$$P_i + 42{,}500\frac{(2)(10)}{(2)(10) + (1.5)(30)} = 20{,}000$$

whence

$$P_i = +6920 \text{ lb. (initial tension)}$$

(For the steel rod)

$$P_i + 42{,}500\frac{(1.5)(30)}{(2)(10) + (1.5)(30)} = 22{,}500$$

whence

$$P_i = -6920 \text{ lb. (initial compression)}$$

If the member were not prestressed, the unit stress in the steel would always be just three times as great as that in the aluminum, because it would sustain the same unit deformation and its modulus of elasticity is three times as great. Therefore, when the steel reached its allowable stress of 15,000 lb. per sq. in., the aluminum would be stressed to only 5000 lb. per sq. in., and the allowable load on the composite member would be only 32,500 lb. instead of 42,500 lb.

28. Trusses.—A conventional truss is essentially an assemblage of straight uniform bars, which are subjected to axial tension or compression when the truss is loaded at the joints.

The deflection of any joint of a truss is easily found by the *method of unit loads* (Art. 17). Let p_1, p_2, p_3, etc., denote the total stresses produced in the several members by an *assumed unit load* acting in the direction x at the joint whose deflection is to be found, and let e_1, e_2, e_3, etc., denote the longitudinal deformations produced in the several members by the *actual applied loads.* The deflection D_x in the direction x of the joint in question is given by

$$D_x = p_1e_1 + p_2e_2 + p_3e_3 \cdot \cdot \cdot = \Sigma pe \tag{10}$$

The deflection in the direction y, at right angles to x, can be similarly found by assuming the unit load to act in the y direction, and the resultant deflection is then determined by compounding the x and y deflections. Attention must be given to the *signs* of p and e; p is positive if tension, negative if compression, and e is positive if it represents an elongation and negative if it represents a shortening. A positive value for Σpe means that the deflection is in the direction of the assumed unit load, and a negative value means that it is in the opposite direction. The procedure outlined above is illustrated in Example 1 below.

A statically indeterminate truss can be solved by the *method of least work* (Art. 17). To do this, it is necessary to write down the expression for the total strain energy in the structure, which, being simply the sum of the strain energies of the constituent bars, is given by

$$\frac{1}{2}P_1e_1 + \frac{1}{2}P_2e_2 + \frac{1}{2}P_3e_3 \cdot \cdot \cdot = \sum\frac{1}{2}Pe = \sum\frac{1}{2}\frac{P^2l}{AE} \tag{11}$$

Here P_1, P_2, etc., denote the total stresses in the individual members due to the applied loads and e has the same meaning as above. It is necessary to express each stress P as the sum of two stresses; one of these is the stress the applied loads would produce with the redundant member removed, the other is the stress due to the unknown force (say, F) exerted by this redundant member on the rest of the structure. The total strain energy is thus expressed as a function of F, the stress in the redundant member. The partial derivative with respect to F of this expression for strain energy is then set equal to zero and solved for F. If there are two or more redundant members, the expression for strain energy with all the redundant stresses, F_1, F_2, etc., represented, is differentiated once with respect to each. The equations thus obtained are then solved simultaneously for the unknown stresses. The procedure is illustrated in Example 2 below.

Examples

1. The truss shown in Fig. 5 is composed of tubular steel members, for which $E = 30{,}000{,}000$. The section areas of the members are given in the table below. It is required to determine D_x and D_y, the horizontal and vertical components of the displacement of joint A produced by the indicated loading.

Solution.—The method of unit loads is used. The stress P in each member due to the applied loads is found and the resulting elongation or shortening e is calculated. The stress p_x in each member due to a load of 1 lb. acting to the right at A, and the stress p_y in each member due to a load of 1 lb. acting down at A, are calculated. By Eq. 10, $\Sigma p_x e$ then gives the horizontal and $\Sigma p_y e$ the vertical displacement or deflection of A. Tensile stresses and elongations are denoted by +; compressive stresses and shortenings by −. The work is conveniently tabulated as follows:

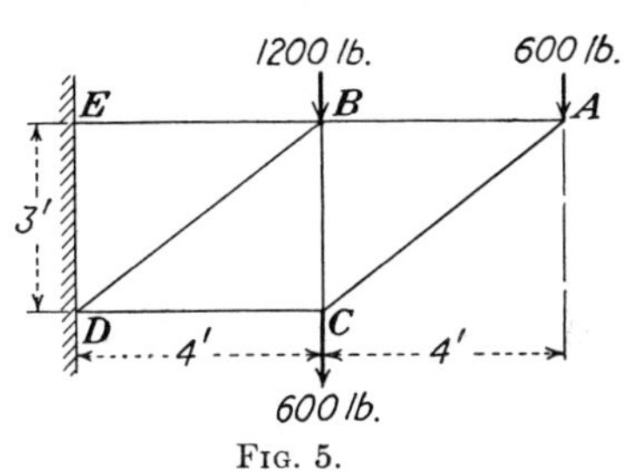

FIG. 5.

Member	Area A, sq. in.	Length l, in.	P, lb.	$e = \frac{Pl}{AE}$, in.	p_x, lb./lb.	$p_x e$, in.	p_y, lb./lb.	$p_y e$, in.
AB	0.07862	48	+ 800	+0.0163	+1.00	+0.0163	+1.33	+0.0217
AC	0.07862	60	−1000	−0.0254	0	0	−1.67	+0.0422
BC	0.1464	36	+1200	+0.0098	0	0	+1.00	+0.0098
BE	0.4142	48	+4000	+0.0154	+1.00	+0.0154	+2.67	+0.0410
BD	0.3318	60	−4000	−0.0241	0	0	−1.67	+0.0400
CD	0.07862	48	− 800	−0.0163	0	0	−1.33	+0.0217
...	....	..	......	....	......	D_x = +0.0317		
						D_y = +0.176		

D_x and D_y are both found to be positive, which means that the displacements are in the directions of the assumed unit loads—to the right and down. Had either been found to be negative, it would have meant that the displacement was in a direction opposite to that of the corresponding unit load.

2. Assume a diagonal member, running from A to D and having a section area 0.3318 sq. in., to be added to the truss of Example 1; the structure is

now statically indeterminate. It is required to determine the stress in each number of the altered truss due to the loads shown.

Solution.—Solution is effected by the method of least work. The truss has one redundant member; either AD or AC may be regarded as redundant, since if either one were removed, the remaining structure would be stable and statically determinate. We select AD to be regarded as redundant, denote the unknown stress in AD by F, and assume F to be compression. We find the stress in each member assuming AD to be removed, then find the stress in each member due to a pull F exerted at A by AD, then add these stresses, thus getting an expression for the stress in each member of the actual truss in terms of F. The expression for the strain energy can then be written out, differentiated with respect to F, equated to zero, and solved for F. F being known, the stress in each member of the truss is easily found. The computations are conveniently tabulated as below:

Member	Stress due to				
	Applied loads, AD out	Pull F exerted by AD		Applied loads, AD in place	
		$F = F$	F = value found	In terms of F	Actual value
	(1)	(2)	(3)	(4) = (1) + (2) = P	(5) = (1) + (3)
AB	+ 800	$+0.470F$	+494	$+800 + 0.470F$	+1290(T)
AC	−1000	$+0.584F$	+612	$-1000 + 0.584F$	− 390(C)
BC	+1200	$-0.351F$	−369	$+1200 - 0.351F$	+ 830(T)
BE	+4000	0	0	+4000	+4000(T)
BD	−4000	$+0.584F$	+612	$-4000 + 0.584F$	−3390(C)
CD	− 800	$+0.470F$	+494	$-800 + 0.470F$	− 306(C)
AD	0	F	1050	F	1050(C)

$$U = \sum \frac{1}{2}\frac{P^2 l}{AE} = \frac{1}{2E}\left[\frac{(800 + 0.470F)^2(48)}{0.07862} + \frac{(-1000 + 0.584F)^2(60)}{0.07862}\right.$$

$$+ \frac{(1200 - 0.351F)^2(36)}{0.1464} + \frac{(4000)^2(48)}{0.4142} + \frac{(-4000 + 0.584F)^2(60)}{0.3318}$$

$$\left. + \frac{(-800 + 0.470F)^2(48)}{0.07862} + \frac{F^2(102.6)}{0.3318}\right]$$

$$\frac{\partial U}{\partial F} = \frac{1}{2E}\left[\frac{2(800 + 0.470F)(48)(0.470)}{0.07862} + \text{etc.}\right]$$

$$\frac{\partial U}{\partial F} = 0 \text{ gives } F = +1050$$

The + sign here simply means that F is *compression, as assumed.* If F had mistakenly been assumed to be tension, a negative result would have been obtained, showing that the assumption was incorrect and that F was really compression.

29. Body under Pure Shear Stress.—A condition of pure shear may be produced by any one of the methods of loading shown in Fig. 6. In (*a*), a rectangular block of length a, height b, and uniform thickness t is shown loaded by forces P_1 and P_2, uniformly distributed over the surfaces to which they are applied and satisfying the equilibrium equation $P_1b = P_2a$. There are equal shear stresses on all vertical and horizontal planes, so that any contained cube oriented like $ABCD$ has on each of four faces the shear stress $s_s = P_1/at = P_2/bt$, and no other stress.

In (*b*) a rectangular block is shown under equal and opposite biaxial stresses s_t and s_c. There are equal shear stresses on all

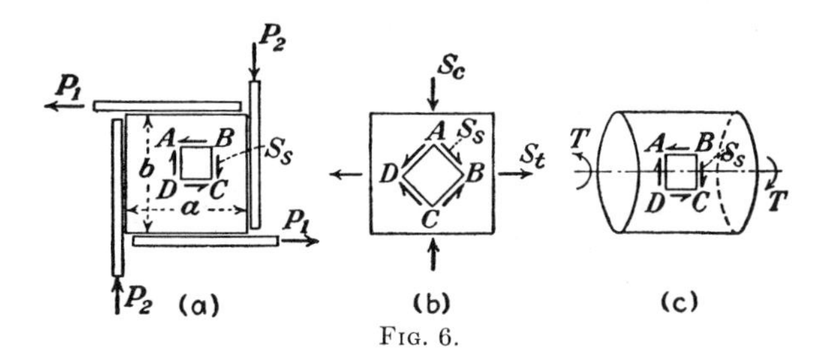

FIG. 6.

planes inclined at 45 deg. to the top and bottom faces, so that a contained cube oriented like $ABCD$ has on each of four faces the shear stress $s_s = s_t = s_c$, and no other stress.

In (*c*) a circular shaft is shown under a twisting moment T; a cube of infinitesimal dimensions, distant z from the axis and oriented like $ABCD$, has on each of four faces an essentially uniform shear stress $s_s = Tz/J$ (Art. 49), and no other stress.

In whatever way the loading is accomplished, the result is to impose on an elementary cube of the loaded body the condition of stress represented in Fig. 7, *i.e.*, shearing stress alone on each of four faces, these stresses being equal and so directed as to satisfy the equilibrium condition $T_x = 0$ (Art. 13).

Behavior.—The strains produced by pure shear are as shown in Fig. 7; the cube $ABCD$ is deformed into the rhombohedron $A'B'C'D'$. On any vertical plane and on any horizontal plane there is a shear stress s_s; on any oblique plane bb there is a normal stress s_n and a shear stress s_p.

Formulas.—Let all stresses be expressed in pounds per square inch, let ϵ_s denote unit shear strain, and let G denote the modulus of rigidity in pounds per square inch. Then

$$s_n = s_s \sin 2\theta; \max s_n = s_s \text{ (when } \theta = 45^\circ)$$
$$s_p = s_s \cos 2\theta$$
$$\epsilon_s = \tan \alpha = \alpha = \frac{s_s}{G} \qquad (12)$$

Strain energy per unit volume =

$$\frac{1}{2}\frac{s_s^2}{G} \quad \text{(in.-lb. per cu. in.)} \qquad (13)$$

The relations between s_s, s_n, and the strains represented in Fig. 7 make it possible to express G in terms of E and Poisson's ratio ν. The formula is

$$G = \frac{E}{2(1+\nu)} \qquad (14)$$

From known values of E (determined by a tensile test) and G (determined by a torsion test) it is thus possible to calculate ν.

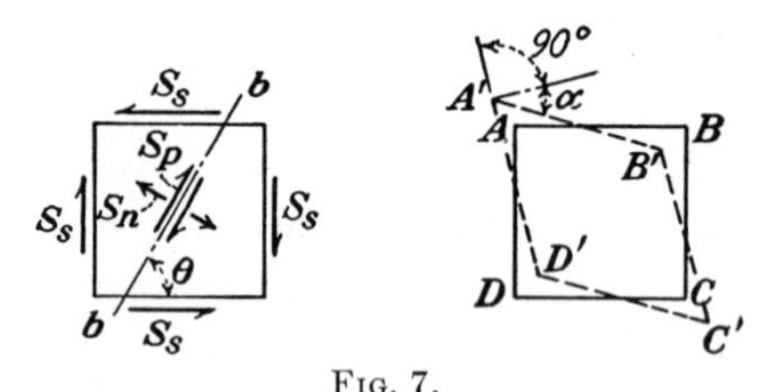

FIG. 7.

30. Cases of Direct Shear Loading.—By direct shear loading is meant any case in which a member is acted on by equal, parallel, and opposite forces so nearly colinear that the material between them is subjected primarily to shear stress, with negligible bending. Examples of this are provided by rivets, bolts, and pins, shaft splines and keys, screw threads, short lugs, etc. These are not really cases of pure shear; the actual stress distribution is complex and usually indeterminate because of the influence of fit and other factors. In designing such parts, however, it is usually assumed that the shear is uniformly distributed on the critical section, and since working stresses are selected with due allowance for the approximate nature of this assumption, the practice is usually permissible. In *beams* subject to transverse shear, this assumption cannot as a rule be made.

Shear and other stresses in rivets, pins, keys, etc., are discussed more fully in Chap. 13, shear stresses in beams in Chap. 8, shear stresses in torsion members in Chap. 9.

31. Combined Stress.—Under certain circumstances of loading, a body is subjected to a combination of tensile and compressive stress (usually designated as biaxial or triaxial stress) or to a combination of tensile, compressive and shear stresses (usually designated as combined stress). For example, the material at the inner surface of a thick cylindrical pressure vessel is subjected to triaxial stress (radial compression, longitudinal tension, and circumferential tension); a shaft simultaneously bent and twisted is subjected to combined stress (longitudinal tension or compression, and torsional shear).

In most instances the normal and shear stresses on each of three mutually perpendicular planes are due to torsion, beam shear, flexure, axial loading, or some combination of these, and can be readily calculated by the appropriate formulas. The principal stresses, the maximum shear stress, and the normal and shear stresses on any given plane can then be found by the formulas given in Table II.

The *strains* produced by any combination of stresses can be found by superposition. Consideration of the strains produced by equal triaxial stress leads to an expression for the bulk modulus of elasticity:

$$K = \frac{E}{3 - 6\nu} \qquad (15)$$

Examples

1. A rectangular block 12 in. long, 4 in. high, and 2 in. thick is subjected to a longitudinal tensile stress $s_x = 12{,}000$ lb. per sq. in., a vertical compressive stress $s_y = 15{,}000$ lb. per sq. in., and a lateral compressive stress $s_z = 9000$ lb. per sq. in. The material is steel, for which $E = 30{,}000{,}000$ and $\nu = 0.30$. It is required to find the total change in length.

Solution.—The longitudinal deformation is found by superposition: The unit strain due to each stress is computed separately by Eq. 2. these results are added to give the resultant longitudinal unit strain, and this is multiplied by the length to give the total elongation. Denoting unit longitudinal strain by ϵ_x and total longitudinal strain by e_x, we have:

$$\epsilon_x = +\frac{12{,}000}{E} + \nu\frac{15{,}000}{E} + \nu\frac{9000}{E} = +0.000400 + 0.000150 + 0.000090$$
$$= +0.00064$$
$$e_x = 12 \times 0.00064 = 0.00768 \text{ in.}$$

The lateral dimensions have nothing to do with the result, since the lateral stresses, not the lateral loads, are given.

2. A piece of "standard extra-strong" pipe, 2 in. nominal diameter, is simultaneously subjected to an internal pressure of 2000 lb. per sq. in. and to a twisting moment of 5000 in.-lb. caused by tightening a cap screwed on at one end. It is required to determine the maximum tensile stress and the maximum shear stress thus produced in the pipe.

Solution.—The calculations will be made, first, for a point at the outer surface, secondly, for a point at the inner surface.

Dimensions of the pipe and properties of the cross section are as follows: Inner radius, $R_0 = 0.9695$; outer radius, $R_1 = 1.1875$; cross-sectional area of bore, $A_b = 2.955$; cross-sectional area of pipe wall, $A_w = 1.475$; polar moment of inertia, $J = 1.735$.
We take axis 1 parallel to the axis of the pipe, axis 2 tangent to the cross section, axis 3 radial. For a point at the outer surface the stress conditions are those of Case 5, Table II, where s_1 is the longitudinal tensile stress due to pressure, s_2 is the circumferential stress due to pressure, and s_s is the shear stress due to torsion. Using the formula for stress in thick cylinders (Case 20, Table XIII) to calculate s_2, the formula for axial stress (Eq. 1) to calculate s_1, and the formula for torsional stress (Eq. 2, Chap. 9) to calculate s_s, we have

$$s_1 = \frac{pA_b}{A_w} = \frac{(2000)(2.955)}{1.475} = 4000$$
$$s_2 = p\frac{R_0^2(R_1^2 + R_1^2)}{R_1^2(R_1^2 - R_0^2)} = 2000\frac{(0.9695^2)(1.1875^2 + 1.1875^2)}{(1.1875^2)(1.1875^2 - 0.9695^2)} = 8000$$
$$s_s = \frac{TR_1}{J} = \frac{(5000)(1.1875)}{1.735} = 3420$$
$$\text{Max. } s = \frac{1}{2}(s_1 + s_2) + \sqrt{\left(\frac{s_1 - s_2}{2}\right)^2 + s_s^2} = \frac{1}{2}(4000 + 8000) +$$
$$\sqrt{\left(\frac{4000 - 8000}{2}\right)^2 + 3420^2} = 9970$$
$$\text{Max } s_p = \sqrt{\left(\frac{4000 - 8000}{2}\right)^2 + 3420^2} = 3970$$

For a point at the inner surface the stress conditions are those of Case 7, with s_1 the longitudinal tension due to pressure, s_2 the circumferential tension due to pressure, s_3 the radial compression due to the direct pressure of the contained liquid, s_{s_3} the shear stress due to torsion, and s_{s_1} and s_{s_2} equal to zero. We have:

$$s_1 = 4000$$
$$s_2 = p\frac{R_1^2 + R_0^2}{R_1^2 - R_0^2} = 2000\frac{1.1875^2 + 0.9695^2}{1.1875^2 - 0.9695^2} = 10{,}000$$

$$s_3 = -p = -2000$$

$$s_{s_3} = \frac{TR_0}{J} = \frac{(5000)(0.9695)}{1.735} = 2790$$

$$s_{s_1} = s_{s_2} = 0$$

$$s^3 - (4000 + 10{,}000 - 2000)s^2 + [(4000)(10{,}000) + 10{,}000)(-2000) + (4000)(-2000) - 0 - 0 - 2790^2]s - [(4000)(10{,}000)(-2000) + 0 - 0 - 0 - (-2000)(2790^2)] = 0$$

Solving, $s = +11{,}100, \ +2900, \ -2000$. These are the three principal stresses. Obviously the maximum stress is 11,100 tension. The maximum shear stress is $\frac{1}{2}\,[11{,}100 - (-2000)] = 6550$. For this particular case, with s_{s_1} and $s_{s_2} = 0$, the principal stresses $+11{,}100$ and $+2900$, are in the plane of axes 1 and 2 and the third principal stress, -2000, is s_3.

TABLE II.—FORMULAS FOR COMBINED STRESS

All stresses are unit stresses, and are positive when acting as shown, negative when acting in opposite direction. θ is positive when measured counterclockwise from the horizontal as shown.

Condition of stress	Formulas for s_n, s_p, principal stresses and maximum shear stress
1. Axial stress 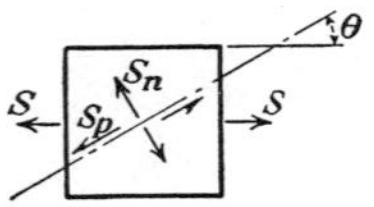	$s_n = s \sin^2 \theta$ $s_p = \frac{1}{2}s \sin 2\theta$ Principal stresses $= s$ and 0 (when $\theta = 90°$ and $0°$) Max $s_p = \frac{1}{2}s$ (when $\theta = 45°$ and $135°$)
2. Pure shear 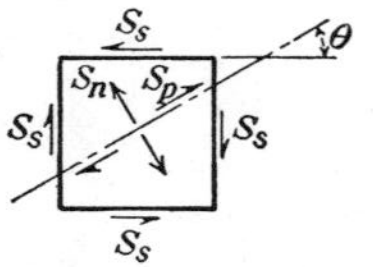	$s_n = s_s \sin 2\theta$ $s_p = s_s \cos 2\theta$ Principal stresses $= +s_s$ and $-s_s$ (when $\theta = 45°$ and $135°$) Max $s_p = s_s$ (when $\theta = 0°$ and $90°$)
3. Axial stress combined with shear 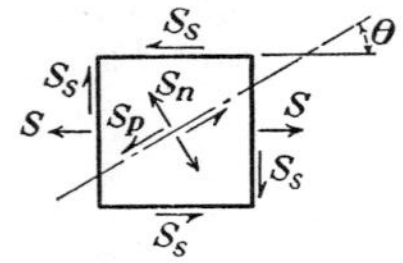	$s_n = \frac{1}{2}s(1 - \cos 2\theta) + s_s \sin 2\theta$ $s_p = \frac{1}{2}s \sin 2\theta + s_s \cos 2\theta$ Principal stresses $= \frac{1}{2}s \pm \sqrt{\left(\frac{1}{2}s\right)^2 + s_s^2}$ when $\theta = \frac{1}{2} \text{arc tan} \frac{-2s_s}{s}$ Max $s_p = \sqrt{\left(\frac{1}{2}s\right)^2 + s_s^2}$ when $\theta = \frac{1}{2} \text{arc tan} \frac{s}{2s_s}$ (Planes of maximum shear stress are at 45° to principal planes)
4. Biaxial stress 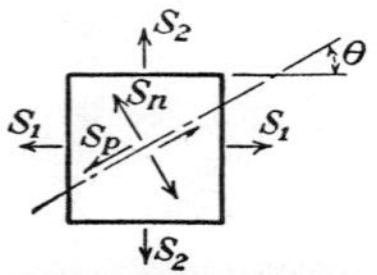	$s_n = s_1 \sin^2 \theta + s_2 \cos^2 \theta$ $s_p = \frac{1}{2}(s_1 - s_2) \sin 2\theta$ Principal stresses $= s_1$ and s_2 (when $\theta = 90°$ and $0°$) Max $s_p = \frac{1}{2}(s_1 - s_2)$ (when $\theta = 45°$ and $135°$). This is the maximum shear stress on any plane normal to the common plane of s_1 and s_2, but when s_1 and s_2 are of the same sign the greatest shear stress occurs on a plane parallel to the lesser of these stresses and inclined at 45° to the greater, and equals half this greater stress

Condition of stress	Formulas for s_n, s_p, principal stresses and maximum shear stress
5. Biaxial stress combined with shear 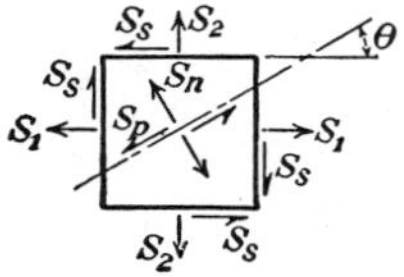	$s_n = \frac{1}{2}(s_1 + s_2) + \frac{1}{2}(s_2 - s_1)\cos 2\theta + s_s \sin 2\theta$ $s_p = \frac{1}{2}(s_1 - s_2)\sin 2\theta + s_s \cos 2\theta$ Principal stresses $= \frac{1}{2}(s_1 + s_2) \pm \sqrt{\left(\frac{s_1 - s_2}{2}\right)^2 + s_s^2}$ when $\theta = \frac{1}{2}\text{arc tan}\frac{2s_s}{s_2 - s_1}$ Max $s_p = \sqrt{\left(\frac{s_1 - s_2}{2}\right)^2 + s_s^2}$ when $\theta = \frac{1}{2}\text{arc tan}\frac{s_1 - s_2}{2s_s}$ (Planes of maximum shear stress are at 45° to principal planes)
6. Triaxial stress 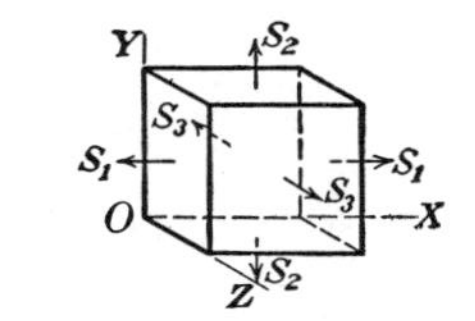	Let l, m, n be the cosines of the angles made by any axis OX' with the axes OX, OY, and OZ, respectively. Then on a plane normal to OX': $s_n = s_1 l^2 + s_2 m^2 + s_3 n^2$ $s_p = \sqrt{s_1^2 l^2 + s_2^2 m^2 + s_3^2 n^2 - s_n^2}$ Principal stresses are s_1, s_2, and s_3 Max s_p occurs on each of the two planes inclined at 45° to the two principal stresses whose algebraic difference is greatest, and is equal to one-half that algebraic difference
7. Triaxial stress combined with shear (general case of stress) 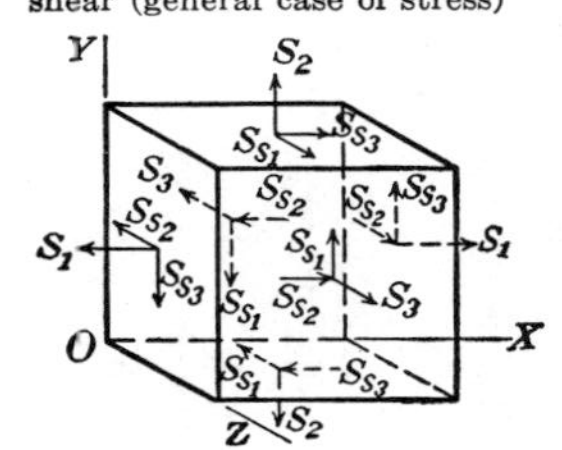	Let OX', OY', OZ' be rectangular axes with origin at O. OX' makes with OX, OY, OZ angles whose cosines are l_1, m_1, n_1; OY' makes with OX, OY, OZ angles whose cosines are l_2, m_2, n_2; OZ' makes with OX, OY, OZ angles whose cosines are l_3, m_3, n_3. Then on a plane normal to OX': $s_n = l_1^2 s_1 + m_1^2 s_2 + n_1^2 s_3 + 2m_1 n_1 s_{s_1} + 2n_1 l_1 s_{s_2} + 2l_1 m_1 s_{s_3}$ s_{p_y}(shear stress parallel to OY') $= l_1 l_2 s_1 + m_1 m_2 s_2 + n_1 n_2 s_3 + s_{s_1}(m_2 n_1 + m_1 n_2) + s_{s_2}(n_2 l_1 + n_1 l_2) + s_{s_3}(l_2 m_1 + l_1 m_2)$ s_{p_z}(shear stress parallel to OZ') $= l_1 l_3 s_1 + m_1 m_3 s_2 + n_1 n_3 s_3 + s_{s_1}(m_3 n_1 + m_1 n_3) + s_{s_2}(n_3 l_1 + n_1 l_3) + s_{s_3}(l_3 m_1 + l_1 m_3)$ s_p(resultant shear) $= \sqrt{(s_{p_y})^2 + (s_{p_z})^2}$ The three principal stresses s are given by the three roots of the equation $s^3 - (s_1 + s_2 + s_3)s^2 + (s_1 s_2 + s_2 s_3 + s_1 s_3 - s_{s_1}^2 - s_{s_2}^2 - s_{s_3}^2)s - (s_1 s_2 s_3 + 2s_{s_1} s_{s_2} s_{s_3} - s_1 s_{s_1}^2 - s_2 s_{s_2}^2 - s_3 s_{s_3}^2) = 0$ The direction of each principal stress is defined by the cosines l, m, n of the angles it makes with OX, OY, OZ and these direction cosines are found by substituting the value of the s in question in the following equations: $(s - s_1)l - s_{s_3}m - s_{s_2}n = 0$; $-s_{s_3}l + (s - s_2)m - s_{s_1}n = 0$; $-s_{s_2}l - s_{s_1}m + (s - s_3)n = 0$ and solving for l, m, and n. The maximum shear stress occurs on each of the two planes inclined at 45° to the two principal stresses whose algebraic difference is greatest, and is equal to one-half that algebraic difference

CHAPTER 8

BEAMS; FLEXURE OF STRAIGHT AND CURVED BARS

32. Straight Beams (Common Case) Elastically Stressed.—The formulas of this article are based on the following assumptions: (1) The beam is of homogeneous material which has the same modulus of elasticity in tension and compression. (2) The beam is straight or nearly so; if slightly curved, the curvature is in the plane of bending, and the radius of curvature is at least 10 times the depth. (3) The cross section is uniform. (4) The beam has at least one longitudinal plane of symmetry. (5) All loads and reactions are perpendicular to the axis of the beam and lie in the same plane, which is a longitudinal plane of symmetry. (6) The beam is long in proportion to its depth, the span/depth ratio being 8 or more for metal beams of compact section, 15 or more for beams with relatively thin webs, and 24 or more for rectangular timber beams. (7) The beam is not disproportionately wide. (8) The maximum stress does not exceed the proportional limit.

Applied to any case for which these assumptions are not valid, the formulas given yield results which at best are approximate and which may be grossly in error; such cases are discussed in subsequent articles. The limitations here stated with respect to straightness and proportions of the beam correspond to a maximum error in calculated results of about 5 per cent.

In the following discussion, it is assumed for convenience that the beam is horizontal and the loads and reactions vertical.

Behavior.—The beam bends; fibers on the convex side lengthen, fibers on the concave side shorten. The neutral surface is normal to the plane of the loads and contains the centroids of all sections, hence the neutral axis of any section is the horizontal central axis. Plane sections remain plane, hence unit fiber strains and stresses are proportional to distance from the neutral surface. Longitudinal displacements of points on the neutral surface are negligible. Vertical deflection is largely due to bending, that due to shear being usually negligible under the conditions stated.

There is at any point a longitudinal fiber stress s, tensile if the point lies between the neutral surface and the convex surface of the beam, compressive if the point lies between the neutral surface and the concave surface of the beam. This fiber stress s may usually be assumed uniform across the width of the beam (see Arts. 36, 37).

There is at any point a longitudinal shear stress s_s on the horizontal plane and an equal vertical shear stress on the transverse plane. These shear stresses may be assumed uniform across the width of the beam (see page 100).

In Fig. 8, (a) and (b) represent a beam under load and show the various dimensions that appear in the formulas; (c) shows a small prism at a point q, acted on by the stresses s and s_s.

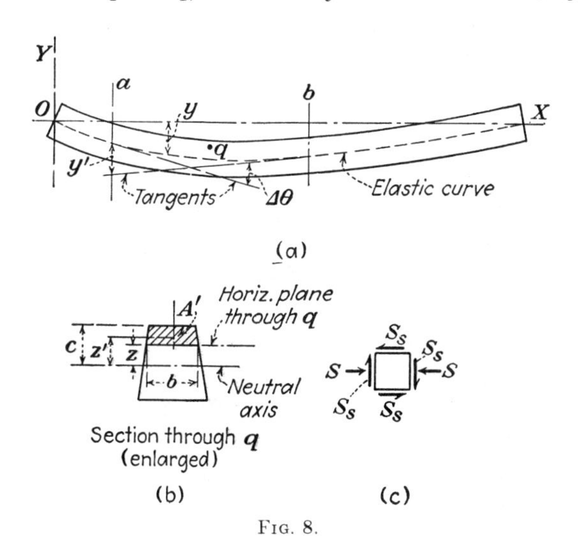

FIG. 8.

Formulas.—Let I = the moment of inertia of the section of the beam with respect to the neutral axis and E = modulus of elasticity of the material.

The fiber stress s at any point q is

$$s = \frac{Mz}{I} \tag{1}$$

where M is the bending moment at the section containing q, and z is the distance from the neutral axis to q.

The shear stress s_s at any point q is

$$s_s = \frac{VA'z'}{Ib} \tag{2}$$

where V is the vertical shear at the section containing q, A' is the area of that part of the section above (or below) q, z' is the distance from the neutral axis to the centroid of A', and b is the net breadth of the section measured through q.

The strain energy of flexure U_f (inch-pounds) is

$$U_f = \int \frac{M^2}{2EI} dx \tag{3}$$

where M represents the bending moment equation in terms of x, the distance (inches) from the left end of the beam to any section.

The radius of curvature, R, of the elastic curve at any section is

$$R = \frac{EI}{M} \tag{4}$$

where M is the bending moment at the section in question.

The general differential equation of the elastic curve is

$$EI\frac{d^2y}{dx^2} = M \tag{5}$$

where M has the same meaning as in Eq. 3. Solution of this equation for the vertical deflection y (inches) is effected by writing out the expression for M, integrating twice, and determining the constants of integration by the boundary conditions.

The vertical deflection y at any point is found by the method of unit loads to be

$$y = \int \frac{Mm}{EI} dx \tag{6}$$

or by Castigliano's first theorem to be

$$y = \frac{\partial U}{\partial P} \tag{7}$$

where M has the same meaning as in Eq. 3 and m is the equation of the bending moment due to a load of 1 lb. acting vertically at the section where y is to be found. The integration indicated must be performed over each portion of the beam for which either

M or m is expressed by a different equation. A positive result for y means that the deflection is in the direction of the assumed unit load; a negative result means it is in the opposite direction (see Example 2).

In Eq. 7, U is given by Eq. 3, and P is a vertical load, real or imaginary, applied at the section where y is to be found. It is most convenient to perform the differentiation within the integral sign. As with Eq. 6, the integration must extend over the entire length of the beam, and the sign of the result is interpreted as before.

The change in slope of the elastic curve $\Delta\theta$ (radians) between any two sections a and b is

$$\Delta\theta = \int \frac{M}{EI} dx \tag{8}$$

where M has the same meaning as in Eq. 3 and the integration extends over that part of the beam between a and b.

The deflection y' at any section a, *measured vertically from a tangent drawn to the elastic curve at any section* b, is

$$y' = \int \frac{M}{EI} x \, dx \tag{9}$$

where x is the distance from a to any section between a and b and the integration indicated extends over that part of the beam between a and b.

Important relations between the bending moment and shear equations are

$$V = \frac{dM}{dx} \tag{10}$$

$$M = \int V \, dx \tag{11}$$

These relations are useful in constructing shear and moment diagrams and in locating the section or sections of maximum bending moment, since Eq. 10 shows that the maximum moment occurs when V, its first derivative, passes through zero, and Eq. 11 shows that the increment in bending moment that occurs between any two sections is equal to the area under the shear diagram between those sections.

Maximum Fiber Stress.—The maximum fiber stress at any section occurs at the point or points most remote from the neutral axis, and is given by Eq. 1 when $z = c$; hence

$$\text{Max } s = \frac{Mc}{I} = \frac{M}{I/c} \tag{12}$$

The maximum fiber stress in the beam occurs at the section of greatest bending moment; if the section is not symmetrical about the neutral axis, the stresses should be investigated at both the section of greatest positive moment and the section of greatest negative moment.

Maximum Shear Stress—The maximum shear stress in the beam occurs at the section of greatest vertical shear. The maximum shear stress at any section occurs at the neutral axis, provided the net width b is as small there as anywhere else; if the section is narrower elsewhere, the maximum shear stress may not occur at the neutral axis. This maximum shear stress can conveniently be expressed by the formula

$$\text{Max } s_s = \alpha\frac{V}{A} \tag{13}$$

where V/A is the *average* shear stress on the section and α is a factor that depends on the form of the section. For a rectangular section $\alpha = \frac{3}{2}$ and the maximum stress is at the neutral axis; for a solid circular section $\alpha = \frac{4}{3}$ and the maximum stress is at the neutral axis; for a triangular section $\alpha = \frac{3}{2}$ and the maximum stress is halfway between the top and bottom of the section; for a diamond-shaped section of depth d, $\alpha = \frac{9}{8}$ and the maximum stress is at points distant $\frac{1}{8}d$ above and below the neutral axis.

In the derivation of Eq. 2 and in the above discussion, it is assumed that the shear stress is uniform across the width of the beam, *i.e.*, it is the same at all points on any transverse line parallel to the neutral axis. Actually this is not the case; exact analysis (Ref. 1) shows that the shear stress varies across the width, and that for a rectangle the maximum intensity occurs at the ends of the neutral axis, where, for a wide beam, it is twice the average. Photoelastic investigation of beams under concentrated loading shows that localized shearing stresses about four times as great as the maximum stress given by Eq. 2 occur near the points of loading and support (Ref. 2). But experience shows that this variation may be ignored and design based on the average value as determined by Eq. 2.

For some sections the greatest horizontal shear stress at a

given point occurs, not on a horizontal plane, but on an inclined longitudinal plane which cuts the section so as to make b a minimum. Thus, for a circular tube or pipe the greatest horizontal shear stress at any point occurs on a *radial* plane; the corresponding shear stress in the plane of the section is not vertical but tangential, and in computing s_s by Eq. 2, b should be taken as twice the thickness of the tube instead of the net horizontal breadth of the member. (See Table VIII, Cases 24 to 27, for instances where this shear stress in a tube is of importance.)

In an I, T, or box section there is a horizontal shear stress on any vertical longitudinal plane through the flange, and this stress is usually a maximum at the juncture of flange and web. It may be calculated by Eq. 2, taking A' as the area outside of the vertical plane (for outstanding flanges) or between the vertical plane and the center of the beam section (for box girders), and b as the flange thickness (see Example 1*b*). The other terms have the same meaning as explained before.

Shear stresses are not often of controlling importance except in wood beams, or in metal beams which have thin webs or which have a small span/depth ratio. For beams that conform to the assumptions stated above, strength will practically always be governed by fiber stress.

Change in Projected Length Due to Bending.—The apparent shortening of a beam due to bending—*i.e.*, the difference between its original length and the horizontal projection of the elastic curve—is given by

$$\Delta l = \frac{1}{2}\int_0^l \left(\frac{dy}{dx}\right)^2 dx \qquad (14)$$

To evaluate Δl, dy/dx is expressed in terms of x (Eq. 5) and the square of this integrated as indicated.

The extreme fibers of the beam undergo a change in actual length due to stress given by

$$e = \int_0^l \frac{Mc}{EI}\, dx \qquad (15)$$

By means of these equations the actual relative horizontal displacement of points on the upper or lower surface of the beam can be predicted and the necessary allowance made in the design of rocker bearings, clearance for the corners, etc.

Tabulated Formulas.—In Table III are given formulas for the end reactions, end moments, vertical shears, bending moments, deflections, and end slopes of beams supported and loaded in various ways.

By superposition, the formulas can be made to apply to almost any type of loading and support, including combinations of beams such as rigid frames. A few formulas for rigid frames derived in this way are included in the table, but in most cases are limited to expressions for such forces and moments as leave a statically determinate problem. Very extensive compilations of formulas for rigid frames are available, notably those of Kleinlogel (Ref. 7) and of Leontovich (Ref. 72). When as in a framed building, the number of members is large, some relaxation method, such as moment distribution, is to be preferred. In all rigid frames, corner or "knee" design is important; much information and experimental data relating to this problem are to be found in the reports published by the Fritz Engineering Laboratory of Lehigh University. The use of the tabulated formulas and of the fundamental formulas given above is illustrated in the following examples.

Examples

1. For a beam supported and loaded as shown in Fig. 9, it is required to determine the maximum tensile stress, maximum shear stress, and maximum compressive stress, assuming first, the beam to be of wood with section as shown in (*a*); second, the beam to be of wood with section as shown in (*b*); third, the beam to be a 4-in., 7.7-lb. steel I-beam.

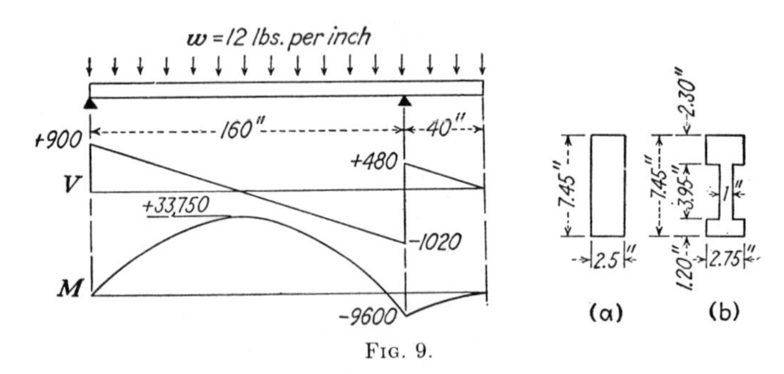

FIG. 9.

Solution.—By using the equations of equilibrium (Art. 13) the left and right reactions are found to be 900 and 1500 lb., respectively. The shear and moment equations are therefore

$$(x = 0 \text{ to } x = 160) \qquad V = 900 - 12x$$
$$M = 900x - 12x(\tfrac{1}{2}x)$$
$$(x = 150 \text{ to } x = 200) \qquad V = 900 - 12x + 1500$$
$$M = 900x - 12x(\tfrac{1}{2}x) + 1500(x - 160)$$

These equations are plotted, giving the shear and moment diagrams shown. The maximum positive moment evidently occurs between the supports; the exact location is found by setting the first shear equation equal to zero and solving for x. This gives $x = 75$, and substitution of this value of x in the first moment equation gives $M = 33{,}750$ in.-lb. The maximum negative moment occurs at the right support where the shear diagram again passes through zero and is 9600 in.-lb.

The results so far obtained are independent of the cross section of the beam. The stresses will now be calculated for each of the sections (*a*), (*b*), and (*c*).

a. For the rectangular section, $I = \frac{1}{12}bd^3 = 86.2$, $I/c = \frac{1}{6}bd^2 = 23.1$, $A = bd = 18.60$.
Therefore

$$\text{(by Eq. 12)} \qquad \text{Max } s = \frac{\text{Max } M}{I/c} = \frac{33{,}750}{23.1} = 1460 \text{ lb. per sq. in.}$$

This stress occurs at $x = 75$, and is tension in the bottom fibers of the beam, compression in the top.

$$\text{(by Eq. 13)} \qquad \text{Max } s_s = \frac{3}{2}\frac{\text{Max } V}{A} = \frac{3}{2}\frac{1020}{18.60} = 82 \text{ lb. per sq. in.}$$

This is the horizontal and vertical shear stress at the neutral axis of the section just to the left of the right support.

b. For the routed section it is found (Chap. 6) that the neutral axis is 4 in. from the base of the section and $I = 82.6$. The maximum shear stress on a horizontal plane occurs at the neutral axis, since b is as small there as anywhere, and so in Eq. 2 the product $A'z'$ represents the statical moment about the neutral axis of all that part of the section above the neutral axis. Taking the moment of the flange and web portions separately, we find $A'z' = (2.75)(2.3)(2.30) + (1)(1.15)(0.575) = 15.2$. Also, $b = 1.00$.

Since the section is not symmetrical about the neutral axis, the fiber stresses will be calculated at the section of maximum positive moment and at the section of maximum negative moment. We have

(At $x = 75$)

$$s = \frac{(33750)(4)}{82.6} = 1630 \text{ lb. per sq. in. (tension in bottom fiber)}$$

$$s = \frac{(33750)(3.45)}{82.6} = 1410 \text{ lb. per sq. in. (compression in top fiber)}$$

(At $x = 160$)

$$s = \frac{(9600)(4)}{82.6} = 465 \text{ lb. per sq. in. (compression in bottom fiber)}$$

$$s = \frac{(9600)(3.45)}{82.6} = 400 \text{ lb. per sq. in. (tension in top fibers)}$$

It is seen that for this beam the maximum fiber stresses in both tension and compression occur at the section of maximum positive bending moment.

$$\text{(By Eq. 2)} \qquad \text{Max } s_s = \frac{(1020)(15.2)}{(82.6)(1)} = 188 \text{ lb. per sq. in.}$$

TABLE III.—SHEAR, MOMENT, AND DEFLECTION FORMULAS FOR BEAMS; REACTION FORMULAS FOR RIGID FRAMES

Notation: W = load (lb.); w = unit load (lb. per linear in.). M is positive when clockwise; V is positive when upward; y is positive when upward. Constraining moments, applied couples, loads, and reactions are positive when acting as shown. All forces are in pounds, all moments in inch-pounds; all deflections and dimensions in inches. θ is in radians and $\tan\theta = \theta$

Statically Determinate Cases

Loading, support, and reference number	Reactions R_1 and R_2, vertical shear V	Bending moment M and maximum bending moment	Deflection y, maximum deflection, and end slope θ
1. Cantilever, end load	$R_2 = +W$ $V = -W$	$M = -Wx$ Max $M = -Wl$ at B	$y = -\frac{1}{6}\frac{W}{EI}(x^3 - 3l^2x + 2l^3)$ Max $y = -\frac{1}{3}\frac{Wl^3}{EI}$ at A $\theta = +\frac{1}{2}\frac{Wl^2}{EI}$ at A
2. Cantilever, intermediate load	$R_2 = +W$ (A to B) $V = 0$ (B to C) $V = -W$	(A to B) $M = 0$ (B to C) $M = -W(x - b)$ Max $M = -Wa$ at C	(A to B) $y = -\frac{1}{6}\frac{W}{EI}(-a^3 + 3a^2l - 3a^2x)$ (B to C) $y = -\frac{1}{6}\frac{W}{EI}[(x - b)^3 - 3a^2(x - b) + 2a^3]$ Max $y = -\frac{1}{6}\frac{W}{EI}(3a^2l - a^3)$ $\theta = +\frac{1}{2}\frac{Wa^2}{EI}$ (A to B)
3. Cantilever, uniform load	$R_2 = +W$ $V = -\frac{W}{l}x$	$M = -\frac{1}{2}\frac{W}{l}x^2$ Max $M = -\frac{1}{2}Wl$ at B	$y = -\frac{1}{24}\frac{W}{EIl}(x^4 - 4l^3x + 3l^4)$ Max $y = -\frac{1}{8}\frac{Wl^3}{EI}$ $\theta = +\frac{1}{6}\frac{Wl^2}{EI}$ at A
4. Cantilever, partial uniform load	$R_2 = +W$ (A to B) $V = 0$ (B to C) $V = -\frac{W}{b - a}(x - l + b)$ (C to D) $V = -W$	(A to B) $M = 0$ (B to C) $M = -\frac{1}{2}\frac{W}{b - a}(x - l + b)^2$ (C to D) $M = -\frac{1}{2}W(2x - 2l + a + b)$ Max $M = -\frac{1}{2}W(a + b)$ at D	(A to B) $y = -\frac{1}{24}\frac{W}{EI}[4(a^2 + ab + b^2)(l - x) - a^3 - ab^2 - a^2b - b^3]$ (B to C) $y = -\frac{1}{24}\frac{W}{EI}\left[6(a + b)(l - x)^2 - 4(l - x)^3 + \frac{(l - x - a)^4}{b - a}\right]$ (C to D) $y = -\frac{1}{12}\frac{W}{EI}[3(a + b)(l - x)^2 - 2(l - x)^3]$ Max $y = -\frac{1}{24}\frac{W}{EI}[4(a^2 + ab + b^2)l - a^3 - ab^2 - a^2b - b^3]$ at A $\theta = +\frac{1}{6}\frac{W}{EI}[a^2 + ab + b^2]$ (A to B)

	$V = -\frac{W}{l^2}x^2$	Max $M = -\frac{1}{3}Wl$ at B	Max $y = -\frac{1}{15}\frac{Wl^3}{EI}$ at A $\theta = +\frac{1}{12}\frac{Wl^2}{EI}$ at A
6. Cantilever, partial triangular load	$R_2 = +W$ $(A$ to $B)$ $V = 0$ $(B$ to $C)$ $V = -\frac{W(x-l+b)^2}{(b-a)^2}$ $(C$ to $D)$ $V = -W$	$(A$ to $B)$ $M = 0$ $(B$ to $C)$ $M = -\frac{1}{3}\frac{W(x-l+b)^3}{(b-a)^2}$ $(C$ to $D)$ $M = -\frac{1}{3}W(3x - 3l + b + 2a)$ Max $M = -\frac{1}{3}W(b + 2a)$ at D	$(A$ to $B)$ $y = -\frac{1}{60}\frac{W}{EI}[(5b^2 + 10ba + 15a^2)(l - x) - 4a^3 - 2ab^2 - 3a^2b - b^3]$ $(B$ to $C)$ $y = -\frac{1}{60}\frac{W}{EI}\left[(20a + 10b)(l-x)^2 - 10(l-x)^3 + 5\frac{(l-x-a)^4}{b-a} - \frac{(l-x-a)^5}{(b-a)^2}\right]$ $(C$ to $D)$ $y = -\frac{1}{6}\frac{W}{EI}[(2a + b)(l-x)^2 - (l-x)^3]$ Max $y = -\frac{1}{60}\frac{W}{EI}[(5b^2 + 10ba + 15a^2)l - 4a^3 - 2ab^2 - 3a^2b - b^3]$ at A $\theta = +\frac{1}{12}\frac{W}{EI}(3a^2 + 2ab + b^2)$ $(A$ to $B)$
7. Cantilever, triangular load	$R_2 = +W$ $V = -W\left(\frac{2lx - x^2}{l^2}\right)$	$M = -\frac{1}{3}\frac{W}{l^2}(3lx^2 - x^3)$ Max $M = -\frac{2}{3}Wl$ at B	$y = -\frac{1}{60}\frac{W}{EIl^2}(-x^5 - 15l^4x + 5lx^4 + 11l^5)$ Max $y = -\frac{11}{60}\frac{Wl^3}{EI}$ at A $\theta = +\frac{1}{4}\frac{W}{EI}l^2$ at A
8. Cantilever, partial triangular load	$R_2 = +W$ $(A$ to $B)$ $V = 0$ $(B$ to $C)$ $V = -W\left[1 - \frac{(l-a-x)^2}{(b-a)^2}\right]$ $(C$ to $D)$ $V = -W$	$(A$ to $B)$ $M = 0$ $(B$ to $C)$ $M = -\frac{1}{3}W\left[\frac{3(x-l+b)^2}{b-a} - \frac{(x-l+b)^3}{(b-a)^2}\right]$ $(C$ to $D)$ $M = -\frac{1}{3}W(-3l + 3x + 2b + a)$ Max $M = -\frac{1}{3}W(2b + a)$ at D	$(A$ to $B)$ $y = -\frac{1}{60}\frac{W}{EI}[(5a^2 + 10ab + 15b^2)(l-x) - a^3 - 2a^2b - 3ab^2 - 4b^3]$ $(B$ to $C)$ $y = -\frac{1}{60}\frac{W}{EI}\left[\frac{(l-x-a)^5}{(b-a)^2} - 10(l-x)^3 + (10a + 20b)(l-x)^2\right]$ $(C$ to $D)$ $y = -\frac{1}{6}\frac{W}{EI}[(a + 2b)(l-x)^2 - (l-x)^3]$ Max $y = -\frac{1}{60}\frac{W}{EI}[(5a^2 + 10ab + 15b^2)l - a^3 - 2a^2b - 3ab^2 - 4b^3]$ at A $\theta = +\frac{1}{12}\frac{W}{EI}(a^2 + 2ab + 3b^2)$ $(A$ to $B)$

TABLE III.—SHEAR, MOMENT, AND DEFLECTION FORMULAS FOR BEAMS; REACTION FORMULAS FOR RIGID FRAMES.—(*Continued*)

Loading, support, and reference number	Reactions R_1 and R_2, vertical shear V	Bending moment M and maximum bending moment	Deflection y, maximum deflection, and end slope θ
9. Cantilever, end couple	$R_2 = 0$ $V = 0$	$M = M_0$ Max $M = M_0 (A \text{ to } B)$	$y = \frac{1}{2}\frac{M_0}{EI}(l^2 - 2lx + x^2)$ Max $y = +\frac{1}{2}\frac{M_0 l^2}{EI}$ at A $\theta = -\frac{M_0 l}{EI}$ at A
10. Cantilever, intermediate couple	$R_2 = 0$ $V = 0$	$(A \text{ to } B)\ M = 0$ $(B \text{ to } C)\ M = M_0$ Max $M = M_0\ (B \text{ to } C)$	$(A \text{ to } B)\ y = \frac{M_0 a}{EI}\left(l - \frac{1}{2}a - x\right)$ $(B \text{ to } C)\ y = \frac{1}{2}\frac{M_0}{EI}[(x - l + a)^2 - 2a(x - l + a) + a^2]$ Max $y = \frac{M_0 a}{EI}\left(l - \frac{1}{2}a\right)$ at A $\theta = -\frac{M_0 a}{EI}\ (A \text{ to } B)$
11. End supports, center load	$R_1 = +\frac{1}{2}W \quad R_2 = +\frac{1}{2}W$ $(A \text{ to } B)\ V = +\frac{1}{2}W$ $(B \text{ to } C)\ V = -\frac{1}{2}W$	$(A \text{ to } B)\ M = +\frac{1}{2}Wx$ $(B \text{ to } C)\ M = +\frac{1}{2}W(l - x)$ Max $M = +\frac{1}{4}Wl$ at B	$(A \text{ to } B)\ y = -\frac{1}{48}\frac{W}{EI}(3l^2 x - 4x^3)$ Max $y = -\frac{1}{48}\frac{Wl^3}{EI}$ at B $\theta = -\frac{1}{16}\frac{Wl^2}{EI}$ at A, $\quad \theta = +\frac{1}{16}\frac{Wl^2}{EI}$ at C
12. End supports, intermediate load	$R_1 = +W\frac{b}{l} \quad R_2 = +W\frac{a}{l}$ $(A \text{ to } B)\ V = +W\frac{b}{l}$ $(B \text{ to } C)\ V = -W\frac{a}{l}$	$(A \text{ to } B)\ M = +W\frac{b}{l}x$ $(B \text{ to } C)\ M = +W\frac{a}{l}(l - x)$ Max $M = +W\frac{ab}{l}$ at B	$(A \text{ to } B)\ y = -\frac{Wbx}{6EIl}[2l(l - x) - b^2 - (l - x)^2]$ $(B \text{ to } C)\ y = -\frac{Wa(l - x)}{6EIl}[2lb - b^2 - (l - x)^2]$ Max $y = -\frac{Wab}{27EIl}(a + 2b)\sqrt{3a(a + 2b)}$ at $x = \sqrt{\frac{1}{3}a(a + 2b)}$ when $a > b$ $\theta = -\frac{1}{6}\frac{W}{EI}\left(bl - \frac{b^3}{l}\right)$ at A; $\quad \theta = +\frac{1}{6}\frac{W}{EI}\left(2bl + \frac{b^3}{l} - 3b^2\right)$ at C
13. End supports, uniform load	$R_1 = +\frac{1}{2}W \quad R_2 = +\frac{1}{2}W$ $V = \frac{1}{2}W\left(1 - \frac{2x}{l}\right)$	$M = \frac{1}{2}W\left(x - \frac{x^2}{l}\right)$ Max $M = +\frac{1}{8}Wl$ at $x = \frac{1}{2}l$	$y = -\frac{1}{24}\frac{Wx}{EIl}(l^3 - 2lx^2 + x^3)$ Max $y = -\frac{5}{384}\frac{Wl^3}{EI}$ at $x = \frac{1}{2}l$ $\theta = -\frac{1}{24}\frac{Wl^2}{EI}$ at $A \quad \theta = +\frac{1}{24}\frac{Wl^2}{EI}$ at B

14. End supports, partial uniform load $d=l-\frac{1}{2}b-\frac{1}{2}a$; $W=wc$	$R_1 = W\frac{d}{l}$ $R_2 = \frac{W}{l}\left(a+\frac{1}{2}c\right)$ (A to B) $V = R_1$ (B to C) $V = R_1 - W\frac{x-a}{c}$ (C to D) $V = R_1 - W$	(A to B) $M = R_1x$ (B to C) $M = R_1x - W\frac{(x-a)^2}{2c}$ (C to D) $M = R_1x - W(x - \frac{1}{2}a - \frac{1}{2}b)$ Max $M = W\frac{d}{l}\left(a+\frac{cd}{2l}\right)$ at $x = a + \frac{cd}{l}$	(A to B) $y = \frac{1}{48EI}\left\{8R_1(x^3 - l^2x) + Wx\left[\frac{8d^3}{l} - \frac{2bc^2}{l} + \frac{c^3}{l} + 2c^2\right]\right\}$ (B to C) $y = \frac{1}{48EI}\left\{8R_1(x^3 - l^2x) + Wx\left[\frac{8d^3}{l} - \frac{2bc^2}{l} + \frac{c^3}{l} + 2c^2\right] - 2W\frac{(x-a)^4}{c}\right\}$ (C to D) $y = \frac{1}{48EI}\left\{8R_1(x^3 - l^2x) + Wx\left[\frac{8d^3}{l} - \frac{2bc^2}{l} + \frac{c^3}{l}\right] - 8W(x - \frac{1}{2}a - \frac{1}{2}b)^3 + W(2bc^2 - c^3)\right\}$ $\theta = \frac{1}{48EI}\left[-8R_1l^2 + W\left(\frac{8d^3}{l} - \frac{2bc^2}{l} + \frac{c^3}{l} + 2c^2\right)\right]$ at A; $\theta = \frac{1}{48EI}\left[16R_1l^2 - W\left(24d^2 - \frac{8d^3}{l} + \frac{2bc^2}{l} - \frac{c^3}{l}\right)\right]$ at D
15. End supports, triangular load $W=\frac{1}{2}wl$	$R_1 = \frac{1}{3}W$ $R_2 = \frac{2}{3}W$ $V = W\left(\frac{1}{3} - \frac{x^2}{l^2}\right)$	$M = \frac{1}{3}W\left(x - \frac{x^3}{l^2}\right)$ Max $M = 0.128Wl$ at $x = l\left(\frac{\sqrt{3}}{3}\right) = 0.5774l$	$y = -\frac{1}{180}\frac{Wx}{EIl^2}(3x^4 - 10l^2x^2 + 7l^4)$ Max $y = -0.01304\frac{Wl^3}{EI}$ at $x = 0.519l$ $\theta = -\frac{7}{180}\frac{Wl^2}{EI}$ at A; $\theta = +\frac{8}{180}\frac{Wl^2}{EI}$ at B.
16. End supports, partial triangular load $d=l-\frac{1}{3}a-\frac{2}{3}b$; $W=\frac{1}{2}wc$	$R_1 = W\frac{d}{l}$ $R_2 = W\frac{l-d}{l}$ (A to B) $V = +R_1$ (B to C) $V = R_1 - \left(\frac{x-a}{c}\right)^2 W$ (C to D) $V = R_1 - W$	(A to B) $M = R_1x$ (B to C) $M = R_1x - W\frac{(x-a)^3}{3c^2}$ (C to D) $M = R_1x - \frac{1}{3}W(3x - a - 2b)$ Max. $M = W\frac{d}{l}\left(a + \frac{2}{3}c\sqrt{\frac{d}{l}}\right)$ at $x = a + c\sqrt{\frac{d}{l}}$	(A to B) $y = \frac{1}{6EI}\left\{R_1(x^3 - l^2x) + Wx\left[\frac{d^3}{l} + \frac{1}{6}c^2\left(1 - \frac{b}{l}\right) + \frac{17}{270}\frac{c^3}{l}\right]\right\}$ (B to C) $y = \frac{1}{6EI}\left[R_1(x^3 - l^2x) - \frac{1}{10}W\frac{(x-a)^5}{c^2} + Wx\left(\frac{d^3}{l} + \frac{1}{6}c^2 - \frac{1}{6}c^2\frac{b}{l} + \frac{17}{270}\frac{c^3}{l}\right)\right]$ (C to D) $y = \frac{1}{6EI}\left\{R_1(x^3 - l^2x) - W\left[\left(x - \frac{1}{3}a - \frac{2}{3}b\right)^3 - d^3\frac{x}{l} - \frac{1}{6}bc^2\left(1 - \frac{x}{l}\right) + \frac{17}{270}c^3\left(1 - \frac{x}{l}\right)\right]\right\}$ $\theta = \frac{1}{6EI}\left[-R_1l^2 + W\left(\frac{d^3}{l} + \frac{1}{6}c^2 + \frac{17}{270}\frac{c^3}{l} - \frac{1}{6}\frac{c^2b}{l}\right)\right]$ at A $\theta = \frac{1}{6EI}\left[2R_1l^2 + W\left(\frac{d^3}{l} + \frac{17}{270}\frac{c^3}{l} - \frac{1}{6}\frac{c^2b}{l} - 3d^2\right)\right]$ at D

TABLE III.—SHEAR, MOMENT, AND DEFLECTION FORMULAS FOR BEAMS; REACTION FORMULAS FOR RIGID FRAMES.—(*Continued*)

Loading, support, and reference number	Reactions R_1 and R_2, vertical shear V	Bending moment M and maximum bending moment	Deflection y, maximum deflection, and end slope θ
17. End supports, triangular load 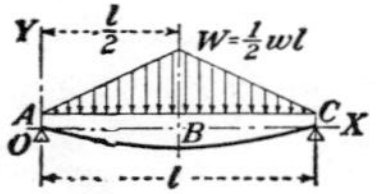	$R = \frac{1}{2}W$ $R_2 = \frac{1}{2}W$ $(A \text{ to } B)\ V = \frac{1}{2}W\left(1 - 4\frac{x^2}{l^2}\right)$ $(B \text{ to } C)\ V = -\frac{1}{2}W\left(1 - 4\frac{(l-x)^2}{l^2}\right)$	$(A \text{ to } B)\ M = \frac{1}{6}W\left(3x - 4\frac{x^3}{l^2}\right)$ $(B \text{ to } C)\ M = \frac{1}{6}W\left[3(l-x) - 4\frac{(l-x)^3}{l^2}\right]$ Max $M = \frac{1}{6}Wl$ at B	$(A \text{ to } B)\ y = \frac{1}{6}\frac{Wx}{EIl^2}\left(\frac{1}{2}l^2x^2 - \frac{1}{5}x^4 - \frac{5}{16}l^4\right)$ Max $y = -\frac{1}{60}\frac{Wl^3}{EI}$ at B $\theta = -\frac{5}{96}\frac{Wl^2}{EI}$ at A; $\theta = +\frac{5}{96}\frac{Wl^2}{EI}$ at C
18. End supports, triangular load 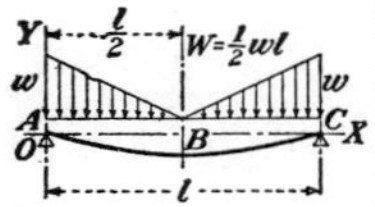	$R_1 = \frac{1}{2}W$ $R_2 = \frac{1}{2}W$ $(A \text{ to } B)\ V = \frac{1}{2}W\left(\frac{l-2x}{l}\right)^2$ $(B \text{ to } C)\ V = -\frac{1}{2}W\left(\frac{2x-l}{l}\right)^2$	$(A \text{ to } B)\ M = \frac{1}{2}W\left(x - 2\frac{x^2}{l} + \frac{4}{3}\frac{x^3}{l^2}\right)$ $(B \text{ to } C)\ M = \frac{1}{2}W\left[(l-x) - 2\frac{(l-x)^2}{l} + \frac{4}{3}\frac{(l-x)^3}{l^2}\right]$ Max $M = \frac{1}{12}Wl$ at B	$(A \text{ to } B)\ y = \frac{1}{12}\frac{W}{EI}\left(x^3 - \frac{x^4}{l} + \frac{2}{5}\frac{x^5}{l^2} - \frac{3}{8}l^2x\right)$ Max $y = -\frac{3}{320}\frac{Wl^3}{EI}$ at B $\theta = -\frac{1}{32}\frac{Wl^2}{EI}$ at A; $\theta = +\frac{1}{32}\frac{Wl^2}{EI}$ at B
19. End supports, end couple 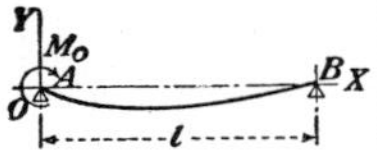	$R_1 = -\frac{M_0}{l}$ $R_2 = +\frac{M_0}{l}$ $V = R_1$	$M = M_0 + R_1x$ Max $M = M_0$ at A	$y = \frac{1}{6}\frac{M_0}{EI}\left(3x^2 - \frac{x^3}{l} - 2lx\right)$ Max $y = -0.0642\frac{M_0l^2}{EI}$ at $x = 0.422l$ $\theta = -\frac{1}{3}\frac{M_0l}{EI}$ at A $\theta = +\frac{1}{6}\frac{M_0l}{EI}$ at B
20. End supports, intermediate couple 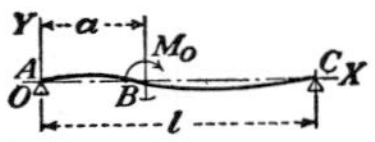	$R_1 = -\frac{M_0}{l}$ $R_2 = +\frac{M_0}{l}$ $(A \text{ to } C)\ V = R_1$	$(A \text{ to } B)\ M = R_1x$ $(B \text{ to } C)\ M = R_1x + M_0$ Max $-M = R_1a$ just left of B Max $+M = R_1a + M_0$ just right of B	$(A \text{ to } B)\ y = \frac{1}{6}\frac{M_0}{EI}\left[\left(6a - 3\frac{a^2}{l} - 2l\right)x - \frac{x^3}{l}\right]$ $(B \text{ to } C)\ y = \frac{1}{6}\frac{M_0}{EI}\left[3a^2 + 3x^2 - \frac{x^3}{l} - \left(2l + 3\frac{a^2}{l}\right)x\right]$ $\theta = -\frac{1}{6}\frac{M_0}{EI}\left(2l - 6a + 3\frac{a^2}{l}\right)$ at A; $\theta = +\frac{1}{6}\frac{M_0}{EI}\left(l - 3\frac{a^2}{l}\right)$ at C $\theta = \frac{M_0}{EI}\left(a - \frac{a^2}{l} - \frac{1}{3}l\right)$ at B

Statically Indeterminate Cases

Loading, support, and reference number	Reactions R_1 and R_2, constraining moments M_1 and M_2, and vertical shear V	Bending moment M and maximum positive and negative bending moments	Deflection y, maximum deflection, and end slope θ
21. One end fixed, one end supported Center load 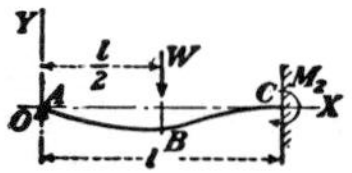	$R_1 = \frac{5}{16}W \qquad R_2 = \frac{11}{16}W$ $M_2 = \frac{3}{16}Wl$ $(A \text{ to } B)\ V = +\frac{5}{16}W$ $(B \text{ to } C)\ V = -\frac{11}{16}W$	$(A \text{ to } B)\ M = \frac{5}{16}Wx$ $(B \text{ to } C)\ M = W(\frac{1}{2}l - \frac{11}{16}x)$ Max $+M = \frac{5}{32}Wl$ at B Max $-M = -\frac{3}{16}Wl$ at C	$(A \text{ to } B)\ y = \frac{1}{96}\frac{W}{EI}(5x^3 - 3l^2x)$ $(B \text{ to } C)\ y = \frac{1}{96}\frac{W}{EI}\left[5x^3 - 16\left(x - \frac{l}{2}\right)^3 - 3l^2x\right]$ Max $y = -0.00932\frac{Wl^3}{EI}$ at $x = 0.4472l$ $\theta = -\frac{1}{32}\frac{Wl^2}{EI}$ at A
22. One end fixed, one end supported Intermediate load 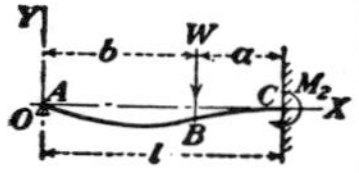	$R_1 = \frac{1}{2}W\left(\frac{3a^2l - a^3}{l^3}\right) \qquad R_2 = W - R_1$ $M_2 = \frac{1}{2}W\left(\frac{a^3 + 2al^2 - 3a^2l}{l^2}\right)$ $(A \text{ to } B)\ V = +R_1$ $(B \text{ to } C)\ V = R_1 - W$	$(A \text{ to } B)\ M = R_1x$ $(B \text{ to } C)\ M = R_1x - W(x - l + a)$ Max $+M = R_1(l - a)$ at B; max possible value $= 0.174\ Wl$ when $a = 0.634l$ Max $-M = -M_2$ at C; max possible value $= -0.1927\ Wl$ when $a = 0.4227l$	$(A \text{ to } B)\ y = \frac{1}{6EI}[R_1(x^3 - 3l^2x) + 3Wa^2x]$ $(B \text{ to } C)\ y = \frac{1}{6EI}\{R_1(x^3 - 3l^2x) + W[3a^2x - (x - b)^3]\}$ If $a < 0.586l$, max y is between A and B at: $x = l\sqrt{1 - \frac{2l}{3l - a}}$ If $a > 0.586l$, max y is at: $x = \frac{l(l^2 + b^2)}{3l^2 - b^2}$ If $a = 0.586l$, max y is at B and $= -0.0098\frac{Wl^3}{EI}$, max possible deflection $\theta = \frac{1}{4}\frac{W}{EI}\left(\frac{a^3}{l} - a^2\right)$ at A
23. One end fixed, one end supported Uniform load 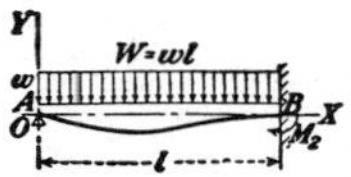	$R_1 = \frac{3}{8}W \qquad R_2 = \frac{5}{8}W$ $M_2 = \frac{1}{8}Wl$ $V = W\left(\frac{3}{8} - \frac{x}{l}\right)$	$M = W\left(\frac{3}{8}x - \frac{1}{2}\frac{x^2}{l}\right)$ Max $+M = \frac{9}{128}Wl$ at $x = \frac{3}{8}l$ Max $-M = -\frac{1}{8}Wl$ at B	$y = \frac{1}{48}\frac{W}{EIl}(3lx^3 - 2x^4 - l^3x)$ Max $y = -0.0054\frac{Wl^3}{EI}$ at $x = 0.4215l$ $\theta = -\frac{1}{48}\frac{Wl^2}{EI}$ at A

TABLE III.—SHEAR, MOMENT, AND DEFLECTION FORMULAS FOR BEAMS; REACTION FORMULAS FOR RIGID FRAMES.—(*Continued*)

Loading, support, and reference number	Reactions R_1 and R_2, constraining moments M_1 and M_2, and vertical shear V	Bending moment M and maximum positive and negative bending moments	Deflection y, maximum deflection, and end slope θ
24. One end fixed, one end supported Partial uniform load 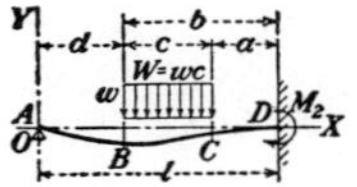	$R_1 = \frac{1}{8}\frac{W}{l^3}[4l(a^2+ab+b^2) - a^3 - ab^2 - a^2b - b^3]$ $R_2 = W - R_1$ $M_2 = -R_1 l + \frac{1}{2}W(a+b)$ (A to B) $V = +R_1$ (B to C) $V = R_1 - W\left(\frac{x-d}{c}\right)$ (C to D) $V = R_1 - W$	(A to B) $M = R_1 x$ (B to C) $M = R_1 x - W\frac{(x-d)^2}{2c}$ (C to D) $M = R_1 x - W(x - d - \frac{1}{2}c)$ Max $+M = R_1\left(d + \frac{1}{2}\frac{R_1}{W}c\right)$ at $x = d + \frac{R_1}{W}c$ Max $-M = -M_2$	(A to B) $y = \frac{1}{EI}\left[R_1\left(\frac{1}{6}x^3 - \frac{1}{2}l^2x\right) + Wx(\frac{1}{2}a^2 + \frac{1}{2}ac + \frac{1}{6}c^2)\right]$ (B to C) $y = \frac{1}{EI}\left[R_1\left(\frac{1}{6}x^3 - \frac{1}{2}l^2x\right) + Wx\left(\frac{1}{2}a^2 + \frac{1}{2}ac + \frac{1}{6}c^2\right) - W\frac{(x-d)^4}{24c}\right]$ (C to D) $y = \frac{1}{EI}\left\{R_1\left(\frac{1}{6}x^3 - \frac{1}{2}l^2x + \frac{1}{3}l^3\right) + W[\frac{1}{6}(a+\frac{1}{2}c)^3 - \frac{1}{2}(a+\frac{1}{2}c)^2l - \frac{1}{6}(x-d-\frac{1}{2}c)^3 + \frac{1}{2}(a+\frac{1}{2}c)^2x]\right\}$ $\theta = -\frac{1}{EI}\left[\frac{1}{2}R_1l^2 - W\left(\frac{1}{2}a^2 + \frac{1}{2}ac + \frac{1}{6}c^2\right)\right]$ at A
25. One end fixed, one end supported Triangular load 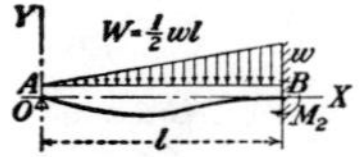	$R_1 = \frac{1}{5}W \qquad R_2 = \frac{4}{5}W$ $M_2 = \frac{2}{15}Wl$ $V = W\left(\frac{1}{5} - \frac{x^2}{l^2}\right)$	$M = W\left(\frac{1}{5}x - \frac{1}{3}\frac{x^3}{l^2}\right)$ Max $+M = 0.06Wl$ at $x = 0.4474l$ Max $-M = -M_2$	$y = \frac{1}{60}\frac{W}{EIl}\left(2lx^3 - l^3x - \frac{x^5}{l}\right)$ Max $y = -0.00477\frac{Wl^3}{EI}$ at $x = l\sqrt{\frac{1}{5}}$ $\theta = -\frac{1}{60}\frac{Wl^2}{EI}$ at A
26. One end fixed, one end supported Partial triangular load 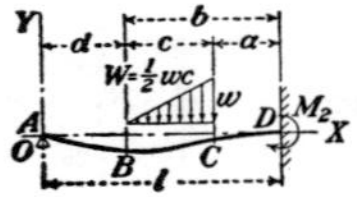	$R_1 = \frac{1}{20}\frac{W}{l^3}[(10ab + 15a^2 + 5b^2)l - 4a^3 - 2ab^2 - 3a^2b - b^3]$ $R_2 = W - R_1 \qquad M_2 = -R_1l + \frac{1}{3}W(2a+b)$ (A to B) $V = R_1$ (B to C) $V = R_1 - W\left(\frac{x-d}{c}\right)^2$ (C to D) $V = R_1 - W$	(A to B) $M = R_1x$ (B to C) $M = R_1x - \frac{1}{3}W\frac{(x-d)^3}{c^2}$ (C to D) $M = R_1x - W(x - d - \frac{2}{3}c)$ Max $+M = R_1\left(d + \frac{2}{3}c\sqrt{\frac{R_1}{W}}\right)$ at $x = d + c\sqrt{\frac{R_1}{W}}$ Max $-M = -M_2$	(A to B) $y = \frac{1}{EI}\left[R_1\left(\frac{1}{6}x^3 - \frac{1}{2}l^2x\right) + Wx(\frac{1}{2}a^2 + \frac{1}{3}ac + \frac{1}{12}c^2)\right]$ (B to C) $y = \frac{1}{EI}\left[R_1\left(\frac{1}{6}x^3 - \frac{1}{2}l^2x\right) + Wx\left(\frac{1}{2}a^2 + \frac{1}{3}ac + \frac{1}{12}c^2\right) - W\frac{(x-d)^5}{60c^2}\right]$ (C to D) $y = \frac{1}{EI}\left\{R_1\left(\frac{1}{6}x^3 - \frac{1}{2}l^2x + \frac{1}{3}l^3\right) + W[\frac{1}{2}(a+\frac{1}{3}c)^2x - \frac{1}{6}(x-d-\frac{2}{3}c)^3 + \frac{1}{6}(a+\frac{1}{3}c)^3 - \frac{1}{2}(a+\frac{1}{3}c)^2l]\right\}$ $\theta = -\frac{1}{EI}\left[\frac{1}{2}R_1l^2 - W\left(\frac{1}{12}c^2 + \frac{1}{3}ac + \frac{1}{2}a^2\right)\right]$ at A

Loading	Reactions, shear	Moments	Deflections, slopes
Triangular load	$M_2 = \frac{7}{60}Wl$ $V = W\left(\frac{11}{20} - \frac{2x}{l} + \frac{x^2}{l^2}\right)$	Max $+M = 0.0846Wl$ at $x = 0.329l$ Max $-M = -\frac{7}{60}Wl$ at B	Max $y = -0.00609\frac{Wl^3}{EI}$ at $x = 0.402l$ $\theta = -\frac{1}{40}\frac{Wl^2}{EI}$ at A
28. One end fixed, one end supported Partial triangular load	$R_1 = \frac{1}{20}\frac{W}{l^3}[(10ab + 5a^2 + 15b^2)l - a^3 - 2a^2b - 3ab^2 - 4b^3]$, $R_2 = W - R_1$ $M_2 = -R_1l + \frac{1}{3}W(a + 2b)$ $(A$ to $B)$ $V = R_1$ $(B$ to $C)$ $V = R_1 - \frac{2(x-d)}{c}W + \frac{(x-d)^2}{c^2}W$ $(C$ to $D)$ $V = R_1 - W$	$(A$ to $B)$ $M = R_1x$ $(B$ to $C)$ $M = R_1x - \frac{(x-d)^2}{c}W + \frac{(x-d)^3}{3c^2}W$ $(C$ to $D)$ $M = R_1x - W(x - d - \frac{1}{3}c)$ Max $+M = R_1\left(d + c - c\sqrt{1 - \frac{R_1}{W}}\right) - \frac{1}{3}Wc\left(1 - \sqrt{1 - \frac{R_1}{W}}\right)^2\left(2 + \sqrt{1 - \frac{R_1}{W}}\right)$ at $x = d + c\left(1 - \sqrt{1 - \frac{R_1}{W}}\right)$ Max $-M = -M_2$ at D	$(A$ to $B)$ $y = \frac{1}{EI}\left\{R_1\left(\frac{1}{6}x^3 - \frac{1}{2}l^2x\right) + Wx(\frac{1}{2}a^2 + \frac{2}{3}ac + \frac{1}{6}c^2)\right\}$ $(B$ to $C)$ $y = \frac{1}{EI}\left\{R_1\left(\frac{1}{6}x^3 - \frac{1}{2}l^2x\right) + W\left[\frac{1}{60}\frac{(x-d)^5}{c^2} - \frac{1}{12}\frac{(x-d)^4}{c} + (\frac{1}{2}a^2 + \frac{2}{3}ac + \frac{1}{6}c^2)x\right]\right\}$ $(C$ to $D)$ $y = \frac{1}{EI}\left\{R_1\left(\frac{1}{6}x^3 - \frac{1}{2}l^2x + \frac{1}{3}l^3\right) - \frac{1}{2}W(l - x)^2\left[\left(a + \frac{2}{3}c\right) - \frac{l - x}{3}\right]\right\}$ $\theta = -\frac{1}{EI}\left[\frac{1}{2}R_1l^2 - W\left(\frac{1}{2}a^2 + \frac{2}{3}ac + \frac{1}{4}c^2\right)\right]$ at A
29. One end fixed, one end supported End couple	$R_1 = -\frac{3}{2}\frac{M_0}{l}$ $R_2 = +\frac{3}{2}\frac{M_0}{l}$ $M_2 = \frac{1}{2}M_0$ $V = -\frac{3}{2}\frac{M_0}{l}$	$M = \frac{1}{2}M_0\left(2 - 3\frac{x}{l}\right)$ Max $+M = M_0$ at A Max $-M = -\frac{1}{2}M_0$ at B	$y = \frac{1}{4}\frac{M_0}{EI}\left(2x^2 - \frac{x^3}{l} - lx\right)$ Max $y = -\frac{1}{27}\frac{M_0l^2}{EI}$ at $x = \frac{1}{3}l$ $\theta = -\frac{1}{4}\frac{M_0l}{EI}$ at A
30. One end fixed, one end supported Intermediate couple	$R_1 = -\frac{3}{2}\frac{M_0}{l}\left(\frac{l^2 - a^2}{l^2}\right)$ $R_2 = +\frac{3}{2}\frac{M_0}{l}\left(\frac{l^2 - a^2}{l^2}\right)$ $M_2 = \frac{1}{2}M_0\left(1 - 3\frac{a^2}{l^2}\right)$ $(A$ to $B)$ $V = R_1$ $(B$ to $C)$ $V = R_1$	$(A$ to $B)$ $M = R_1x$ $(B$ to $C)$ $M = R_1x + M_0$ Max $+M = M_0\left[1 - \frac{3a(l^2 - a^2)}{2l^3}\right]$ at B (to right) Max $-M = -M_2$ at C (when $a < 0.275l$) Max $-M = R_1a$ at B (to left) (when $a > 0.275l$)	$(A$ to $B)$ $y = \frac{M_0}{EI}\left[\frac{l^2 - a^2}{4l^3}(3l^2x - x^3) - (l - a)x\right]$ $(B$ to $C)$ $y = \frac{M_0}{EI}\left[\frac{l^2 - a^2}{4l^3}(3l^2x - x^3) - lx + \frac{1}{2}(x^2 + a^2)\right]$ $\theta = \frac{M_0}{EI}\left(a - \frac{1}{4}l - \frac{3}{4}\frac{a^2}{l}\right)$ at A

TABLE III.—SHEAR, MOMENT, AND DEFLECTION FORMULAS FOR BEAMS; REACTION FORMULAS FOR RIGID FRAMES.—(*Continued*)

Loading, support, and reference number	Reactions R_1 and R_2, constraining moments M_1 and M_2, and vertical shear V	Bending moment M and maximum positive and negative bending moments	Deflection y, maximum deflection, and end slope θ
31. Both ends fixed. Center load	$R_1 = \frac{1}{2}W \quad R_2 = \frac{1}{2}W$ $M_1 = \frac{1}{8}Wl \quad M_2 = \frac{1}{8}Wl$ $(A \text{ to } B)\ V = +\frac{1}{2}W$ $(B \text{ to } C)\ V = -\frac{1}{2}W$	$(A \text{ to } B)\ M = \frac{1}{8}W(4x - l)$ $(B \text{ to } C)\ M = \frac{1}{8}W(3l - 4x)$ Max $+M = \frac{1}{8}Wl$ at B Max $-M = -\frac{1}{8}Wl$ at A and C	$(A \text{ to } B)\ y = -\frac{1}{48}\frac{W}{EI}(3lx^2 - 4x^3)$ Max $y = -\frac{1}{192}\frac{Wl^3}{EI}$ at B
32. Both ends fixed. Intermediate load	$R_1 = \frac{Wb^2}{l^3}(3a + b) \quad R_2 = \frac{Wa^2}{l^3}(3b + a)$ $M_1 = W\frac{ab^2}{l^2} \quad M_2 = W\frac{a^2b}{l^2}$ $(A \text{ to } B)\ V = R_1$ $(B \text{ to } C)\ V = R_1 - W$	$(A \text{ to } B)\ M = -W\frac{ab^2}{l^2} + R_1x$ $(B \text{ to } C)\ M = -W\frac{ab^2}{l^2} + R_1x - W(x - a)$ Max $+M = -W\frac{ab^2}{l^2} + R_1a$ at B; max possible value $= \frac{1}{8}Wl$ when $a = \frac{1}{2}l$ Max $-M = -M_1$ when $a < b$; max possible value $= -0.1481Wl$ when $a = \frac{1}{3}l$ Max $-M = -M_2$ when $a > b$; max possible value $= -0.1481\ Wl$ when $a = \frac{2}{3}l$	$(A \text{ to } B)\ y = \frac{1}{6}\frac{Wb^2x^2}{EIl^3}(3ax + bx - 3al)$ $(B \text{ to } C)\ y = \frac{1}{6}\frac{Wa^2(l - x)^2}{EIl^3}[(3b + a)(l - x) - 3bl]$ Max $y = -\frac{2}{3}\frac{W}{EI}\frac{a^3b^2}{(3a + b)^2}$ at $x = \frac{2al}{3a + b}$ if $a > b$ Max $y = -\frac{2}{3}\frac{W}{EI}\frac{a^2b^3}{(3b + a)^2}$ at $x = l - \frac{2bl}{3b + a}$ if $a < b$
33. Both ends fixed. Uniform load	$R_1 = \frac{1}{2}W \quad R_2 = \frac{1}{2}W$ $M_1 = \frac{1}{12}Wl \quad M_2 = \frac{1}{12}Wl$ $V = \frac{1}{2}W\left(1 - \frac{2x}{l}\right)$	$M = \frac{1}{2}W\left(x - \frac{x^2}{l} - \frac{1}{6}l\right)$ Max $+M = \frac{1}{24}Wl$ at $x = \frac{1}{2}l$ Max $-M = -\frac{1}{12}Wl$ at A and B	$y = \frac{1}{24}\frac{Wx^2}{EIl}(2lx - l^2 - x^2)$ Max $y = -\frac{1}{384}\frac{Wl^3}{EI}$ at $x = \frac{1}{2}l$
34. Both ends fixed Partial uniform load $d = l - \frac{1}{2}a - \frac{1}{2}b$	$R_1 = \frac{1}{4}\frac{W}{l^2}\left(12d^2 - 8\frac{d^3}{l} + 2\frac{bc^2}{l} - \frac{c^3}{l} - c^2\right)$ $R_2 = W - R_1$ $M_1 = -\frac{1}{24}\frac{W}{l}\left(24\frac{d^3}{l} - 6\frac{bc^2}{l} + 3\frac{c^3}{l} + 4c^2 - 24d^2\right)$ $M_2 = \frac{1}{24}\frac{W}{l}\left(24\frac{d^3}{l} - 6\frac{bc^2}{l} + 3\frac{c^3}{l} + 2c^2 - 48d^2 + 24dl\right)$ $(A \text{ to } B)\ V = R_1 \quad (B \text{ to } C)\ V = R_1 - W\frac{x - a}{c}$ $(C \text{ to } D)\ V = R_1 - W$	$(A \text{ to } B)\ M = -M_1 + R_1x$ $(B \text{ to } C)\ M = -M_1 + R_1x - \frac{1}{2}W\frac{(x - a)^2}{c}$ $(C \text{ to } D)\ M = -M_1 + R_1x - W(x - l + d)$ Max $+M$ is between B and C at $x = a + \frac{R_1}{W}c$ Max $-M = -M_1$ when $a < l - b$	$(A \text{ to } B)\ y = \frac{1}{6EI}(R_1x^3 - 3M_1x^2)$ $(B \text{ to } C)\ y = \frac{1}{6EI}\left(R_1x^3 - 3M_1x^2 - \frac{1}{4}W\frac{(x - a)^4}{c}\right)$ $(C \text{ to } D)\ y = \frac{1}{6EI}[R_2(l - x)^3 - 3M_2(l - x)^2]$

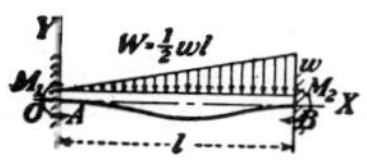	$M_1 = \frac{1}{15}Wl$ $M_2 = \frac{1}{10}Wl$ $V = W\left(\frac{3}{10} - \frac{x^2}{l^2}\right)$	Max $+M = 0.043Wl$ at $x = 0.548l$ Max $-M = -\frac{1}{10}Wl$ at B	Max $y = -0.002617\frac{Wl^3}{EI}$ at $x = 0.525l$
36. Both ends fixed **Partial triangular load** 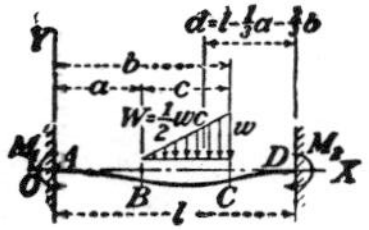	$R_1 = \frac{W}{l^2}\left(3d^2 - \frac{1}{6}c^2 + \frac{1}{3}\frac{bc^2}{l} - \frac{17}{135}\frac{c^3}{l} - 2\frac{d^3}{l}\right)$ $R_2 = W - R_1$ $M_1 = -\frac{W}{l}\left(\frac{d^3}{l} + \frac{1}{9}c^2 + \frac{51}{810}\frac{c^3}{l} - \frac{1}{6}\frac{c^2b}{l} - d^2\right)$ $M_2 = \frac{W}{l}\left(\frac{d^3}{l} + \frac{1}{18}c^2 + \frac{51}{810}\frac{c^3}{l} - \frac{1}{6}\frac{c^2b}{l} - 2d^2 + dl\right)$ (A to B) $V = R_1$ (B to C) $V = R_1 - W\frac{(x-a)^2}{c^2}$ (C to D) $V = R_1 - W$	(A to B) $M = -M_1 + R_1x$ (B to C) $M = -M_1 + R_1x - W\frac{(x-a)^3}{3c^2}$ (C to D) $M = -M_1 + R_1x - W(x - l + d)$ Max $+M$ at $x = a + c\sqrt{\frac{R_1}{W}}$ Max $-M = M_1$ when $d > \frac{l}{2}$, $-M_2$ when $d < \frac{l}{2}$	(A to B) $y = \frac{1}{6EI}(R_1x^3 - 3M_1x^2)$ (B to C) $y = \frac{1}{EI}\left(\frac{1}{6}R_1x^3 - \frac{1}{2}M_1x^2 - \frac{1}{60}W\frac{(x-a)^5}{c^2}\right)$ (C to D) $y = \frac{1}{6EI}\{R_1(x^3 - 3l^2x + 2l^3) - 3M_1(l-x)^2$ $+ W[3d^2x + d^3 - 3d^2l - (x - l + d)^3]\}$
37. Both ends fixed Intermediate couple 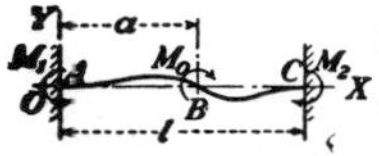	$R_1 = -6\frac{M_0}{l^3}(al - a^2)$ $R_2 = 6\frac{M_0}{l^3}(al - a^2)$ $M_1 = -\frac{M_0}{l^2}(4la - 3a^2 - l^2)$ $M_2 = \frac{M_0}{l^2}(2la - 3a^2)$ $V = R_1$	(A to B) $M = -M_1 + R_1x$ (B to C) $M = -M_1 + R_1x + M_0$ Max $+M = M_0\left(4\frac{a}{l} - 9\frac{a^2}{l^2} + 6\frac{a^3}{l^3}\right)$ just right of B Max $-M = M_0\left(4\frac{a}{l} - 9\frac{a^2}{l^2} + 6\frac{a^3}{l^3} - 1\right)$ just left of B	(A to B) $y = -\frac{1}{6EI}(3M_1x^2 - R_1x^3)$ (B to C) $y = \frac{1}{6EI}[(M_0 - M_1)(3x^2 - 6lx + 3l^2)$ $- R_1(3l^2x - x^3 - 2l^3)]$ Max $+y$ at $x = \frac{2M_1}{R_1}$ if $a > \frac{1}{3}l$ Max $-y$ at $x = l - \frac{2M_2}{R_2}$ if $a < \frac{2}{3}l$
38. Continuous beam, each span uniformly loaded; spans, loads and sections different 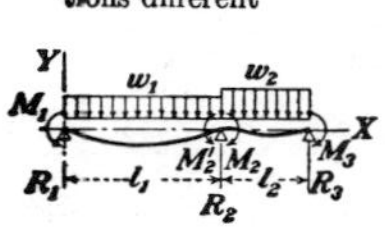	$\frac{M_1l_1}{I_1} + 2M_2\left[\frac{l_1}{I_1} + \frac{l_2}{I_2}\right] + \frac{M_3l_2}{I_2} = \frac{w_1l_1^3}{4I_1} + \frac{w_2l_2^3}{4I_2}$ (Theorem of Three Moments: I_1 and I_2 refer to 1st and 2d spans. Equation gives M_2 when M_1 and M_3 are known, or can be written for each pair of spans of a continuous beam and resulting equations solved. M_2 acts on span 1, M_2' on span 2.)	Superpose cases 13 and 19	Superpose cases 13 and 19

TABLE III.—SHEAR, MOMENT, AND DEFLECTION FORMULAS FOR BEAMS; REACTION FORMULAS FOR RIGID FRAMES.—(*Continued*)

Loading, support, and reference number	Formulas for statically indeterminate forces and moments
39. Pinned supports, concentrated load on horizontal member	$H = \frac{1}{2} W \frac{L_1L_3b + 2L_2L_3b - 3L_2b^2 - (b^3/L_3)(L_1 - L_2)}{L_1L_2L_3 + L_1^2L_3 + L_2^2L_3 + L_1^3(I_3/I_1) + L_2^3(I_3/I_2)}$ $V_1 = \frac{Wb - H(L_2 - L_1)}{L_3}$
40. Pinned supports, concentrated load on one vertical member	$H_2 = W \frac{\frac{2L_1^3}{I_1} - \frac{2b^3}{I_1} - \frac{3ab^2}{I_1} + \frac{2L_1^2L_3}{I_3} - \frac{2L_1L_3b}{I_3} + \frac{L_1L_2L_3}{I_3} - \frac{L_2L_3b}{I_3}}{\frac{2L_2^3}{I_2} + \frac{2L_2^2L_3}{I_3} + \frac{2L_1L_2L_3}{I_3} + \frac{2L_1^3}{I_1} + \frac{2L_1^2L_3}{I_3}}$ $V = \frac{Wa - H_2(L_1 - L_2)}{L_3}$
41. Pinned supports, uniform load on horizontal member	$H = W \frac{L_3^3(L_1 + L_2)}{8L_1^2L_3 + 4L_1L_2L_3 + 8L_1^3(I_3/I_1) + 8L_2^3(I_3/I_2) + 8L_2^2L_3 + 4L_1L_2L_3}$ $V_1 = \frac{\frac{1}{2}WL_3 + H(L_1 - L_2)}{L_3}$

42. Pinned supports, uniform load on vertical member	$H_2 = \frac{1}{8} W \frac{5L_1^3(I_3/I_1) + 2L_1L_2L_3 + 4L_1^2L_3}{L_1^3(I_3/I_1) + L_2^3(I_3/I_2) + L_1^2L_3 + L_2^2L_3 + L_1L_2L_3}$ $V = \frac{\frac{1}{2}WL_1 - H_2(L_1 - L_2)}{L_3}$
43. Fixed supports, concentrated load on horizontal member	$-\frac{\frac{1}{3}HL_1^3}{I_1} + \frac{\frac{1}{2}M_1L_1^2}{I_1} = \frac{\frac{1}{3}HL_2^3}{I_2} - \frac{\frac{1}{2}M_2L_2^2}{I_2}$ $-\frac{\frac{1}{2}HL_1^2}{I_1} + \frac{M_1L_1}{I_1} = -\frac{\frac{1}{3}M_1L_3}{I_3} + \frac{\frac{1}{6}W(bL_3 - b^3/L_3)}{I_3} - \frac{\frac{1}{6}M_2L_3}{I_3}$ $\frac{\frac{1}{2}HL_2^2}{I_2} - \frac{M_2L_2}{I_2} = \frac{\frac{1}{3}M_2L_3}{I_3} + \frac{\frac{1}{6}M_1L_3}{I_3} - \frac{\frac{1}{6}W[2bL_3 + (b^3/L_3) - 3b^2]}{I_3}$
44. Fixed supports, concentrated load on one vertical member	$\frac{\frac{1}{3}Wa^3}{I_1} + \frac{\frac{1}{2}Wa^2b}{I_1} - \frac{\frac{1}{3}H_2L_1^3}{I_1} - \frac{\frac{1}{2}M_1L_1^2}{I_1} = \frac{\frac{1}{3}H_2L_2^3}{I_2} - \frac{\frac{1}{2}M_2L_2^2}{I_2}$ $\frac{\frac{1}{2}Wa^2}{I_1} - \frac{\frac{1}{2}H_2L_1^2}{I_1} - \frac{M_1L_1}{I_1} = \frac{\frac{1}{3}M_1L_3}{I_3} - \frac{\frac{1}{6}M_2L_3}{I_3}$ $\frac{\frac{1}{2}HL_2^2}{I_2} - \frac{M_2L_2}{I_2} = \frac{\frac{1}{3}M_2L_3}{I_3} - \frac{\frac{1}{6}M_1L_3}{I_3}$

TABLE III.—SHEAR, MOMENT, AND DEFLECTION FORMULAS FOR BEAMS; REACTION FORMULAS FOR RIGID FRAMES.—(*Continued*)

Loading, support, and referance number	Formulas for statically indeterminate forces and moments
45. Fixed supports, uniform load on horizontal member 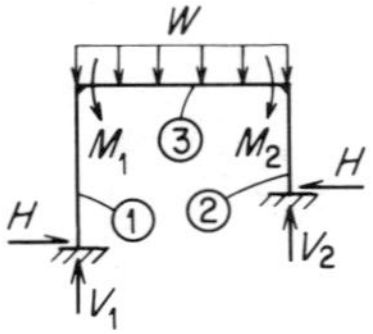	$\frac{\frac{1}{2}M_1L_1^2}{I_1} - \frac{\frac{1}{3}HL_1^3}{I_1} = \frac{\frac{1}{3}HL_2^3}{I_2} - \frac{\frac{1}{2}M_2L_2^2}{I_2}$ $\frac{-\frac{1}{2}HL_1^2}{I_1} + \frac{M_1L_1}{I_1} = \frac{-\frac{1}{3}M_1L_3}{I_3} - \frac{\frac{1}{6}M_2L_3}{I_3} + \frac{\frac{1}{24}WL_3^2}{I_3}$ $\frac{\frac{1}{2}HL_2^2}{I_2} - \frac{M_2L_2}{I_2} = \frac{\frac{1}{3}M_2L_3}{I_3} + \frac{\frac{1}{6}M_1L_3}{I_3} - \frac{\frac{1}{24}WL_3^2}{I_3}$
46. Fixed supports, uniform load on vertical member 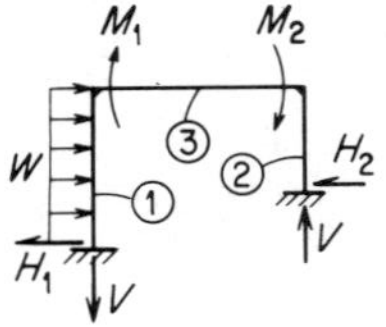	$\frac{\frac{1}{8}WL_1^3}{I_1} - \frac{\frac{1}{2}M_1L_1^2}{I_1} - \frac{\frac{1}{3}H_2L_1^3}{I_1} = \frac{\frac{1}{3}H_2L_2^3}{I_2} - \frac{\frac{1}{2}M_2L_2^2}{I_2}$ $\frac{\frac{1}{6}WL_1^2}{I_1} - \frac{\frac{1}{2}H_2L_1^2}{I_1} - \frac{M_1L_1}{I_1} = \frac{\frac{1}{3}M_1L_3}{I_3} - \frac{\frac{1}{6}M_2L_3}{I_3}$ $\frac{\frac{1}{2}H_2L_2^2}{I_2} - \frac{M_2L_2}{I_2} = \frac{\frac{1}{3}M_2L_3}{I_3} - \frac{\frac{1}{6}M_1L_3}{I_3}$
47. Rectangular frame or tube under uniform outward (or inward) pressure w 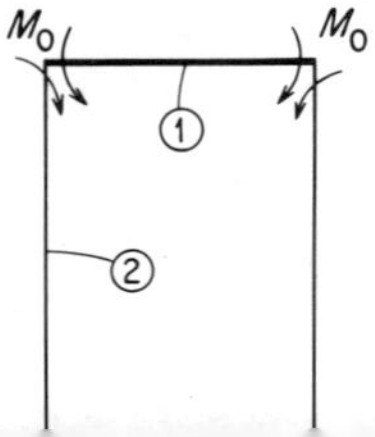	$M_0 = \frac{1}{12} w \frac{\frac{L_1^3}{I_1} + \frac{L_2^3}{I_2}}{\frac{L_1}{I_1} + \frac{L_2}{I_2}}$ (For frame with arched top see Ref. 77)

48. Uniform rectangular frame or tube with rounded corners under uniform outward or inward pressure w

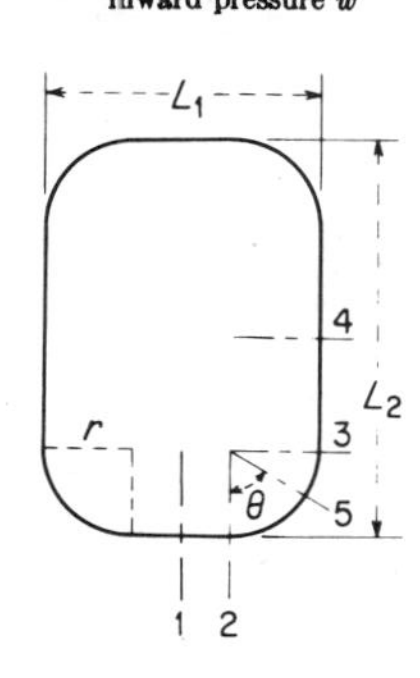

Bending moment at any numbered section $= CwL_2^2$, where C has value given in table below. Subscript of C corresponds to number of section; maximum moment is at section 5 defined by θ; plus sign means that moment due to internal pressure produces tension at inner surface. In calculating stress at corners, appropriate curved beam formula (Table VII) or stress concentration factor (Table XVII) should be used.

$\frac{r}{L_2}$	$\frac{L_1}{L_2}$	C_1	C_2	C_3	C_4	C_5	θ (deg)
0	0	+0.0833	+0.0833	+0.0833	−0.0417	+0.0833	0
	0.2	+0.0650	+0.0700	+0.0700	−0.0550	+0.0700	11.3
	0.4	+0.0433	+0.0633	+0.0633	−0.0617	+0.0633	21.8
	0.6	+0.0183	+0.0633	+0.0633	−0.0617	+0.0633	31
	0.8	−0.0100	+0.0700	+0.0700	−0.0550	+0.0700	38.7
	1.0	−0.0417	+0.0833	+0.0833	−0.0417	+0.0833	45
0.1	0.2	+0.0711	+0.0711	+0.0311	−0.0489	+0.0711	0
	0.4	+0.0482	+0.0532	+0.0232	−0.0568	+0.0544	14
	0.6	+0.0227	+0.0427	+0.0227	−0.0573	+0.0474	26.6
	0.8	−0.0057	+0.0393	+0.0293	−0.0507	+0.0493	36.8
	1.0	−0.0372	+0.0428	+0.0428	−0.0372	+0.0594	45
0.2	0.4	+0.0551	+0.0551	−0.0049	−0.0499	+0.0551	0
	0.6	+0.0289	+0.0339	−0.0061	−0.0511	+0.0371	18.4
	0.8	+0.0003	+0.0203	+0.0003	−0.0447	+0.0323	33.7
	1.0	−0.0309	+0.0141	+0.0141	−0.0310	+0.0389	45
0.3	0.6	+0.0371	+0.0371	−0.0229	−0.0429	+0.0371	0
	0.8	+0.0083	+0.0133	−0.0167	−0.0367	+0.0203	26.6
	1.0	−0.0228	−0.0028	−0.0028	−0.0228	+0.0220	45
0.4	0.8	+0.0185	−0.0215	−0.0215	−0.0265	+0.0185	0
	1.0	−0.0125	−0.0076	−0.0076	−0.0125	+0.0091	45
0.5	1.0	0	0	0	0	0	

This is the maximum shear stress on a horizontal plane, and occurs at the neutral axis of the section just to the left of the right support.

The shear stress at the junction of each flange with the web will also be computed at the section of maximum vertical shear.

For the upper flange, $b = 2.30$; $A' = 2.01$; $z' = 2.30$. Hence

$$s_s = \frac{(1020)(2.01(2.30)}{(82.6)(2.30)} = 25 \text{ lb. per sq. in.}$$

For the lower flange, $b = 1.20$; $A' = 1.05$; $z' = 3.40$. Hence

$$s_s = \frac{(1020)(1.05)(3.40)}{(82.6)(1.20)} = 37 \text{ lb. per sq. in.}$$

c. For the steel I-beam, the structural-steel handbook gives $I/c = 3.00$ $t = 0.190$. Therefore

$$\text{Max } s = \frac{33{,}750}{3} = 11{,}250 \text{ lb. per sq. in.}$$

This stress occurs at $x = 75$, and is tension in the bottom fibers, compression in the top.

$$\text{Approx. Max } s_s = \frac{1020}{(4)(0.19)} = 1340 \text{ lb. per sq. in.}$$

Although this method of calculating s_s is only approximate, it is usually sufficiently accurate to show whether or not the shear stress is important. If it indicates that shear stress may govern, then the stress at the neutral axis may be calculated by Eq. 2. For standard I-beams, the allowable vertical shear is given by the structural-steel handbooks, making computation unnecessary.

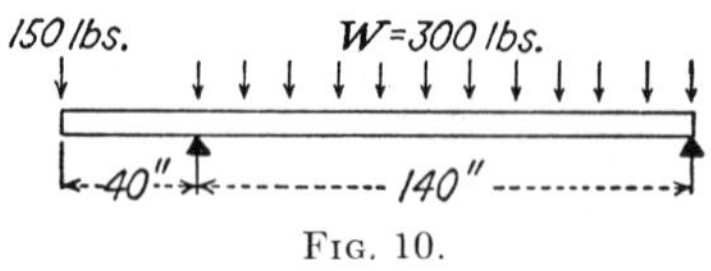

FIG. 10.

2. The beam shown in Fig. 10 has a rectangular section 2 in. wide and 4 in deep, and is of spruce, for which $E = 1{,}300{,}000$. It is required to determine the deflection of the left end.

Solution.—Solution will be first effected by superposition, using the formulas of Table III. The deflection y of the left end is the sum of the deflection y_1 produced by the distributed load and the deflection y_2 produced by the concentrated load. Each of these is computed independently of the other. Thus

$$y_1 = -40\theta = (-40)\left(-\frac{1}{24}\frac{(300)(140^2)}{EI}\right) = +\frac{9{,}800{,}000}{EI} \text{ (by formula for } \theta \text{ at } A\text{, Case 13)}$$

y_2 is calculated as the sum of the deflection the 150-lb. load would produce if the beam were *fixed* at the left support and the deflection due to the fact that it actually assumes a slope there. The first part of the deflection is given by the formula for max y, Case 1; the second part is found by multiplying the overhang (40 in.) by the slope produced at the left end of the 140-in. span by a couple equal to $150 \times 40 = 6000$ applied at that point (formula for θ at A, Case 19). Thus

$$y_2 = -\frac{1}{3}\frac{(150)(40^3)}{EI} + (-40)\left[-\frac{1}{3}\frac{(-6000)(140)}{EI}\right] = -\frac{14,400,000}{EI}$$

Adding algebraically,

$$y = y_1 + y_2 = -\frac{4,600,000}{EI} = -0.33 \text{ in. (deflection is downward)}$$

Solution of this problem can also be effected readily by using Eq. 6. The reaction at the left support due to the actual loads is 343; the reaction due to a unit load acting down at the left end is 1.29. For the part of the beam from $x = 0$ to $x = 40$,

$$M = -150x \qquad \text{and} \qquad m = -x$$

For the part of the beam from $x = 40$ to $x = 180$,

$$M = -150x + 343(x - 40) - \frac{300}{140}\frac{(x-40)^2}{2} \qquad \text{and} \qquad m = -x + 1.286\,(x - 40)$$

Simplifying the equations, we have

$$y = \int \frac{Mm}{EI}\,dx = \frac{1}{EI}\left[\int_0^{40} (-150x)(-x)dx + \int_{40}^{180} (-1.071x^2 + 278.8x - 15,430)(0.286x - 51.6)dx\right] = +0.33 \text{ in.}$$

Here the + sign means that y is in the direction of the assumed unit load, *i.e.*, downward.

This second solution involves much more labor than the first, and the calculations must be carried out with great accuracy if the possibility of a large error in the final result is to be avoided.

3. A timber beam is used to carry a center load of 3000 lb. on a span of 100 in. The cross section is 6 in. wide and 8 in. deep ($I = 256$, $I/c = 64$). The modulus of elasticity of the wood is 1,200,000 lb. per sq. in. It is desired to determine the relative displacement of the lower edges of the end sections.

With origin at the left support the moment is $M = 1500x$ up to $x = 50$ Therefore

$$EI\frac{d^2y}{dx^2} = 1500x, \qquad EI\frac{dy}{dx} = 750x^2 + C = 0$$

at $x = 50$; hence $C = -1,875,000$ and

$$\frac{dy}{dx} = \frac{1}{EI}(750x^2 - 1,875,000)$$

Then

$$\Delta l = \frac{1}{2}(2)\int_0^{50}\left(\frac{750x^2 - 1,875,000}{(1,200,000)(256)}\right)^2 dx = 0.0022 \text{ in.}$$

Also

$$e = 2\int_0^{50}\frac{1500x}{(1,200,000)(64)}\,dx = 0.0488 \text{ in.}$$

Therefore the lower edges of the end sections move farther apart by an amount $0.0488 - 0.0022 = 0.0466$ in., while the centers of the end sections move 0.0022 in. closer together and the top edges move 0.0510 in. closer together.

33. Three-moment Equation.—The equation given for Case 38, Table III, is obtained by equating the slopes of the first and second spans at the second support. By superposition, a similar equation can readily be derived for any kind of loading. The slope of either span is the sum of the slope produced on a simply supported span by the given loading (found from Table III, Cases 11 to 20) and the slope produced by end couples M_1, M_2, (Fig. 11) as given below:

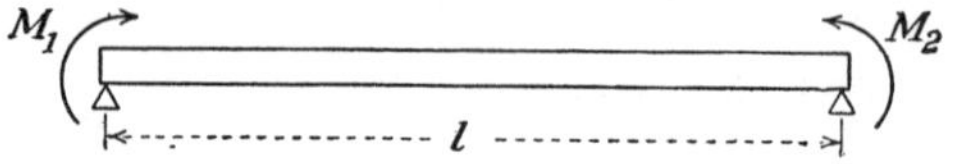

FIG. 11.

At $x = 0$,

$$\theta = \frac{1}{EI}\left(-\frac{1}{3}M_1 l - \frac{1}{6}M_2 l\right)$$

At $x = l$,

$$\theta = \frac{1}{EI}\left(\frac{1}{6}M_1 l + \frac{1}{3}M_2 l\right)$$

At x,

$$y = \frac{1}{EI}\left[\frac{1}{2}M_1(x^2 - lx) + \frac{1}{6}(M_2 - M_1)\left(\frac{x^3}{l} - xl\right)\right]$$

If the end supports settle or deflect unequal amounts y_1, y_2, the increment of slope thus produced is obviously the same at both ends and is

$$\theta = \frac{1}{l}(y_2 - y_1)$$

where, according to the usual convention, y is positive when *upward.*

Example

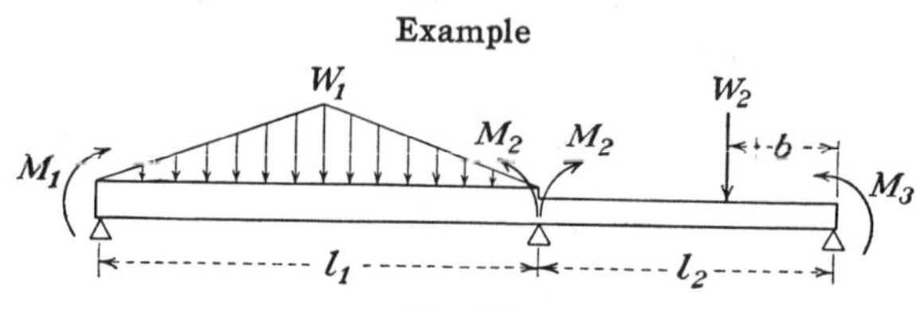

FIG. 12.

Consider two contiguous spans loaded as shown in Fig. 12. The slopes at the right end of Span 1 and at the left end of Span 2 are, respectively,

$$\theta = \frac{1}{E_1 I_1}\left(\frac{1}{6}M_1 l_1 + \frac{1}{3}M_2 l_2\right) \text{ (from above equation) } + \frac{5Wl_1^2}{96E_1 I_1} \text{ (from Case 17) } + \frac{1}{l}(y_2 - y_1)$$

and

$$\theta = \frac{1}{E_2 I_2}\left(-\frac{1}{3}M_2 l_2 - \frac{1}{6}M_3 l_2\right) \text{ (from above equation) } - \frac{W_2}{6E_2 I_2}\left(bl_2 - \frac{b^3}{l_2}\right) \text{ (Case 12) } + \frac{1}{l}(y_3 - y_2).$$

These slopes are set equal, giving the desired equation. If M_1 and M_3 are determinate (ends simply supported or overhanging) the equation can be solved at once for M_2 and the reactions then found by statics. If the ends are fixed, the slopes at those points can be set equal to zero; this provides two additional equations, and the three unknowns M_1, M_2, and M_3 can be found. If the two spans are parts of a continuous beam, a similar equation can be written for each successive pair of contiguous spans and these equations solved simultaneously for the unknown moments.

The three-moment equation can also be applied to beams carrying axial compression or tension in addition to transverse loading. The procedure is exactly the same as that described above except that the slope formulas to be used are those given in Table VI. For the case of two successive spans l_1, l_2 carrying unequal uniform loads w_1, w_2 and unequal axial compressions P_1, P_2 the equation is given in Table VI. If the supports undergo unequal deflections y_1, y_2, y_3, then to the right-hand side of this equation must be added:

$$\frac{6E(y_1 - y_2)}{l_1} + \frac{6E(y_3 - y_2)}{l_2}$$

A complete discussion of this problem, with equations for various loadings and tables of numerical values of the functions which greatly facilitate calculations, is given in Ref. 34.

34. Straight Uniform Beam (Common Case); Ultimate Strength.—When a beam is stressed beyond the elastic limit, plane sections remain plane or nearly so, but unit stresses are no longer proportional to strains and hence no longer proportional to distance from the neutral surface. If the material has similar stress-strain curves in tension and compression, the stress distribution above and below the neutral surface will be similar and the neutral axis of any section will still pass through the centroid; if the material has different properties in tension and compression, then the neutral axis will shift away from the side on which the fibers yield the most; this shift causes an additional departure from the stress distribution assumed by the theory outlined in Art. 32.

Failure in Bending.—The strength of a beam of ordinary proportions is determined by the maximum bending moment it can sustain. For beams of nonductile material (cast iron, concrete, seasoned wood) this moment may be calculated by the formula $M_m = s'(I/c)$ if s', the modulus of rupture, is known. The modulus of rupture depends on the material and on other factors (see Art. 9). Attempts have been made to calculate the modulus of rupture for a given material and section from the form of the complete stress-strain diagram. Thus for cast iron an approximate value of s' may be found by the formula $s' = K\sqrt{c/z'}\,s_t$, where c is the distance to the extreme fiber, z' is the distance from the neutral axis to the centroid of the tensile part of the section, and K is an experimental coefficient equal to $\frac{6}{5}$ for sections flat at top and bottom (rectangle, I, T, etc.), and $\frac{4}{3}$ for sections pointed or convex at top and bottom (circle, diamond, etc.) (Ref. 4). Some tests indicate that this method of calculating the breaking strength of cast iron is sometimes inaccurate, but generally errs on the side of safety (Ref. 5).

In general, the breaking strength of a beam can best be predicted from experimentally determined values of the rupture factor and tensile strength, or form factor and modulus of rupture. In Table IV are given the rupture factors and form factors for a number of sections and materials. The rupture factors are based on the ultimate tensile strength for all materials except wood, for which it is based on ultimate compressive strength. The form factors are based on a rectangular section; for wood this section is 2 by 2 in., and for beams of greater depth a scale correction must be made by the formula given. For structural steel, wrought aluminum, and other ductile metals, beams of which do not actually break, modulus of rupture means the computed fiber stress at maximum bending moment (Refs. 6, 7, 8, 9).

The values given in Table IV are for ratios of span to depth of from about 15 to 20. The effect of the span/depth ratio on the strength of cast-iron and plaster (brittle material) beams is shown by the following table, which gives the modulus of rupture (determined by center loading) for various span/depth ratios (s/d) in percentages of the modulus of rupture for $s/d = 20$ (Refs. 7, 10).

Material and section	s/d = span/depth ratio								
	30	20	15	10	5	4	3	2	1
Cast iron, circular..........	97	100	102	105	110	112	114	118	123
Cast iron, rectangular.......	99	100	101	102	111				
Plaster, rectangular.........	100	100	101	102	110				

The table shows that the modulus of rupture increases as the span/depth ratio decreases, but the variation is slight except for relatively small values of s/d.

When the maximum bending moment occurs at but one section, as for a single concentrated load, the modulus of rupture is higher than when the maximum moment extends over a considerable part of the span. For instance, the modulus of rupture of short beams of brittle material is about 20 per cent higher when determined by center loading than when determined by third-point loading. The disparity decreases as the s/d ratio increases.

Beams of ductile material (structural steel or aluminum) do not ordinarily fracture under static loading but fail through excessive deflection. For such beams, if of relatively thick section so as to preclude local buckling, the maximum bending moment is that which corresponds to plastic yielding throughout the section. This maximum or "plastic" moment is usually denoted by M_p and can be calculated by the formula $M_p = s_y Z$, where s_y is the lower yield point of the material, and Z, called the plastic section modulus, is the arithmetical sum of the statical moments about the neutral axis of the parts of the cross section above and below that axis. Thus, for a rectangular section of depth d and width b, $Z = (\frac{1}{2}bd)(\frac{1}{4}d) + (\frac{1}{2}bd)(\frac{1}{4}d) = \frac{1}{4}bd^2$. This method of calculating the maximum resisting moment of a ductile-material beam is widely used in "plastic design," and is discussed further in Art. 48. It is important to note that when the plastic moment has been developed, the neutral axis divides the cross-section area into halves, and so is not always a centroidal axis. It is also important to note that the plastic moment is always greater than the moment required to just stress the extreme fiber to the lower yield point. This moment, which may be denoted by M_y, is equal to $s_y \frac{I}{c}$, and so $\frac{M_p}{M_y} = \frac{z}{I/c}$. This ratio $\frac{z}{I/c}$, called the *shape factor*, depends on the form of the cross section. For a solid rectangle it would be $\frac{1}{4}bd^2/\frac{1}{6}bd^2$ or 1.5; for an I section it is usually about 1.15. In tubes and in beams of thin open section, local buckling or crippling will sometimes occur before the full plastic resisting moment is realized, and the length of the member will have an influence. Tubes of steel or aluminum alloy will generally develop a modulus of rupture

TABLE IV.—FORM FACTORS FOR BEAMS

Form of section (Tensile side down)	Form factors F and rupture factors R			
	Cast iron	Cast al. alloy 195	Plaster	Wood
1. (square, side d)	$F = 1$ $R = 2.3 - 0.02S$ where S = tensile strength in thousands of lb./sq. in.	$F = 1$ $R = 1.75$	$F = 1$ $R = 1.60$	For $d = 2$ in., $F = 1$ For $d > 2$ in., $F = 1 - 0.07\left(\sqrt{\frac{d}{2}} - 1\right)$ $R = 1.84$
2. (diamond)	$F = 1.35$	$F = 1.26$	$F = 1.23$	$F = 1.414$
3. (circle)	$F = 1.20$ $R = 2.80 - 0.025S$	$F = 1.12$	$F = 1.15$	$F = 1.18$
4. (triangle)	$F = 0.98$	$F = 0.88$	$F = 1.00$	

TABLE IV.—FORM FACTORS FOR BEAMS.—(*Continued*)

Form of section (Tensile side down)	Form factors F and rupture factors R			
	Cast iron	Cast al. alloys 195	Plaster	Wood
5.	$F = 1.27$	$F = 1.43$	$F = 1.27$	
6. t_2, t_c, t_1, t_t, d, $\frac{1}{2}t_1$	$F = 0.5 + 0.5\left[\frac{k(t_2 - t_1)}{t_2} + \frac{t_1}{t_2}\right]$ where $k = 3.6\frac{t_t}{d}$ (for $d = 2.36$, $t_1 = 0.41$, $t_2 = 2.36$, $t_c = t_t = 0.4$, $F = 0.84$)	$F = 0.75$ (for $d = t_2 = 6t_1 = 6t_c = 6t_t$)	$F = 0.91$ (for $d = t_2 = 6t_1 = 6t_c = 6t_t$)	$F = 0.5 + 0.5\left[\frac{k(t_2 - t_1)}{t_2} + \frac{t_1}{t_2}\right]$ where $k = 1.6\frac{t_c}{d} - 0.07$, up to $\frac{t_c}{d} = 0.6$
7. t_2, t_c, d, t_1, t_t, t_3	$F = 0.88$ (for $d = 2.36$, $t_1 = 0.33$, $t_2 = 1.18$, $t_3 = 2.44$, $t_c = 0.39$, $t_t = 0.55$			

exceeding the ultimate tensile strength when the ratio of diameter to wall thickness is less than 50 for steel or 35 for aluminum. Wide-flanged steel beams will develop the full plastic resisting moment when the outstanding width to thickness ratio is less than 8.7 for $s_y = 33{,}000$ or 8.3 for $s_y = 36{,}000$. Charts giving the effective modulus of rupture of steel, aluminum, and magnesium tubes of various proportions are given in Ref. 70.

Failure in Shear.—Failure by an actual shear fracture is unlikely to occur in any save wood beams, in which the shear strength parallel to the grain is, of course, small.

In I-beams and similar thin-webbed sections, the diagonal compression that accompanies shear (Art. 29) may lead to a buckling failure (see discussion of *web buckling* below), and in beams of cast iron and concrete the diagonal tension that similarly accompanies shear may cause rupture. The formula for shear stress (Eq. 2) may be considered valid as long as the *fiber* stresses do not exceed the proportional limit, and it may therefore be used to calculate the vertical shear necessary to produce failure in any case where the ultimate shearing strength of the beam is reached while the fiber stresses, at the section of maximum shear, are still within the proportional limit.

Web Buckling; Local Failure.—An I-beam or similar thin-webbed member may fail by buckling of the web owing to diagonal compression when the shear stress reaches a certain value. Ketchum and Draffin (Ref. 11) and Wendt and Withey (Ref. 12) found that in light I-beams this type of buckling occurs when the shear stress, calculated by $s_s = 1.25V/\text{web area}$ (Ref. 11), or $s_s = V/\text{web area}$ (Ref. 12), reaches a value equal to the unit load a vertical strip of the beam can carry as a round-ended column. For the thin webs of the beams tested, such a thin strip would be computed as an Euler column; for heavier beams an appropriate parabolic or other formula should be used (Chap. 11). In plate girders, web buckling may be prevented by vertical or diagonal stiffeners, usually consisting of double angles riveted or welded one on each side of the web. Steel-construction specifications (Ref. 13) require that such stiffeners be provided when h/t exceeds 70 and v exceeds $64{,}000{,}000 \div (h/t)^2$. Such stiffeners should have a moment of inertia (figured for an axis at the center line of the web) at least equal to $0.00000016H^4$, and should be spaced so the clear distance between successive stiffeners is not more than $11{,}000t/\sqrt{v}$ or 84 in., whichever is least. Here h is the clear depth of the web between flanges, t is the web thickness, v is the shear stress V/ht, and H is the total depth of the web. In light-metal airplane construction, the stiffeners are sometimes designed to have a moment of inertia about an axis parallel to the web given by $I = (2.29d/t)(Vh/33E)^{\frac{4}{3}}$, where V = the (total) vertical shear and d = the stiffener spacing center-to-center (Ref. 14).

Failure may also occur owing to vertical compression at a support or concentrated load, either by column-type buckling of the web (Refs. 11, 12) or by crippling of the web at the toe of the fillet (Ref. 15). To guard against this latter type of failure, present specifications provide that for interior loads $R/t(N + 2k) \leq 24{,}000$ and for end reactions $R/t(N + k) \leq 24{,}000$, where R is the concentrated load or end reaction, t the web thickness, N the length of bearing, and k the distance from the outer face of the flange to the web toe of fillet. Here R is in pounds, and all linear dimensions are in inches.

Wood beams will crush locally if the supports are too narrow or if a load is applied over too small a bearing area. The unit bearing stress in either case is calculated by dividing the force by the nominal bearing area, no allowance being made for the nonuniform distribution of pressure consequent upon bending (Ref. 9). Metal beams also may be subjected to high local pressure stresses; these are discussed in Chap. 13.

Longitudinal Buckling.—The compression flange of an I-beam or similar member may fail as a column by lateral buckling if unsupported. Such buckling may be *elastic* or *plastic*, that is, may occur at a maximum fiber stress below or above the elastic limit. In the first case the buckling represents an example of elastic instability, for which relevant formulas are given in Table XV of Chap. 14. For buckling above the elastic range analytical solutions are difficult to obtain, and recourse is generally had to empirical expressions based on experiment, as will be shown to be true also of columns in Chap. 11.

Moore (Ref. 16) found standard I-beams to fail by lateral buckling when $s' = 40{,}000 - 60ml/r$, where s' is the compressive stress in the extreme fiber (computed by Eq. 1), l is the span (inches), r is the radius of gyration (inches) of the beam section about a central axis parallel to the web, and m is a coefficient which depends on the manner of loading and support and has the following values:

Loading and Support	Value of m
End supports, uniform load	0.667
End supports, mid-point load	0.500
End supports, single load at any point	0.500
End supports, loads at third-points	0.667
End supports, loads at quarter-points	0.750
End supports, loads at sixth-points	0.833
Cantilever beam, uniform load	0.667
Cantilever beam, end load	1.000
Fixed-ended beam, uniform load	0.281
Fixed-ended beam, mid-point load	0.250

For very light I-beams, Ketchum and Draffin (Ref. 11) found that the lower limit of test results was given by

$$s' = 24{,}000 - 40\,\frac{ml}{r}$$

where the terms have the same meaning and m the same values as given above.

The beams tested by Moore generally failed at stresses below but very close to the yield point, and so could probably be regarded as representing plastic buckling. The lighter beams tested by Ketchum and Draffin, however, failed at stresses below the limit of proportionality, and illustrate elastic buckling.

In Ref. 13 rules are given for the reduction in allowable compressive stress according to the unbraced length of the compression flange.

A review of the literature on this subject of the lateral buckling of structural members and a bibliography up through 1959 are to be found in Ref. 73.

Narrow rectangular beams also may fail by buckling of the compression edge. When this buckling occurs below the elastic limit, the strength is determined by elastic stability; formulas covering this case are given in Table XV. For buckling at stresses beyond the elastic limit, no simple formula for the critical stress can be given, but methods for calculating this critical stress are given for aluminum beams by Dumont and Hill (Ref. 17) and for wood beams by Trayer and March (Ref. 18).

35. Beams of Relatively Great Depth.—In beams of small span/depth ratio, the shear stresses are likely to be high, and the resulting deflection due to shear may not be negligible. For span/depth ratios of 3 or more, the deflection y_s due to shear is found by the method of unit loads to be

$$y_s = F \int \frac{Vv}{AG}\, dx \tag{16}$$

or by Castigliano's first theorem to be

$$y_s = \frac{\partial U_s}{\partial P} \tag{17}$$

In Eq. 16, V is the vertical shear due to the actual loads, v is the vertical shear due to a load of 1 lb. acting at the section where the deflection is desired, A is the area of the section, G is the modulus of rigidity, F is a factor depending on the form of the cross section, and the integration extends over the entire length of the beam, with due regard to the sign of V and v. For a rectangular section, $F = \frac{6}{5}$; for a solid circular section, $F = \frac{10}{9}$; for a thin-walled hollow circular section, $F = 2$; for an I or box section having flanges and web of uniform thickness,

$$F = \left[1 + \frac{3(D_2^2 - D_1^2)D_1}{2D_2^3}\left(\frac{t_2}{t_1} - 1\right)\right]\frac{4D_2^2}{10r^2}$$

where D_1 = distance from neutral axis to the nearest surface of the flange.

D_2 = distance from neutral axis to extreme fiber.

t_1 = thickness of web (or webs, in box beams).

t_2 = width of flange.

r = radius of gyration of section with respect to the neutral axis.

If the I or box beam has flanges of nonuniform thickness, it may be replaced by an "equivalent" section whose flanges, of uniform thickness, have the same width and area as those of the actual section (Ref. 19). Approximate results may be obtained for I-beams using $F = 1$ and taking for A the area of the web.

Application of Eq. 16 to several common cases of loading yields results as follows:

End support, center load P . . . $y_s = \frac{1}{4} F \left(\frac{Pl}{AG} \right)$

End support, uniform load W . . . $y_s = \frac{1}{8} F \left(\frac{Wl}{AG} \right)$

Cantilever, end load P . . . $y_s = F \left(\frac{Pl}{AG} \right)$

Cantilever, uniform load W . . . $y_s = \frac{1}{2} F \left(\frac{Wl}{AG} \right)$

In Eq. 17, $U_s = F \int \frac{V^2}{2AG} dx$, P is a vertical load, real or imaginary, applied at the section where y_s is to be found, and the other terms have the same meaning as in Eq. 16.

The deflection due to shear will usually be found negligible in metal beams unless the span/depth ratio is extremely small; in wood beams, because of the small value of G compared to E, deflection due to shear is much more important. It may be allowed for, in computing deflections, by using for E a value obtained from bending tests (shear deflection ignored) on beams of similar proportions, or by using a value about 10 per cent less than that found by testing in direct compression if the span/depth ratio is between 12 and 24. For larger ratios the effect of shear is negligible, and for lower ratios it should be calculated by the above method.

For extremely short deep beams, the assumption of linear stress distribution on which the simple theory of flexure is based is no longer valid. Equation 1 gives sufficiently accurate results for span/depth ratios down to about 3; for still smaller ratios it was formerly believed that the actual stresses were smaller than the formula indicates (Refs. 1, 2), but more recent analyses by numerical methods (Refs. 53, 54) indicate the contrary to be true. These show that at s/d between 1.5 and 1, depending on the manner of loading and support, the stress distribution changes radically and the ratio of maximum stress to Mc/I becomes greater than one and increases rapidly as s/d becomes still smaller. In the table below, the influence of s/d on both maximum fiber stress and maximum horizontal shear stress is shown in accordance with the solution given in Ref. 53. Reference 54 gives comparable results, and both strain-gauge measurements (Ref. 55) and photoelastic studies (Ref. 56) support the conclusions reached in these analyses.

These established facts concerning elastic stresses in short beams seem incompatible with the contrary influence of s/d on modulus of rupture, discussed in Art. 34, unless it is assumed that there is a very radical redistribution of stress as soon as plastic action sets in.

Ratio l/d	Ratio span$/d$	l, d, Span = 23/24 l Uniform load over entire l			l, d, Span = 23/24 l Uniform load over middle $\frac{1}{12}l$		
		$\frac{\text{Max } s_t}{Mc/I}$	$\frac{\text{Max } s_c}{Mc/I}$	$\frac{\text{Max } s_s}{V/A}$	$\frac{\text{Max } s_t}{Mc/I}$	$\frac{\text{Max } s_c}{Mc/I}$	$\frac{\text{Max } s_s}{V/A}$
3	2.875	1.025	1.03	1.58	0.970	1.655	1.57
2.5	2.395	1.046	1.035	1.60	0.960	1.965	1.60
2.0	1.915	1.116	1.022	1.64	0.962	2.525	1.70
1.5	1.4375	1.401	0.879	1.80	1.038	3.585	1.92
1	0.958	2.725	0.600	2.43	1.513	6.140	2.39
0.5	0.479	10.95	2.365	4.53	5.460	15.73	3.78
$\frac{1}{3}$	0.3193	24.70	5.160	6.05	12.35	25.55	7.23

The stress produced by a concentrated load acting on a very short *cantilever* beam or projection (gear tooth, sawtooth, screw thread) can be found by the following formula, due to Heywood (Ref. 49, Chap. 3) and modified by Kelley and Pedersen (Ref. 74). As given here, the formula follows this modification, with some changes in notation. Figure 13 represents the profile of the beam, assumed to be of uniform thickness t. ED is the axis or center line of the beam; it bisects the angle between the sides if these are straight and otherwise is drawn through the centers of two unequal inscribed circles. W represents the load; its line of action or load line intersects the beam profile at C and the beam axis at O. The inscribed parabola, with vertex at O, is tangent to the fillet on the tension side of the beam at A, which is the point of maximum tensile stress. (A can be located by making AF equal to FE by trial, F being the intersection of a perpendicular to the axis at O and a trial tangent to the fillet.) B is the corresponding point on the compression side, and D is the intersection of the beam axis with section AB. The dimensions a and e are perpendicular, respectively, to the load line and to the beam

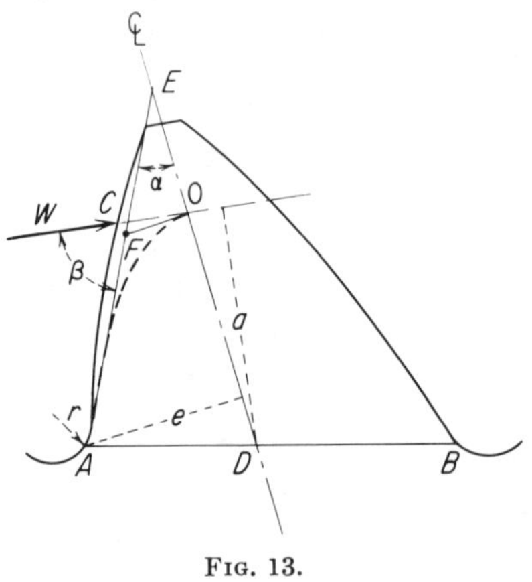

FIG. 13.

axis; r is the fillet radius; and b is the straight line distance from A to C. The tensile stress at A is given by

$$s = \frac{W}{t}\left[1 + 0.26\left(\frac{e}{r}\right)^{0.7}\right]\left[\frac{1.5a}{e^2} + \frac{\cos\beta}{2e} + \frac{0.45}{(be)^{\frac{1}{2}}}\right]$$

Here the quantity in the first pair of brackets is the factor of stress concentration for the fillet. In the second pair of brackets, the first term represents the bending moment divided by the section modulus; the second term represents the effect of the component of the load along the tangent line, positive when tensile; and the third term represents what Heywood called the "proximity effect," and may be regarded as an adjustment for the very small span/depth ratio. Kelley and Pedersen suggested a further refinement in locating the point of maximum stress, putting it at an angular distance equal to $25° - \frac{1}{2}\alpha$, positive toward the root of the fillet. Heywood suggested locating this point at 30 deg. from the outer end of the fillet, reducing this to 12 deg. as the ratio of b to e increases, and he also took the moment of W about a point halfway between A and B instead of about D. For most cases the slightly different procedures seem to give comparable results, and to agree well with photoelastic analysis. However, some more recent (1963) experimental studies, including fatigue tests, appear to indicate that actual stresses may considerably exceed those computed by the formula (Ref. 78).

36. Beams of Relatively Great Width.—Because of prevention of the lateral deformation that would normally accompany the fiber stresses, wide beams, such as thin metallic strips, are more rigid than the formulas of Art. 32 would indicate. This stiffening effect is taken into account by using, in the formulas for deflection and curvature, $E/(1 - \nu^2)$ instead of E (Ref. 21).

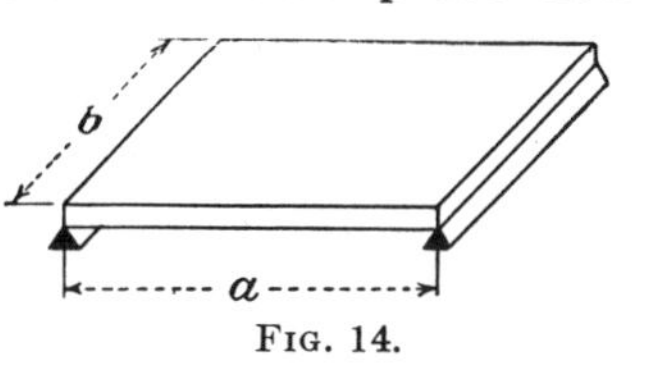

FIG. 14.

In very short wide beams, such as the concrete slabs used as highway-bridge flooring, the deflection and fiber-stress distribution cannot be regarded as uniform across the width. It is convenient, in calculating the strength of such a slab, to make use of the concept of "effective width," *i.e.*, the width of a spanwise strip which, acting as a beam with uniform extreme fiber stress equal to the maximum stress in the slab, would develop the same resisting moment as does the slab. The effective width depends on the manner of support, manner of loading, and on the ratio of breadth to span, b/a. The effective width has been determined by Holl (Ref. 22) for a number of assumed conditions, the results, for a slab freely supported at each of two opposite edges (Fig. 14), being as given in the following table. Two kinds of loading are considered, *viz.*, uniform load over the entire slab, and load uni-

Loading	Values of $\frac{e}{a}$ for				
	$\frac{b}{a} = 1$	$\frac{b}{a} = 1.2$	$\frac{b}{a} = 1.6$	$\frac{b}{a} = 2$	$\frac{b}{a} = \infty$
Uniform	0.96	1.145	1.519	1.90	
Central, $c = 0$	0.568	0.599	0.633	0.648	0.656
Central, $c = 0.125h$	0.581	0.614	0.649	0.665	0.673
Central, $c = 0.250h$	0.599	0.634	0.672	0.689	0.697
Central, $c = 0.500h$	0.652	0.694	0.740	0.761	0.770

formly distributed over a central circular area of radius c. The ratio of the effective width e to the span a is given for each of a number of ratios of c to slab thickness h and each of a number of b/a values.

For the same case (slab supported at opposite edges and loaded on a central circular area) Westergaard (Ref. 23) gives, as an approximate expression for effective width, $e = 0.58a + 4c$. Morris (Ref. 24) gives as an approximate expression for the effective width for mid-span *off-center* loading, $e = \frac{1}{2}e_c + d$, where e_c is the effective width for central loading and d is the distance from the load to the nearer unsupported edge.

For a slab *fixed* at two opposite edges and uniformly loaded, the stresses and deflections may, with sufficient accuracy, be calculated by the ordinary beam formulas, replacing E by $E/(1 - \nu^2)$. For a slab thus supported and loaded at the center, the maximum stresses occur under the load, except for relatively large values of c, when they occur at the mid-points of the fixed edges. The effective widths are approximately as given in the following table (values from curves of Ref. 22). Here b/a and c have the same meaning as in the table above, but it should be noted that values of e/b are given instead of e/a, as formerly.

Values of c	Values of $\frac{e}{b}$ for				Max stress at
	$\frac{b}{a} = 1$	$\frac{b}{a} = 1.2$	$\frac{b}{a} = 1.6$	$\frac{b}{a} = 2.0$	
0	0.51	0.52	0.53	0.53	Load
$0.01a$	0.52	0.54	0.55	0.55	Load
$0.03a$	0.58	0.59	0.60	0.60	Load
$0.10a$	0.69	0.73	0.81	0.86	Fixed edges

Holl (Ref. 22) also discusses the deflections of a wide beam with two edges supported, and the distribution of pressure under the supported edges. The problem of determining the effective width in concrete slabs, and tests made for that purpose, are discussed by Kelley (Ref. 25), who also gives a brief bibliography on the subject.

The case of a very wide *cantilever* slab under a concentrated load has been discussed by MacGregor (Ref. 26), Holl (Ref. 27),

Jaramillo (Ref. 57), Wellauer and Seireg (Ref. 58), Little (Ref. 59), Small (Ref. 60), and others. For the conditions represented in Fig. 15, a cantilever plate of infinite length loaded by a concentrated load, the bending stress s at any point can be expressed by $s = K_m(6P/t^2)$, and the deflection y at any point by

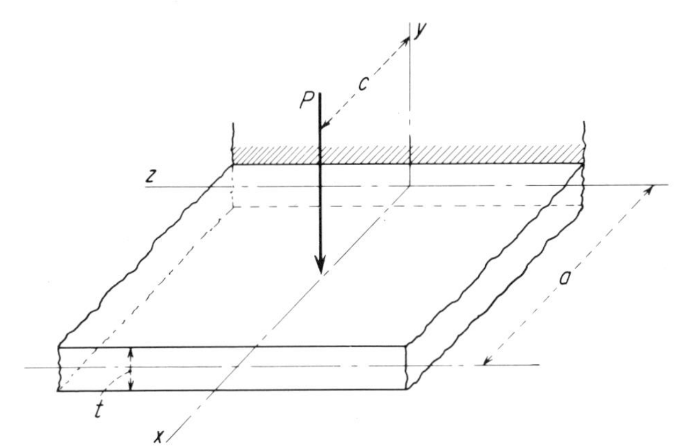

FIG. 15.

$y = K_y(Pa^2/\pi D)$, where K_m and K_y are dimensionless coefficients that depend upon the location of the load and the point, and D is as defined in Table XIII. For the load at $x = c$, $z = 0$, the stress at any point on the fixed edge $x = 0$, $z = z$, and the deflection at any point on the free edge $x = a$, $z = z$, can be found by using the values of K_m and K_y tabulated below.

c/a \ z/a		0	0.25	0.50	1.0	1.5	2	∞
1.0	K_M	0.509	0.474	0.390	0.205	0.091	0.037	0
	K_y	0.524	0.470	0.380	0.215	0.108	0.049	0
0.75	K_M	0.428	0.387	0.284	0.140	0.059	0.023	0
	K_y	0.318	0.294	0.243	0.138	0.069	0.031	0
0.50	K_M	0.370	0.302	0.196	0.076	0.029	0.011	0
0.25	K_M	0.332	0.172	0.073	0.022	0.007	0.003	0

These values are based on the analysis of Jaramillo, who assumed an infinite length for the plate, and are in good agreement, so far as comparable, with coefficients given by MacGregor. They differ but little from results obtained by Holl for a length/span ratio of 4 and by Little for a length/span ratio of 5, and are in good agreement with available test data.

Wellauer and Seireg discuss the results of tests on beams of various proportions and explain and illustrate an empirical method by which the K_m values obtained by Jaramillo for the infinite plate under concentrated load can be used to determine approximately the stress in a finite plate under any arbitrary transverse loading.

The stresses corresponding to the tabulated values of K_m are *spanwise* stresses; the maximum *crosswise* stress occurs under the load when the load is applied at the mid-point of the free edge, and is approximately equal to the maximum spanwise stress for that loading.

Although the above formulas are based on the assumption of infinite width of slab, tests (Ref. 26) on a plate of which the width was $8\frac{1}{2}$ in. and the span (a) $1\frac{1}{4}$ in. showed close agreement between calculated and measured deflections, and Holl's analysis, based on the assumption of a plate width four times the span, gives results that differ but little from MacGregor's. The formulas given should, therefore, be applicable to slabs of breadth as small as four times the span.

37. Beams with Wide Flanges; Shear Lag.—In thin metal construction, box, T-, or I-beams with very wide thin cover plates or flanges are sometimes used, and when a thin plate is stiffened by an attached member, a portion of the plate may be considered as a flange, acting integrally with the attached member which forms the web. Examples of this are to be found in ship hulls, floors, tanks, and aircraft. In either type of construction the question arises as to what width of flange or plate may be considered effective; *i.e.*, what width, uniformly stressed to the maximum stress that actually occurs, would provide a resisting moment equal to that of the actual stresses, which are greatest near the web and diminish as the distance therefrom increases.

This problem has been considered by several investigators; the results tabulated on page 138 are due to Hildebrand and Reissner (Ref. 48), to Winter (Ref. 49), and to Miller (Ref. 28).

Let b = actual net width of flange (or clear distance between webs in continuous plate and stiffener construction); let l = span, and let b' = effective width of flange at the section of maximum bending moment. Then the approximate value of b'/b, which varies with the loading and with the ratio l/b, can be found for beams of uniform section in the table on p. 138. (In this table the case numbers refer to the manner of loading and support represented in Table III.)

Some of the more important conclusions stated in Ref. 48 can be summarized as follows:

The amount of shear lag depends not only on the method of loading and support, and the ratio of span to flange width, but also on the ratio of G to E and on the ratio $m = (3I_w + I_s)/(I_w + I_s)$, where I_w and I_s are the moments of inertia about the neutral axis of the beam of the side plates and cover plates, respectively. (The values tabulated from Ref. 48 are for $G/E = 0.375$ and for $m = 2$.) The value of b'/b increases with increasing m, but for values of m between 1.5 and 2.5 the variation is small enough to be disregarded. Shear lag at the critical section does not seem to be appreciably affected by taper of the beam in width, but taper in cover-plate thickness may have an important effect. In beams with fixed ends the effect of shear lag at the end sections is the same as for a cantilever of span equal to the distance from the point of inflection to the adjacent end.

In Ref. 49 it is stated that for a given l/b ratio the effect of shear lag is practically the same for box beams, I-beams, T-beams, and U-beams.

Flange in Compression.—The above discussion and tabulated factors apply to any case in which the flange is subjected to tension, or to compression less than that required to produce elastic instability (see Chap. 14). When a thin flange or sheet is on the compression side, however, it may be stressed beyond the stability limit. For this condition, the effective width decreases with the actual stress. A formula for effective width used in aircraft design may be written

$$b' = Kt\sqrt{\frac{E}{s}}$$

where s is the maximum compressive stress (adjacent to the supporting web or webs), and K is a coefficient which may be con-

RATIO EFFECTIVE WIDTH TO TOTAL WIDTH b'/b FOR WIDE FLANGES

Case No.	Ref. No.	l/b													
		1	1.25	1.50	1.75	2	2.5	3	4	5	6	8	10	15	20
1	48	0.571	0.638	0.690	0.730	0.757	0.801	0.830	0.870	0.895	0.913	0.934	0.946		
3	48	.....	.....	0.550	0.600	0.632	0.685	0.724	0.780	0.815	0.842	0.876	0.899		
5	48	.....	.....	.....	.....	.....	0.609	0.650	0.710	0.751	0.784	0.826	0.858		
11	48	.....	.....	.....	0.530	0.571	0.638	0.686	0.757	0.801	0.830	0.870	0.895	0.936	0.946
	49	.....	.....	.....	.....	.....	.....	0.550	0.670	0.732	0.779	0.850	0.894	0.945	
	28	.....	.....	.....	.....	.....	0.525	.....	.....	0.750					
12	48	.....	.....	.....	0.455	0.495	0.560	0.610	0.686	0.740	0.778	0.826	0.855	0.910	0.930
13	48	.....	.....	.....	0.640	0.690	0.772	0.830	0.897	0.936	0.957	0.977	0.985	0.991	0.995
	49	.....	.....	.....	.....	.....	.....	0.850	0.896	0.928	0.950	0.974	0.984	0.995	
	28	.....	.....	.....	.....	.....	0.725	.....	.....	0.875					

servatively taken as 0.85 for box beams and as 0.60 for a T- or I-beam having flanges with unsupported outer edges.

A theoretical analysis that takes into account both compressive buckling and shear lag is described in Ref. 50. Problems involving shear lag and buckling are most frequently encountered in design with thin-gauge metal; good guides to such design are the books "Light Gage Cold-formed Steel Design Manual" (and commentary), published by the American Iron and Steel Institute, and "Alcoa Structural Handbook," Aluminum Company of America.

Curved Beam with Wide Flange.—In reinforcing rings for large pipes, airplane fuselages, and ship hulls, the combination of a curved sheet and attached web or stiffener forms a curved beam with wide flanges. Formulas for the effective width of flange in such a curved beam are given in Ref. 29 and are as follows:

When the flange is indefinitely wide (*e.g.*, inner flange of pipe stiffener ring), the effective width is

$$b' = 1.56\sqrt{Rt}$$

where b' is the total width assumed effective, R is the mean radius of curvature of the flange, and t is the thickness of the flange, all dimensions being in inches.

When the flange has a definite unsupported width b (gross width less web thickness), the ratio of effective to actual width b'/b is a function of qb, where

$$q = \sqrt[4]{\frac{3(1-\nu^2)}{R^2t^2}}$$

Corresponding values of qb and of b'/b are as follows:

qb	1	2	3	4	5	6	7	8	9	10	11
b'/b	0.980	0.850	0.610	0.470	0.380	0.328	0.273	0.244	0.217	0.200	0.192

For the curved beam each flange should be considered as replaced by one of corresponding effective width b', and all calculations for direct, bending, and shear stresses, including corrections for curvature (Art. 44), should be based on this transformed section.

Bleich (Ref. 61) has shown that the radial components of the longitudinal flange stresses bend both flanges toward the web.

The maximum transverse stress s' due to this bending occurs at the junction of flange and web and is given by $s' = \beta s_m$; here s_m is the longitudinal bending stress at the middle surface of the flange, and β is a coefficient that depends on the ratio c^2/Rt, where c is the actual unsupported projecting width of the flange to either side of the web, and R and t have the same meaning as before. Values of β may be found from the following table; they were taken from Ref. 61, where values of b' are similarly tabulated.

$c^2/Rt =$	0	0.1	0.2	0.3	0.4	0.5	0.6	0.8
$\beta =$	0	0.297	0.580	0.836	1.056	1.238	1.382	1.577
$c^2/Rt =$	1	1.2	1.4	1.5	2	3	4	5
$\beta =$	1.677	1.721	1.732	1.732	1.707	1.671	1.680	1.700

38. Beam with Very Thin Web.—In beams with extremely thin webs, such as are used in airplane construction, buckling due to shear will occur at stresses well below the elastic limit. This can be prevented if the web is made "shear resistant" by the addition of stiffeners such as are used in plate girders, but the number of these required may be excessive. Instead of thus making the web shear resistant, it may without damage be permitted to buckle elastically, the shear being carried wholly in *diagonal tension.* This tension tends to pull the upper and lower flanges together, and to prevent this, vertical struts are provided which carry the vertical component of the diagonal web tension. A girder so designed is in effect a Pratt truss, the web replacing the diagonal-tension members and the vertical struts constituting the compression members. In appearance, these struts resemble the stiffeners of an ordinary plate girder, but their function is obviously quite different.

A beam of this kind is called a diagonal-tension field beam, or Wagner beam, after Professor Wagner, of Danzig, to whom the development of the theory is largely due. Because of its rather limited field of application, only one example of the Wagner-type beam will be here considered, *viz.*, a cantilever under end load.

Let P = end load; h = depth of beam; t = thickness of web; d = spacing of vertical struts; x = distance from the loaded end to the section in question; H_t and H_c = the total stresses in the tension and compression flanges, respectively, at the given section; C = total compression on a vertical strut; and f = unit diagonal tensile stress in the web. Then

$$H_t = \frac{Px}{h} - \frac{1}{2}P; \qquad H_c = \frac{Px}{h} + \frac{1}{2}P; \qquad C = \frac{Pd}{h}; \qquad f = \frac{2P}{ht}$$

The vertical component of the web tension constitutes a beam loading on each individual flange between struts; the maximum value of the resulting bending moment occurs at the struts, and is given by $M_f = \frac{1}{12}\frac{Pd^2}{h}$. The flexural stresses due to M_f must be added to the stresses due to H_t or H_c, which may be found by simply dividing H_t or H_c by the area of the corresponding flange.

The horizontal component of the web tension causes a bending moment $M = \frac{1}{8}Ph$ in the vertical strut at the end of the beam, unless bending there is prevented by some system of bracing. This end strut must also distribute the load to the web, and should be designed to carry the load as a pin-ended column of length $\frac{1}{2}h$, as well as to resist the moment imposed by the web tension.

The intermediate struts are designed as pin-ended columns with length somewhat less than h. An adjacent portion of the web is included in the area of the column, the width of the strip considered effective being $30t$ in the case of aluminum and $60t$ in the case of steel.

Obviously the above formulas will also apply to a beam with end supports and center load if P is replaced by the reaction, $\frac{1}{2}P$. Because of various simplifying assumptions made in the analysis the formulas given above are conservative; in particular the formula for stress in the vertical struts or stiffeners gives results much larger than the actual stresses that have been discovered experimentally. A more accurate analysis, together with experimental data from various sources, will be found in Refs. 30, 44, 45.

39. Beam Not Loaded in Plane of Symmetry; Flexural Center. The formulas for stress and deflection given in Art. 32 are valid if the beam is loaded in a plane of symmetry; they are also valid if the applied loads are parallel to either principal central axis of the beam section, but unless the loads also pass through the *elastic axis*, the beam will be subjected to torsion as well as bending.

For the general case of a beam of any section, loaded by a transverse load P in any plane, solution therefore involves the

TABLE V.—POSITION OF FLEXURAL CENTER Q FOR DIFFERENT SECTIONS

Form of section	Position of Q
1. Any narrow section symmetrical about the x axis. Centroid at $x = 0$, $y = 0$ 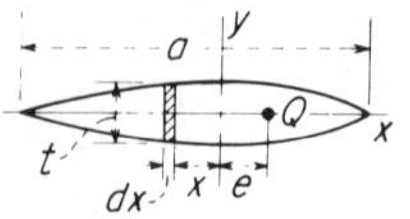	$e = \frac{1+3\nu}{1+\nu} \frac{\int x t^3\,dx}{\int t^3\,dx}$ For narrow triangle (with $\nu = 0.25$), $e = 0.187a$ For any equilateral triangle, $e = 0$ (Refs. 32, 62)
2. Sector of thin circular tube 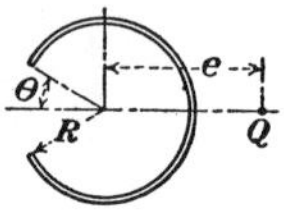	$e = \frac{2R}{(\pi - \theta) + \sin\theta\cos\theta}[(\pi - \theta)\cos\theta + \sin\theta]$ For complete tube split along element ($\theta = 0$), $e = 2R$
3. Semicircular area 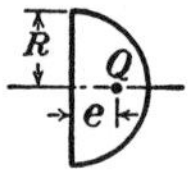	$e = \left(\frac{8}{15\pi}\frac{3+4\nu}{1+\nu}\right)R$ (Q is to right of centroid) (Refs. 1, 79) For sector of solid or hollow circular area, see Ref. 32
4. Angle 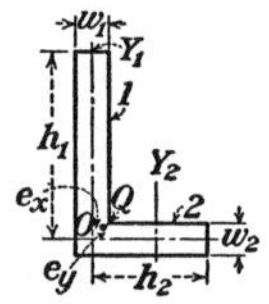	Leg 1 = rectangle w_1h_1; leg 2 = rectangle w_2h_2 I_1 = moment of inertia of leg 1 about Y_1 (central axis) I_2 = moment of inertia of leg 2 about Y_2 (central axis) $e_x = \frac{1}{2}h_2\left(\frac{I_2}{I_1+I_2}\right)$ $e_y = \frac{1}{2}h_1\left(\frac{I_1}{I_1+I_2}\right)$ (Ref. 31) If w_1 and w_2 are small, $e_x = e_y = 0$ (practically) and Q is at 0
5. Channel 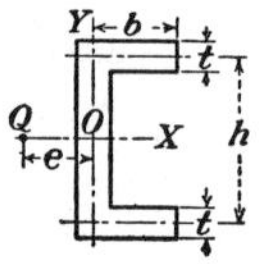	$e = h\left(\frac{H_{xy}}{I_x}\right)$ where H_{xy} = product of inertia of the half section (above X) with respect to axes X and Y, and I_x = moment of inertia of whole section with respect to axis X If t is uniform, $e = \frac{b^2h^2t}{4I_x}$
6. Tee 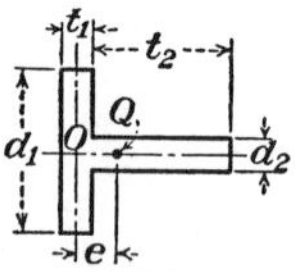	$e = \frac{1}{2}(t_1 + t_2)\left[\frac{1}{1+\frac{d_1^3t_1}{d_2^3t_2}}\right]$ For a T-beam of ordinary proportions, Q may be assumed to be at 0
7. I with unequal flanges and thin web 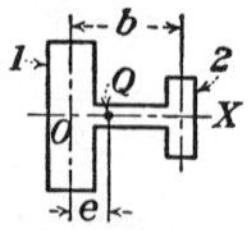	$e = b\left(\frac{I_2}{I_1+I_2}\right)$ where I_1 and I_2, respectively, denote moments of inertia about X-axis of flange 1 and flange 2
8. Beam composed of n elements, of any form, connected or separate, with common neutral axis (*e.g.*, multiple-spar airplane wing) 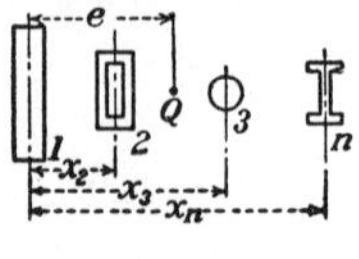	$e = \frac{E_2I_2x_2 + E_3I_3x_3 \ldots + E_nI_nx_n}{E_1I_1 + E_2I_2 + E_3I_3 \ldots + E_nI_n}$ where I_1, I_2, etc., are moments of inertia of the several elements about the X-axis (*i.e.*, Q is at the centroid of the products EI for the several elements)

TABLE V.—POSITION OF FLEXURAL CENTER Q.—(*Continued*)

Form of section	Position of Q

d channel (t small) — Values of e/h

c/h \ b/h	1.0	0.8	0.6	0.4	0.2
0	0.430	0.330	0.236	0.141	0.055
0.1	0.477	0.380	0.280	0.183	0.087
0.2	0.530	0.425	0.325	0.222	0.115
0.3	0.575	0.470	0.365	0.258	0.138
0.4	0.610	0.503	0.394	0.280	0.155
0.5	0.621	0.517	0.405	0.290	0.161
					(Ref. 51)

section (t small) — Values of e/h

c/h \ b/h	1.0	0.8	0.6	0.4	0.2
0	0.430	0.330	0.236	0.141	0.055
0.1	0.464	0.367	0.270	0.173	0.080
0.2	0.474	0.377	0.280	0.182	0.090
0.3	0.453	0.358	0.265	0.172	0.085
0.4	0.410	0.320	0.235	0.150	0.072
0.5	0.355	0.275	0.196	0.123	0.056
0.6	0.300	0.225	0.155	0.095	0.040
					(Ref. 51)

ction (A = enclosed area) — Values of $e(h/A)$

t_1/t_s \ S/h	1	1.5	2	3	4	5	6	7
0.5	.....	.....	1.0	0.800	0.665	0.570	0.500	0.445
0.6	.....	.....	0.910	0.712	0.588	0.498	0.434	0.386
0.7	.....	0.980	0.831	0.641	0.525	0.443	0.384	0.338
0.8	.....	0.910	0.770	0.590	0.475	0.400	0.345	0.305
0.9	.....	0.850	0.710	0.540	0.430	0.360	0.310	0.275
1.0	1.0	0.800	0.662	0.500	0.400	0.330	0.285	0.250
1.2	0.905	0.715	0.525	0.380	0.304	0.285	0.244	0.215
1.6	0.765	0.588	0.475	0.345	0.270	0.221	0.190	0.165
2.0	0.660	0.497	0.400	0.285	0.220	0.181	0.155	0.135
3.0	0.500	0.364	0.285	0.200	0.155	0.125	0.106	0.091
								(Ref. 51)

following steps: (1) The load P is resolved into an equal and parallel force P' passing through the flexural center Q of the section, and a twisting couple T equal to the moment of P about Q. (2) P' is resolved at Q into rectangular components P_u', P_v', each parallel to a principal central axis of the section. (3) The flexural stresses and deflections due to P_u' and P_v' are calculated independently by the formulas of Art. 32 and superposed to find the effect of P'. (4) The stresses due to T are computed independently and superposed on the stresses due to P', giving the stresses due to the actual loading. (It is to be noted that T may cause longitudinal fiber stresses as well as shear stresses. See Art. 51 and example below.) If there are several loads, the effect of each is calculated separately and these effects superposed. For a distributed load the same procedure is followed as for a concentrated load.

The above procedure requires the determination of the position of the flexural center Q. For any section having two or more axes of symmetry (rectangle, I-beam, etc.) and for any section having a point of symmetry (equilateral triangle, Z bar, etc.), Q is at the centroid. For any section having but one axis of symmetry, Q is on that axis, but in general not at the centroid. For such sections, and for unsymmetrical sections in general, the position of Q must be determined by calculation, by direct experiment, or by the soap-film method (Art. 23).

Table V gives the position of the flexural center for each of a number of sections.

Neutral Axis.—When a beam is bent by one or more loads that lie in a plane not parallel to either principal central axis of the section, the neutral axis passes through the centroid but is not perpendicular to the plane of the loads. Let axes 1 and 2 be the principal central axes of the section and I_1 and I_2 represent the corresponding moments of inertia. Then, if the plane of the loads makes with axis 1 an angle α, the neutral axis makes with axis 2 an angle β such that $\tan \beta = \tan \alpha(I_2/I_1)$. It can be seen from this equation that the neutral axis tends to approach that one of the principal central axes about which the moment of inertia is least.

Examples

Figure 16a represents a cantilever beam of channel section under a diagonal end load applied at one corner. It is required to determine the maximum resulting fiber stress.

Solution.—For the section (Fig. 16b) $I_u = 5.61$; $I_v = 19.9$; $b = 3.875$; $h = 5.75$; $t = \frac{1}{4}$.

By the formula from Table V, $e = b^2h^2t/4I_v = 1.55$ in. Therefore the flexural center is at Q, as shown. When the load is resolved into vertical and horizontal components at Q and a couple, the results are as shown in Fig. 16b. (Vertical and horizontal components are used because the *principal central axes* U and V are vertical and horizontal.)

The maximum fiber stress will occur at the corner where the stresses due to the vertical and horizontal bending moments are of the same kind; at the upper right corner f both stresses are tensile, and since f is farther from the U-axis than the lower left corner g where both stresses are compressive, it will sustain the greater stress. This stress will simply be the sum of the stresses due to the vertical and horizontal components of the load, or

$$s = \frac{(940)(36)(3)}{19.9} + \frac{(342)(36)(2.765)}{5.61} = 5100 + 6070 = 11{,}200 \text{ lb. per sq. in.}$$

The effect of the couple depends on the way in which the inner end of the beam is supported. If it is simply constrained against rotation in the planes of bending and twisting, the twisting moment will be wholly resisted by

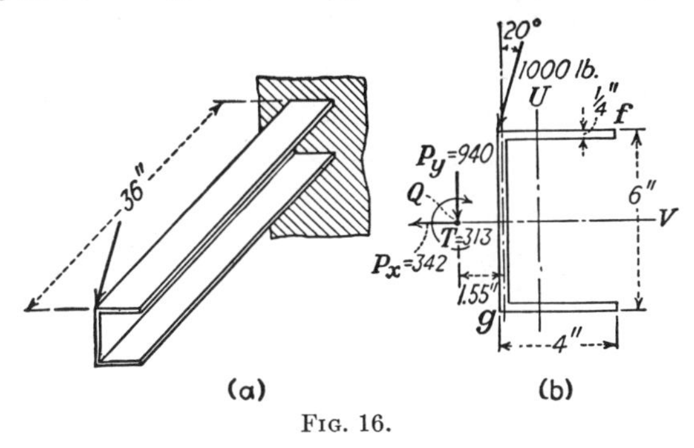

FIG. 16.

shear stress on the cross section, and these stresses can be found by the appropriate torsion formula of Table IX. If, however, the beam is built in so that the flanges are fixed in the *horizontal* plane, then part of the torque is resisted by the bending rigidity of the flanges and the corresponding moment causes a further fiber stress. This can be found by using the formulas of Art. 51. For the channel section, K is given with sufficient accuracy by the formula $K = \frac{1}{3}Ut^3$ (Case 13, Table IX), which gives $K = 0.07$. Taking $G = 12{,}000{,}000$ and $E = 30{,}000{,}000$, and solving for a, we have

$$a = \frac{h}{2}\sqrt{\frac{I_u E}{KG}} = 40$$

Therefore $l/a = 0.9$, $\tanh l/a = 0.72$, and the fiber stress due to the bending produced in the flange by the twisting moment is 1600 lb. per sq. in. At f this stress is compressive, hence is subtracted from the stress of 11,200 produced there by the vertical and horizontal beam moments.

40. Beam under Simultaneous Axial and Transverse Loading.

Under certain conditions a beam may be subjected to axial tension or compression in addition to the transverse loads; examples are afforded by airplane wing spars and the chord members of a bridge truss. Axial tension tends to straighten the beam and thus reduce the bending moments produced by the transverse loads, but axial compression has the opposite effect and may greatly increase the maximum bending moment and deflection. In either case solution cannot be effected by simple superposition but must be arrived at by methods that take into account the change in deflection produced by the axial load.

For any condition of loading, the maximum stress in the extreme fiber is given by

$$\text{Max } s = \frac{P}{A} \pm \frac{M'}{I/c} \tag{18}$$

where P is the axial load, A is the cross-sectional area of the beam, I/c is the section modulus, and M' is the maximum bending moment due to the combined effect of the axial and transverse loads. (The + sign is used for the fibers in which the direct stress $\frac{P}{A}$ and the bending stress $\frac{M'}{I/c}$ are alike, the − sign for the fibers in which they are unlike.)

It is the determination of M' that offers difficulty. For some cases it is permissible to ignore the deflection and to take M' as equal to M, the bending moment due to transverse loads only. For many cases M' is given with sufficient accuracy by the approximate formula (Ref. 33):

$$M' = \frac{M}{\left(1 \pm \alpha \frac{Pl^2}{EI}\right)} \tag{19}$$

where M is the maximum moment (inch-pounds) due to transverse loads alone; P is the axial load (pounds); l is the length of the beam (inches); E is the modulus of elasticity; I is the moment of inertia (inches^4) of the section about a central axis normal to the plane of bending, and α is a coefficient which depends on the manner of loading and support and which has the following values:

Manner of Loading and Support	Value of α
Cantilever, end load	$\frac{1}{3}$
Cantilever, uniform load	$\frac{1}{4}$
End supports, center load	$\frac{1}{12}$
End supports, uniform load	$\frac{5}{48}$
Equal and opposite end couples	$\frac{1}{8}$
Fixed ends, center load	$\frac{1}{24}$
Fixed ends, uniform load	$\frac{1}{32}$ (for end moments)
	$\frac{1}{16}$ (for center moments)

The + sign is used in the denominator when P is tension, the − sign when P is compression. The formula is appropriate only for beams in which the maximum bending moment and maximum deflection occur at the same section.

For relatively long and slender members, it is often necessary to use a more precise method of analysis, and formulas derived by such a method (Refs. 34, 35) are given in Table VI. Most of these formulas are for axial compression, since this is the more important case. Formulas for axial tension may be derived from those for axial compression by making the following substitutions: $-P$ for P; l/U for j; $U\sqrt{-1}$ for U; $-\sinh U$ for $\sin U$; and $\cosh U$ for $\cos U$. This has been done for some of the more usual kinds of loading and the resulting formulas are given under Cases 13 to 19 and 21 to 23. Cases 24 and 25 represent a limiting condition of perfect flexibility. The use of the formulas of Table VI is greatly facilitated by a table of trigonometric functions for angles in radians (Ref. 34) and a table of hyperbolic functions (Ref. 36).

While the principle of superposition does not apply to the problem here considered, this modification of the principle can be used: The moment (or deflection) for a combination of transverse loads can be found by adding the moments (or deflections) for each transverse load combined with the axial load. Thus a beam supported at the ends and subjected to a uniform load, a center load, and an axial compression, would have a maximum bending moment (or deflection) given by the sum of the maximum moments (or deflections) for Cases 3 and 4, the end load being included once for each transverse load.

The criterion for judging whether a given problem can be solved with sufficient accuracy without taking deflection into account at all, whether Eq. 19 will be satisfactory, or whether the precise formulas of Table VI should be used, is the ratio of the end compression P to the critical Euler load (see Chap. 11) for the beam regarded as a column, with end conditions like those that obtain for the beam, and free to buckle in the plane of bending. (This does not mean that the beam must be so slender that it would actually constitute an Euler column; the criterion applies to a beam of any slenderness ratio.) Approximately, the error in ignoring deflections is equal to the ratio of the actual load P to the Euler load P'.

This means that if an error of over, say, 5 per cent is to be avoided, deflection should be taken into account (by using Eq. 19 or the precise formulas) for cantilever beams if $P > 0.125EI/l^2$; for beams with end support if $P > 0.5EI/l^2$; for beams with fixed ends if $P > 2EI/l^2$. The precise formulas should be used for cantilevers if $P > 0.8EI/l^2$; for beams with end supports if $P > 3EI/l^2$; for beams with fixed ends if $P > 4EI/l^2$.

TABLE VI.—FORMULAS FOR BEAMS UNDER COMBINED AXIAL AND TRANSVERSE LOADING

Notation: M = bending moment (in.-lb.) due to the combined loading, positive when clockwise, negative when counterclockwise; M_1 and M_2 are applied external couples (in.-lb.) positive when acting as shown; y = deflection (in.), positive when upward, negative when downward; θ = slope of beam (radians) to horizontal, positive when upward to the right; $j = \sqrt{\frac{EI}{P}}$ where E = modulus of elasticity, I = moment of inertia (in.^{4}) of cross section about horizontal central axis, P = axial load (lb.); $U = \frac{l}{j}$; W = transverse load (lb.); w = transverse unit load (lb. per linear in.). All dimensions are in inches, all forces in pounds, all angles in radians

Manner of loading and support	Formulas for maximum bending moment, maximum deflection, end slope, and constraining moments
1. Cantilever beam under axial compression and transverse end load	Max $M = -Wj \tan U$ at $x = l$ Max $y = -\frac{W}{P}(j \tan U - l)$ at $x = 0$ $\theta = \frac{W}{P}\left(\frac{1 - \cos U}{\cos U}\right)$ at $x = 0$
2. Cantilever beam under axial compression and uniform transverse load	Max $M = -wj[j(1 - \sec U) + l \tan U]$ at $x = l$ Max $y = -\frac{wj}{P}\left[j\left(1 + \frac{1}{2}U^2 - \sec U\right) + l(\tan U - U)\right]$ at $x = 0$ $\theta = \frac{w}{P}\left[\frac{l}{\cos U} - j\frac{1 - \cos 2U}{\sin 2U}\right]$
3. Beam on end supports under axial compression and transverse center load	Max $M = \frac{1}{2}Wj \tan \frac{1}{2}U$ at $x = \frac{1}{2}l$ Max $y = -\frac{1}{2}\frac{Wj}{P}\left(\tan\frac{1}{2}U - \frac{1}{2}U\right)$ at $x = \frac{1}{2}l$ $\theta = -\frac{W}{2P}\left(\frac{1 - \cos\frac{1}{2}U}{\cos\frac{1}{2}U}\right)$ at $x = 0$

4. Be... end supports under axial compression and uniform transverse load 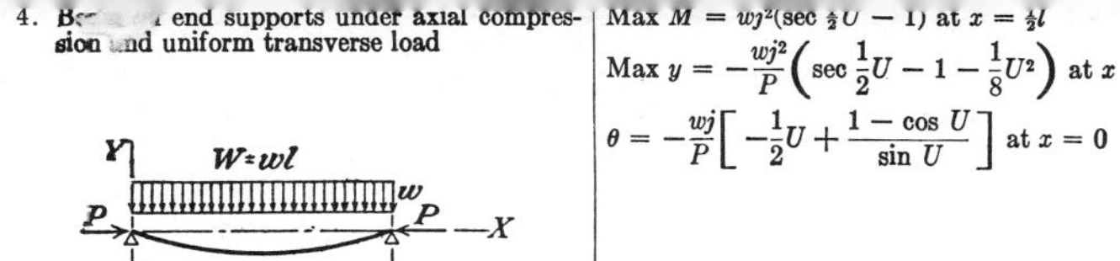 	Max $M = wj^2(\sec \frac{1}{2}U - 1)$ at $x = \frac{1}{2}l$ Max $y = -\frac{wj^2}{P}\left(\sec \frac{1}{2}U - 1 - \frac{1}{8}U^2\right)$ at $x = \frac{1}{2}l$ $\theta = -\frac{wj}{P}\left[-\frac{1}{2}U + \frac{1 - \cos U}{\sin U}\right]$ at $x = 0$
5. Beam on end supports under axial compression and intermediate transverse load	Moment equation: $x = 0$ to $x = a$: $M = \frac{Wj \sin \frac{b}{j} \sin \frac{x}{j}}{\sin U}$; Max M at $x = \frac{1}{2}\pi j$ if $\frac{1}{2}\pi j < a$ Moment equation: $x = a$ to $x = l$: $M = \frac{Wj \sin \frac{a}{j} \sin \frac{l - x}{j}}{\sin U}$; Max M at $x = \left(l - \frac{1}{2}\pi j\right)$ if $\left(l - \frac{1}{2}\pi j\right) > a$ If $\frac{1}{2}\pi j > a$ and $(l - \frac{1}{2}\pi j) < a$, Max M is at $x = a$ Deflection equation: $x = 0$ to $x = a$: $y = \frac{Wj}{P}\left(\frac{\sin \frac{b}{j} \sin \frac{x}{j}}{\sin U} - \frac{bx}{lj}\right)$ Deflection equation: $x = a$ to $x = l$: $y = \frac{Wj}{P}\left(\frac{\sin \frac{a}{j} \sin \frac{l - x}{j}}{\sin U} - \frac{a(l - x)}{lj}\right)$ $\theta = -\frac{W}{P}\left(\frac{b}{l} + \frac{\sin \frac{a}{j}}{\tan U} - \cos \frac{a}{j}\right)$ at $x = 0$ $\qquad \theta = \frac{W}{P}\left(\frac{a}{l} - \frac{\sin \frac{a}{j}}{\sin U}\right)$ at $x = l$
6. Beam on end supports under axial compression and triangular transverse load	Moment equation: $x = 0$ to $x = 1$; $M = wj^2\left(\frac{\sin \frac{x}{j}}{\sin U} - \frac{x}{l}\right)$ Max M at $x = j \text{ arc cos } \left(\frac{\sin U}{U}\right)$ Deflection equation: $x = 0$ to $x = l$; $x = -\frac{w}{P}\left(\frac{x^3}{6l} + \frac{j^2 \sin \frac{x}{j}}{\sin U} - \frac{jx}{U} - \frac{1}{6}lx\right)$ $\theta = -\frac{w}{P}\left(\frac{j}{\sin U} - \frac{j}{U} - \frac{1}{6}l\right)$ at $x = 0$ $\qquad \theta = \frac{w}{P}\left(-\frac{j}{\tan U} + \frac{j}{U} - \frac{1}{3}l\right)$ at $x = l$

TABLE VI.—FORMULAS FOR BEAMS UNDER COMBINED AXIAL AND TRANSVERSE LOADING.—(*Continued*)

Manner of loading and support	Formulas for maximum bending moment, maximum deflection, end slope, and constraining moments
7. Beam under axial compression and equal and opposite end couples 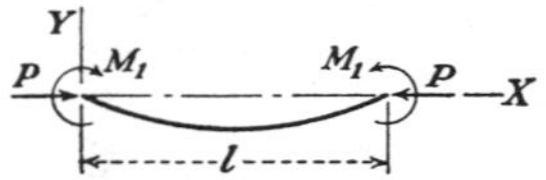	Max $M = M_1 \sec \frac{1}{2}U$ at $x = \frac{1}{2}l$ Max $y = -\frac{M_1}{P}\left(\frac{1 - \cos \frac{1}{2}U}{\cos \frac{1}{2}U}\right)$ at $x = \frac{1}{2}l$ $\theta = -\frac{M_1}{Pj} \tan \frac{1}{2}U$ at $x = 0$
8. Beam on end supports under axial compression and unequal end couples 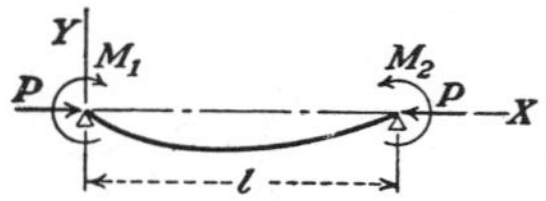	Moment equation: $x = 0$ to $x = l$: $M = \left(\frac{M_2 - M_1 \cos U}{\sin U}\right) \sin \frac{x}{j} + M_1 \cos \frac{x}{j}$ Max M at $x = j \arctan \left(\frac{M_2 - M_1 \cos U}{M_1 \sin U}\right)$ Deflection equation: $x = 0$ to $x = l$: $y = \frac{1}{P}\left[M_1 + (M_2 - M_1)\frac{x}{l} - (M_2 - M_1 \cos U)\frac{\sin \frac{x}{j}}{\sin U} - M_1 \cos \frac{x}{j}\right]$ $\theta = \frac{1}{P}\left[\frac{M_2 - M_1}{l} - \frac{M_2 - M_1 \cos U}{j \sin U}\right]$ at $x = 0$ $\theta = \frac{1}{P}\left[\frac{M_2 - M_1}{l} - \frac{M_2 - M_1 \cos U}{j \sin U} \cos U + \frac{M_1}{j} \sin U\right]$ at $x = l$
9. Beam with fixed ends under axial compression and transverse center load 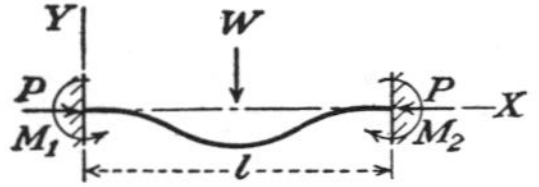	$M_1 = M_2 = \frac{1}{2}Wj\left(\frac{1 - \cos \frac{1}{2}U}{\sin \frac{1}{2}U}\right)$ At $x = \frac{l}{2}$ $M = \frac{1}{2}Wj\left(\tan \frac{1}{2}U - \frac{1 - \cos \frac{1}{2}U}{\sin \frac{1}{2}U \cos \frac{1}{2}U}\right)$ Max $y = -\frac{Wj}{2P}\left[\tan \frac{1}{2}U - \frac{1}{2}U - \frac{(1 - \cos \frac{1}{2}U)^2}{\sin \frac{1}{2}U \cos \frac{1}{2}U}\right]$
10. Beam with fixed ends under axial compression and uniform transverse load 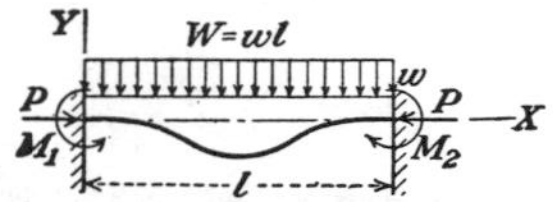	$M_1 = M_2 = wj^2\left(1 - \frac{\frac{1}{2}U}{\tan \frac{1}{2}U}\right)$ At $x = \frac{l}{2}$ $M = wj^2\left(\frac{\frac{1}{2}U}{\sin \frac{1}{2}U} - 1\right)$ Max $y = -\frac{wj^2}{P}\left[-\left(1 - \frac{\frac{1}{2}U}{\tan \frac{1}{2}U}\right)\left(\frac{1 - \cos \frac{1}{2}U}{\cos \frac{1}{2}U}\right) + \sec \frac{1}{2}U - \frac{1}{8}U^2 - 1\right]$

11. Beam with one end fixed, other end supported, under axial compression and transverse center load	Max $M = M_1 = \frac{Wl}{2}\left[\frac{j \tan U(\sec \frac{1}{2}U - 1)}{j \tan U - l}\right]$ $R = \frac{1}{2}W - \frac{M_1}{l}$ Moment equation: $x = \frac{l}{2}$ to $x = l$: $M = M_1\left(\frac{\sin \frac{x}{j}}{\tan U} - \cos \frac{x}{j}\right) + Wj\left(\sin \frac{1}{2}U \cos \frac{x}{j} - \frac{\sin \frac{1}{2}U \sin \frac{x}{j}}{\tan U}\right)$ Deflection equation: $x = \frac{l}{2}$ to $x = l$: $y = -\frac{1}{P}\left\{M_1\left(1 - \frac{x}{l} + \frac{\sin \frac{x}{j}}{\tan U} - \cos \frac{x}{j}\right) - Wj\left[\frac{l-x}{2j} + \frac{\sin \frac{1}{2}U \sin \frac{x}{j}}{\tan U} - \sin \frac{1}{2}U \cos \frac{x}{j}\right]\right\}$
12. Beam with one end fixed, other end supported, under axial compression and uniform transverse load	Max $M = M_1 = wlj\left[\frac{\tan U(\tan \frac{1}{2}U - \frac{1}{2}U)}{\tan U - U}\right]$ $R = \frac{1}{2}wl - \frac{M_1}{l}$ Moment equation: $x = 0$ to $x = l$: $M = M_1\left(\cot U \sin \frac{x}{j} - \cos \frac{x}{j}\right) + wj^2\left[\frac{\sin \frac{x}{j}}{\sin U}(1 - \cos U) + \cos \frac{x}{j} - 1\right]$ Deflection equation: $x = 0$ to $x = l$: $y = -\frac{1}{P}\left[M_1\left(1 - \frac{x}{l} + \cot U \sin \frac{x}{j} - \cos \frac{x}{j}\right) - wj^2\left(\cot U \sin \frac{x}{j} - \frac{\sin \frac{x}{j}}{\sin U} - \cos \frac{x}{j} + \frac{lx - x^2}{2j^2} + 1\right)\right]$
13. Same as Case 1 (cantilever with end load) except that P is tension	Max $M = -Wj \tanh U$ at $x = l$ Max $y = -\frac{W}{P}(l - j \tanh U)$ at $x = 0$
14. Same as Case 2 (cantilever with uniform load) except that P is tension	Max $M = -wj[l \tanh U - j(1 - \operatorname{sech} U)]$ at $x = l$ Max $y = -\frac{wj}{P}\left[j\left(1 - \frac{1}{2}U^2 - \operatorname{sech} U\right) - l(\tanh U - U)\right]$ at $x = 0$
15. Same as Case 3 (end supports, center load) except that P is tension	Max $M = \frac{1}{2}Wj \tanh \frac{1}{2}U$ at $x = \frac{1}{2}l$ Max $y = -\frac{W}{P}\left(\frac{1}{4}l - \frac{1}{2}j \tanh \frac{1}{2}U\right)$ at $x = \frac{1}{2}l$
16. Same as Case 4 (end supports, uniform load) except that P is tension	Max $M = wj^2(1 - \operatorname{sech} \frac{1}{2}U)$ Max $y = -\frac{w}{P}\left[\frac{1}{8}l^2 - j^2\left(1 - \operatorname{sech} \frac{1}{2}U\right)\right]$
17. Same as Case 9 (fixed ends, center load) except that P is tension	$M_1 = M_2 = \frac{1}{2}Wj\left(\frac{\cosh \frac{1}{2}U - 1}{\sinh \frac{1}{2}U}\right)$, Max $+M = \frac{1}{2}Wj\left(\frac{1 - \cosh \frac{1}{2}U}{\sinh \frac{1}{2}U \cosh \frac{1}{2}U} + \tanh \frac{1}{2}U\right)$ at $x = \frac{1}{2}l$ Max $y = -\frac{Wj}{2P}\left[\frac{1}{2}U - \tanh \frac{1}{2}U - \frac{(1 - \cosh \frac{1}{2}U)^2}{\sinh \frac{1}{2}U \cosh \frac{1}{2}U}\right]$

TABLE VI.—FORMULAS FOR BEAMS UNDER COMBINED AXIAL AND TRANSVERSE LOADING.—(*Continued*)

Manner of loading and support	Formulas for maximum bending moment, maximum deflection, end slope, and constraining moments
18. Same as Case 10 (fixed ends, uniform load) **except** that P is tension	$M_1 = M_2 = wj^2\left(\frac{\frac{1}{2}U - \tanh\frac{1}{2}U}{\tanh\frac{1}{2}U}\right)$, Max $+M = wj^2\left(1 - \frac{\frac{1}{2}U}{\sinh\frac{1}{2}U}\right)$ at $x = \frac{1}{2}l$ Max $y = -\frac{wj^2}{8P}\left[\frac{4U(1 - \cosh\frac{1}{2}U)}{\sinh\frac{1}{2}U} + U^2\right]$ at $x = \frac{1}{2}l$
19. Beam with ends pinned to rigid supports so horizontal displacement is prevented. Uniform transverse load and unknown axial tension $W = wl$; P, P, X, Y, l	$\frac{E^2A^2k^6}{w^2l^8}U^9 = \frac{1}{24}U^3 - \frac{5}{4}U + \frac{5}{2}\tanh\frac{U}{2} + \frac{U}{4}\tanh^2\frac{U}{2}$ where $k = \sqrt{\frac{I}{A}}$ This equation is solved for U, and P determined therefrom When $C = \frac{wl^4}{16EAk^3}$ is small (less than 4), $P = \frac{68}{630}\frac{EIC^2}{l^2}\left(1 - \frac{62}{2835}C^2\right)$ When C is large (greater than 15), $P = \frac{4EI}{l^2}\left[\left(\frac{C^2}{6}\right)^{\frac{1}{3}} - 2\right]$ When P has been found by one of the above formulas, M and y may be found by the formulas of Case 16
20. Continuous beam, spans 1 and 2 unequal and unequally loaded w_1, w_2, P_1, P_2, M_1, M_2', M_2, M_3, l_1, l_2	$\frac{M_1l_1}{I_1}\left(\frac{U_1 \operatorname{cosec} U_1 - 1}{U_1^2}\right) + \frac{M_3l_2}{I_2}\left(\frac{U_2 \operatorname{cosec} U_2 - 1}{U_2^2}\right)$ $+ M_2\left[\frac{l_1}{I_1}\left(\frac{1 - U_1 \cot U_1}{U_1^2}\right) + \frac{l_2}{I_2}\left(\frac{1 - U_2 \cot U_2}{U_2^2}\right)\right]$ $= \frac{w_1l_1^3}{I_1}\left(\frac{\tan\frac{1}{2}U_1 - \frac{1}{2}U_1}{U_1^3}\right) + \frac{w_2l_2^3}{I_2}\left(\frac{\tan\frac{1}{2}U_2 - \frac{1}{2}U_2}{U_2^3}\right)$ (Theorem of Three Moments: Subscripts with P, l, w, I, and U refer to first and second spans. M_2 acts on span 1, M_2' on span 2)

21. Same as Case 19 except ends fixed as well as held to prevent horizontal displacement	$2\pi^4 EIy + \frac{1}{8}\pi^4 EAy^3 = \frac{1}{2}wl^4$ (Here y = Max y; A = cross-section area) $P = \frac{1}{4}\pi^2 y^2 \frac{EA}{l^2}$ Solve first equation for y, then second equation for P; then solve for M_1, M_2, and Max M by formulas for Case 18
22. Same as Case 19 except load is W concentrated at center	$\frac{1}{2}\pi^4 EIy + \frac{1}{8}\pi^4 EAy^3 = Wl^3$ (Here y = Max y; A = cross-section area) $P = \frac{1}{4}\pi^2 y^2 \frac{EA}{l^2}$ Solve first equation for y, then second equation for P; then solve for Max M by formulas for Case 15
23. Same as Case 21 except load is W concentrated at center	$2\pi^4 EIy + \frac{1}{8}\pi^4 EAy^3 = Wl^3$ (Here y = Max y; A = cross-section area) $P = \frac{1}{4}\pi^2 y^2 \frac{EA}{l^2}$ Solve first equation for y, then second equation for P; then solve for M_1, M_2, and Max M by formulas for Case 9
24. Same as Case 19 except beam is perfectly flexible like a cable or chain and has natural length l	Max $y = l\left(\frac{3wl}{64EA}\right)^{\frac{1}{3}}$ (Here A = cross-section area) $P = \frac{1}{8}\frac{wl^2}{\text{Max } y}$
25. Same as Case 24 except load is W concentrated at center [diagram labels: W, P, P, θ, l]	$\tan\theta - \sin\theta = \frac{1}{2}\frac{W}{EA}$ (Here A = cross-section area) $P = \frac{1}{2}W \cot\theta$

Examples

A 4-in. 7.7-lb. I-beam 20 ft. long is supported at the ends and simultaneously subjected to a transverse load of 50 lb. per ft. (including its own weight) and an axial compression of 3000 lb. It is required to determine the maximum deflection, maximum moment, and maximum fiber stress.

Solution.—Here $P = 3000$; $l = 240$; $I = 6$; $I/c = 3$; $A = 2.21$; $w = \frac{50}{12} = 4.17$; $W = 50 \times 20 = 1000$; $j = \sqrt{EI/P} = 245$; $U = l/j = 0.98$; $\alpha = \frac{5}{48}$. Solution will be carried out: (*a*) ignoring deflection; (*b*) using Eq. 19; (*c*) using the precise formula.

(*a*) $M = \frac{1}{8}WL = \frac{1}{8}(1{,}000)(240) = 30{,}000$ in.-lb.

$$\text{Max } s = \frac{P}{A} + \frac{M}{(I/c)} = \frac{3000}{2.21} + \frac{30{,}000}{3} = 11{,}360 \text{ lb. per sq. in.}$$

(this is compressive stress, and occurs in the top fibers at the center of the beam)

$$y = \frac{5}{384}\frac{Wl^3}{EI} = \frac{5}{384}\frac{(1000)(240^3)}{(30{,}000{,}000)(6)} = 1.00 \text{ in.}$$

$$(b)\ M' = \frac{M}{\left(1 - \alpha\dfrac{Pl^2}{EI}\right)} = \frac{30{,}000}{1 - \dfrac{5}{48}\dfrac{(3000)(240^2)}{(30{,}000{,}000)(6)}} = 33{,}300 \text{ in.-lb.}$$

$$\text{Max } s = \frac{3000}{2.21} + \frac{33{,}300}{3} = 12{,}460 \text{ lb. per sq. in.}$$

(*c*) The formula for Case 4, Table VI, is used.

$$M = wj^2(\sec \tfrac{1}{2}U - 1) = (4.17)(245^2)(1.1334 - 1) = 33{,}250 \text{ in.-lb.}$$

$$\text{Max } s = \frac{3000}{2.21} + \frac{33{,}250}{3} = 12{,}440 \text{ lb. per sq. in.}$$

$$y = -\frac{wj^2}{P}\left(\sec\frac{1}{2}U - 1 - \frac{1}{8}U^2\right)$$

$$= -\frac{(4.17)(245^2)}{3000}\left(1.1334 - 1 - \frac{1}{8}(0.98^2)\right) = 1.107 \text{ in.}$$

(The Euler load for this beam is $P' = \pi^2 EI/l^2 = 30{,}800$ lb. Hence $P = 0.10P'$, and it will be noted that the error in neglecting the effect of deflection, as in solution (*a*), is about 10 per cent, while Eq. 19 yields practically the same value for M' as does the precise method.)

If P is assumed to be tension instead of compression, Eq. 19 gives $M' = 27{,}260$ in.-lb. while the precise formula (Case 16) gives

$$M = wj^2(1 - \operatorname{sech} \tfrac{1}{2}U) = (4.17)(245^2)(1 - 0.8913) = 27{,}200 \text{ in.-lb.}$$

$$y = -\frac{w}{P}\left[\frac{1}{8}l^2 - j^2\left(1 - \operatorname{sech}\frac{1}{2}U\right)\right]$$

$$= -\frac{4.17}{3000}\left[\frac{1}{8}(240^2) - (245^2)(1 - 0.8913)\right] = 0.943 \text{ in.}$$

41. Beam on an Elastic Foundation.—There are cases in which a very long beam is supported continuously along its length by a surface that may be regarded as elastic, in the sense that it may be considered to deflect in proportion to the intensity of the applied pressure. The most familiar example of this is a track rail. Three conditions of loading will be considered: (1) a bar of infinite length under a single concentrated load; (2) a bar of infinite length under a uniform load applied over a finite portion; (3) a very long bar with a couple and a concentrated load applied at one end. By superposition, the results for these three cases may be applied to a variety of loading conditions.

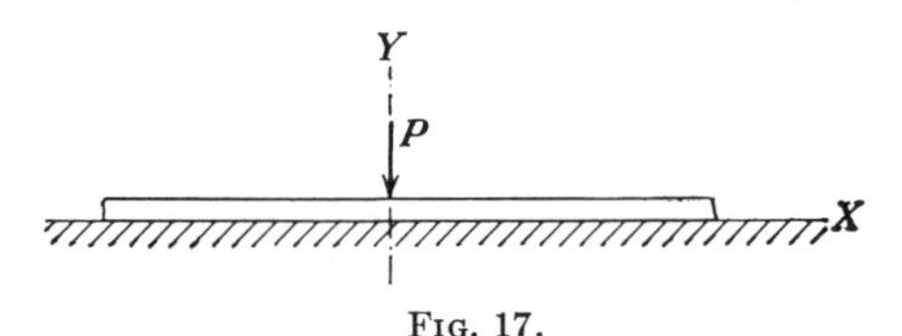

FIG. 17.

1. The arrangement is shown in Fig. 17. Let P = applied load, I = moment of inertia of the beam section; E = the modulus of elasticity of the beam; k = modulus of the foundation, defined by the equation $p = ky$, where p is the pressure (pounds per linear inch) required to produce the vertical deflection y (inches) of the foundation (either up or down, it being assumed that the supporting pressure can be either up or down). Also let M = bending moment, V = vertical shear, and y = deflection of the beam at any point distant x from P. Also let

$$\beta = \sqrt[4]{\frac{k}{4EI}}$$

Then:

$$M = -\frac{P}{4\beta} e^{-\beta x}(\sin \beta x - \cos \beta x)$$

$$V = -\tfrac{1}{2}Pe^{-\beta x} \cos \beta x$$

$$y = \frac{P}{8\beta^3 EI} e^{-\beta x}(\cos \beta x + \sin \beta x)$$

$$\text{Max } M = \frac{P}{4\beta} \text{ (at the load)}$$

$$\text{Max } y = \frac{P\beta}{2k} \text{ (at the load)}$$

(e = 2.71828, the base of the Napierian logarithm system; βx is to be expressed in radians when evaluating $\sin \beta x$, etc.)

2. The arrangement is shown in Fig. 18. Let M, V, and y denote, respectively, the moment, vertical shear, and deflection at a point distant $x(x < l)$ from the left end of the uniform load; w = intensity of distributed load (pounds per inch); l = distance

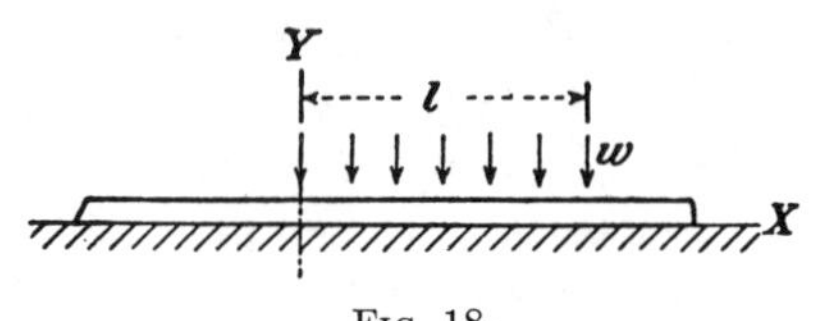

FIG. 18.

over which the load extends, and let other symbols have the meaning given in (1). Then

$$M = \frac{w}{4\beta^2}[e^{-\beta x} \sin \beta x + e^{-\beta(l-x)} \sin \beta(l - x)]$$

$$V = \frac{w}{4\beta}\{e^{-\beta x}(\cos \beta x - \sin \beta x) + e^{-\beta(l-x)}[\sin \beta(l - x) - \cos \beta(l - x)]\}$$

$$y = \frac{w}{2k}[2 - e^{-\beta(l-x)} \cos \beta(l - x) - e^{-\beta x} \cos \beta x]$$

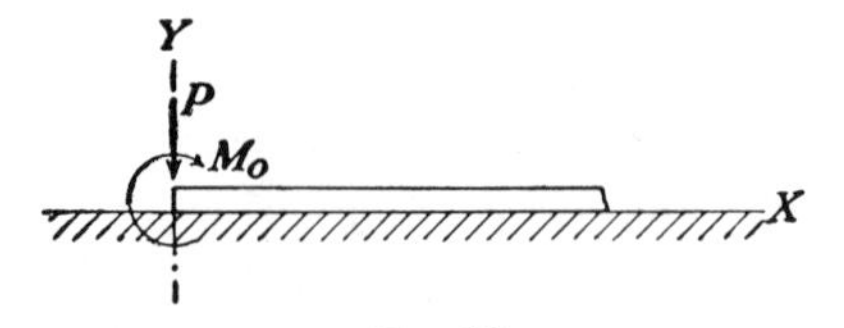

FIG. 19.

3. The arrangement is shown in Fig. 19. Let M_0 = the couple applied at the end of the beam, and let the other symbols have the meaning given in (1). Then

$$M = \frac{e^{-\beta x}}{\beta}[\beta M_0(\cos \beta x + \sin \beta x) - P \sin \beta x]$$

$$V = e^{-\beta x}[2\beta M_0 \sin \beta x + P(\sin \beta x - \cos \beta x)]$$

$$y = \frac{e^{-\beta x}}{2\beta^3 EI}[P \cos \beta x - \beta M_0(\cos \beta x - \sin \beta x)]$$

The formulas given above for Cases 1, 2, and 3 are based on the solution given by Timoshenko (Ref. 3), who also gives tabulated values of functions that greatly facilitate the evaluation of the equations. A more precise solution for the bar of infinite length with a single concentrated load is given by Biot (Ref. 37). Hetenyi (Ref. 63) discusses this problem of the beam on an elastic foundation extensively, and shows how the solutions can be adapted to other elements such as hollow cylinders.

Cantilever with Elastic Support.—The formulas in Tables III and VI for deflection of a cantilever beam are based on the assumption that the support is rigid and holds the fixed end of the beam truly horizontal. The slight yielding that actually occurs at the support permits the beam to assume there a slope $\Delta\theta$, which for the conditions represented in Fig. 20—that is, a beam integral with a semi-infinite supporting foundation—is given by

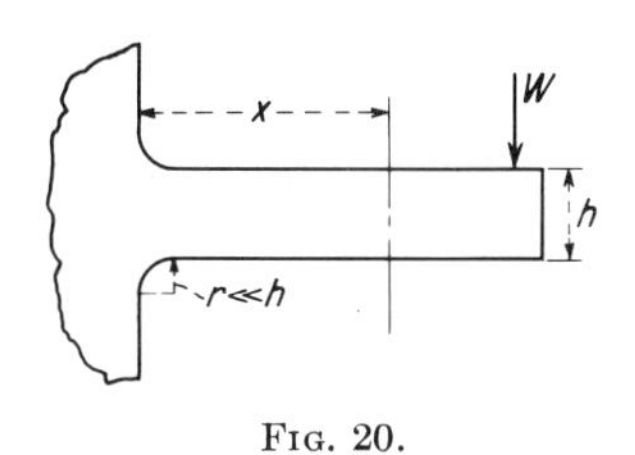

FIG. 20.

$$\Delta\theta = \frac{16.67M}{\pi E h_1^2} + \frac{(1 - \nu)V}{E h_1}$$

Here M is the bending moment, and V the shear per unit width of beam at the support, inch-pounds per inch and pounds per inch, respectively; E is the modulus of elasticity; ν is Poisson's ratio for the foundation material; and $h_1 = h + 1\frac{1}{2}r$ (Ref. 64). The effect of this yielding is to increase the deflection of the beam at any section distance x from the support by the amount $x\,\Delta\theta$.

42. Beams of Variable Section.—For a beam, the cross section of which changes gradually, Eqs. 1, 4, 10, 11, and 12 (Art. 32) apply with sufficient accuracy. Equations 3, 5, 6, and 7 apply if I is treated as a variable, as in the examples below. All the formulas given in Table III for vertical shear and bending moments in *statically determinate* beams apply, but those given for statically indeterminate beams, and those given for deflection and slope, are inapplicable to beams of nonuniform section unless the section varies in such a way that I is constant.

Accurate analysis (Ref. 3) shows that in an end-loaded cantilever beam of rectangular section which is symmetrically tapered in the plane of bending the maximum fiber stress is somewhat less than is indicated by Eq. 12, the error amounting to about 5 per cent for a surface slope of 15 deg. (wedge angle 30 deg.) and to about 10 per cent for a surface slope of 20 deg. The maximum horizontal and vertical shear stress is shown to occur at the upper and lower surfaces instead of at the neutral axis, and to be approximately three times as great as the average shear stress on the section for slopes up to 20 deg. It is very doubtful, however, if this shear stress is often critical even in wood beams, although it may possibly start failure in short, heavily reinforced concrete beams that are deepened or "haunched" at the ends. Such a failure, if observed, would probably be ascribed to compression, since it would occur at a point of high compressive stress. It is also, of course, conceivable that this shear stress might be of importance in certain metal parts subject to repeated stress.

Abrupt changes in the section of a beam cause high local stresses, the effect of which is taken into account by using the proper factor of stress concentration (Art. 8, Table XVII).

Examples

1. Figure 21 represents a wood beam supported at the ends and carrying a uniformly distributed load of 30 lb. per in. The left half of the beam has a uniform cross section whose moment of inertia is 12 in.^{4}; the right half has a uniform cross section whose moment of inertia is 20 in.^{4}. It is required to determine the deflection of this beam at a point 25 in. to the right of the left support.

Solution.—The method of unit loads (Eq. 6) will be used. The bending-moment equations are

$$(x = 0 \text{ to } x = 100) \qquad M = 1500x - 15x^2$$
$$(x = 0 \text{ to } x = 25) \qquad m = \tfrac{3}{4}x$$
$$(x = 25 \text{ to } x = 100) \qquad m = \tfrac{3}{4}x - 1(x - 25) = 25 - \tfrac{1}{4}x$$

(m is the bending moment due to a downward load of 1 lb. applied at the point whose deflection is desired.)

$$y = \int \frac{mM}{EI}\,dx = \int_0^{25} \frac{(1500x - 15x^2)(\frac{3}{4}x)dx}{12E} + \int_{25}^{50} \frac{(1500x - 15x^2)(25 - \frac{1}{4}x)dx}{12E} + \int_{50}^{100} \frac{(1500x - 15x^2)(25 - \frac{1}{4}x)dx}{20E} = \frac{2{,}000{,}000}{E}$$

Assuming that the beam is spruce with $E = 1{,}300{,}000$, $y = 1.54$ in. (It is to be noted that a new integral must be written every time that m, M, or I changes. The shape of the section is obviously immaterial, but it is assumed that E is the same throughout and that stress concentration due to the change in section at mid-span does not affect the deflection.)

2. A beam of length l is fixed at one end and supported at the other. In section the beam is rectangular, with constant depth d and with a varying breadth which increases linearly from b at the supported end to $2b$ at the fixed end. This beam carries a uniformly distributed load of w lb. per in. (Fig. 22). It is required to determine the reaction R at the supported end and the moment at the fixed end.

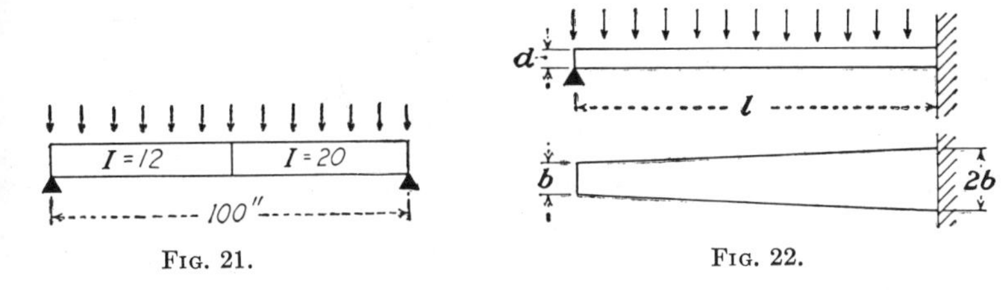

FIG. 21. FIG. 22.

Solution.—R will be found by making use of Eq. 5 and the boundary conditions: (a) that the slope $dy/dx = 0$ at the fixed end, (b) that the deflection $y = 0$ at the supported end, and (c) that $y = 0$ at the fixed end.

Obviously the breadth at any point distant x from the left end is

$$b + \frac{x}{l} b = b\left(\frac{l + x}{l}\right)$$

Therefore I at any point $= \frac{1}{12} d^3 b \left(\frac{l + x}{l}\right)$, and putting all constant quantities on the left side, Eq. 5 can be written:

$$E\left(\frac{d^3 b}{12l}\right)\frac{d^2y}{dx^2} = R\frac{x}{l + x} - \frac{1}{2} w \frac{x^2}{l + x}$$

Letting the coefficient of d^2y/dx^2 be denoted by K for convenience and integrating, we have

$$K\frac{dy}{dx} = R[l + x - l \log (l + x)] - \frac{1}{2} w \left[\frac{1}{2}(l + x)^2 - 2l(l + x) + l^2 \log (l + x)\right] + C_1$$

Using the boundary conditions that $dy/dx = 0$ when $x = 0$, it is found that $C_1 = -R(2l - l \log 2l) + \frac{1}{2}w(-2l^2 + l^2 \log 2l)$. Substituting this value of C_1 and integrating again, we have

$$\begin{aligned} Ky = {} & R\{lx + \tfrac{1}{2}x^2 - l[(l + 2) \log (l + x) - (l + x)]\} - \tfrac{1}{2}w\{\tfrac{1}{6}(l + x)^3 \\ & -l(l + x)^2 + l^2[(l + x) \log (l + x) - (l + x)]\} - R(2l - l \log 2l)x \\ & + \tfrac{1}{2}w(-2l^2 + l^2 \log 2l)x + C_2 \end{aligned}$$

Using the boundary conditions that $y = 0$ when $x = 0$, it is found that $C_2 = R(l^2 \log l - l^2) + \frac{1}{2}w(-\frac{11}{6} l^3 + l^3 \log l)$. Substituting this value of C_2 and using the boundary condition that $y = 0$ when $x = l$, we have

$$R(\tfrac{1}{2}l^2 - l^2 \log 2l + l^2 \log l) - \tfrac{1}{2}w(-\tfrac{5}{6}l^3 + l^3 \log 2l - l^3 \log l) = 0$$

Transposing and dividing by l^2 gives

$$R(\tfrac{1}{2} - \log 2l + \log l) = \tfrac{1}{2}wl(-\tfrac{5}{6} + \log 2l - \log l)$$

or

$$R(\tfrac{1}{2} - \log 2) = \tfrac{1}{2}wl(-\tfrac{5}{6} + \log 2)$$

whence

$$R = 0.363wl = 0.363W$$

and the moment at the fixed end is

$$M = 0.363wl^2 - 0.5wl^2 = -0.137wl^2 = -0.137Wl$$

If this beam were of uniform section, the reaction R would be $0.375W$ and the moment at the fixed end would be $-0.125Wl$ (Table III, Case 23).

The effect in any statically indeterminate beam of varying section is to thus increase the moment at the larger sections and decrease the moments at the smaller sections. Unless there is a great variation in moment of inertia, however, the difference in moment distribution from that obtaining in a beam of constant section is not likely to be marked.

When the beam section varies in such a way that it cannot be expressed as a function of x, Eq. 6 can be solved by numerical integration. The beam is divided into arbitrary segments Δl; M, m, and I are computed for the middle section of each segment; and then the quantities Mm/I (or Mm/EI if E is not constant) are summed. The procedure will be illustrated by applying it to the tapered beam of this example, taking $\Delta l = \frac{1}{4}l$ and numbering the segments in order from left to right. (If the actual deflection of the beam at some point other than the end were being computed, it would be necessary to multiply each term Mm by $\frac{1}{4}l$, representing dx, but here the dx term can be omitted as it is common to both sides of the final equation.) The calculations can conveniently be tabulated thus:

Segment no.	Breadth at center	I at center	M at center	m at center	Mm	Mm/I (omitting b and d)
1	$\frac{9}{8}b$	$\frac{9}{96}bd^3$	$\frac{1}{8}Rl - \frac{1}{128}wl^2$	$\frac{1}{8}l$	$\frac{1}{64}Rl^2 - \frac{1}{1024}wl^3$	$0.167Rl^2 - 0.010wl^3$
2	$\frac{11}{8}b$	$\frac{11}{96}bd^3$	$\frac{3}{8}Rl - \frac{9}{128}wl^2$	$\frac{3}{8}l$	$\frac{9}{64}Rl^2 - \frac{27}{1024}wl^3$	$1.227Rl^2 - 0.230wl^3$
3	$\frac{13}{8}b$	$\frac{13}{96}bd^3$	$\frac{5}{8}Rl - \frac{25}{128}wl^2$	$\frac{5}{8}l$	$\frac{25}{64}Rl^2 - \frac{125}{1024}wl^3$	$2.882Rl^2 - 0.901wl^3$
4	$\frac{15}{8}b$	$\frac{15}{96}bd^3$	$\frac{7}{8}Rl - \frac{49}{128}wl^2$	$\frac{7}{8}l$	$\frac{49}{64}Rl^2 - \frac{343}{1024}wl^3$	$4.900Rl^2 - 2.142wl^3$

$\Sigma Mm/I = 9.176Rl^2 - 3.282wl^3$.

Since $\Sigma Mm/I$ represents deflection at left end $= 0$, $R = 0.358wl$. By taking Δl smaller, closer agreement with the result previously obtained by integration could be obtained.

43. Slotted Beam.—If the web of a beam is pierced by a hole or slot (Fig. 23), the stresses in the extreme fibers a and b at any section B are given by

$$s_a = \frac{M_A}{I/c} + \frac{V_A x[I_1/(I_1 + I_2)]}{(I/c)_1} \text{ (compression)}$$

$$s_b = \frac{M_A}{I/c} + \frac{V_A x[I_2/(I_1 + I_2)]}{(I/c)_2} \text{ (tension)}$$

Here M_A is the bending moment at A (mid-length of the slot), V_A is the vertical shear at A; I/c is the section modulus of the net beam section at B; I_1 and I_2 are the moments of inertia, and $(I/c)_1$ and $(I/c)_2$ the section moduli of the cross sections of parts 1 and 2 about their own central axes. M and V are positive or negative according to the usual convention, and x is positive when measured to the right.

The above formulas are derived by replacing all forces acting on the beam to the left of A by an equivalent couple M_A and shear V_A acting at A. The couple produces a bending stress given by the first term of the formula. The shear divides between parts 1 and 2 in proportion to their respective I's and produces in each part an additional bending stress given by the second term of the formula.

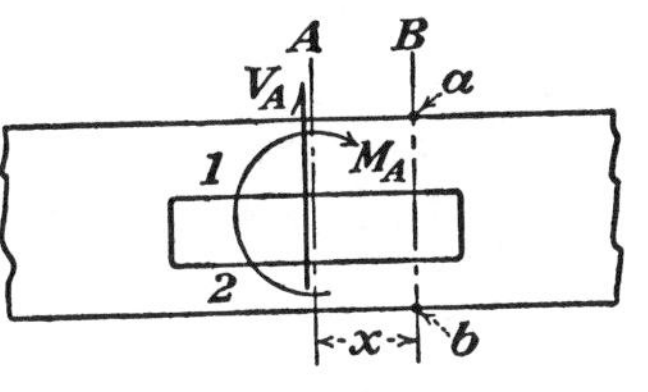

FIG. 23.

The stress at any other point in the cross section can be found by similarly adding the stresses due to M_A and those due to this secondary bending caused by the shear. At the ends of the slot there is a stress concentration at the corners which is not here taken into account.

The above analysis applies also to a beam with multiple slots of equal length; all that is necessary is to modify the term in brackets so that the numerator is the I of the part in question and the denominator is the sum of the I's of all the parts 1, 2, 3, etc. The formulas can also be used for a rigid frame consisting of beams of equal length joined at their ends by rigid members; thus in Fig. 23 parts 1 and 2 might equally well be two separate beams joined at their ends by rigid crosspieces.

44. Curved Beams.—When a curved beam is bent in the plane of initial curvature, plane sections remain plane, but because of the different lengths of fibers on the inner and outer sides of the beam the distribution of strain and stress is not linear; the neutral axis therefore does not pass through the centroid of the section and Eqs. 1 and 2 of Art. 32 do not apply. The error involved in their use is slight as long as the radius of curvature is more than about 10 times the depth of the beam, but becomes large for sharp curvatures. In Table VII are given formulas for the position of the neutral axis and for the maximum fiber stresses in curved beams having different degrees of curvature and various forms of cross section. In large part the formulas and tabulated coefficients are taken from the University of Illinois Circular by Wilson and Quereau (Ref. 38).

Shear Stress.—Although Eq. 2 of Art. 32 does not apply to curved beams, Eq. 13, used as for a straight beam, gives the *maximum* shear stress with sufficient accuracy in most instances. A solution for the shear stress in a curved beam of narrow rectangular section is given by Case (Ref. 39); his formula shows that even for very sharp curvature (radius of beam axis equal to depth) the maximum shear stress is only about 10 per cent in excess of the value $\frac{3}{2}V/A$ given by Eq. 13. It should be noted that this maximum shear stress occurs at the neutral axis of the curved beam, and not at the central axis.

Radial Stress.—Owing to the radial components of the fiber stresses, there are set up radial stresses in a curved beam; these are tensile when the bending moment tends to straighten the beam and compressive under the reverse condition. Case (Ref. 39) gives a formula for this radial stress at any point in a beam of narrow rectangular section; the formula shows that the radial stress does not become equal to even the smaller of the extreme fiber stresses until the curvature is very sharp (ratio of outer to inner radius = 7). It can thus be seen that radial stresses are unlikely to be important in curved beams of rectangular section. In beams of I or T section, however, the radial stress may become critical when the web thickness is small. Seely and James (Ref. 40) discuss this question; they explain a method of calculating the stress and give experimental results secured with plaster models. Their conclusion is that the radial web stress is probably less important than the fiber stress for all values of R/c (radius of curvature divided by distance from centroid of section to extreme fiber on inner side of beam) greater than about 2, provided that the web thickness is not less than about $\frac{1}{5}$ the flange breadth and provided stress concentration at the junction of flange and web is negligible. (This is with reference to tensile stresses in a curved beam under a *straightening* moment; in a beam with very thin web, the web might buckle under the radial compression produced by a moment that tended to increase the curvature.)

Deflection.—The change in slope of a curved beam can be found, with sufficient accuracy, by using Eq. 8 with dx replaced by ds, where s represents distance measured along the axis of the beam. The displacement in a direction y can be found by using Eq. 9, letting x represent distance measured normal to the y-axis and again replacing dx by ds. Deflection can also be found by Eq. 6, replacing dx by ds (see example below).

Distortion of Tubular Sections.—In curved beams of thin tubular section, the distortion of the cross section produced by the radial components of the fiber stresses reduces both the strength and stiffness. If the beam curvature is not so sharp as to make Eqs. 1 and 4 inapplicable, the effect of this distortion of the section can be taken into account as follows:

In calculating deflection of curved beams of hollow circular section, replace I by KI, where $K = 1 - \dfrac{9}{[10 + 12(tR/a^2)^2]}$. (Here R = radius of curvature of the beam axis; a = outer radius of tube section; t = thickness of tube wall.)

In calculating the maximum stress in curved beams of hollow circular section, use the formula, $S_{\max} = \dfrac{Ma}{I}\left(\dfrac{2}{3K\sqrt{3\beta}}\right)$ where $\beta = \dfrac{6}{5 + 6(tR/a^2)^2}$ and K has the value given above. This maximum stress does not occur at the extreme fiber, but at a distance $a\sqrt{1/3\beta}$ from the central axis.

In calculating deflection or stress in a curved beam of hollow square section and uniform wall thickness, replace I by

$$\left(\frac{1 + 0.0270n}{1 + 0.0656n}\right) I$$

where $n = \dfrac{b^4}{R^2t^2}$. (Here R = the radius of curvature of the

TABLE VII.—FORMULAS FOR CURVED BEAMS

Notation: R = radius of curvature measured to centroid of section; c = distance from centroidal axis to extreme fiber on concave side of beam; A = area of section; h = distance from centroidal axis to neutral axis, measured toward center of curvature; I = moment of inertia of cross section about centroidal axis perpendicular to plane of curvature; $k_i = \frac{s_i}{s}$ and $k_o = \frac{s_o}{s}$ where s_i = actual stress in extreme fiber on concave side, s_o = actual stress in extreme fiber on convex side, and s = fictitious unit stress in corresponding fiber as computed by ordinary flexure formula for a straight beam

Form and dimensions of cross section, reference number	Precise formula for h and approximate formula for k_i	Values of k_i, k_o, and $\frac{h}{R}$ for various values of $\frac{R}{c}$										
1. Solid rectangular section	$h = R - \dfrac{d}{\log_e\left(\dfrac{R+c}{R-c}\right)}$	$\frac{R}{c}$ =	1.2	1.4	1.6	1.8	2.0	3.0	4.0	6.0	8.0	10
	$k_i = 1 + 0.5\dfrac{I}{bc^2}\left[\dfrac{1}{R-c} + \dfrac{1}{R}\right]$	k_i =	2.89	2.13	1.79	1.63	1.52	1.30	1.20	1.12	1.09	1.07
		k_o =	0.57	0.63	0.67	0.70	0.73	0.81	0.85	0.90	0.92	0.94
		$\frac{h}{R}$ =	0.305	0.204	0.149	0.112	0.090	0.041	0.021	0.0093	0.0052	0.0033
2. Solid circular section	$h = R - \dfrac{\frac{1}{2}c^2}{R - \sqrt{R^2 - c^2}}$	$\frac{R}{c}$ =	1.2	1.4	1.6	1.8	2.0	3.0	4.0	6.0	8.0	10
	$k_i = 1 + 1.05\dfrac{I}{dc^2}\left[\dfrac{1}{R-c} + \dfrac{1}{R}\right]$	k_i =	3.41	2.40	1.96	1.75	1.62	1.33	1.23	1.14	1.10	1.08
		k_o =	0.54	0.60	0.65	0.68	0.71	0.79	0.84	0.89	0.91	0.93
		$\frac{h}{R}$ =	0.224	0.151	0.108	0.084	0.069	0.030	0.016	0.0070	0.0039	0.0025
3. Hollow circular section	$h = R - \dfrac{\frac{1}{2}(c^2 - c_1^2)}{\sqrt{R^2 - c_1^2} - \sqrt{R^2 - c^2}}$	(When $c = 2c_1$)										
	$k_i = 1 + 1.05\dfrac{I}{dc^2}\left[\dfrac{1}{R-c} + \dfrac{1}{R}\right]$	$\frac{R}{c}$ =	1.2	1.4	1.6	1.8	2.0	3.0	4.0	6.0	8.0	10
		k_i =	3.28	2.31	1.89	1.70	1.57	1.31	1.21	1.13	1.10	1.07
		k_o =	0.58	0.64	0.68	0.71	0.73	0.81	0.85	0.90	0.92	0.93
		$\frac{h}{R}$ =	0.269	0.182	0.134	0.104	0.083	0.038	0.020	0.0087	0.0049	0.0031
4. Solid elliptical section	$h = R - \dfrac{\frac{1}{2}c^2}{R - \sqrt{R^2 - c^2}}$	Same as for solid circular section										
	$k_i = 1 + 1.05\dfrac{I}{bc^2}\left[\dfrac{1}{R-c} + \dfrac{1}{R}\right]$											

5. Hollow elliptical section

$$h = R - \frac{\frac{1}{2}(bc - b_1c_1)}{b\left[\frac{R}{c} - \sqrt{\left(\frac{R}{c}\right)^2 - 1}\right] - b_1\left[\frac{R}{c_1} - \sqrt{\left(\frac{R}{c_1}\right)^2 - 1}\right]}$$

$$k_i = 1 + 1.05\frac{I}{bc^2}\left[\frac{1}{R-c} + \frac{1}{R}\right]$$

$\frac{R}{c}$ =	1.2	1.4	1.6	1.8	2.0	3.0	4.0	6.0	8.0	10
k_i =	3.03	2.15	1.82	1.65	1.53	1.29	1.20	1.12	1.09	1.07
k_o =	0.58	0.64	0.68	0.71	0.73	0.81	0.85	0.90	0.92	0.93
$\frac{h}{R}$ =	0.295	0.195	0.146	0.114	0.085	0.041	0.021	0.0088	0.005	0.0032

6. Triangular section

$$h = R - \frac{\frac{1}{2}d^2}{(R + c_1)\log_e\frac{R + c_1}{R - c} - d}$$

$$k_i = 1 + 0.5\frac{I}{bc^2}\left[\frac{1}{R-c} + \frac{1}{R}\right]$$

(When $d = 0.6b$)

$\frac{R}{c}$ =	1.2	1.4	1.6	1.8	2.0	3.0	4.0	6.0	8.0	10
k_i =	3.26	2.39	1.99	1.78	1.66	1.37	1.27	1.16	1.12	1.09
k_o =	0.44	0.50	0.54	0.57	0.60	0.70	0.75	0.82	0.86	0.88
$\frac{h}{R}$ =	0.361	0.251	0.186	0.144	0.116	0.052	0.029	0.013	0.0060	0.0039

7. Trapezoidal section

$$h = R - \frac{A}{\frac{b(R + c_1) - b_1(R - c)}{d}\log_e\frac{R + c_1}{R - c} - (b - b_1)}$$

$$k_i = 1 + 0.5\frac{I}{bc^2}\left[\frac{1}{R-c} + \frac{1}{R}\right]$$

(When $b = 2b_1$ and $d = 3b_1$)

$\frac{R}{c}$ =	1.2	1.4	1.6	1.8	2.0	3.0	4.0	6.0	8.0	10
k_i =	3.09	2.25	1.91	1.73	1.61	1.37	1.26	1.17	1.13	1.11
k_o =	0.56	0.62	0.66	0.70	0.73	0.81	0.86	0.91	0.94	0.95
$\frac{h}{R}$ =	0.336	0.229	0.168	0.128	0.102	0.046	0.024	0.011	0.0060	0.0039

8. T-beam or channel section

$$h = R - \frac{A}{b\log_e\left(\frac{R + t - c}{R - c}\right) + b_1\log_e\left(\frac{R + c_1}{R + t - c}\right)}$$

$$k_i = 1 + 0.5\frac{I}{bc^2}\left[\frac{1}{R-c} + \frac{1}{R}\right]$$

When $b = 4b_1$, $t = \frac{3}{2}b_1$, $d = 6b_1$

$\frac{R}{c}$ =	1.2	1.4	1.6	1.8	2.0	3.0	4.0	6.0	8.0	10
k_i =	3.63	2.54	2.14	1.89	1.73	1.41	1.29	1.18	1.13	1.10
k_o =	0.58	0.63	0.67	0.70	0.72	0.79	0.83	0.88	0.91	0.92
$\frac{h}{R}$ =	0.418	0.299	0.229	0.183	0.149	0.069	0.040	0.018	0.010	0.0065

9. Symmetrical I-beam or hollow rectangular section

$$h = R - \frac{A}{b\log_e\left(\frac{R + t - c}{R - c}\right) + b_1\log_e\left(\frac{R + c - t}{R + t - c}\right) + b\log_e\left(\frac{R + c}{R + c - t}\right)}$$

$$k_i = 1 + 0.5\frac{I}{bc^2}\left[\frac{1}{R-c} + \frac{1}{R}\right]$$

When $b = 3t$, $b_1 = t$, $d = 6t$

$\frac{R}{c}$ =	1.2	1.4	1.6	1.8	2.0	3.0	4.0	6.0	8.0	10
k_i =	2.52	1.90	1.63	1.50	1.41	1.23	1.16	1.10	1.07	1.05
k_o =	0.67	0.71	0.75	0.77	0.79	0.86	0.89	0.92	0.94	0.95
$\frac{h}{R}$ =	0.408	0.285	0.208	0.160	0.127	0.058	0.030	0.013	0.0076	0.0048

10. Unsymmetrical I-beam section

$$h = R - \frac{A}{b\log_e\left(\frac{R+t-c}{R-c}\right) + b_2\log_e\left(\frac{R+c_1-t_1}{R+t-c}\right) + b_1\log_e\left(\frac{R + c_1}{R+c_1-t_1}\right)}$$

$$k_i = 1 + 0.5\frac{I}{bc^2}\left[\frac{1}{R-c} + \frac{1}{R}\right]$$

When $b = 6t_1$, $t = 2t_1$, $b_1 = 4t_1$, $d = 6t_1$, $b_2 = t_1$

$\frac{R}{c}$ =	1.2	1.4	1.6	1.8	2.0	3.0	4.0	6.0	8.0	10
k_i =	3.55	2.48	2.07	1.83	1.69	1.38	1.26	1.15	1.10	1.08
k_o =	0.67	0.72	0.76	0.78	0.80	0.86	0.89	0.92	0.94	0.95
$\frac{h}{R}$ =	0.409	0.292	0.224	0.178	0.144	0.067	0.038	0.018	0.010	0.0065

beam axis; b = length of the side of the square section; t = thickness of the section wall.)

The above formulas for circular sections are due to von Kármán (Ref. 41); the formulas for square sections are due to Timoshenko (Ref. 42), who also gives formulas for rectangular sections.

U-shaped Members.—A U-shaped member having a semicircular inner boundary and a rectangular outer boundary is sometimes used as a punch or riveter frame. Such a member can usually be analyzed as a curved beam having a concentric outer boundary, but when the back thickness is large, a more accurate analysis may be necessary. In Ref. 51 are presented the results of a photoelastic stress analysis of such members, in which the effects of variations in the several dimensions were determined.

Example

Figure 24 represents a slender uniform bar curved to form the quadrant of a circle; it is fixed at the lower end and at the upper end is loaded by a vertical force V, a horizontal force H, and a couple M_0. It is desired to find the vertical deflection D_y, the horizontal deflection D_x, and the rotation θ, of the upper end, here denoted respectively by D_y, D_x, and θ. According to Castigliano's first theorem, $D_y = \partial U/\partial V$; $D_x = \partial U/\partial H$, and $\theta = \partial U/\partial M_0$. Denoting the angular position of any section by x, it is evident that the moment there is $M = VR \sin x + HR(1 - \cos x) + M_0$. Disregarding shear and axial stress, and replacing ds by $R\,dx$, we have (Eq. 3)

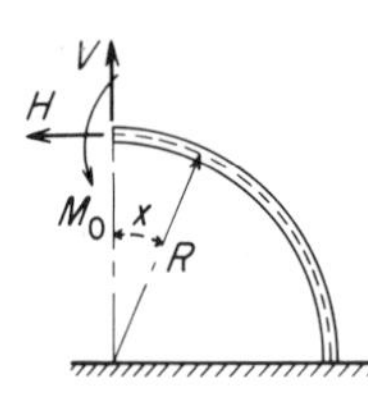

FIG. 24.

$$U = U_f = \int_0^{\pi/2} \frac{[VR \sin x + HR(1 - \cos x) + M_0]^2 R\,dx}{2EI}$$

Instead of integrating this and then carrying out the partial differentiations, we differentiate first and then integrate, and for convenience suppress the constant term EI until all computations are completed. Thus:

$$D_y = \frac{\partial U}{\partial V} = \int_0^{\pi/2} [VR \sin x + HR(1 - \cos x) + M_0](R \sin x)R\,dx$$

$$= VR^3(\tfrac{1}{2}x - \tfrac{1}{2} \sin x \cos x) - HR^3(\cos x - \tfrac{1}{2} \sin^2 x) - M_0R^2 \cos x \Big|_0^{\pi/2}$$

$$= \frac{(\pi/4)VR^3 + \frac{1}{2}HR^3 + M_0R^2}{EI}$$

$$D_x = \frac{\partial U}{\partial H} = \int_0^{\pi/2} [VR \sin x + HR(1 - \cos x) + M_0]R(1 - \cos x)R\, dx$$

$$= VR^3(-\cos x - \tfrac{1}{2}\sin^2 x) + HR^3(\tfrac{3}{2}x - 2\sin x + \tfrac{1}{2}\sin x \cos x) + M_0R^2(x - \sin x)\Big|_0^{\pi/2}$$

$$= \frac{\frac{1}{2}VR^3 + \left(\frac{3}{4}\pi - 2\right)HR^3 + \left(\frac{\pi}{2} - 1\right)M_0R^2}{EI}$$

$$\theta = \frac{\partial U}{\partial M_0} = \int_0^{\pi/2} [VR \sin x + HR(1 - \cos x) + M_0]R\, dx$$

$$-VR\cos x + HR(x - \sin x) + M_0x\Big|_0^{\pi/2}$$

$$= \frac{VR^2 + \left(\frac{\pi}{2} - 1\right)HR^2 + \frac{\pi}{2}M_0R}{EI}$$

The deflection produced by any one or by any combination of two loads is found by setting the other loads or load equal to zero; thus, V alone would produce $D_x = \frac{1}{2}VR^3/EI$, and M alone would produce $D_y = M_0R^2/EI$. In this example all results are positive, indicating that D_x is in the direction of H, D_y in the direction of V, and θ in the direction of M_0.

45. Curved Beam Loaded Normal to Plane of Curvature.—This type of beam usually presents a statically indeterminate problem, the degree of indeterminacy depending upon the manner of loading and support. Both bending and twisting occur, and it is necessary to distinguish between an analysis applicable to compact or flangeless sections (circular, rectangular, etc.) in which torsion does not produce secondary bending and one applicable to flanged sections (I-beams, channels, etc.) in which torsion may be accompanied by such secondary bending (see Art. 51). It is also necessary to distinguish three kinds of constraint that may or may not occur at the supports, namely: (*a*) The beam is prevented from *sloping*, its horizontal axis is held horizontal by a bending couple. (*b*) The beam is prevented from *rolling*, its vertical axis is held vertical by a twisting couple. (*c*) In the case of a flanged section, the flanges are prevented from turning about their vertical axes by horizontal secondary bending couples. These types of constraint will here be designated thus: (*a*) fixed as to slope; (*b*) fixed as to roll; (*c*) flanges fixed.

Below there are given, for each of several conditions of support and loading, equations that (when the appropriate numerical values have been substituted) either give or can be solved simultaneously for the statically indeterminate end reactions V, constraining twisting couples T, and constraining bending couples M. For the sake of clarity, these couples are represented in Fig. 25 by vectors according to the usual convention, the vector points in the direction in which the couple would advance a right-hand screw. These couples are to be regarded as positive when acting as shown. The usual rule of sign is followed in writing the general equations for the bending moment at any section, and the twisting moment at any section is regarded as positive when it has the same sense as a positive end torque.

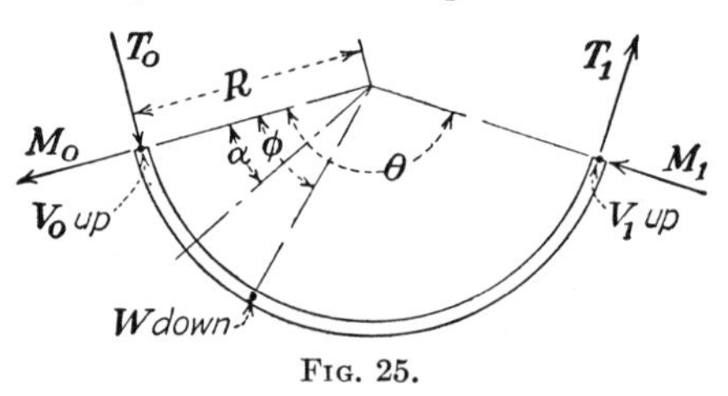

FIG. 25.

When the bending and twisting moments at any section of the girder have been found by the above formulas, the stresses at that section can be found by the formulas given for straight bars in Chaps. 8 and 9. The error in results thus obtained, due to curvature of the beam, will seldom be important in comparison with the unavoidable errors due to uncertain end conditions.

The angle of twist and the vertical deflection can be calculated by the method of unit loads or by Castigliano's first theorem (Art. 17), using the expressions for strain energy of bending $U = \int \frac{M^2R}{2EI}\,d\alpha$ and strain energy of twisting $U = \int \frac{T^2R}{2GK}\,d\alpha$.

The equations, though given for single spans, are equally applicable to continuous ring girders under conditions of symmetrical loading and support. Each section of such a ring, between supports, constitutes a single span and comes under classification I if free to roll at supports and under II if fixed against roll at supports.

FLANGELESS SECTIONS

I. Single span with ends supported and fixed as to slope but not fixed as to roll.

1. *Uniformly distributed load w lb. per linear inch.*

$$T_0 = T_1 = 0$$
$$V_0 = V_1 = \tfrac{1}{2}wR\theta$$
$$M_0 = M_1 = wR^2\left(\frac{\sin\frac{1}{2}\theta - \frac{1}{2}\theta\cos\frac{1}{2}\theta}{\sin\frac{1}{2}\theta}\right) \qquad (\text{Max } -M)$$
$$M = -M_0\cos\alpha + \tfrac{1}{2}wR^2\theta\sin\alpha - wR^2(1-\cos\alpha)$$
$$T = -M_0\sin\alpha + \tfrac{1}{2}wR^2\theta(1-\cos\alpha) - wR^2(\alpha - \sin\alpha)$$

2. *Concentrated load W at mid-span.*

$$T_0 = T_1 = 0$$
$$V_0 = V_1 = \tfrac{1}{2}W$$
$$M_0 = WR\left(\frac{\sin\frac{1}{2}\theta - \frac{1}{2}\sin\theta}{1-\cos\theta}\right) \qquad (\text{Max } -M)$$
$$M = -M_0\cos\alpha + \tfrac{1}{2}WR\sin\alpha \qquad (\text{Max } +M \text{ at } \alpha = \tfrac{1}{2}\theta)$$
$$T = -M_0\sin\alpha + \tfrac{1}{2}WR(1-\cos\alpha) \qquad (\text{Max at } \alpha = \tfrac{1}{4}\theta)$$

3. *Concentrated load W at any point ϕ.*

$T_0 = T_1 = 0$. Let $s = \sin\theta$, $c = \cos\theta$, $n = \sin\phi$, $e = \cos\phi$. Then

$$M_0\left\{\frac{1}{EI}\left[\theta + sc - \frac{2s^3}{1-c} + \left(\frac{s}{1-c}\right)^2(\theta - sc)\right]\right.$$
$$\left. + \frac{1}{KG}\left[\theta - sc + \frac{s}{1-c}(4c + 2s^2 - 4) + \left(\frac{s}{1-c}\right)^2(3\theta - 4s + sc)\right]\right\}$$
$$+ WR\left\{\frac{1}{EI}\left[n(\phi - \theta - sc) + es^2 + \frac{1-\cos(\theta-\phi)}{1-c}\left(\frac{s\theta - s^2}{1-c}\right)\right.\right.$$
$$\left. + \frac{s}{1-c}(sce - e\theta + s^2n + e\phi - n)\right]$$
$$+ \frac{1}{KG}\left[n(sc - \theta + \phi) + \frac{1-\cos(\theta-\phi)}{1-c}\left(2c + s^2 - 2 + \frac{3s\theta + s^2c - 4s^2}{1-c}\right)\right.$$
$$+ \frac{s}{1-c}(2s - 2\theta + 2se - 2cn - e\theta - sce - s^2n + e\phi - n + 2\phi)$$
$$\left.\left. - 2c - s^2e + 2e\right]\right\} = 0$$

II. Single span with ends supported and fixed as to both slope and roll.

1. *Uniformly distributed load w lb. per linear in.*

$$V_0 = V_1 = \tfrac{1}{2}wR\theta$$
$$\frac{1}{EI}\left[T_0(\theta - \sin\theta\cos\theta)\right.$$
$$+ M_0\sin^2\theta - wR^2\left(\frac{1}{2}\theta^2 - \frac{1}{2}\theta\sin\theta\cos\theta + 2\cos\theta\right.$$
$$\left.\left. + \sin^2\theta - 2\right)\right] + \frac{1}{GK}\left[2T_0\left(\frac{1}{2}\theta + \frac{1}{2}\sin\theta\cos\theta\right) - M_0\sin^2\theta\right.$$
$$\left. - wR^2\left(\frac{1}{2}\theta^2 + \frac{1}{2}\theta\sin\theta\cos\theta + 2\cos\theta - \sin^2\theta + \theta\sin\theta - 2\right)\right] = 0$$
$$M_0\sin\theta - T_0(1+\cos\theta) - wR^2(\sin\theta - \tfrac{1}{2}\theta - \tfrac{1}{2}\theta\cos\theta) = 0$$
$$M = -M_0\cos\alpha - T_0\sin\alpha + \tfrac{1}{2}wR^2\theta\sin\alpha - wR^2(1-\cos\alpha)$$
$$(\text{Max } -M = M_0, \qquad \text{Max } +M \text{ at } \alpha = \tfrac{1}{2}\theta)$$

$T = T_0 \cos\alpha - M_0 \sin\alpha + \frac{1}{2}wR^2\theta(1 - \cos\alpha) - wR^2(\alpha - \sin\alpha)$

2. *Concentrated load W at mid-span.*

$V_0 = V_1 = \frac{1}{2}W$

$$\frac{1}{EI}\left[M_0 \cos\frac{1}{2}\theta(\theta + \sin\theta) + T_0 \sin\frac{1}{2}\theta(\theta + \sin\theta) + \frac{1}{2}WR\left(1 - \cos\theta - \theta\sin\frac{1}{2}\theta - \sin\theta\sin\frac{1}{2}\theta\right)\right] + \frac{1}{KG}\left[M_0\cos\frac{1}{2}\theta(\theta - \sin\theta) + T_0\sin\frac{1}{2}\theta(\theta - \sin\theta) + \frac{1}{2}WR\left(3 + \cos\theta - 4\cos\frac{1}{2}\theta - \theta\sin\frac{1}{2}\theta + \sin\theta\sin\frac{1}{2}\theta\right)\right] = 0$$

$M_0(1 - \cos\theta) - T_0\sin\theta - WR(\sin\frac{1}{2}\theta - \frac{1}{2}\sin\theta) = 0$

$M = -M_0\cos\alpha - T_0\sin\alpha + \frac{1}{2}WR\sin\alpha$

(Max $-M = M_0$, Max $+M$ at $\alpha = \frac{1}{2}\theta$)

$T = T_0\cos\alpha - M_0\sin\alpha + \frac{1}{2}WR(1 - \cos\alpha)$

3. *Concentrated load W at any point ϕ.*

$$\frac{1}{EI}\left[\frac{1}{2}T_0\sin^2\theta + \frac{1}{2}M_0(\theta + \sin\theta\cos\theta) - \frac{1}{2}V_0R\sin^2\theta + \frac{1}{2}WR(\sin^2\theta\cos\phi - \theta\sin\phi - \sin\phi\sin\theta\cos\theta + \phi\sin\phi)\right] + \frac{1}{GK}\left[-\frac{1}{2}T_0\sin^2\theta + \frac{1}{2}M_0(\theta - \sin\theta\cos\theta) + V_0R\left(\cos\theta + \frac{1}{2}\sin^2\theta - 1\right) + \frac{1}{2}WR(\phi\sin\phi - 2\cos\theta - \cos\phi\sin^2\theta - \theta\sin\phi + \sin\phi\sin\theta\cos\theta + 2\cos\phi)\right] = 0$$

$$\frac{1}{EI}\left[\frac{1}{2}T_0(\theta - \sin\theta\cos\theta) + \frac{1}{2}M_0\sin^2\theta + \frac{1}{2}V_0R(\sin\theta\cos\theta - \theta) + \frac{1}{2}WR(\theta\cos\phi - \cos\phi\sin\theta\cos\theta - \sin\phi\sin^2\theta - \phi\cos\phi + \sin\phi)\right] + \frac{1}{GK}\left[\frac{1}{2}T_0(\theta + \sin\theta\cos\theta) - \frac{1}{2}M_0\sin^2\theta + \frac{1}{2}V_0R(2\sin\theta - \theta - \sin\theta\cos\theta) + \frac{1}{2}WR(\theta\cos\phi - 2\sin\theta + \cos\phi\sin\theta\cos\theta + \sin\phi\sin^2\theta + \sin\phi - \phi\cos\phi)\right] = 0$$

$$\frac{1}{EI}\left[\frac{1}{2}T_0(\sin\theta\cos\theta - \theta) - \frac{1}{2}M_0\sin^2\theta + \frac{1}{2}V_0R(\theta - \sin\theta\cos\theta) + \frac{1}{2}WR(\sin\phi\sin^2\theta + \cos\phi\sin\theta\cos\theta - \theta\cos\phi + \phi\cos\phi - \sin\phi)\right] + \frac{1}{GK}\left[\frac{1}{2}T_0(2\sin\theta - \theta - \sin\theta\cos\theta) + M_0\left(\cos\theta + \frac{1}{2}\sin^2\theta - 1\right) + \frac{1}{2}V_0R(3\theta - 4\sin\theta + \sin\theta\cos\theta) + \frac{1}{2}WR(2\sin\theta\cos\phi - 2\theta - 2\cos\theta\sin\phi + 2\sin\theta - \theta\cos\phi - \cos\theta\cos\phi\sin\theta - \sin^2\theta\sin\phi + 2\phi + \phi\cos\phi - \sin\phi)\right] = 0$$

Further discussion of this problem can be found in Refs. 46, 66, and 67.

FLANGED SECTIONS

The above equations for flangeless sections apply also to flanged sections when fixed as to slope only or when fixed as to slope and roll but not as to flange bending. If the flanges are fixed, however, the additional torsional stiffness contributed by the bending resistance of the flanges may appreciably affect the value and distribution of twisting and bending moments, and the flange stresses caused by the secondary bending may exceed the primary bending stresses. A method applicable to this case is given in Refs. 46 and 66, which include coefficients that facilitate solution and a bibliography relevant to this problem. Approximate results (judging from agreement secured with such test data as are available) can be secured by ignoring the effect of secondary bending on torsional stiffness (*i.e.*, by using the equations given for flangeless sections) and by computing the stress due to the secondary bending by Eq. 6, Art. 51, taking for l half the length from the concentrated load to the nearest support (in the case of concentrated loading) or one-fourth the span (in the case of distributed loading).

46. Circular Rings and Arches.—In large pipe lines, tanks, aircraft, and submarines the circular ring is an important structural element, and for correct design it is often necessary to calculate the stresses and deflections produced in such a ring under various conditions of loading and support. The circular arch of uniform section is often employed in light building construction and finds other applications.

A closed circular ring may be regarded as a statically indeterminate beam, and analyzed as such by Eqs. 6, 8, and 9 of Art. 32. In Table VIII are given formulas thus derived for the bending moments, tensions, shears, and horizontal and vertical deflections of rings loaded and supported in various ways.[1] By superposition, these formulas can be combined so as to cover almost any condition of loading and support likely to occur. The table also gives formulas for the end thrusts, moments, and

[1] Many of the formulas here given were taken (with some modification of notation) from Formulas for the Stress Analysis of Circular Rings in a Monocoque Fuselage, by R. A. Miller and K. D. Wood, *Nat. Adv. Comm. Aeron., Tech. Note* 462, and from Stress Coefficients for Large Horizontal Pipes, by J. M. Paris, *Eng. News-Record,* Vol. 87, No. 19, November, 1921.

TABLE VIII.—FORMULAS FOR CIRCULAR RINGS AND ARCHES

M_1, T_1, V_1, M, T, and V are positive when as shown, negative when reversed. All applied forces and couples are positive when as shown, negative when reversed. The following notation is employed: E = modulus of elasticity (lb. per sq. in.); I = moment of inertia of ring cross section (in.^{4}); W or F as shown = applied load or reaction (lb.); w = applied load (lb. per lin. in.); k = weight of contained liquid (lb. per cu. in.); $z = \sin x$, $u = \cos x$; $s = \sin \theta$, $c = \cos \theta$; $n = \sin \phi$, $e = \cos \phi$; $p = \sin \beta$, $q = \cos \beta$. All angles in radians, distances in inches, forces in pounds, moments in inch-pounds. $+D_x$ or $+D_y$ means increase, $-D_x$ or $-D_y$ means decrease in diameters. $+\Delta R$ means increase, $-\Delta R$ means decrease, in upper half of vertical diameter.

Loading, support, and case number	Formulas for bending moment M, circumferential tension T, radial shear V at angular distance x from bottom of ring and for D_x, change in horizontal diameter, and D_y, change in vertical diameter
1.	$M = WR\left(0.3183 - \frac{1}{2}z\right)$ Max $+M = 0.3183\ WR$ at $x = 0$ Max $-M = -0.1817\ WR$ at $x = \frac{\pi}{2}$ $T = -\frac{1}{2}Wz$ $V = -\frac{1}{2}Wu$ $D_x = +0.137\frac{WR^3}{EI}$ $D_y = -0.149\frac{WR^3}{EI}$ For greater accuracy when the ring is relatively thick, multiply D_x by k_x and D_y by k_y, where k_x and k_y are corrective factors that depend on the ratio of outer radius R_o to inner radius R_i and have following values: R_o/R_i = 1.3, 1.4, 1.5, 1.6, 1.7, 1.8, 1.9 k_x = 1.05, 1.115, 1.175, 1.225, 1.275, 1.325, 1.360 k_y = 1.03, 1.055, 1.090, 1.114, 1.155, 1.180, 1.225 (Ref. 68)
2.	$(x = 0$ to $x = \theta)$ $M = WR[0.3183(s - c\theta + u\theta - usc) - u + c]$ $T = W[0.3183u(\theta - sc) - u]$ $V = W[0.3183z(sc - \theta) + z]$ $(x = \theta$ to $x = \pi)$ $M = WR[0.3183(s - c\theta + u\theta - usc)]$ $T = W[0.3183u(\theta - sc)]$ $V = W[0.3183z(sc - \theta)]$ $D_x = \frac{WR^3}{EI}\left[0.6366(s - c\theta) + \frac{1}{2}(sc - \theta)\right]$ $D_y = \frac{WR^3}{EI}\left[0.6366(s - c\theta) + c + \frac{1}{2}s^2 - 1\right]$ $\Delta R = \frac{WR^3}{EI}\left[0.3183\left(s - c\theta + \frac{1}{2}\theta - \frac{1}{2}sc\right) - \frac{1}{2}s + \frac{1}{2}\theta c\right]$ when $\theta < 90°$
3. Ring under two equal and opposite localized couples M_0	$\left(x = 0 \text{ to } x = \frac{\pi}{2}\right) M = M_0\left(0.6366u - \frac{1}{2}\right)$ $\left(x = \frac{\pi}{2} \text{ to } x = \pi\right) M = M_0\left(0.6366u + \frac{1}{2}\right)$ Max $+M = +\frac{1}{2}M_0$ just above M_0 Max $-M = -\frac{1}{2}M_0$ just below M_0 $(x = 0$ to $x = \pi)$ $T = \frac{M_0}{R}(0.6366u)$, $V = -\frac{M_0}{R}(0.6366z)$ $D_x = 0$ $D_y = 0$ $\Delta R = \frac{M_0R^2}{EI}(0.0329)$

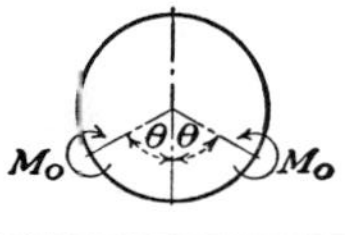

$V = \frac{M_0}{R}(0.6366zs)$ $\qquad$ $V = -\frac{M_0}{R}(0.6366zs)$

$D_x = \frac{M_0R^2}{EI}(0.6366\theta - s)$

$D_y = \frac{M_0R^2}{EI}(0.6366\theta + c - 1) \qquad \Delta R = \frac{M_0R^2}{EI}(0.3183s - 0.1817\theta) \qquad \text{when } \theta < 90°$

5.

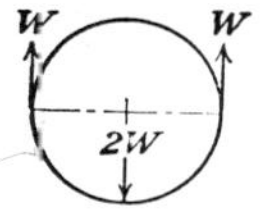

$\left(x = 0 \text{ to } x = \frac{\pi}{2}\right) M = WR(0.3183u + z - 0.8183)$ $\qquad$ $\left(x = \frac{\pi}{2} \text{ to } x = \pi\right) M = WR(0.1817 + 0.3183u)$

$T = W(0.3183u + z)$ $\qquad$ $T = W(0.3183u)$

$V = W(u - 0.3183z)$ $\qquad$ $V = -W(0.3183z)$

$D_x = \frac{WR^3}{EI}(-0.1366)$

$D_y = \frac{WR^3}{EI}(0.1488) \qquad \Delta R = \frac{WR^3}{EI}(0.0554)$

6.

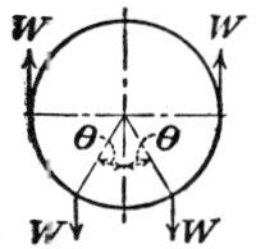

$(x = 0 \text{ to } x = \theta) M = WR[0.3183(uc^2 - s\theta - c) + s - \tfrac{1}{2}]$ $\qquad$ $\left(x = \theta \text{ to } x = \frac{\pi}{2}\right) M = WR[0.3183(uc^2 - s\theta - c) + z - \tfrac{1}{2}]$

$\left(x = \frac{\pi}{2} \text{ to } x = \pi\right) M = WR[0.3183(uc^2 - s\theta - c) + \tfrac{1}{2}]$

$T = W(0.3183uc^2)$ $\qquad$ $T = W(0.3183uc^2 + z)$ $\qquad$ $T = W(0.3183uc^2)$

$V = -W(0.3183zc^2)$ $\qquad$ $V = W(u - 0.3183zc^2)$ $\qquad$ $V = -W(0.3183zc^2)$

$D_x = \frac{WR^3}{EI}\left[\frac{1}{2}(s^2 + 1) - 0.6366(s\theta + c)\right]$

$D_y = \frac{WR^3}{EI}\left[s - \frac{1}{2}(sc + \theta) - 0.6366(s\theta + c) + 0.7854\right] \qquad \Delta R = \frac{WR^3}{EI}\left[\frac{c^2}{2\pi} + 0.1817(c + \theta s) - 0.2854\right]$

7.

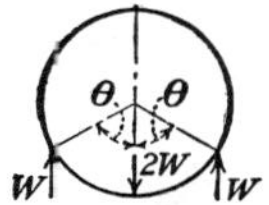

$(x = 0 \text{ to } x = \theta)\ M = WR[0.3183(s\theta + c + us^2 - 1) - s + z]$ $\qquad$ $(x = \theta \text{ to } x = \pi)\ M = WR[0.3183(s\theta + c + us^2 - 1)]$

$T = W(0.3183us^2 + z)$ $\qquad$ $T = W(0.3183us^2)$

$V = W(u - 0.3183zs^2)$ $\qquad$ $V = -W(0.3183zs^2)$

$D_x = \frac{WR^3}{EI}\left[\frac{1}{2}(s^2 + 2) + 0.6366(s\theta + c - 1) - 2s\right] \text{ when } \theta > 90° \qquad Dx = \frac{WR^3}{EI}\left[0.6366(s\theta + c - 1) - \frac{1}{2}s^2\right] \text{ when } \theta < 90°$

$D_y = \frac{WR^3}{EI}\left[\frac{1}{2}(sc + \theta) + 0.6366(s\theta + c - 1) - s\right] \qquad \Delta R = \frac{WR^3}{EI}\left[1.6366(c + \theta s) - \pi s + cs + \theta - \frac{c^2}{\pi} - 0.8891\right]$

8.

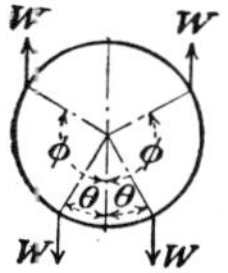

$(x = 0 \text{ to } x = \theta)\ M = WR[0.3183(n\phi + e - s\theta - c - us^2 + un^2) - n + s]$ $\qquad$ $(x = \theta \text{ to } x = \phi)\ M = WR[0.3183(n\phi + e - s\theta - c - us^2 + un^2) - n + z]$

$T = W[0.3183u(n^2 - s^2) + z]$

$V = W[0.3183z(s^2 - n^2) + u]$

$T = W[0.3183u(n^2 - s^2)]$

$V = W[0.3183z(s^2 - n^2)]$

$(x = \phi \text{ to } x = \pi)\ M = WR[0.3183(n\phi + e - s\theta - c - us^2 + un^2)]$

$T = W[0.3183u(n^2 - s^2)]$

$V = W[0.3183z(s^2 - n^2)]$

$D_x = \frac{WR^3}{EI}\left[\frac{1}{2}(s^2 + n^2) + 0.6366(n\phi + e - s\theta - c) + 1 - 2n\right] \qquad \Delta R = \frac{WR^3}{EI}[0.1592(c^2 + e^2) + 0.8183(e + \phi n)$

$D_y = \frac{WR^3}{EI}\left[\frac{1}{2}(ne + \phi - sc - \theta) + 0.6366(n\phi + e - s\theta - c) + s - n\right] \qquad + 0.1817(c + \theta s) - 0.5(\pi n - \phi - en) - 0.7854]$

TABLE VIII.—FORMULAS FOR CIRCULAR RINGS AND ARCHES.—(*Continued*)

Loading, support and case number	Formulas for bending moment M, circumferential tension T, radial shear V at angular distance x from bottom of ring and for D_x, change in horizontal diameter, and D_y, change in vertical diameter
9. Ring under any number of equal radial forces equally spaced	$(x = 0 \text{ to } x = \theta)\ M = \frac{1}{2}WR\left(\frac{u}{s} - \frac{1}{\theta}\right)$; Max + $M = \frac{1}{2}WR\left(\frac{1}{s} - \frac{1}{\theta}\right)$ at $x = 0, 2\theta, 4\theta$, etc. Max − $M = -\frac{1}{2}WR\left(\frac{1}{\theta} - \cot\theta\right)$ at each load Max $T = \frac{1}{2}W\left(\frac{1}{s}\right)$ at $x = 0, 2\theta$, etc. $T = \frac{1}{2}W\cot\theta$ at loads. Radial displacement of each load point $= \frac{WR^3}{2EI}\left[\frac{1}{s^2}\left(\frac{1}{2}\theta + \frac{1}{2}sc\right) - \frac{1}{\theta}\right]$ outward Radial displacement at $x = 0, 2\theta, 4\theta$, etc. $= \frac{WR^3}{4EI}\left(\frac{2}{\theta} - \frac{1}{s} - \theta\frac{c}{s^2}\right)$ inward
10.	$M_1 = wR^2[\frac{1}{4} + \frac{1}{2}s^2 + 0.3183(s - \frac{1}{2}\theta s^2 - \frac{1}{3}s^3 - \frac{3}{4}sc - \frac{1}{4}\theta)]$ $T_1 = -0.1061wRs^3$ $(x = 0 \text{ to } x = \theta)\ M = M_1 - wR^2[sz - 0.1061s^3(1-u)]$ $T = -wR(0.1061s^3u + sz)$ $V = wR(0.1061s^3z - su)$ $(x = \theta \text{ to } x = \pi)\ M = M_1 + wR^2[0.1061s^3(1-u) - \frac{1}{2}(s^2 + z^2)]$ $T = -wR(0.1061s^3u + z^2)$ $V = wR(0.1061s^3z - zu)$ $D_x = \frac{2wR^4}{EI}\left[\frac{1}{4} - \frac{1}{2}s + \frac{1}{2}s^2 - \frac{1}{12}s^3 - 0.3183\left(\frac{1}{4}\theta + \frac{3}{4}sc + \frac{1}{2}\theta s^2 - s\right)\right]$ $D_y = \frac{2wR^4}{EI}\left[\frac{1}{12} + \frac{1}{4}s^2 - \frac{1}{12}s^2c - \frac{1}{4}\theta s - \frac{1}{6}c - 0.3183\left(\frac{1}{2}\theta s^2 + \frac{3}{4}sc + \frac{1}{4}\theta - s\right)\right]$ $\Delta R = \frac{wR^4}{EI}\left[0.3094 + 0.6037s + \frac{\pi}{4}s^2 - \frac{1}{3}c - 0.6132sc - \frac{1}{6}s^2c - 0.2046\theta - \frac{1}{2}\theta s - 0.4092\theta s^2 - \frac{1}{6\pi}s^3\right]$
11.	$M_1 = wR^2[0.3183(\frac{1}{2}\theta + \theta s^2 + \frac{3}{2}sc) - \frac{1}{2}s^2]$ $T_1 = 0$ $(x = 0 \text{ to } x = \theta)\ M = M_1 - wR^2(\frac{1}{2}z^2)$ $T = -wRz^2$ $V = -wRzu$ $(x = \theta \text{ to } x = \pi - \theta)\ M = M_1 - wR^2(sz - \frac{1}{2}s^2)$ $T = -wRsz$ $V = -wRsu$ $D_x = -\frac{wR^4}{EI}\left[s + \frac{1}{3}s^3 - 0.3183(\theta + 3sc + 2\theta s^2)\right]$ $D_y = -\frac{wR^4}{EI}\left[-0.3183(2\theta s^2 + 3sc + \theta) + s^2 - \theta s + \frac{1}{2}\pi s + \frac{1}{3}c^3 + \frac{2}{3} - c\right]$
12.	$M_1 = 0.305wR^2$ $T_1 = -wR(0.02653)$ $\left(x = 0 \text{ to } x = \frac{\pi}{2}\right)\ M = M_1 - T_1R(1-u) - \frac{1}{2}wR^2z$ $T = T_1u - \frac{1}{2}wRz$ $V = -T_1z - \frac{1}{2}wRu$ $\left(x = \frac{\pi}{2} \text{ to } x = \pi\right)\ M = M_1 - T_1R(1-u) - \frac{1}{2}wR^2z - \frac{1}{6}wR^2(1-z)^3$ $T = T_1u - \frac{1}{2}wRz + \frac{1}{2}wR(1-z)^2z$ $V = -T_1z - \frac{1}{2}wRu + \frac{1}{2}wR(1-z)^2u$ $D_x = +\frac{0.1228wR^4}{EI}$ $D_y = \frac{0.1315wR^4}{}$

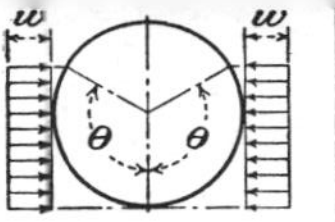	$T = T_1u + wR(1-u)u$ $V = -T_1z - wR(1-u)z$	$T = T_1u + wR(1-c)u$ $V = -T_1z - wR(1-c)z$
14. 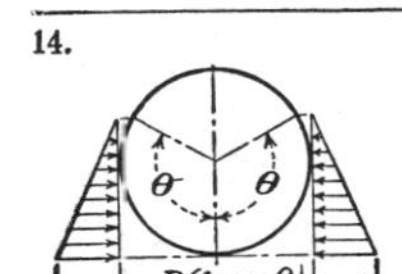	$M_1 = wR^3[0.3183(\frac{1}{3}\theta + \frac{1}{9}s - \frac{1}{4}\theta c - \frac{13}{24}sc + \frac{11}{36}sc^2 + \frac{1}{2}\theta c^2 - \frac{1}{12}sc^3 - \frac{1}{6}\theta c^3) - \frac{1}{6}(1-c)^3]$ $(x = 0$ to $x = \theta)$ $M = M_1 - T_1R(1-u) + wR^3[\frac{1}{6}(1-u)^3 - \frac{1}{2}(1-c)(1-u)^2]$ $T = T_1u + wR^2[\frac{1}{2}(1-2c+u)(1-u)u]$ $V = -T_1z - wR^2[\frac{1}{2}(1-2c+u)(1-u)z]$	$T_1 = wR^2[0.3183(\frac{1}{3}\theta + \frac{1}{2}\theta c^2 - \frac{13}{24}sc - \frac{1}{12}sc^3) - \frac{1}{2}(1-c)^2]$ $(x = \theta$ to $x = \pi)$ $M = M_1 - T_1R(1-u) - wR^3[\frac{1}{2}(1-c)^2(\frac{2}{3} + \frac{1}{3}c - u)]$ $T = T_1u + wR^2[\frac{1}{2}u(1-c)^2]$ $V = -T_1z - wR^2[\frac{1}{2}z(1-c)^2]$
15. 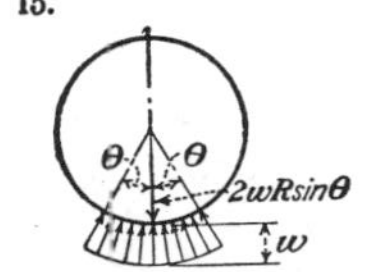	$M_1 = wR^2[c - 0.3183(\theta c - \theta) - 1]$ $\quad T_1 = wR[0.3183(s - \theta c) + c - 1]$ $(x = 0$ to $x = \theta)$ $M = M_1 - T_1R(1-u) - wR^2(1-u-sz)$ $T = T_1u + wR(sz + u - 1)$ $V = -T_1z + wR(su - z)$ $D_x = \frac{2wR^4}{EI}\left[\frac{1}{4}\theta c + 0.3183\theta - 0.5683s\right]$ when $\theta < \frac{\pi}{2}$ $D_y = \frac{2wR^4}{EI}\left[\frac{1}{4}\theta s + 0.3183\theta + \frac{1}{2}c - 0.3183s - \frac{1}{2}\right]$	$(x = \theta$ to $x = \pi)$ $M = M_1 - T_1R(1-u) - wR^2(cu - u)$ $T = T_1u + wR(u - cu)$ $V = -T_1z + wR(cz - z)$
16. 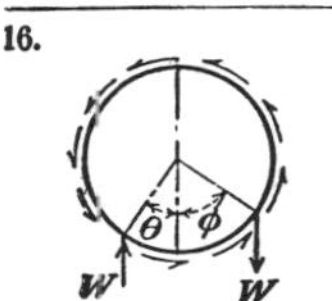	$(x = 0$ to $x = \theta)$ $M = WR\{0.15915[s\theta + c - n\phi - e + u(s^2 - n^2) - z(sc + \theta + ne + \phi) - x(s + n)] - \frac{1}{2}(s - n) + z\}$ $(x = \theta$ to $x = 2\pi - \phi)$ $M = WR\{0.15915[s\theta + c - n\phi - e + u(s^2 - n^2) - z(sc + \theta + ne + \phi) - x(s + n)] + \frac{1}{2}(s + n)\}$ $(x = 2\pi - \phi$ to $2\pi)$ $M = WR\{0.15915[s\theta + c - n\phi - e + u(s^2 - n^2) - z(sc + \theta + ne + \phi) - x(s + n)] + \frac{1}{2}(s + 3n) + z\}$ $(x = 0$ to $x = \theta$ and $x = 2\pi - \phi$ to $x = 2\pi)$ $T = W[0.15915(us^2 - un^2 - zsc - z\theta - zne - z\phi) + z]$ $(x = \theta$ to $x = 2\pi - \phi)$ $T = W[0.15915(us^2 - un^2 - zsc - z\theta - zne - z\phi)]$	$V = W[0.15915(-s - n - zs^2 + zn^2 - usc - u\theta - une - u\phi) + u]$ $V = W[0.15915(-s - n - zs^2 + zn^2 - usc - u\theta - une - u\phi)]$
17. Ring under localized couple M_0 and uniform tangential shear of $(M_0 \div 2\pi R^2)$ lb. per linear in. 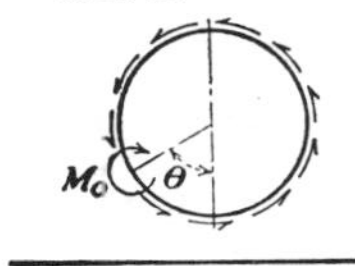	$(x = 0$ to $x = \theta)$ $M = M_0[0.3183(us - zc + \frac{1}{2}\theta - \frac{1}{2}x) - \frac{1}{2}]$ $T = -\frac{M_0}{R}[0.318\ (zc - us)]$ $V = -\frac{M_0}{R}\left[0.3183\left(zs + uc + \frac{1}{2}\right)\right]$	$(x = \theta$ to $x = 2\pi)$ $M = M_0[0.3183(us - zc + \frac{1}{2}\theta - \frac{1}{2}x) + \frac{1}{2}]$ $T = -\frac{M_0}{R}[0.3183(zc - us)]$ $V = -\frac{M_0}{R}\left[0.3183\left(zs + uc + \frac{1}{2}\right)\right]$

TABLE VIII.—FORMULAS FOR CIRCULAR RINGS AND ARCHES.—(*Continued*)

Loading, support and case number	Formulas for bending moment M, circumferential tension T, radial shear V at angular distance x from bottom of ring and for D_x, change in horizontal diameter, and D_y, change in vertical diameter
18. Ring supported at base and loaded by own weight of w lb. per linear in.	$M = wR^2(1 + \frac{1}{2}u - \pi z + xz)$ Max $+M = M_1 = \frac{3}{2}wR^2$ Max $-M = -0.642wR^2$ at $x = 1.3$ rad (74.6°) $T = wR(xz - \frac{1}{2}u - \pi z)$ $V = wR(xu + \frac{1}{2}z - \pi u)$ $D_x = \frac{wR^4}{EI}(0.4292)$ $D_y = -\frac{wR^4}{EI}(0.4674)$ $\Delta R = -\frac{wR^4}{EI}(0.18765)$
19. Ring symmetrically supported and loaded by own weight of w lb. per linear in.	$M_1 = wR^2(\frac{1}{2} + c + \theta s - \pi s + s^2)$ $T_1 = wR(s^2 - \frac{1}{2})$ $(x = 0$ to $x = \theta)$ $M = M_1 - T_1R(1 - u) + wR^2(xz + u - 1)$ $T = T_1u + wRxz$ $V = -T_1z + wRxu$ $(x = \theta$ to $x = \pi)$ $M = M_1 - T_1R(1 - u) + wR^2(xz + u - 1 - \pi z + \pi s)$ $T = T_1u + wR(xz - \pi z)$ $V = -T_1z + wR(xu - \pi u)$ $D_x = \frac{2wR^4}{EI}\left[c + \theta s - \frac{1}{4}\pi(1 + s^2)\right]$ $D_y = \frac{wR^4}{EI}\left[-2.4674 + \frac{1}{2}\pi(sc + \theta - 2s) + 2(\theta s + c)\right]$ $\Delta R = \frac{wR^4}{EI}\left[0.38315 - 0.5708(c + \theta s) + \frac{1}{2}s^2\right]$
20. 1-in. segment of pipe filled with liquid of specific weight k lb. per cu. in. and supported at base	$M_1 = \frac{3}{4}kR^3$ $T_1 = \frac{5}{4}kR^2$ Max $+M = M_1$ Max $-M = -0.321kR^3$ at $x = 1.3$ rad (74.6°) $M = kR^3(\frac{1}{2} + \frac{1}{4}u - \frac{1}{2}\pi z + \frac{1}{2}xz)$ $T = kR^2(1 + \frac{1}{4}u - \frac{1}{2}\pi z + \frac{1}{2}xz)$ $V = kR^2(\frac{1}{2}xu + \frac{1}{4}z - \frac{1}{2}\pi u)$ $D_x = \frac{kR^5}{EI}(0.2146)$ $D_y = -\frac{kR^5}{EI}(0.2337)$ $\Delta R = -\frac{kR^5}{EI}(0.093825)$

of specific weight k lb. per cu. in. and supported at base

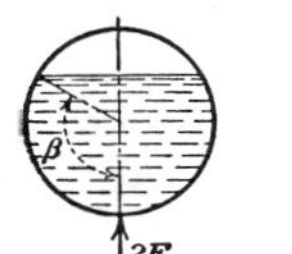

$$T = T_1u - Fz + kR^2(\tfrac{1}{2}xz - q + qu) \qquad T = T_1u - Fz + kR^2[\tfrac{1}{2}z(\beta - pq) + u(q - q^2 - \tfrac{1}{2}p^2)]$$
$$V = -T_1z - Fu + kR^2(\tfrac{1}{2}xu + \tfrac{1}{2}z - qz) \qquad V = -T_1z - Fu + kR^2[\tfrac{1}{2}u(\beta - pq) - z(q - q^2 - \tfrac{1}{2}p^2)]$$

When $\beta < \frac{1}{2}\pi$: $D_x = \dfrac{kR^5}{EI}\left[\dfrac{2}{\pi}(\beta q - p) + 0.6933(\beta - pq) - \dfrac{1}{4}\beta p^2\right]$

When $\beta > \frac{1}{2}\pi$: $D_x = \dfrac{kR^5}{EI}\left[\dfrac{2}{\pi}(\beta q - p) - 0.5567(\beta - pq) - 2q + \dfrac{1}{4}\beta p^2 + \dfrac{1}{4}\pi q^2 + \dfrac{3}{8}\pi\right]$

$$D_y = \frac{kR^5}{EI}\left[\frac{1}{\pi}(2\beta q + \beta - pq - 2p) - \frac{5}{8}p^2 - q + \frac{1}{4}\beta pq - \frac{1}{8}\beta^2 + 1\right]$$

$$\Delta R = \frac{kR^5}{EI}\left[\frac{1}{4\pi}\beta p^2 + 0.1825(\beta - pq) + 0.8183(\beta q - p) - \frac{\pi}{2}q + \frac{7}{8}q^2 + \frac{1}{4}\beta pq - \frac{1}{8}\beta^2 + 0.6916\right] \text{ when } \beta > 90^\circ$$

22. 1-in. segment of pipe filled with liquid of specific weight k lb. per cu. in. and supported symmetrically along two elements

½kπR² ½kπR²

$$M_1 = kR^3\left(\frac{1}{4} - \frac{\pi}{2}s + \frac{1}{2}\theta s + \frac{1}{2}c + \frac{1}{2}s^2\right) \qquad T_1 = kR^2(\tfrac{1}{2}s^2 + \tfrac{5}{4})$$

$(x = 0 \text{ to } x = \theta)$
$$M = kR^3(\tfrac{1}{4}u + \tfrac{1}{2}xz - \tfrac{1}{2}\pi s + \tfrac{1}{2}\theta s + \tfrac{1}{2}c + \tfrac{1}{2}us^2)$$
$$T = kR^2(1 + \tfrac{1}{4}u + \tfrac{1}{2}xz + \tfrac{1}{2}us^2)$$
$$V = kR^2(\tfrac{1}{2}xu + \tfrac{1}{4}z - \tfrac{1}{2}zs^2)$$

$(x = \theta \text{ to } x = \pi)$
$$M = kR^3(\tfrac{1}{4}u - \tfrac{1}{2}\pi z + \tfrac{1}{2}xz + \tfrac{1}{2}\theta s + \tfrac{1}{2}c + \tfrac{1}{2}us^2)$$
$$T = kR^2(1 + \tfrac{1}{4}u - \tfrac{1}{2}\pi z + \tfrac{1}{2}xz + \tfrac{1}{2}us^2)$$
$$V = kR^2(\tfrac{1}{2}xu + \tfrac{1}{4}z - \tfrac{1}{2}\pi u - \tfrac{1}{2}zs^2)$$

$$D_x = \frac{kR^5}{EI}\left[\theta s + c - \frac{1}{4}\pi(1 + s^2)\right]$$

$$D_y = -\frac{kR^5}{EI}\left[\frac{1}{4}\pi(2s - sc - \theta) - c - \theta s + \frac{1}{8}\pi^2\right]$$

$$\Delta R = \frac{kR^5}{2EI}\left[1 + c + s\left(\theta + \frac{1}{2}s\right) - \frac{\pi}{2}\left(\frac{\pi}{8} + \theta s + c\right)\right]$$

23. 1-in. segment of pipe partly filled with liquid of specific weight k lb. per cu. in. and supported symmetrically along two elements

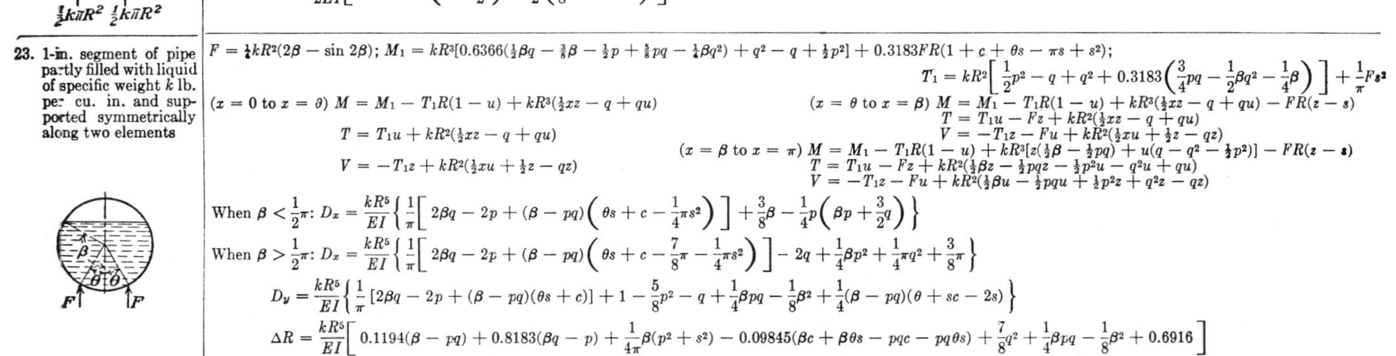

$$F = \tfrac{1}{4}kR^2(2\beta - \sin 2\beta); \quad M_1 = kR^3[0.6366(\tfrac{1}{2}\beta q - \tfrac{3}{8}\beta - \tfrac{1}{2}p + \tfrac{5}{8}pq - \tfrac{1}{4}\beta q^2) + q^2 - q + \tfrac{1}{2}p^2] + 0.3183FR(1 + c + \theta s - \pi s + s^2);$$

$$T_1 = kR^2\left[\frac{1}{2}p^2 - q + q^2 + 0.3183\left(\frac{3}{4}pq - \frac{1}{2}\beta q^2 - \frac{1}{4}\beta\right)\right] + \frac{1}{\pi}Fs^2$$

$(x = 0 \text{ to } x = \theta)$
$$M = M_1 - T_1R(1 - u) + kR^3(\tfrac{1}{2}xz - q + qu)$$
$$T = T_1u + kR^2(\tfrac{1}{2}xz - q + qu)$$
$$V = -T_1z + kR^2(\tfrac{1}{2}xu + \tfrac{1}{2}z - qz)$$

$(x = \theta \text{ to } x = \beta)$
$$M = M_1 - T_1R(1 - u) + kR^3(\tfrac{1}{2}xz - q + qu) - FR(z - s)$$
$$T = T_1u - Fz + kR^2(\tfrac{1}{2}xz - q + qu)$$
$$V = -T_1z - Fu + kR^2(\tfrac{1}{2}xu + \tfrac{1}{2}z - qz)$$

$(x = \beta \text{ to } x = \pi)$
$$M = M_1 - T_1R(1 - u) + kR^3[z(\tfrac{1}{2}\beta - \tfrac{1}{2}pq) + u(q - q^2 - \tfrac{1}{2}p^2)] - FR(z - s)$$
$$T = T_1u - Fz + kR^2(\tfrac{1}{2}\beta z - \tfrac{1}{2}pqz - \tfrac{1}{2}p^2u - q^2u + qu)$$
$$V = -T_1z - Fu + kR^2(\tfrac{1}{2}\beta u - \tfrac{1}{2}pqu + \tfrac{1}{2}p^2z + q^2z - qz)$$

When $\beta < \frac{1}{2}\pi$: $D_x = \dfrac{kR^5}{EI}\left\{\dfrac{1}{\pi}\left[2\beta q - 2p + (\beta - pq)\left(\theta s + c - \dfrac{1}{4}\pi s^2\right)\right] + \dfrac{3}{8}\beta - \dfrac{1}{4}p\left(\beta p + \dfrac{3}{2}q\right)\right\}$

When $\beta > \frac{1}{2}\pi$: $D_x = \dfrac{kR^5}{EI}\left\{\dfrac{1}{\pi}\left[2\beta q - 2p + (\beta - pq)\left(\theta s + c - \dfrac{7}{8}\pi - \dfrac{1}{4}\pi s^2\right)\right] - 2q + \dfrac{1}{4}\beta p^2 + \dfrac{1}{4}\pi q^2 + \dfrac{3}{8}\pi\right\}$

$$D_y = \frac{kR^5}{EI}\left\{\frac{1}{\pi}[2\beta q - 2p + (\beta - pq)(\theta s + c)] + 1 - \frac{5}{8}p^2 - q + \frac{1}{4}\beta pq - \frac{1}{8}\beta^2 + \frac{1}{4}(\beta - pq)(\theta + sc - 2s)\right\}$$

$$\Delta R = \frac{kR^5}{EI}\left[0.1194(\beta - pq) + 0.8183(\beta q - p) + \frac{1}{4\pi}\beta(p^2 + s^2) - 0.09845(\beta c + \beta\theta s - pqc - pq\theta s) + \frac{7}{8}q^2 + \frac{1}{4}\beta pq - \frac{1}{8}\beta^2 + 0.6916\right]$$

TABLE VIII.—FORMULAS FOR CIRCULAR RINGS AND ARCHES.—(*Continued*)

Loading, support and case number	Formulas for bending moment M, circumferential tension T, radial shear V at angular distance x from bottom of ring and for D_x, change in horizontal diameter and D_y, change in vertical diameter
24. Bulkhead or supporting ring in pipe, supported at sides and carrying total load W transferred by tangential shear of s lb. per linear in. distributed as shown $\frac{W}{2}$ $\frac{W}{2}$ $s = \frac{W \sin x}{\pi R}$	$M_1 = -0.01132WR$ $T_1 = -0.07958W$; Max $+ M = 0.01456WR$ at $x = 1.166$ rad (66.8°); Max $- M = -0.01456WR$ at $x = 1.975$ rad (113.2°); M at $x = -M$ at $(\pi - x)$; $M = 0$ at $x = \frac{\pi}{2}$ $\left(x = 0 \text{ to } x = \frac{\pi}{2}\right) M = WR\left(0.23868u + 0.15915xz - \frac{1}{4}\right)$ $T = W(0.15915xz - 0.07958u)$ $V = W(0.15915xu - 0.07958z)$ $\left(x = \frac{\pi}{2} \text{ to } x = \pi\right) M = WR\left(0.23868u + 0.15915xz - \frac{1}{2}z + \frac{1}{4}\right)$ $T = W(0.15915xz - 0.07958u - \frac{1}{2}z)$ $V = W(0.15915xu - 0.07958z - \frac{1}{2}u)$ $D_x = 0$ $D_y = 0$
25. Same as Case 24 except supported as shown 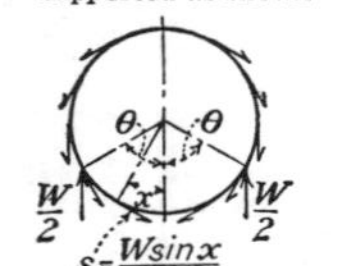	$(x = 0 \text{ to } x = \theta)$ $M = WR[0.23868u - \frac{1}{2}s + 0.15915(xz + \theta s + c - uc^2)]$ $T = W[0.15915(xz - uc^2) - 0.07958u]$ $V = W[0.15915(xu - \frac{1}{2}z + zc^2)]$ $(x = \theta \text{ to } x = \pi)$ $M = WR[0.23868u - \frac{1}{2}z + 0.15915(xz + \theta s + c - uc^2)]$ $T = W[0.15915(xz - uc^2) - 0.07958u - \frac{1}{2}z]$ $V = W[0.15915(xu - \frac{1}{2}z + zc^2) - \frac{1}{2}u]$ $D_x = \frac{WR^3}{EI}\left[0.3183(s\theta + c) - \frac{1}{4}(s^2 + 1)\right]$ $D_y = \frac{WR^3}{EI}\left[0.3183(s\theta + c) + \frac{1}{4}(sc + \theta) - \frac{1}{2}s - \frac{\pi}{8}\right]$ $\Delta R = \frac{WR^3}{EI}\left[\frac{1}{\pi}\left(\frac{1}{2}c + \frac{1}{2}\theta s + \frac{1}{4}s^2 + \frac{1}{2}\right) - \frac{1}{4}c - \frac{1}{4}\theta s - \frac{\pi}{32}\right]$ when $\theta < 90°$
26. 1-in. segment of pipe between supports, loaded by own weight of w lb. per linear in. and supported by tangential shear of s lb. per linear in. distributed as shown	All moments $= 0$

Loading, support, and case number	Formulas for end reactions: Circular arch	Formulas for end reactions: Parabolic arch; l = span; f = rise; a = distance load from left end, b from right
27. Ends pinned; concentrated load W at any point ϕ 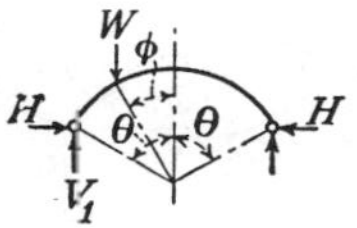	$H = \frac{1}{2}W\left[\frac{s^2 - n^2 - 2c(\theta s - \phi n + c - e) - \alpha(s^2 - n^2)}{\theta - 3sc + 2\theta c^2 + \alpha(\theta + sc)}\right]$ $V_1 = \frac{1}{2}W\left(\frac{s + n}{s}\right)$ $\left(\text{Here } \alpha = \frac{I}{AR^2} \text{ where } A = \text{cross-sectional area}\right)$	$H = W\frac{5b}{8f}\left[1 - 2\left(\frac{b}{l}\right)^2 + \left(\frac{b}{l}\right)^3\right]$ $V_1 = W\frac{b}{l}$ (Ref. 72)
28. Like Case 27 except ends fixed 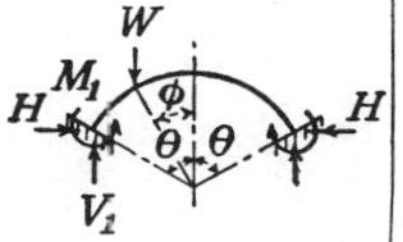	$H = \frac{1}{2}W\left[\frac{\frac{2}{\theta}(se + \phi sn - sc) - s^2 - n^2 - \alpha(s^2 - n^2)}{\theta + sc - \frac{2s^2}{\theta} + \alpha(\theta + sc)}\right]$ $V_1 = \frac{1}{2}W\left(\frac{\theta + \phi - cs + en - 2nc}{\theta - cs}\right)$ $M_1 = V_1Rs + HR\left(\frac{\theta c - s}{\theta}\right) + \frac{1}{2}WR\left(\frac{c - e - \phi n - \theta n}{\theta}\right)$ (α as for Case 27)	$H = \frac{15W}{4}\left(\frac{a^2b^2}{l^3f}\right)$ $V_1 = W\left[1 - \left(\frac{a}{l}\right)^2 - \frac{2a^2b}{l^3}\right]$ $M_1 = Wa\left(\frac{5ab^2}{2l^3} - \frac{b^2}{l^2}\right)$ (Ref. 72)
29. Ends pinned; uniform load w lb. per linear in. 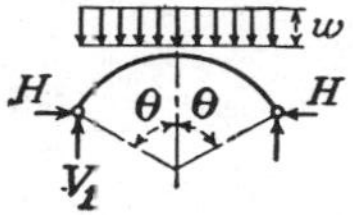	$H = \frac{1}{2}wR\left[\frac{\frac{4}{3}s^3 + \theta c - 2\theta s^2c - sc^2 + 2\alpha(\theta c^2 - \frac{1}{2}\theta - \frac{3}{2}sc)}{2\theta c^2 + \theta - 3sc + \alpha(\theta + sc)}\right]$ $V_1 = wRs$ (α as for Case 27)	$H = \frac{wl^2}{8f}$ $V_1 = \frac{1}{2}wl$ (Ref. 72)
30. Like Case 29 except ends fixed 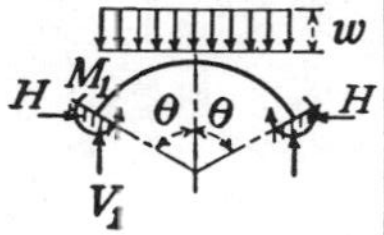	$H = wR\left[\frac{\frac{1}{4}\left(\frac{s^2c}{\theta} - s\right) + \frac{1}{6}s^3 + \alpha\left(\frac{1}{4}\theta - \frac{1}{2}\theta c^2 + \frac{1}{4}sc\right)}{\frac{(\theta - s)^2}{\theta} - \frac{3}{2}\theta + 2s - \frac{1}{2}sc - \alpha\left(\frac{1}{2}\theta + \frac{1}{2}sc\right)}\right]$ $M_1 = wR^2\left(\frac{1}{2}s^2 - \frac{1}{4} + \frac{1}{4}\frac{sc}{\theta}\right) - HR\left(\frac{s}{\theta} - c\right)$ $V_1 = wRs$ (α as for Case 27)	$H = \frac{wl^2}{8f}$ $V_1 = \frac{1}{2}wl$ $M_1 = 0$ (Ref. 72)

TABLE VIII.—FORMULAS FOR CIRCULAR RINGS AND ARCHES.—(*Continued*)

Loading, support, and case number	Formulas for end reactions	
	Circular arch	Parabolic arch; l = span, f = rise; a = distance load from left end, b from right
31. Ends pinned; concentrated load W at any point ϕ	$V = \frac{1}{2} W \left(\frac{n-s}{c}\right)$ $H_1 = W\left(\frac{\pi - \theta - \phi + \pi sn - 3sc - 2\theta s^2 + \pi s^2 - ne - 2se - 2\phi ns}{\pi + 2\pi s^2 - 2\theta - 6sc - 4\theta s^2}\right)$	
32. Like Case 31 except ends fixed	$V = W\left(\frac{2\theta ec + \theta s^2 + \theta n^2 - 2\theta}{2\theta sc - 2\theta^2}\right)$ $H_2 = W\left(\frac{s^2 - \frac{1}{2}\theta en + \phi es - ns - \frac{1}{2}\theta sc - \frac{1}{2}\theta^2 + \frac{1}{2}\theta\phi}{2s^2 - \theta^2 - \theta sc}\right)$ $M_0 = WR\left(\frac{ec + \frac{1}{2}s^2 + \theta ne - \phi ne - sn - e^2 + \frac{1}{2}n^2}{2\theta n}\right) + \frac{H_2R(2sn - 2\theta en) + VR(\theta - sc + 2\theta n^2)}{2\theta n}$	
33. Ends pinned; uniform load w lb. per linear in.	$V = \frac{1}{4} wR \frac{(1-s)^2}{c}$ $H_1 = wR\left[\frac{\pi(\frac{1}{2} - \frac{5}{4}s + s^2 - \frac{3}{2}s^3) + \theta(-1 + \frac{5}{2}s - 2s^2 + 3s^3) - 3sc + \frac{2}{3}c^3 + \frac{11}{2}s^2c}{\pi + 2\pi s^2 - 2\theta - 6sc - 4\theta s^2}\right]$	$V = \frac{1}{2} W \frac{f}{l}$ $H_1 = \frac{5}{7} W$ $(W = wf)$ (Ref. 72)
34. Like Case 33 except ends fixed	$V = wR\left(\frac{4 - 3c - 3s^2 + c^3}{6\theta - 6sc}\right)$ $H_2 = wR\left(\frac{\theta^2 - \frac{1}{6}\theta s + \theta sc - 2s^2 + \frac{1}{2}s^2c - \frac{1}{3}\theta sc^2}{2\theta^2 - 4s^2 + 2\theta sc}\right)$ $M_0 = \frac{1}{4} wR^2\left(\frac{2}{3} - 2\frac{s}{\theta} + \frac{1}{2}\frac{sc}{\theta}\right) - H_2R\left(1 - \frac{s}{\theta}\right)$	$V = \frac{1}{4} W \frac{f}{l}$ $H_2 = \frac{55}{256} W$ $M_1 = \frac{373}{2048} Wf$ $(W = wf)$ (Ref. 72)
35. Circular cantilever with end loading and uniform radial pressure p lb. per linear in.	$M = M_0 + HR[\sin(\theta - x) - s] + VR[\cos(\theta - x) - c] + pR^2(1 - u)$ Vertical deflection $= \frac{1}{EI}\left[M_0R^2(s - \theta c) + VR^3\left(\frac{1}{2}\theta + c^2\theta - \frac{3}{2}sc\right) + HR^3\left(\frac{1}{2} - c + sc\theta + \frac{1}{2}c^2 - s^2\right) + pR^4\left(s + sc - \frac{3}{2}\theta c - \frac{1}{2}s^3 - \frac{1}{2}c^2s\right)\right]$ Horizontal deflection $= \frac{I}{EI}\left[M_0R^2(1 - \theta s - c) + VR^3\left(\frac{1}{2} - c + \theta sc + \frac{1}{2}c^2 - s^2\right) + HR^3\left(-2s + \theta s^2 + \frac{1}{2}\theta + \frac{3}{2}sc\right) + pR^4\left(1 - \frac{3}{2}\theta s + s^2 - c\right)\right]$ Rotation $= \frac{1}{EI}[M_0R\theta + VR^2(s - \theta c) + HR^2(1 - \theta s - c) + pR^3(\theta - s)]$	

vertical reactions for arches. When these are known, the arch becomes statically determinate, and the compression, shear, moment, and deflection at any section can readily be calculated.

The ring formulas are based on the following assumptions: (1) The ring is of uniform cross section. (2) It is of such large radius in comparison with its radial thickness that the deflection theory for straight beams is applicable. (3) Its deflection is due solely to bending, the effect of direct axial tension or compression, and the effect of shear, being negligible. (4) It is nowhere stressed beyond the elastic limit. (5) It is not so severely deformed as to lose its essentially circular shape. (6) In the case of pipes acting as beams between widely spaced supports, the distribution of shear stress across the section of the pipe is in accordance with Eq. 2, and the direction of the resultant shear stress at any point of the cross section is tangential. Some of the arch formulas take into account the effect of axial tension and compression but disregard the effect of shear.

It will be noted that most of the formulas consist of the algebraic sum of a number of terms, each of which may be large in comparison with the end result. For this reason, accurate results will be obtained only when the calculations are made with great care, and all terms should be given to at least four significant figures.

The use of the formulas and the way in which they may be combined by superposition are illustrated in the following examples.

Examples

1. A pipe, diameter 13 ft., thickness $\frac{1}{4}$ in., is supported at intervals of 44 ft. by rings, each ring being supported at the extremities of its horizontal diameter by vertical reactions acting at the centroids of the ring sections. It is required to determine the bending moments in a ring at the bottom, sides, and top, and the maximum bending moment, when the pipe is filled with water.

Solution.—Solution is effected by the formulas for Case 24. Taking the weight of water as 62.4 lb. per cu. ft. and the weight of the shell as 10.2 lb. per sq. ft., the total weight W of 44 ft. of pipe carried by one ring is found to be 382,400 lb. Therefore

(At bottom) $M = M_1 = -0.01132 \times 382{,}400 \times 6\frac{1}{2} \times 12 = -338{,}000$ in.-lb.

$\left(\text{At sides, } x = \frac{\pi}{2}, u = 0, z = 1\right) \quad M = (382{,}400)(78)\left[\left(0.15915 \times \frac{\pi}{2} \times 1\right) - 0.25\right] = 0$

(At top, $x = \pi$, $u = -1$, $z = 0$) $\quad M = 338{,}000$ in.-lb.

(At $x = 66.8°$) $\quad M = +0.01456 \times 382{,}400 \times 78 = +434{,}000$ in.-lb. (maximum positive moment)

(At $x = 113.2°$) $\quad M = -434{,}000$ in.-lb. (maximum negative moment)

By applying the supporting reactions outside the center line of the ring, at a distance a from the centroid of the section, side couples, each equal to $\frac{1}{2}Wa$, would be introduced. The effect of these, found by the formulas for Case 3, would be to reduce the maximum moments, and it can be shown that the optimum condition obtains when $a = 0.04R$.

2. The pipe of Example 1 rests on soft ground, with which it is in contact over 60 deg. of its circumference at the bottom. The supporting pressure of the soil may be assumed to be radial and uniform. It is required to determine the bending moment at the bottom of the pipe.

Solution.—A section of the pipe 1 in. long is considered. The loading may be considered as a combination of Cases 15, 18, and 20, the *assumed* downward center load in Case 15 being equal to the sum of the *assumed* reactions for Cases 20 and 18. This load is therefore simply the weight of a 1-in. length of pipe and water, or 725 lb. We have:

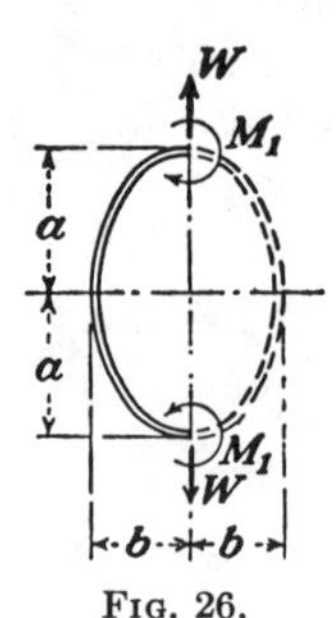

FIG. 26.

Due to weight of pipe ($w = 0.0708$, Case 18):

$$M = M_1 = \frac{3}{2} \times 0.0708 \times 78^2 = +644 \text{ in.-lb.}$$

Due to weight of contained water ($k = 0.0361$, Case 20):

$$M = M_1 = \frac{3}{4} \times 0.0361 \times 78^3 = 12{,}860 \text{ in.-lb.}$$

Due to earth pressure and the reversed reaction, ($\theta = 30° = 0.524$ rad, $c = 0.866$, $2wR \sin\theta = 725$, $w = 9.3$, Case 15):

$$M = (9.3)(78^2)[0.866 - 0.3183(0.4537 - 0.524) - 1] = -6310 \text{ in.-lb.}$$

The resultant bending moment per linear inch at the bottom of the pipe is therefore

$$M = 644 + 12{,}860 - 6310 = +7190 \text{ in.-lb.}$$

47. Elliptical Rings.—For an elliptical ring of semiaxes a and b, under equal and opposite forces W (Fig. 26) the bending moment M_1 at the extremities of the major axis is given by $M_1 = K_1Wa$, and for equal and opposite outward forces applied at the ends of the minor axis the moment M_1 at the ends of the major axis is given by $M_1 = -K_2Wa$, where K_1 and K_2 are coefficients which depend on the ratio a/b and have values as follows:

a/b	1	1.1	1.2	1.3	1.4	1.5	1.6	1.7
K_1	0.318	0.295	0.274	0.255	0.240	0.227	0.216	0.205
K_2	0.182	0.186	0.191	0.195	0.199	0.203	0.206	0.208

a/b	1.8	1.9	2.0	2.1	2.2	2.3	2.4	2.5
K_1	0.195	0.185	0.175	0.167	0.161	0.155	0.150	0.145
K_2	0.211	0.213	0.215	0.217	0.219	0.220	0.222	0.223

Burke (Ref. 43) gives charts by which the moments and tensions in elliptical rings under various conditions of concentrated loading can be found. The tabulated values of K given above were taken from these charts.

Timoshenko (Ref. 3) gives an analysis of an elliptical ring (or other ring with two axes of symmetry) under the action of a uniform outward pressure. This would apply to a tube of elliptical section under internal pressure. For this case $M = Kpa^2$, where M is the bending moment at a section distant x along the ring from the end of the minor axis, p is the outward normal pressure per linear inch, and K is a coefficient that depends on the ratios b/a and x/S, where S is one-quarter of the perimeter of the ring. Values of K are tabulated below. M is positive when it produces tension at the inner surface of the ring.

x/S \ b/a	0.3	0.5	0.6	0.7	0.8	0.9
0	−0.172	−0.156	−0.140	−0.115	−0.085	−0.045
0.1	−0.167	−0.152	−0.135	−0.112	−0.082	−0.044
0.2	−0.150	−0.136	−0.120	−0.098	−0.070	−0.038
0.4	−0.085	−0.073	−0.060	−0.046	−0.030	−0.015
0.6	0.020	0.030	0.030	0.028	0.022	0.015
0.7	0.086	0.090	0.082	0.068	0.050	0.022
0.8	0.160	0.150	0.130	0.105	0.075	0.038
0.9	0.240	0.198	0.167	0.130	0.090	0.046
1.0	0.282	0.218	0.180	0.140	0.095	0.050

Values of M calculated by the above coefficients are correct only for a ring of uniform moment of inertia I; if I is not uniform, then a correction ΔM must be added. This correction is given by

$$\Delta M = -\int_0^x \left(\frac{M}{I}\right) dx \div \int_0^x \frac{dx}{I}$$

The integrals can be evaluated graphically.

Charts for the calculation of moments in elliptical rings under uniform radial loading are presented in Ref. 52, from which the above values of K were taken.

48. Plastic or Ultimate Strength Design.—The foregoing discussion of beams and frames is based for the most part on the assumption of purely elastic action and on the acceptance of maximum fiber stress as the primary criterion of safety. These constitute the basis of *elastic* analysis and design. An alternative and often preferred method of design, applicable to rigid frames and statically indeterminate beams made of materials capable of plastic action, is the method of *plastic* or *ultimate strength* design. It is based on the fact that such a frame or beam cannot deflect indefinitely or collapse until the full plastic moment M_p (see Art. 34) has been developed at each of several critical sections. If it is assumed that the plastic moment—a determinable couple—does indeed act at each such section, then the problem becomes a statically determinate one, and the load corresponding to the collapse condition can be readily calculated.

A simple illustration of the procedure is afforded by the beam of Fig. 27a, corresponding to Case 21 of Table III. Suppose it is desired to determine the maximum value of the load W that the beam can support. It is shown by elastic analysis, and is indeed apparent from inspection, that the maximum bending moments

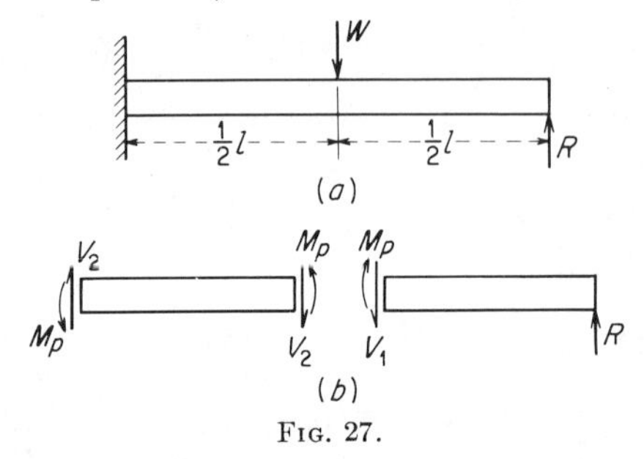

FIG. 27.

occur at the load and at the left end of the beam. The maximum possible value of each such moment is M_p. It is evident that the beam cannot collapse until the moment at each of these points reaches this value. Therefore, when W has reached its maximum value and collapse is imminent, the beam is acted on by the force system represented in Fig. 27b; there is a *plastic hinge* and a known couple M_p at each of the critical sections, and the problem is statically determinate. For equilibrium of the right half, $R = \frac{M_p}{l/2}$ and $V_1 = R$; for equilibrium of the left half, $V_2 = W - R$, and $\left(W - \frac{M_p}{l/2}\right)\frac{l}{2} = 2M_p$, whence $W = \frac{6M_p}{l}$.

If one attempted to predict the collapse load on the basis of elastic analysis, it would be easy to fall into the error of equating the maximum elastic moment $\frac{3}{16}Wl$ at the wall (Table III) to M_p, thus getting $W = \frac{16}{3}M_p/l$. This erroneous procedure fails to take into account the fact that as W increases, and yielding commences and progresses at the wall section, there is a redistribution of moments; the moment at the wall becomes less than $\frac{3}{16}Wl$, and the moment at the load becomes greater than $\frac{5}{32}Wl$, until finally each moment becomes equal to M_p. An important point to note is that although the elastic moments are affected by even a very slight departure from the assumed conditions—perfect fixity at one end and rigid support at the other—the collapse load is not thus affected. So long as the constraints are rigid enough to develop the plastic hinges as indicated, the ultimate load will be the same. Similarly, the method does not require that the beam be uniform in section, although a local reduction in section, leading to the formation of a hinge at some point other than those assumed, would, of course, alter the solution.

This example may, because of its simplicity, give an exaggerated impression of the ease of plastic analysis, but it does indicate that for any indeterminate structure whose strength is determined primarily by resistance to bending, the method is well suited to the determination of ultimate load, and—through the use of a suitable factor of safety—to design. Its accuracy has been proved by good agreement between computed and experimental ultimate loads for a variety of frames. An extended discussion of the procedure is not appropriate here; the interested reader will find an extensive literature on the subject (Refs. 75, 76).

References

1. TIMOSHENKO, S.: "Theory of Elasticity," Engineering Societies Monograph, McGraw-Hill Book Company, 1934.
2. FROCHT, M. M.: A Photoelastic Investigation of Shear and Bending Stresses in Centrally Loaded Simple Beams, *Eng. Bull., Carnegie Inst. Technology,* 1937.

3. TIMOSHENKO, S.: "Strength of Materials," D. Van Nostrand Company, Inc., 1930.
4. BACH, C.: Zur Beigungsfestigkeit des Gusseisens, *Zeits. Vereines Deutscher Ing.*, Vol. 32, p. 1089, 1888.
5. SCHLICK, W. J., and B. A. MOORE: Strength and Elastic Properties of Cast Iron, *Iowa Eng. Exp. Sta., Iowa State College, Bull.* 127, 1930.
6. Symposium on Cast Iron, *Proc. Am. Soc. Testing Materials,* Vol. 33, Part II, p. 115, 1933.
7. ROARK, R. J., R. S. HARTENBERG, and R. Z. WILLIAMS: The Effect of Form and Scale on Strength, *Eng. Exp. Sta., Univ. Wis., Bull.* 82, 1938.
8. NEWLIN, J. A., and G. W. TRAYER: Form Factors of Beams Subjected to Transverse Loading Only, *Nat. Adv. Comm. Aeron., Report* 181, 1924.
9. "Wood Handbook," Forest Products Laboratory, U.S. Dept. of Agriculture.
10. MACKENZIE, J. T., and C. K. DONOHO: A Study of the Effect of Span on the Transverse Test Results of Cast Iron, *Proc. Am. Soc. Testing Materials,* Vol. 37, Part II, 1937.
11. KETCHUM, M. S., and J. O. DRAFFIN: Strength of Light I-beams, *Eng. Exp. Sta. Univ. Ill., Bull.* 241, 1932.
12. WENDT, K. F., and M. O. WITHEY: The Strength of Light Steel Joists, *Eng. Exp. Sta., Univ. Wis., Bull.* 79, 1934.
13. American Institute of Steel Construction, Specifications for the Design, Fabrication and Erection of Structural Steel for Buildings, 1961.
14. YOUNGER, J. E.: "Structural Design of Metal Airplanes," McGraw-Hill Book Company, 1935.
15. LYSE, I., and H. J. GODFREY: Investigation of Web Buckling in Steel Beams, *Trans. Am. Soc. Civil Eng.*, Vol. 100, p. 675, 1935.
16. MOORE, H. F.: The Strength of I-beams in Flexure, *Eng. Exp. Sta., Univ. Ill., Bull.* 68, 1913.
17. DUMONT, C., and H. N. HILL: The Lateral Instability of Deep Rectangular Beams, *Nat. Adv. Comm. Aeron., Tech. Note* 601, 1937.
18. TRAYER, G. W., and H. W. MARCH: Elastic Instability of Members having Sections Common in Aircraft Construction, *Nat. Adv. Comm. Aeron., Report* 382, 1931.
19. NEWLIN, J. A., and G. W. TRAYER: Deflection of Beams with Special Reference to Shear Deformation, *Nat. Adv. Comm. Aeron., Report* 180, 1924.
20. PEARSON, K.: On the Flexure of Heavy Beams Subjected to Continuous Systems of Load, *Quarterly Jour. Pure Appl. Math.*, Vol. 24, p. 63, 1890.
21. TIMOSHENKO, S.: Mathematical Determination of the Modulus of Elasticity, *Mech. Eng.*, Vol. 45, p. 259, 1923.
22. HOLL, D. L.: Analysis of Thin Rectangular Plates Supported on Opposite Edges, *Iowa Eng. Exp. Sta., Iowa State College, Bull.* 129, 1936.
23. WESTERGAARD, H. M.: Computation of Stress Due to Wheel Loads, *Public Roads,* U.S. Dept. of Agriculture, Bureau of Public Roads, Vol. 11, p. 9, March, 1930.
24. MORRIS, C. T.: Concentrated Loads on Slabs, *Ohio State Univ. Eng. Exp. Sta. Bull.* 80, 1933.

25. Kelley, E. F.: Effective Width of Concrete Bridge Slabs Supporting Concentrated Loads, *Public Roads*, U.S. Dept. of Agriculture, Bureau of Public Roads, Vol. 7, No. 1, 1926.
26. MacGregor, C. W.: Deflection of Long Helical Gear Tooth, *Mech. Eng.* Vol. 57, p. 225, 1935.
27. Holl, D. L.: Cantilever Plate with Concentrated Edge Load, *Am. Soc. Mech. Eng. Paper* A-8, *Jour. Appl. Mech.*, Vol. 4, No. 1, 1937.
28. Miller, A. B.: Die mittragende Breite, and Über die mittragende Breite, *Luftfahrtforschung*, Vol. 4, No. 1, 1929.
29. "Penstock Analysis and Stiffener Design," U.S. Dept. of Agriculture, Bureau of Reclamation, Boulder Canyon Project Final Reports, Part V, *Bull.* 5, 1940.
30. Kuhn, P., J. P. Peterson, and L. R. Levin: A Summary of Diagonal Tension, Parts I and II, *Nat. Adv. Comm. Aeron., Tech. Notes* 2661 and 2662, 1952.
31. Schwalbe, W. L. S.: The Center of Torsion for Angle and Channel Sections, *Trans. Am. Soc. Mech. Eng.*, Vol. 54, No. 11, p. 125, 1932.
32. Young, A. W., E. M. Elderton, and K. Pearson: "On the Torsion Resulting from Flexure in Prisms with Cross-sections of Uniaxial Symmetry," Drapers' Co. Research Memoirs, Technical Series VII, 1918.
33. Maurer, E. R., and M. O. Withey: "Strength of Materials," John Wiley & Sons, Inc., 1935.
34. Niles, A. S., and J. S. Newell: "Airplane Structures," John Wiley & Sons, Inc., 1929.
35. Timoshenko, S.: "Theory of Elastic Stability," Engineering Societies Monograph, McGraw-Hill Book Company, 1936.
36. Smith, P. F., and W. R. Longley: "Mathematical Tables and Formulas," John Wiley & Sons, Inc., 1929.
37. Biot, M. A.: The Bending of an Infinite Beam on an Elastic Foundation, *Am. Soc. Mech. Eng. Paper* A-1, *Jour. Appl. Mech.*, Vol. 4, No. 1, March, 1937.
38. Wilson, B. J., and J. F. Quereau: A Simple Method of Determining Stress in Curved Flexural Members, *Univ. Ill. Eng. Exp. Sta., Circ.* 16, 1927.
39. Case, J.: "Strength of Materials," Longmans, Green & Company, 1925.
40. Seely, F. B., and R. V. James: The Plaster-model Method of Determining Stresses Applied to Curved Beams, *Univ. Ill. Eng. Exp. Sta. Bull.* 195, 1929.
41. von Kármán, Th: "Über die Formänderung dünnwandiger Rohre, insbesondere federnder Ausgleichrohre," *Zeits. Vereines Deutscher Ing.*, Vol. 55, p. 1889, 1911.
42. Timoshenko, S.: Bending Stresses in Curved Tubes of Rectangular Cross-section, *Trans. Am. Soc. Mech. Eng.*, Vol. 45, p. 135, 1923.
43. Burke, W. F.: Working Charts for the Stress Analysis of Elliptic Rings, *Nat. Adv. Comm. Aeron., Tech. Note* 444, 1933.
44. Peery, D. J.: "Aircraft Structures," McGraw-Hill Book Company, 1950.

45. SECHLER, E. E., and L. G. DUNN: "Airplane Structural Analysis and Design," John Wiley & Sons, Inc., 1942.
46. MOORMAN, R. B. B.: "Stresses in a Curved Beam under Loads Normal to the Plane of Its Axis," *Iowa Eng. Exp. Sta., Iowa State College, Bull.* 145, 1940.
47. REISSNER, E.: Least Work Solutions of Shear Lag Problems, *Jour. Aeron. Sci.*, Vol. 8, No. 7, p. 284, 1941.
48. HILDEBRAND, F. B., and E. REISSNER: Least-work Analysis of the Problem of Shear Lag in Box Beams, *Nat. Adv. Comm. Aeron., Tech. Note* 893, 1943.
49. WINTER, G.: Stress Distribution in and Equivalent Width of Flanges of Wide, Thin-wall Steel Beams, *Nat. Adv. Comm. Aeron., Tech. Note* 784, 1940.
50. TATE, M. B.: Shear Lag in Tension Panels and Box Beams, *Iowa Eng. Exp. Sta. Iowa State College, Eng. Report* 3, 1950.
51. MANTLE, J. B., and T. J. DOLAN: A Photoelastic Study of Stresses in U-shaped Members, *Soc. Exp. Stress Anal.*, Vol. VI, No. 1, 1948.
52. Stressed Skin Structures, Royal Aeronautical Society, Data Sheets.
53. WHITE, RICHARD N.: Rectangular Plates Subjected to Partial Edge Loads: Their Elastic Stability and Stress Distribution, doctor's dissertation, University of Wisconsin, 1961.
54. CHOW, L., HARRY D. CONWAY, and GEORGE WINTER: Stresses in Deep Beams, *Trans. Am. Soc. Civil Eng.*, Vol. 118, p. 686, 1953.
55. KAAR, P. H.: Stress in Centrally Loaded Deep Beams, *Proc. Soc. Exp. Stress Anal.*, Vol. 15, No. 1, p. 77, 1957.
56. SAAD, S., and A. W. HENDRY: Stresses in a Deep Beam with a Central Concentrated Load, *Exp. Mech., Jour. Soc. Exp. Stress Anal.*, Vol. 18, No. 1, p. 192, June, 1961.
57. JARAMILLO, T. J.: Deflections and Moments Due to a Concentrated Load on a Cantilever Plate of Infinite Length, *Am. Soc. Mech. Eng., Jour. Appl. Mech.*, Vol. 17, No. 1, March, 1950.
58. WELLAUER, E. J., and A. SEIREG: Bending Strength of Gear Teeth by Cantilever-plate Theory, *Am. Soc. Mech. Eng., Jour. Eng. for Industry*, Vol. 82, August, 1960.
59. LITTLE, ROBERT W.: Bending of a Cantilever Plate, master's thesis, University of Wisconsin, 1959.
60. SMALL, N. C.: Bending of a Cantilever Plate Supported from an Elastic Half Space, *Am. Soc. Mech. Eng., Jour. Appl. Mech.*, Vol. 28, No. 3, September, 1961.
61. BLEICH, HANS: "Stress Distribution in the Flanges of Curved T and I Beams," Translation 228, Navy Dept., David W. Taylor Model Basin, 1950.
62. DUNCAN, W. J.: The Flexural Center or Center of Shear, *Jour. Roy. Aeron. Soc.*, Vol. 57, September, 1953.
63. HETENYI, MIKLOS: "Beams on Elastic Foundation," University of Michigan Press, 1946.
64. O'DONNELL, W. J.: The Additional Deflection of a Cantilever Due to the Elasticity of the Support, *Am. Soc. Mech. Eng., Jour. Appl. Mech.*, Vol. 27, No. 3, September, 1960.

65. Fisher, G. P.: Design Charts for Symmetrical Ring Girders, *Am. Soc. Mech. Eng., Jour. Appl. Mech.*, Vol. 24, No. 1, March, 1957.
66. Moorman, R. B. B.: Stresses in a Uniformly Loaded Circular-arc I-beam, *Univ. Missouri Bull., Eng. Ser.* 36, 1947.
67. Hogan, M. B.: *Utah Eng. Exp. Sta., Bulls.* 21, 27, and 31.
68. Blake, Alexander: Deflection of a Thick Ring in Diametral Compression, *Am. Soc. Mech. Eng., Jour. Appl. Mech.*, Vol. 26, No. 2, June, 1959.
69. Volterra, Enrico, and Tandall Chung: Constrained Circular Beam on Elastic Foundations, *Trans. Am. Soc. Civil Eng.*, Vol, 120, 1955, *Paper* 2740.
70. ANC Mil-Hdbk-5, Strength of Metal Aircraft Elements, Armed Forces Supply Support Center, March, 1959.
71. Kleinlogel, A.: "Rigid Frame Formulas," Frederick Ungar Publishing Co., 1958.
72. Leontovich, Valerian: "Frames and Arches," McGraw-Hill Book Company, 1959.
73. Lee, G. C.: A Survey of Literature on the Lateral Instability of Beams, *Bull.* 63 *Welding Research Council*, August, 1960.
74. Kelley, B. W., and R. Pedersen: The Beam Strength of Modern Gear Tooth Design, *Trans. S.A.E.*, Vol. 66, 1950.
75. Beedle, Lyman S.: "Plastic Design of Steel Frames," John Wiley & Sons, Inc., 1958.
76. "The Steel Skeleton," Vol. II, "Plastic Behaviour and Design," Cambridge University Press, 1956.
77. Hiltscher, R.: Stress Distribution around Tunnel Openings of Rectangular Basic Profile with Circular Roof, *Der Bauingenieur*, Vol. 8, 1957.
78. Weigle, R. E., R. R. Lasselle, and J. P. Purtell: Experimental Investigation of the Fatigue Behavior of Thread-type Projections, *Exp. Mech.*, Vol. 3, No. 5, May, 1963.
79. Leko, T.: On the Bending Problem of Prismatical Beam by Terminal Transverse Load, *Am. Soc. Mech. Eng., Jour. Appl. Mech.*, Vol. 32, No. 1, March, 1965.

CHAPTER 9

TORSION

49. Straight Bar of Uniform Circular Section under Pure Torsion.—The formulas of this article are based on the following assumptions: (1) The bar is straight, of uniform circular section (solid or concentrically hollow), and of homogeneous isotropic material. (2) The bar is loaded only by equal and opposite twisting couples, which are applied at its ends in planes normal to its axis. (3) The bar is not stressed beyond the elastic limit.

Behavior.—The bar twists, each section rotating about the longitudinal axis. Plane sections remain plane and radii remain straight. There is at any point a shear stress s_s on the plane of the section; the magnitude of this stress is proportional to the

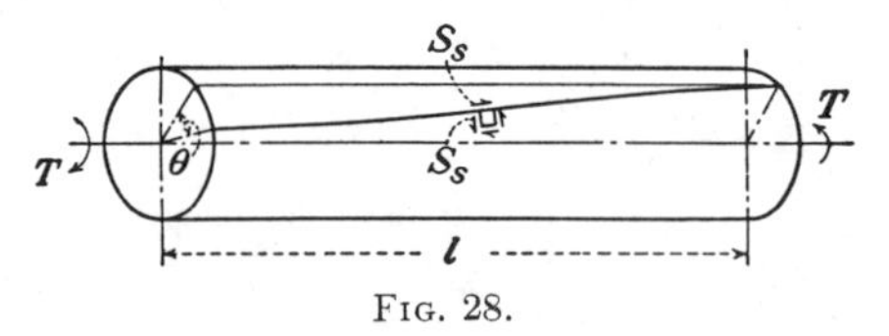

Fig. 28.

distance from the center of the section and its direction is perpendicular to the radius drawn through the point. Accompanying this shear stress there is an equal longitudinal shear stress on a radial plane, and equal tensile and compressive stresses s_t and s_c at 45 deg. (see Art. 30). The deformation and stresses described are represented in Fig. 28.

In addition to these deformations and stresses, there is some longitudinal strain and stress. It has been generally held that the longitudinal strain is a shortening, and the longitudinal stress a tension in the outer part and a balancing compression in the inner part (Ref. 5). Reiner (Ref. 25), on the basis of mathematical analysis, concluded that the longitudinal strain can be either a lengthening, a shortening, or zero, depending on certain physical characteristics of the material, and cites experiments carried out by Poynting (Ref. 26), in which steel and hard copper specimens showed elongation under torsion. In any event, for elastic loading, neither longitudinal deformation nor stress is likely to be large enough to have engineering significance in any case involving pure elastic torsion of a solid circular bar.

Formulas.—Let T = twisting moment; l = length of the member; r = radius of the section; J = polar moment of inertia of the section; z = distance from the center of the section to any point q; s_s = the shear stress; θ = angle of twist (radians); G = modulus of rigidity of the material. Then

$$\theta = \frac{Tl}{JG} \tag{1}$$

(At q)

$$s_s = \frac{Tz}{J} \tag{2}$$

(At surface)

$$\text{Max } s_s = \frac{Tr}{J} \tag{3}$$

$$\text{Strain energy } U = \frac{1}{2}\frac{T^2l}{JG} = \frac{1}{2}\frac{s_s{}^2Jl}{r^2G} \tag{4}$$

Maximum longitudinal tensile stress at surface and maximum longitudinal compressive stress at center

$$s = (\text{Max } s_s)^2 \frac{E}{4G^2} \tag{5}$$

By substituting for J in Eqs. 1 and 3 its value $2I$ from Table I, the following formulas are readily obtained:

For solid section, radius r

$$\theta = \frac{2Tl}{\pi r^4 G}$$

$$\text{Max } s_s = \frac{2T}{\pi r^3}$$

For hollow section, outer radius r_1, inner radius r_0,

$$\theta = \frac{2Tl}{\pi(r_1{}^4 - r_0{}^4)G}$$

$$\text{Max } s_s = \frac{2Tr_1}{\pi(r_1{}^4 - r_0{}^4)}$$

50. Bars of Noncircular Uniform Section under Pure Torsion.—The formulas of this article are based on the same assumptions as those of Art. 49, except that the cross section of the bar is not circular. It is important to note that the condition of loading implies that the end sections of the bar are free to warp, there being no constraining forces to hold them in their respective planes.

Behavior.—The bar twists, each section rotating about its torsional center. Sections do not remain plane, but warp, and radial lines through the torsional center do not remain straight. The distribution of shear stress on the section is not linear, and the direction of the shear stress is not normal to a radius.

Formulas.—The torsional stiffness of the bar can be expressed by the general equation

$$T = \frac{\theta}{l} KG \qquad \text{or} \qquad \theta = \frac{Tl}{KG}$$

where K is a factor dependent on the form and dimensions of the cross section. For a *circular* section K is the polar moment of inertia J (Eq. 1); for other sections K is less than J, and may be only a very small fraction of J. The maximum stress is a function of the twisting moment and of the form and dimensions of the cross section. In Table IX are given formulas for K and for Max s_s for a variety of sections. With one exception, the formulas for Cases 1 to 7, inclusive, are based on rigorous mathematical analysis. The exception is Case 4, the equations for which are given in a simplified form involving an approximation, with a resulting error not greater than 4 per cent. The K formulas for Cases 8 to 16, inclusive, and the stress formulas for Cases 8 to 13, inclusive, are based on mathematical analysis but are approximate (Ref. 2). Their accuracy depends upon how nearly the actual section conforms to the assumptions indicated as to form. The K formulas for the remaining cases and the stress formulas for Cases 14 to 20, inclusive, are based on the membrane analogy and are to be regarded as reasonably close approximations giving results that are rarely as much as 10 per cent in error (Refs. 2, 3, 4).

It will be noted that formulas for K in Cases 17, 18, 19, and 20 are based on the assumption of uniform flange thickness. For slightly tapering flanges, D should be taken as the diameter of the largest circle that can be inscribed in the actual section, and b as the average flange thickness. For sharply tapering flanges the method described by Griffith (Ref. 3) may be used. Charts relating especially to structural H sections and I sections are given in Ref. 11.

The formulas of Table IX make possible the calculation of the strength and stiffness of a bar of almost any form, but an understanding of the membrane analogy (Art. 23) makes it possible to draw certain conclusions as to the *comparative* torsional properties of different sections by simply visualizing the bubbles that would be formed over holes of corresponding size and shape. From the volume relationship, it can be seen that of two sections having the same area, the one more nearly circular is the stiffer, and that while any extension whatever of the section increases its torsional stiffness, narrow outstanding flanges and similar protrusions have little effect. It is also apparent that any member having a narrow section, such as a thin plate, has practically the same torsional stiffness when flat as when bent into the form of an open tube or into a channel or angle section.

From the slope relationship it can be seen that the greatest stresses (slopes) in a given section occur at the boundary adjacent to the thicker portions, and that the stresses are very low at the ends of outstanding flanges or protruding corners, and very high at points where the boundary is sharply concave. A longitudinal slot or groove, if sharp at the bottom or if narrow, will therefore cause high local stresses, and if deep will greatly reduce the torsional stiffness of the member. The direction of the shear stresses at any point is along the contour of the bubble surface at the corresponding point, and at points corresponding to high and low points of the bubble surface the shear stress becomes zero. There may therefore be several points of zero shear stress in a section. Thus for an I section, there are high points of zero slope at the center of the largest inscribed circles (at junction of web and flanges) and a low point of zero slope at the center of the web, and at these points in the section the shear stress is zero.

The above generalizations apply to solid sections, but it is possible to make somewhat similar generalizations concerning hollow or tubular sections from the formulas given for Cases 7 to 11, inclusive. These show that the strength and stiffness of a hollow section depend largely upon the area inclosed by the median boundary. For this reason a circular tube is stiffer and stronger than one of any other form, and the more nearly the form of any hollow section approaches the circular, the greater will be its strength and stiffness. It is also apparent from the formulas for strength that even a local reduction in the thickness of the wall of a tube, such as would be caused by a longitudinal groove, may greatly reduce its strength, though if the groove is narrow the effect on stiffness will be small.

The torsional strength and stiffness of thin-walled multicelled structures such as airplane wings and boat hulls can best be calculated by an arithmetical process of successive approximations (Ref. 12). The method of successive approximations can also be applied to solid sections (*e.g.*, Cases 14 to 16, Table IX), and any desired accuracy can be attained by sufficient repetition (Refs. 13, 14).

Examples

1. It is required to compare the strength and stiffness of a circular steel tube, 4 in. outside diameter and $\frac{5}{32}$ in. thick, with the strength and stiffness of the same tube after it has been split by cutting along an element.

TABLE IX.—FORMULAS FOR TORSIONAL DEFORMATION AND STRESS

General formulas: $\theta = \frac{TL}{KG}$, $s = \frac{T}{Q}$, where θ = angle of twist (rad); T = twisting moment (in.-lb); L = length (in.); s = unit shear stress (lb. per sq. in.); G = modulus of rigidity (lb. per sq. in.); K (in.^{4}) and Q (in.^{3}) are functions of the cross section.

Form and dimensions of cross sections, other quantities involved, and case number	Formula for K in $\theta = \frac{TL}{KG}$	Formula for shear stress
1. Solid circular section (2r)	$K = \frac{1}{2}\pi r^4$	Max $s = \frac{2T}{\pi r^3}$ at boundary
2. Solid elliptical section (2a, 2b)	$K = \frac{\pi a^3 b^3}{a^2 + b^2}$	Max $s = \frac{2T}{\pi a b^2}$ at ends of minor axis
3. Solid square section (a)	$K = 0.1406a^4$	Max $s = \frac{T}{0.208a^3}$ at mid-point of each side
4. Solid rectangular section (2a, 2b)	$K = ab^3\left[\frac{16}{3} - 3.36\frac{b}{a}\left(1 - \frac{b^4}{12a^4}\right)\right]$	Max $s = \frac{T(3a + 1.8b)}{8a^2b^2}$ at mid-point of each longer side

	80	a^3
6. Hollow concentric circular section	$K = \frac{1}{2}\pi(r_1^4 - r_0^4)$	Max $s = \dfrac{2Tr_1}{\pi(r_1^4 - r_0^4)}$ at outer boundary
7. Hollow elliptical section, outer and inner boundaries similar ellipses $q = \dfrac{a_0}{a} = \dfrac{b_0}{b}$	$K = \dfrac{\pi a^3 b^3}{a^2 + b^2}(1 - q^4)$	Max $s = \dfrac{2T}{\pi a b^2(1 - q^4)}$ at ends of minor axis on outer surface
8. Hollow, thin-walled elliptical section of uniform thickness. U = length of median boundary, shown dotted $U = \pi(a + b - t)\left[1 + 0.27\dfrac{(a-b)^2}{(a+b)^2}\right]$, approx.	$K = \dfrac{4\pi^2 t[(a - \frac{1}{2}t)^2(b - \frac{1}{2}t)^2]}{U}$	Average $s = \dfrac{T}{2\pi t(a - \frac{1}{2}t)(b - \frac{1}{2}t)}$ (stress nearly uniform if t is small)
9. Any thin tube of uniform thickness. U = length of median boundary, A = mean of areas enclosed by outer and inner boundaries, or (approx.) area within median boundary	$K = \dfrac{4A^2 t}{U}$	Average $s = \dfrac{T}{2tA}$ (stress nearly uniform if t is small)

TABLE IX.—FORMULAS FOR TORSIONAL DEFORMATION AND STRESS.—(*Continued*)

Form and dimensions of cross sections, other quantities involved, and case number	Formula for K in $\theta = \frac{TL}{KG}$	Formula for shear stress
10. Any thin tube. U and A as for Case 9; t = thickness at any point 	$K = \frac{4A^2}{\int \frac{dU}{t}}$	Average s on any thickness $AB = \frac{T}{2tA}$ (Max s where t is a minimum)
11. Hollow rectangle 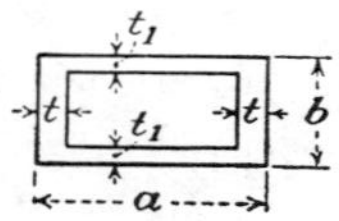	$K = \frac{2tt_1(a-t)^2(b-t_1)^2}{at + bt_1 - t^2 - t_1^2}$	Average $s = \frac{T}{2t(a-t)(b-t_1)}$ near mid-length of short sides Average $s = \frac{T}{2t_1(a-t)(b-t_1)}$ near mid-length of long sides (There will be higher stresses at inner corners unless fillets of fairly large radius are provided)
12. Thin circular open tube of uniform thickness. r = mean radius 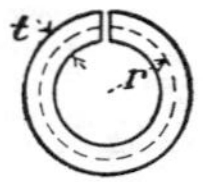	$K = \frac{2}{3}\pi r t^3$	Max $s = \frac{T(6\pi r + 1.8t)}{4\pi^2 r^2 t^2}$, along both edges remote from ends (this assumes t small compared with mean radius; otherwise use formulas given for Cases 14 to 20)
13. Any thin open tube of uniform thickness. U = length of median line, shown dotted 	$K = \frac{1}{3}Ut^3$	Max $s = \frac{T(3U + 1.8t)}{U^2t^2}$, along both edges remote from ends (this assumes t small compared with least radius of curvature of median line; otherwise use formulas given for Cases 14 to 20)

metry OX. U = length, A = area of section, I_x = moment of inertia about axis of symmetry. 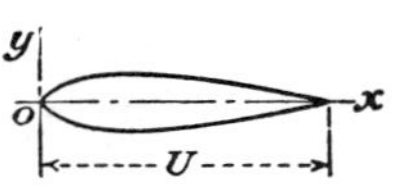	$\left(1 + 16\frac{I_x}{AU^2}\right)$	For all solid sections of i..egular form (Cases 14 to 20, inclusive) the max shear stress occurs at o.. very near one of the points where the largest inscribed circle touches the boundary,* and of these, at the one where the curvature of the boundary is algebraically least. (Convexity represents positive, concavity negative, curvature of the boundary.) At a point where the curvature is positive (boundary of section straight or convex) this max stress is given approximately by: $s = G\frac{\theta}{L}c$ or $s = \frac{T}{K}c$ where $c = \frac{D}{1 + \frac{\pi^2 D^4}{16A^2}}\left[1 + 0.15\left(\frac{\pi^2 D^4}{16A^2} - \frac{D}{2r}\right)\right]$, where D = diameter of largest inscribed circle r = radius of curvature of boundary at the point (positive for this case) A = area of the section At a point where the curvature is negative (boundary of section concave, or reentrant) this max stress is given approximately by $s = G\frac{\theta}{L}c$ or $s = \frac{T}{K}c$ where $c = \frac{D}{1 + \frac{\pi^2 D^4}{16A^2}}\left[1 + \left\{0.118 \log_e\left(1 - \frac{D}{2r}\right) - 0.238\frac{D}{2r}\right\} \tanh \frac{2\phi}{\pi}\right]$ where D, A, and r have same meaning as before and ϕ = angle through which a tangent to the boundary rotates in turning or traveling around the reentrant portion, measured in radians. (Here r is *negative*.) The above formulas should also be used for Cases 12 and 13 when t is relatively large compared with radius of median line
15. Any elongated section or thin open tube. dU = elementary length along median line, t = thickness normal to median line, A = area of section 	$K = \frac{\frac{1}{3}F}{\left(1 + \frac{4}{3}\frac{F}{AU^2}\right)}$ where $F = \int_0^U t^3\,dU$	
16. Any solid, fairly compact section without reentrant angles. J = polar moment of inertia about centroidal axis; A = area of section 	$K = \frac{A^4}{40J}$	
17. I section, flange thickness uniform. r = fillet radius, D = diameter largest inscribed circle, $t = b$ if $b < d$, $t = d$ if $d < b$, $t_1 = b$ if $b > d$ $t_1 = d$ if $d > b$ 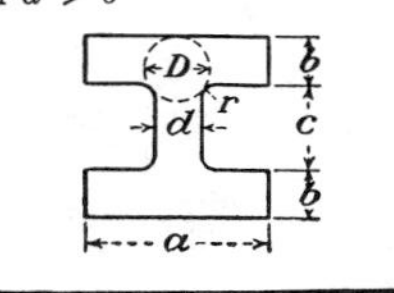	$K = 2K_1 + K_2 + 2\alpha D^4$ where $K_1 = ab^3\left[\frac{1}{3} - 0.21\frac{b}{a}\left(1 - \frac{b^4}{12a^4}\right)\right]$ $K_2 = \frac{1}{3}cd^3$ $\alpha = \frac{t}{t_1}\left(0.15 + 0.1\frac{r}{b}\right)$	

* Unless at some other point on boundary there is a sharp reentrant angle, causing high local stress.

TABLE IX.—FORMULAS FOR TORSIONAL DEFORMATION AND STRESS.—(*Continued*)

Form and dimensions of cross sections, other quantities involved, and case number	Formula for K in $\theta = \frac{TL}{KG}$	Formula for shear stress
18. **T section, flange thickness uniform; r, D, t and t_1 as for Case 17**	$K = K_1 + K_2 + \alpha D^4$ where $K_1 = ab^3\left[\frac{1}{3} - 0.21\frac{b}{a}\left(1 - \frac{b^4}{12a^4}\right)\right]$ $K_2 = cd^3\left[\frac{1}{3} - 0.105\frac{d}{c}\left(1 - \frac{d^4}{192c^4}\right)\right]$ $\alpha = \frac{t}{t_1}\left(0.15 + 0.10\frac{r}{b}\right)$	
19. **L section,** r **and** D as for Cases 17 and 18; $b \gtreqless d$	$K = K_1 + K_2 + \alpha D^4$ where $K_1 = ab^3\left[\frac{1}{3} - 0.21\frac{b}{a}\left(1 - \frac{b^4}{12a^4}\right)\right]$ $K_2 = cd^3\left[\frac{1}{3} - 0.105\frac{d}{c}\left(1 - \frac{d^4}{192c^4}\right)\right]$ $\alpha = \frac{d}{b}\left(0.07 + 0.076\frac{r}{b}\right)$	
20. **U section or Z section**	K = sum of K's of constituent L sections, computed as for Case 19	
21. Eccentric hollow circular section; $\frac{e}{D} = \lambda$, $\frac{d}{D} = n$	$K = \pi(D^4 - d^4)/32Q$ where $Q = 1 + \left[\frac{16n^2}{(1-n^2)(1-n^4)}\right]\lambda^2 + \left[\frac{384n^4}{(1-n^2)^2(1-n^4)^4}\right]\lambda^4$	Max $S = 16TDF/\pi(D^4 - d^4)$ where $F = 1 + \left[\frac{4n^2}{1-n^2}\right]\lambda + \left[\frac{32n^2}{(1-n^2)(1-n^4)}\right]\lambda^2 + \left[\frac{48n^2(1+2n^2+3n^4+2n^6)}{(1-n^2)(1-n^4)(1-n^6)}\right]\lambda^3 + \left[\frac{64n^2(2+12n^2+19n^4+28n^6+18n^8+14n^{10}+3n^{12})}{(1-n^2)(1-n^4)(1-n^6)(1-n^8)}\right]\lambda^4$ (Ref. 10)

α	0°	30°	60°	80°	90°
C	$\frac{1}{2}\pi$	1.47	0.91	0.48	0.296

α	0°	30°	60°	80°	90°
C	$\frac{1}{2}\pi$	1.25	0.80	0.49	0.35

(Ref. 16)

23. Circular sector

$K = Cr^4$
where C depends on α and has values as follows:

α	45°	60°	90°	120°
C	0.0181	0.0349	0.0825	0.148
α	180°	270°	300°	360°
C	0.296	0.528	0.686	0.878

Max $s = \dfrac{T}{Q}$ on radial boundary. Here $Q = Cr^3$, where C has values as follows:

α	60°	120°	180°
C	0.0712	0.227	0.35

(Ref. 17)

24. Isosceles triangle

$$K = \frac{a^3b^3}{15a^2 + 20b^2}$$

For $\alpha = 90°$, $K = 0.0261c^4$
For $\alpha = 60°$, $K = 0.0216c^4$

$Q = 0.0666ab^2$

For $\alpha = 90°$, $Q = 0.0554c^3$
For $\alpha = 60°$, $Q = 0.050c^3$
Max S_s at center longest side

(Ref. 20)

25. Trapezoid

$$K = \tfrac{1}{12}b(m + n)(m^2 + n^2) - V_L m^4 - V_s n^4$$

where

$$V_L = 0.10504 - 0.10s + 0.0848s^2 - 0.06746s^3 + 0.0515s^4$$

$$V_s = 0.10504 + 0.10s + 0.0848s^2 + 0.06746s^3 + 0.0515s^4$$

and $s = \dfrac{m - n}{b}$

Max S as for Cases 14 to 20

(Ref. 11)

26. Circular shaft with opposite sides flattened

$K = cr^4$
where c depends on ratio w/r and has values as follows:

$\frac{w}{r}$	$\frac{7}{8}$	$\frac{3}{4}$	$\frac{5}{8}$	$\frac{1}{2}$
c	1.357	1.076	0.733	0.438

$Q = cr^3$
where c depends on ratio w/r and has values as follows:

$\frac{w}{r}$	$\frac{7}{8}$	$\frac{3}{4}$	$\frac{5}{8}$	$\frac{1}{2}$
c	1.155	0.912	0.638	0.471

(Ref. 21)

Solution.—The strengths will be compared by comparing the twisting moments required to produce the same stress; the stiffnesses by comparing the values of K.

(*a*) For the tube (Case 6), $K = \frac{1}{2}\pi(r_1^4 - r_0^4) = \frac{1}{2}\pi[2^4 - (1\frac{27}{32})^4] = 6.98$ in.^{4}

$$T = s_s\frac{\pi(r_1^4 - r_0^4)}{2r_1} = 3.49\ s_s \text{ in.-lb.}$$

(*b*) For the split tube (Case 12), $K = \frac{2}{3}\pi r t^3 = \frac{2}{3}\pi(1\frac{59}{64})(\frac{5}{32})^3 = 0.0154$ in.^{4}

$$T = s_s\frac{4\pi^2 r^2 t^2}{6\pi r + 1.8t} = 0.097\ s_s \text{ in.-lb.}$$

The closed section is therefore more than 400 times as stiff as the open section, and more than 30 times as strong.

2. It is required to determine the angle through which an airplane wing spar of spruce, 8 ft. long and having the section shown in Fig. 29, would be twisted by end torques of 500 in.-lb., and to find the maximum resulting stress. For the material in question, $G = 100{,}000$ and $E = 1{,}500{,}000$.

Solution.—All relevant dimensions are shown in Fig. 29, with notation corresponding to that used in the formulas. The first step is to compute K by the formula given for Case 17, and we have

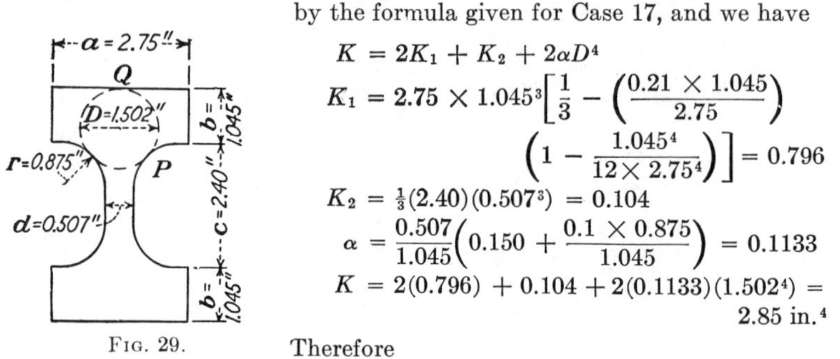

FIG. 29.

$$K = 2K_1 + K_2 + 2\alpha D^4$$

$$K_1 = 2.75 \times 1.045^3\left[\frac{1}{3} - \left(\frac{0.21 \times 1.045}{2.75}\right)\left(1 - \frac{1.045^4}{12 \times 2.75^4}\right)\right] = 0.796$$

$$K_2 = \tfrac{1}{3}(2.40)(0.507^3) = 0.104$$

$$\alpha = \frac{0.507}{1.045}\left(0.150 + \frac{0.1 \times 0.875}{1.045}\right) = 0.1133$$

$$K = 2(0.796) + 0.104 + 2(0.1133)(1.502^4) = 2.85 \text{ in.}^4$$

Therefore

$$\theta = \frac{Tl}{KG} = \frac{(500)(96)}{(2.85)(100{,}000)} = 0.168 \text{ rad.} = 9.64^\circ$$

The maximum stress will probably be at P, the point where the largest inscribed circle touches the section boundary at a fillet. The formula is

$$\text{Max } s_s = \frac{T}{K}C$$

$$C = \frac{1.502}{1 + \dfrac{\pi^2(1.502^4)}{16(7.63^2)}}\left\{1 + \left[0.118 \log_e\left(1 - \frac{1.502}{2(-0.875)}\right) - 0.238\,\frac{1.502}{2(-0.875)}\right]\tanh\left(\frac{2(\pi/2)}{\pi}\right)\right\} = 1.73$$

Substituting the values of T, C, and K, it is found that

$$\text{Max } s_s = \frac{500}{2.85}1.73 = 303 \text{ lb. per sq. in.}$$

It will be of interest to compare this stress with that at Q, the other point where the maximum inscribed circle touches the boundary. Here the formula that applies is

$$s_s = \frac{T}{K}C$$

where

$$C = \frac{1.502}{1 + \pi^2 \frac{(1.502)^4}{16(7.63^2)}} \left[1 + 0.15\left(\frac{\pi^2(1.502^4)}{16(7.63^2)} - \frac{1.502}{\infty}\right)\right] = 1.437$$

(Here r = infinity because the boundary is straight.)

Substituting the values of T, C, and K as before, it is found that s_s = 252 lb. per sq. in.

51. Effect of End Constraint.—It was pointed out in Art. 50 that when noncircular bars are twisted, the sections do not remain plane, but warp, and that the formulas of Table IX are based on the assumption that this warping is not prevented. If one or both ends of the bar are so fixed that warping is prevented, the stresses and angle of twist produced by a given twisting moment are affected. In compact sections—rectangular, elliptical, triangular, etc.—the effect is slight and usually negligible, but in the case of open tubes (Cases 12, 13, 15) or flanged sections (Cases 17, 20) the effect may be considerable.

Consider a member having an I, Z, or channel section, so fixed at one end (as by welding or gluing to a rigid plate or to blocks) that there can be no warping of the section, and then twisted by a couple applied at the other end (Fig. 30*a*). If this twisting couple were applied as two equal and opposite forces, one acting to the left on the lower flange, the other acting to the right on the upper flange, and the web were removed (Fig. 30*b*), it is apparent that the entire twisting moment would be resisted by the flanges acting as cantilever beams, each flange carrying a load equal to T/h and deflecting laterally without twisting. When the web is present, it and the flanges must twist (Fig. 30*c*), and so a part of the twisting moment is resisted by the torsional rigidity of the whole section and a part by the bending rigidity of the flanges. The proportional part of T resisted in each of these ways varies along the member; at sections near the free end the resistance is largely torsional, while at the section adjacent to the fixed end the resistance is wholly flexural, the twisting moment being wholly balanced there by horizontal transverse shear in the flanges.

Timoshenko (Ref. 5) gives a solution for the case of an I-beam of length $2l$ with ends simply restrained against turning and with a torque $2T$ applied at mid-span. (The center section is here fixed against warping, and so the analysis applies equally to a bar of length l fixed at one end and twisted by a torque T at the other.)

Let I_y = the moment of inertia of the section about the vertical central axis; h = depth of section center to center of flanges; b = width of flange; $a = \frac{1}{2}h\sqrt{I_yE/KG}$; M_{max} = the maximum

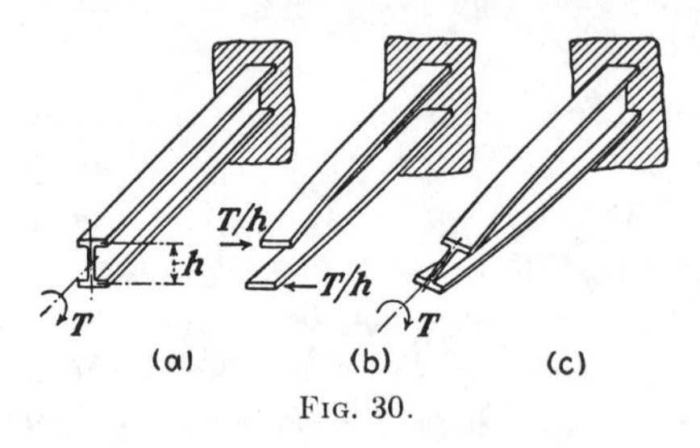

FIG. 30.

bending moment sustained by one flange; T_{max}' = the maximum proportion of the total twisting moment T resisted by torsion; θ = angle of twist in the length l. Then

$$M_{max} = \frac{T}{h}a \tanh \frac{l}{a} \tag{6}$$

$$T_{max}' = T\left(1 - \operatorname{sech} \frac{l}{a}\right) \tag{7}$$

$$\theta = \frac{T}{KG}\left(l - a \tanh \frac{l}{a}\right) \tag{8}$$

For long members Eq. 6 becomes $\frac{T}{h}a$; for very short members it becomes $\frac{T}{h}l$. For long members Eq. 7 becomes T; for short members it may be much less than T. For long members Eq. 8 becomes $(T/KG)(l - a)$.

The maximum bending stress in the flange is given by

$$\text{Max } s = \frac{M_{max}b}{I_y}$$

As stated above, these equations apply to a bar of I section, of length l, fixed at one end, and subjected to a torque T applied at the other end; they apply also to a bar of length $2l$, with ends constrained against twisting and a torque $2T$ applied at mid-length. Equations 6 and 7 will also apply to a bar of length $2l$ with both ends fixed and a torque T applied at each end; for this case Eq. 8 gives $\frac{1}{2}\theta$. They also apply to a channel or Z-bar, where in computing the bending stress b is replaced by twice the distance from the Y-axis to the outer fiber. In an angle, the torsional center is at or very near the junction of the legs, hence twisting causes little or no bending, and is resisted almost wholly by torsional stress even though the ends are fixed. The effect of end fixity on the torsional properties of H and I sections is further discussed in Ref. 11.

For a box girder fixed at one end and subjected to a twisting couple T applied at the other end (Fig. 31) the following formulas

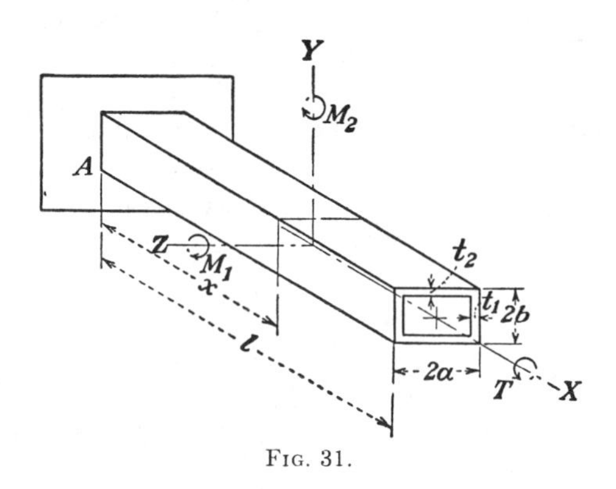

FIG. 31.

are given by Payne (Ref. 15). Bending moment M_1 in either spar or vertical web:

At A:

$$M_1 = \frac{T}{2a}\frac{\eta K_1}{\mu}\tanh \mu l$$

At distance x from A:

$$M_1 = (M_1 \text{ at } A)\frac{\sinh \mu(l - x)}{\sinh \mu l}$$

Bending moment M_2 in either top or bottom flange:

At A:

$$M_2 = -\frac{T}{2b}\frac{\eta K_2}{\mu}\tanh \mu l$$

At distance x from A:

$$M_2 = (M_2 \text{ at } A) \frac{\sinh \mu(l - x)}{\sinh \mu l}$$

Vertical shear V_1 in either spar or vertical web:

$$V_1 = \frac{T}{4a}\left(1 + \eta \frac{\cosh \mu(l - x)}{\cosh \mu l}\right)$$

Transverse shear V_2 on either top or bottom flange:

$$V_2 = \frac{T}{4b}\left(1 - \eta \frac{\cosh \mu(l - x)}{\cosh \mu l}\right)$$

Shear per linear inch along junction of web and flange:

$$s = \frac{T}{8ab}\left[1 - \eta(K_1 - K_2) \frac{\cosh \mu(l - x)}{\cosh \mu l}\right]$$

In these equations the several terms are defined as follows:

$$K_1 = \frac{a^2EI_1}{a^2E_1I_1 + b^2E_2I_2}, \qquad K_2 = 1 - K_1$$

$$\eta = \frac{a^2r_2 - b^2r_1}{a^2r_2 + b^2r_1}, \qquad \mu^2 = \frac{4a^2b^2}{(a^2E_1I_1 + b^2E_2I_2)(a^2r_2 + b^2r_1)}$$

$$r_1 = \frac{1}{2bt_1G_1}, \qquad r_2 = \frac{1}{2at_2G_2}$$

$I_1 = I$ of one web about axis zz; $I_2 = I$ of one flange about axis yy.

E_1 and E_2 are, respectively, moduli of elasticity of material in webs and flanges.

G_1 and G_2 are, respectively, shearing moduli of elasticity of material in webs and flanges.

If instead of being applied at the free end the twisting couple T is applied at a section B distant l_2 from the fixed end and l_3 from the free end, the formulas become:

(From fixed end to B)

$$M_1 = \frac{T}{2a}\frac{\eta K_1}{\mu}\left[\left(\frac{\sinh \mu l - \sinh \mu l_3}{\sinh \mu l \cosh \mu l}\right) \sinh \mu(l - x) - \left(\frac{\sinh \mu l_3}{\sinh \mu l}\right) \sinh \mu x\right]$$

(From B to free end)

$$M_1 = \frac{T}{2a}\frac{\eta K_1}{\mu}\left[\left(\frac{\sinh \mu l - \sinh \mu l_3}{\sinh \mu l \cosh \mu l}\right)\sinh \mu(l - x) - \left(\frac{\sinh \mu l_2}{\sinh \mu l}\right)\sinh \mu(l - x)\right]$$

(At any section)

$$M_2 = -M_1\left(\frac{aK_2}{bK_1}\right)$$

(From fixed end to B)

$$V_1 = \frac{T}{4a}\left[1 + \eta\left(\frac{\cosh \mu(l - x)}{\cosh \mu l}\right) + \eta\left(\frac{\sinh \mu l_3 \sinh \mu x}{\cosh \mu l}\right)\right]$$

$$V_2 = \frac{T}{4b}\left[1 - \eta\left(\frac{\cosh \mu(l - x)}{\cosh \mu l}\right) - \eta\left(\frac{\sinh \mu l_3 \sinh \mu x}{\cosh \mu l}\right)\right]$$

(From B to free end)

$$V_1 = \frac{T}{4a}\left[\eta\left(\frac{\cosh \mu(l - x)}{\cosh \mu l}\right) - \eta\left(\frac{\cosh \mu l_2 \cosh \mu(l - x)}{\cosh \mu l}\right)\right]$$

$$V_2 = \frac{T}{4b}\left[-\eta\left(\frac{\cosh \mu(l - x)}{\cosh \mu l}\right) + \eta\left(\frac{\cosh \mu l_2 \cosh \mu(l - x)}{\cosh \mu l}\right)\right]$$

(At any section)

$$s = \frac{\left(V_1 + \frac{dM_1}{dx}\right)}{2b}$$

52. Effect of Longitudinal Stresses.—It was pointed out in Art. 49 that the elongation of the outer fibers consequent upon twist caused longitudinal stresses, but that in a bar of circular section these stresses were negligible. In a flexible bar, the section of which comprises one or more narrow rectangles, the stresses in the longitudinal fibers may become large, and since after twisting these fibers are inclined, the stresses in them have components, normal to the axis of twist, which contribute to the torsional resistance of the member.

The stress in the longitudinal fibers of a thin twisted strip and the effect of these stresses on torsional stiffness have been considered by Timoshenko (Ref. 5), Green (Ref. 6), and others. The following formulas apply to this case:

Let $2a$ = width of strip; $2b$ = thickness of strip; s_s, s_t, and s_c, respectively, = the maximum shear, maximum tensile, and maximum compressive stress due to twisting; T = the applied twisting moment; θ/l = the angle of twist per unit length. Then

$$s_t = \frac{E s_s^2}{12G^2}\left(\frac{a}{b}\right)^2 \tag{9}$$

$$s_c = \tfrac{1}{2}s_t \tag{10}$$

$$T = KG\frac{\theta}{l} + \frac{8}{45}E\left(\frac{\theta}{l}\right)^3 ba^5 \tag{11}$$

The first term on the right side of Eq. 11 ($KG\ \theta/l$) represents the part of the total applied torque T that is resisted by torsional shear; the second term represents the part that is resisted by the tensile stresses in the (helical) longitudinal fibers. It can be seen that this second part is small for small angles of twist, but increases rapidly as θ/l increases.

To find the stresses produced by a given torque T, the value of θ/l is first found by Eq. 11, taking K as given for Case 4. Then s_s is found by the stress formula for Case 4, taking $KG\ \theta/l$ for the twisting moment. Then s_t and s_c can be found by Eqs. 9 and 10.

This stiffening and strengthening effect of induced longitudinal stress will manifest itself in any bar having a section composed of narrow rectangles, such as an I, T, or channel, provided that the parts are so thin as to permit of a large unit twist without overstressing. At the same time the accompanying longitudinal compression (Eq. 10) may cause failure through elastic instability (see Table XV).

If a thin strip of width a and maximum thickness b is *initially* twisted (as by cold working) to an helical angle β, then there is an initial stiffening effect in torsion that can be expressed by the ratio of effective K to nominal K (as given in Table IX):

$$\frac{\text{Effective } K}{\text{Nominal } K} = 1 + C(1 + \nu)\beta^2\left(\frac{a}{b}\right)^2$$

where C is a numerical coefficient that depends on the shape of the cross section and is $\frac{2}{15}$ for a rectangle, $\frac{1}{8}$ for an ellipse, $\frac{1}{10}$ for a lenticular form, and $\frac{7}{60}$ for a double wedge (Ref. 22).

If a bar of any cross section is independently loaded in tension, then the corresponding longitudinal tensile stress s_t will similarly provide a resisting torque that again depends on the angle of twist, and the total applied torque corresponding to any angle of twist θ is $T = (KG + s_t J)\,\theta/l$, where J is the centroidal polar moment of inertia of the cross section. If the longitudinal loading causes a compressive stress s_c, the equation becomes

$$T = (KG - s_c J)\frac{\theta}{l}$$

Bending also influences the torsional stiffness of a rod unless the cross section (1) has two axes of symmetry, (2) has point symmetry, or (3) has one axis of symmetry that is normal to the plane of bending. The influences of longitudinal loading and of bending are discussed in Ref. 23.

53. Ultimate Strength of Bars in Torsion.—When twisted to failure, bars of ductile material usually break in shear, the surface of fracture being normal to the axis and practically flat. Bars of brittle material usually break in tension, the surface of fracture being helicoidal.

Circular Sections.—The formulas of Art. 49 apply only when the maximum stress does not exceed the elastic limit. If Eq. 3 is used with T equal to the twisting moment at failure, a fictitious value of s_s is obtained which is called the modulus of rupture in torsion, and which for convenience will here be denoted by s_s'.

For solid bars of steel, s_s' slightly exceeds the ultimate tensile strength when the length is only about twice the diameter, but drops to about 80 per cent of the tensile strength when the length becomes 25 times the diameter. For solid bars of aluminum, s_s' is about 90 per cent of the tensile strength.

For tubes, the modulus of rupture decreases with the ratio of diameter D to wall thickness t. Younger (Ref. 7) gives the following approximate formula, applicable to tubes of steel and aluminum:

$$s_s' = \frac{1600 s_{s_0}}{\left(\frac{D}{t} - 2\right)^2 + 1600}$$

where s_s' is the modulus of rupture in torsion of the tube and s_{s_0}' is the modulus of rupture in torsion of a solid circular bar of the same material. Curves giving s_s' as a function of D/t, for various steels and light alloys, may be found in Ref. 18.

For a solid bar of cast iron, the ratio of s_s' to the tensile strength (rupture factor) seems to vary considerably, ranging from a little over 100 to 190 per cent. The variation is probably due in part to differences in length and end conditions of the specimens tested.

Noncircular Sections.—The rupture factors for cast iron and plaster specimens of different sections in torsion are given in Table XVIII. These rupture factors are the ratios of the calculated maximum shear stress at rupture (calculated by the appropriate formula from Table IX) to the tensile strength of the material. As usual, it is seen that the rupture factor increases as the degree of stress localization increases.

Torsion Combined with Bending.—In the case of thin tubular members that fail by buckling, it may be assumed that failure will not occur so long as $(s_s/s_s')^2 + (s/s')^2 < 1$. Here s_s and s are the maximum actual stresses, and s_s' and s' are the moduli of rupture, in torsion and bending, respectively.

54. Torsion of Curved Bars; Helical Springs.—The formulas of Arts. 49 and 50 can be applied to slightly curved bars without significant error, but for sharply curved bars such as helical springs, account must be taken of the influence of curvature and slope. Among others, Wahl (Ref. 8) and Ancker and Goodier (Ref. 24) have discussed this problem, and the former presents charts which greatly facilitate the calculation of stress and deflection for springs of noncircular section. Of the formulas cited below, those for round wire were taken from Ref. 24, and those for square and rectangular wire from Ref. 8, with some changes of notation.

Let R = radius of coil, measured from spring axis to center of section (Fig. 32); d = diameter of circular section; b = thickness of square section; P = load (either tensile or compressive); n = number of active turns in spring; α = pitch angle of spring; f = total stretch or shortening of spring; s_s = maximum shear stress produced.

Then for a spring of *circular* wire,

$$f = \frac{64PR^3n}{Gd^4}\left[1 - \frac{3}{64}\left(\frac{d}{R}\right)^2 + \frac{3+\nu}{2(1+\nu)}(\tan\alpha)^2\right]$$

$$s_s = \frac{16PR}{\pi d^3}\left[1 + \frac{5}{8}\frac{d}{R} + \frac{7}{32}\left(\frac{d}{R}\right)^2\right]$$

For a spring of *square* wire,

$$f = \frac{44.72PR^3n}{Gb^4}$$

$$s_s = \frac{4.8PR}{b^3}\left(1 + \frac{1.2}{c} + \frac{0.56}{c^2} + \frac{0.5}{c^3}\right)$$

where $c = 2R/b$.

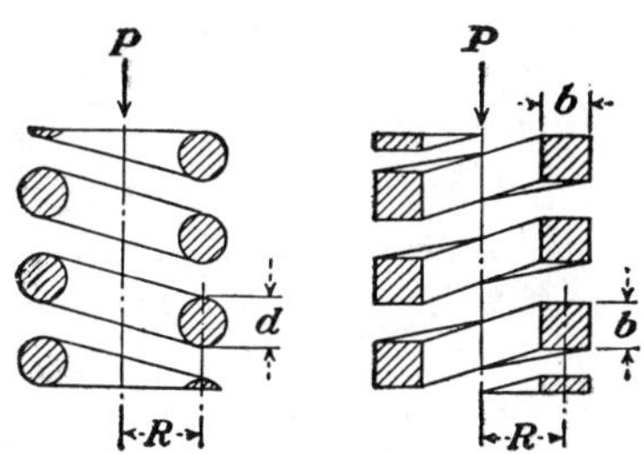

Fig. 32.

For a spring of *rectangular* wire, section $b \times a$ and $b > a$,

$$f = \frac{2\pi PR^3n}{Ga^3}\,\frac{1}{\frac{1}{3}b - 0.209a[\tanh(\pi a/2b) + 0.004]}$$

$$s_s = \frac{PR(3b + 1.8a)}{b^2a^2}\left(1 + \frac{1.2}{c} + \frac{0.56}{c^2} + \frac{0.5}{c^3}\right)$$

It should be noted that in each of these cases the maximum stress is given by the ordinary formula for the section in question (from Table IX) multiplied by a corrective factor that takes account of curvature, and these corrective factors can be used for any curved bar of the corresponding cross section.

For compression springs with the end turns ground down for even bearing, n should be taken as the actual number of turns (including the tapered end turns) less 2. For tension springs n should be taken as the actual number of turns, or slightly more.

Unless laterally supported, compression springs that are relatively long will buckle when compressed beyond a certain critical deflection. This critical deflection depends on the ratio of L, the free length, to D, the mean diameter, and is indicated approximately by the following tabulation, based on Ref. 27.

$L/D =$	1	2	3	4	5	6	7	8
$\frac{\text{Crit. defl.}}{L} =$	0.72	0.71	0.68	0.63	0.53	0.39	0.27	0.17

Precise Formula.—For very accurate calculation of the extension of a spring, as is necessary in designing precision spring scales, account must be taken of the change in slope and radius of the coils caused by stretching. Sayre (Ref. 9) gives a formula which takes into account not only the effect of this change in form, but also the deformation due to direct transverse shear and to flexure. This formula can be written

$$f = P\left\{\left[\frac{R_0^2L}{GK} - \frac{R_0^2H_0^2}{GKL}\left(1 - \frac{GK}{EI}\right) + \frac{FL}{AG}\right] - \left[\frac{R_0^2}{3GKL}\left(3 - \frac{2GK}{EI}\right)(H^2 + HH_0 - 2H_0^2)\right]\right\}$$

where f = stretch of spring; P = load; R_0 = initial radius of coil; H = variable length of the effective portion of the stretched spring; H_0 = initial value of H; L = actual developed length of the wire of which the spring is made; A = cross-sectional area of this wire; K = the torsional-stiffness factor for the wire section, as given in Table IX ($K = \frac{1}{2}\pi r^4$ for circle, $K = 0.1406a^4$ for square, etc.); F = the section factor for shear deformation (Eq. 16, Art. 35; $F = \frac{10}{9}$ for a circle or ellipse, $F = \frac{6}{5}$ for a square or rectangle); I = moment of inertia of the wire section about a central axis parallel to the spring axis.

The first term in brackets represents the initial rate of stretch; the second term in brackets represents the change in this rate due to change in form consequent upon stretch. The final expression shows that f is not a linear function of P.

55. Miscellaneous Formulas for Circular Shafts.—The most common torsion member is the straight shaft of circular cross section, and a number of additional relations and formulas for this case will be given.

Shaft of Varying Diameter.—If the diameter changes gradually, the stress at any section is given with sufficient accuracy by the formulas for uniform bars. If the change in section is abrupt, as at a shoulder with a small fillet, the maximum stress should be found by the use of a suitable factor of stress concentration k. Values of k are given in Table XVII.

Shaft under Combined Torsion and Bending.—The bending stress s and the torsional stress s_s can be found separately and the resultant shear and normal stresses found by the formulas of

Art. 31. Or the equivalent bending moment M' may be used to find the maximum tensile and compressive stresses and the equivalent twisting moment T' to find the maximum shear stress. The following formulas apply to circular sections:

$$M' = \frac{1}{2}(M + \sqrt{M^2 + T^2})$$
$$T' = \sqrt{M^2 + T^2}$$
$$\text{Max } s = \frac{M'r}{I}$$
$$\text{Max } s_s = \frac{T'r}{J}$$

where M = bending moment and T = twisting moment at the section in question. The use of the equivalent bending moment and the equivalent twisting moment is especially convenient in design, since the radius required for a given allowable stress can be found directly.

Relation between Twisting Moment and Power Transmitted.—A shaft rotating uniformly at n rev. per min. and transmitting H hp. is subjected to a steady twisting moment T (inch-pounds) given by

$$T = 63{,}024\,\frac{H}{n}$$

For a solid circular shaft of radius r the resulting stress is

$$s = 40{,}100\,\frac{H}{nr^3}$$

and the resulting unit twist (radians per inch) is

$$\frac{\theta}{l} = 40{,}150\,\frac{H}{nr^4G}$$

References

1. PRESCOTT, J.: "Applied Elasticity," Longmans, Green & Company, 1924.
2. TRAYER, G. W., and H. W. MARCH: The Torsion of Members having Sections Common in Aircraft Construction, *Nat. Adv. Comm. Aeron., Report* 334, 1930.
3. GRIFFITH, A. A.: The Determination of the Torsional Stiffness and Strength of Cylindrical Bars of any Shape, *Reports and Memoranda* 334, *Adv. Comm. Aeron.* (British), 1917.

4. TAYLOR, G. I., and A. A. GRIFFITH: The Use of Soap Films in Solving Torsion Problems, *Reports and Memoranda* 333, *Adv. Comm. Aeron.* (British), 1917.
5. TIMOSHENKO, S.: "Strength of Materials," Part II, D. Van Nostrand Company, Inc., 1930.
6. GREEN, A. E.: The Equilibrium and Elastic Stability of a Thin Twisted Strip, *Proc. Royal Soc. London*, Series *A*, Vol. 154, 1936.
7. YOUNGER, J. E.: "Structural Design of Metal Airplanes," McGraw-Hill Book Company, 1935.
8. WAHL, A. M.: "Mechanical Springs," 2d ed., McGraw-Hill Book Company, 1963. See also (same author) Helical Compression and Tension Springs, *Am. Soc. Mech. Eng., Paper* A-38, *Jour. Appl. Mech.*, Vol. 2, No. 1, 1935.
9. SAYRE, M. F.: New Spring Formulas and New Materials for Precision Spring Scales, *Trans. Am. Soc. Mech. Eng.*, Vol. 58, p. 379, 1936.
10. WILSON, T. S.: The Eccentric Circular Tube, *Aircraft Eng.*, Vol. 14, No. 157, March, 1942.
11. LYSE, I., and B. G. JOHNSTON: Structural Beams in Torsion, *Inst. Research, Lehigh Univ., Circ.* 113, 1935.
12. BARON, F. M.: Torsion of Multi-connected Thin-walled Cylinders, *Am. Soc. Mech. Eng. Paper* A-72, *Jour. Appl. Mech.*, Vol. 9, No. 2, June, 1942.
13. SHORTLEY, G. H., R. WELLS, and B. FRIED: *Eng. Exp. Sta., Ohio State Univ., Bull.* 107, September, 1940.
14. PLETTA, D. H., and F. J. MAHER: The Torsional Properties of Round-edged Flat Bars, *Eng. Exp. Sta., Va. Polytech. Inst., Bull.* 50, 1942.
15. PAYNE, J. H.: Torsion in Box Beams, *Aircraft Eng.*, January, 1942.
16. WEIGAND, A.: The Problem of Torsion in Prismatic Members of Circular Segmental Cross Section, *Nat. Adv. Comm. Aeron., Tech. Memo.* 1182, 1948.
17. TIMOSHENKO, S. P., and J. N. GOODIER: "Theory of Elasticity," 2d ed., McGraw-Hill Book Company, 1951.
18. ANC Mil-Hdbk-5, Strength of Metal Aircraft Elements, Armed Forces Supply Support Center, March, 1959.
19. Bethlehem Steel Co., Booklet 1803, Torsional Stresses in Structural Beams.
20. NUTTALL, HENRY: Torsion of Uniform Rods with Particular Reference to Rods of Triangular Cross Section, *Am. Soc. Mech. Eng., Jour. Appl. Mech.*, Vol. 19, No. 4, December, 1952.
21. CARTER, W. J., and J. B. OLIPHANT: Torsion of a Circular Shaft with Diametrically Opposite Flat Sides, *Am. Soc. Mech. Eng., Jour. Appl. Mech.*, Vol. 19, No. 3, September, 1952.
22. CHU, CHEN: The Effect of Initial Twist on the Torsional Rigidity of Thin Prismatical Bars and Tubular Members, *Proc. 1st U.S. Nat. Congr. Appl. Mech.*, p. 265, 1951.
23. ENGEL, H. L., and J. N. GOODIER: Measurements of Torsional Stiffness Changes and Instability Due to Tension, Compression and Bending, *Am. Soc. Mech. Eng., Jour. Appl. Mech.*, Vol. 20, No. 4, December, 1953.

24. ANCKER, C. J., JR., and J. N. GOODIER: Pitch and Curvature Correction for Helical Springs, *Am. Soc. Mech. Eng., Jour. Appl. Mech.*, Vol. 25, No. 4, December, 1958.
25. REINER, M.: The Complete Elasticity Law for Some Metals According to Poynting's Observations, *Appl. Sci. Research, Sec.* A, Vol. 5.
26. POYNTING, J. H.: *Proc. Roy. Soc. London,* A32, 1909, and A36, 1912.
27. William D. Gibson Co., Division of Associated Spring Corp., "Mechanical Springs: Their Engineering and Design," 1st ed., 1944.

CHAPTER 10

FLAT PLATES

56. Common Case.—The formulas of this article are based on the following assumptions: (1) The plate is flat, of uniform thickness, and of homogeneous isotropic material. (2) The thickness is not more than about one-quarter of the least transverse dimension, and the maximum deflection is not more than about one-half the thickness. (3) All forces—loads and reactions—are normal to the plane of the plate. (4) The plate is nowhere stressed beyond the elastic limit.

For convenience in discussion, it will further be assumed that the plane of the plate is horizontal.

Behavior.—The plate deflects. The middle surface (halfway between top and bottom surfaces) remains unstressed; at other points there are biaxial stresses in the plane of the plate. Straight lines in the plate originally vertical remain straight but become inclined; therefore the intensity of either principal stress at points on any such line is proportional to the distance from the middle surface, and the maximum stresses occur at the surfaces of the plate.

Formulas.—In Table X are given formulas for deflection, edge slope, and stress for plates of various forms loaded and supported in various ways. By superposition, these formulas may be made to cover a wide variety of loadings not specifically considered (see Examples).

Unless otherwise indicated, the formulas are based on very closely approximate mathematical analysis and may be accepted as sufficiently accurate so long as the assumptions stated hold true. Certain additional facts of importance in relation to these formulas are as follows:

Concentrated Loading.—It will be noted that all formulas for maximum stress due to a load applied over a small area give very high values when the radius of the loaded area approaches zero. Analysis by a more precise method (Ref. 12) shows that the actual maximum stress produced by a load concentrated on a very small area of radius r_0 can be found by replacing the actual r_0 by a so-called *equivalent radius* b, which depends largely upon the thickness of the plate t and to a less degree on its least transverse dimension. Holl (Ref. 13) shows how b varies with the width of a flat plate. Westergaard (Ref. 14) gives as an approximate expression for this equivalent radius

$$b = \sqrt{1.6r_0^2 + t^2} - 0.675t$$

This formula, which applies to a plate of any form, may be used for all values of r_0 less than about $1.7t$; for larger values the actual r_0 may be used. According to the equation, b is greater than r_0 until r_0 becomes $0.5t$, after which b becomes slightly less than r_0.

Use of the equivalent radius makes possible the calculation of the finite maximum stresses produced by a (nominal) point loading; whereas the ordinary formula would indicate that these stresses were infinite.

Edge Conditions.—The formulas of Table X are given for one or the other of two ideal conditions of support—either simply supported edges or fixed edges. Neither condition is likely to be realized in ordinary construction; a condition of true edge fixity is especially difficult to obtain. Even a small horizontal force at the line of contact may appreciably reduce the stress and deflection in a supported plate, while on the other hand a very slight yielding at nominally fixed edges will greatly relieve the stresses there, while increasing the deflection and center stresses. For this reason it is usually advisable to design a fixed-edged plate that is to carry uniform load for somewhat higher center stresses than are indicated by theory. The effect of a definite amount of edge yielding, or relaxation of the fixing moments, can usually be taken into account by means of the formulas for edge slope and the principle of superposition, as shown in Example 5.

Use of Formulas.—The formulas as given involve m, the reciprocal of Poisson's ratio. If ν is taken as $\frac{1}{3}$ or $\frac{1}{4}$, so that m is an even number, this is perhaps the most convenient form for calculation. If ν is taken as 0.3 (a value often used for steel) it is more convenient to divide the numerator and denominator of each term by m, leaving the formula in terms of ν. This is done in the illustrative examples below, where ν is taken as 0.3.

TABLE X.—FORMULAS FOR FLAT PLATES

Notation: W = total applied load (lb.); w = unit applied load (lb. per sq. in.); t = thickness of plate (in.); s = unit stress at surface of plate (lb. per sq. in.); y = vertical deflection of plate from original position (in.); θ = slope of plate measured from horizontal (rad); E = modulus of elasticity; m = reciprocal of ν, Poisson's ratio. q denotes any given point on the surface of plate; r denotes the distance of q from the center of a circular plate. Other dimensions and corresponding symbols are indicated on figures. Positive sign for s indicates tension at upper surface and equal compression at lower surface; negative sign indicates reverse condition. Positive sign for y indicates upward deflection, negative sign downward deflection. Subscripts r, t, a, and b used with s denote respectively radial direction, tangential direction, direction of dimension a, and direction of dimension b. All dimensions are in inches. All logarithms are to the base e, ($\log_e x = 2.3026 \log_{10} x$). (See pp. 240 and 242 for stress, slope, and deflection coefficients.)

Manner of loading and Case No.	Formulas for stress and deflection
	Circular and solid (A)
1. Edges supported. Uniform load over entire surface. $W = w\pi a^2$	(At q) $s_r = -\frac{3W}{8\pi m t^2}\left[(3m+1)\left(1-\frac{r^2}{a^2}\right)\right]$ $s_t = -\frac{3W}{8\pi m t^2}\left[(3m+1)-(m+3)\frac{r^2}{a^2}\right]$ $y = -\frac{3W(m^2-1)}{8\pi E m^2 t^3}\left[\frac{(5m+1)a^2}{2(m+1)}+\frac{r^4}{2a^2}-\frac{(3m+1)r^2}{m+1}\right]$ (At center) Max $s_r = s_t = -\frac{3W}{8\pi m t^2}(3m+1)$ Max $y = -\frac{3W(m-1)(5m+1)a^2}{16\pi E m^2 t^3}$ (At edge) $\theta = \frac{3W(m-1)a}{2\pi E m t^3}$
2. Edges supported. Uniform load over concentric circular area of radius r_0. $W = w\pi r_0^2$	(At q, $r < r_0$) $s_r = -\frac{3W}{2\pi m t^2}\left[m+(m+1)\log\frac{a}{r_0}-(m-1)\frac{r_0^2}{4a^2}-(3m+1)\frac{r^2}{4r_0^2}\right]$ $s_t = -\frac{3W}{2\pi m t^2}\left[m+(m+1)\log\frac{a}{r_0}-(m-1)\frac{r_0^2}{4a^2}-(m+3)\frac{r^2}{4r_0^2}\right]$ $y = -\frac{3W(m^2-1)}{16\pi E m^2 t^3}\left[4a^2-5r_0^2+\frac{r^4}{r_0^2}-(8r^2+4r_0^2)\log\frac{a}{r_0}-\frac{2(m-1)r_0^2(a^2-r^2)}{(m+1)a^2}+\frac{8m(a^2-r^2)}{m+1}\right]$ (At q, $r > r_0$) $s_r = -\frac{3W}{2\pi m t^2}\left[(m+1)\log\frac{a}{r}-(m-1)\frac{r_0^2}{4a^2}+(m-1)\frac{r_0^2}{4r^2}\right]$ $s_t = -\frac{3W}{2\pi m t^2}\left[(m-1)+(m+1)\log\frac{a}{r}-(m-1)\frac{r_0^2}{4a^2}-(m-1)\frac{r_0^2}{4r^2}\right]$ $y = -\frac{3W(m^2-1)}{16\pi E m^2 t^3}\left[\frac{(12m+4)(a^2-r^2)}{m+1}-\frac{2(m-1)r_0^2(a^2-r^2)}{(m+1)a^2}-(8r^2+4r_0^2)\log\frac{a}{r}\right]$ (At center) Max $s_r = s_t = -\frac{3W}{2\pi m t^2}\left[m+(m+1)\log\frac{a}{r_0}-(m-1)\frac{r_0^2}{4a^2}\right]$ Max $y = -\frac{3W(m^2-1)}{16\pi E m^2 t^3}\left[\frac{(12m+4)a^2}{m+1}-4r_0^2\log\frac{a}{r_0}-\frac{(7m+3)r_0^2}{m+1}\right]$ For r_0 very small (concentrated load) Max $y = -\frac{3W(m-1)(3m+1)a^2}{4\pi E m^2 t^3}$ (At edge) $\theta = \frac{3W(m-1)a}{\pi E m t^3}$

3. Uniform load on concentric circular ring of radius r_0

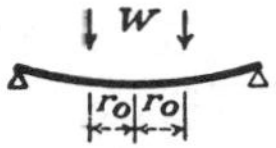

$$y = -\frac{3W(m^2-1)}{2\pi Em^2t^3}\left[\frac{(3m+1)(a^2-r^2)}{2(m+1)} - (r^2+r_0^2)\log\frac{a}{r_0} + (r^2-r_0^2) - \frac{(m-1)r_0^2(a^2-r^2)}{2(m+1)a^2}\right]$$

(At q, $r > r_0$) $s_r = -\frac{3W}{2\pi mt^2}\left[(m+1)\log\frac{a}{r} + (m-1)\frac{r_0^2}{2r^2} - (m-1)\frac{r_0^2}{2a^2}\right]$ $\quad s_t = -\frac{3W}{2\pi mt^2}\left[(m-1) + (m+1)\log\frac{a}{r} - (m-1)\frac{r_0^2}{2r^2} - (m-1)\frac{r_0^2}{2a^2}\right]$

$$y = -\frac{3W(m^2-1)}{2\pi Em^2t^3}\left[\frac{(3m+1)(a^2-r^2)}{2(m+1)} - (r^2+r_0^2)\log\frac{a}{r} - \frac{(m-1)r_0^2(a^2-r^2)}{2(m+1)a^2}\right]$$

(At center) Max $y = -\frac{3W(m^2-1)}{2\pi Em^2t^3}\left[\frac{(3m+1)a^2-(m-1)r_0^2}{2(m+1)} - r_0^2\left(\log\frac{a}{r_0}+1\right)\right]$

---

4. Edges supported. Uniform load over small eccentric circular area of radius r_0

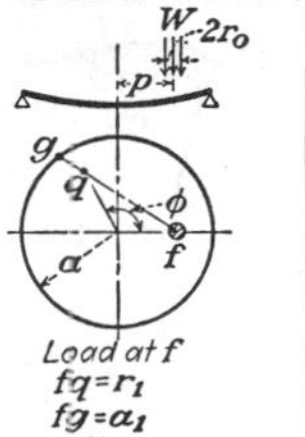

Load at f; $fq = r_1$; $fg = a_1$

(At point of load, f) Max $s_r = s_t = -\frac{3W}{2\pi mt^2}\left[m + (m+1)\log\frac{a-p}{r_0} - (m-1)\left(\frac{r_0^2}{4(a-p)^2}\right)\right]$

(At q) $s_r = (\text{Max } s_r)\left[\frac{(m+1)\log\frac{a_1}{r_1}}{1+(m+1)\log\frac{a_1}{r_0}}\right]$ $\quad s_t = (\text{Max } s_t)\left[\frac{(m+1)\log\frac{a_1}{r_1} + (m-1)}{m+(m+1)\log\frac{a_1}{r_0}}\right]$

$$y = K_0(r^3 - b_0ar^2 + c_0a^3) + K_1(r^4 - b_1ar^3 + c_1a^3r)\cos\phi + K_2(r^4 - b_2ar^3 + c_2a^2r^2)\cos 2\phi$$

Where

$$K_0 = \frac{2(m+1)W(p^3 - b_0ap^2 + c_0a^3)}{9(5m+1)K\pi a^4};\ K_1 = \frac{2(3m+1)W(p^4 - b_1ap^3 + c_1a^3p)}{3(9m+1)K\pi a^6};\ K_2 = \frac{(4m+1)^2W(p^4 - b_2ap^3 + c_2a^2p^2)}{(9m+1)(5m+1)K\pi a^6}$$

Where

$$K = \frac{m^2Et^3}{12(m^2-1)};\ b_0 = \frac{3(2m+1)}{2(m+1)};\ b_1 = \frac{3(4m+1)}{2(3m+1)};\ b_2 = \frac{2(5m+1)}{4m+1};\ c_0 = \frac{4m+1}{2(m+1)};\ c_1 = \frac{6m+1}{2(3m+1)};\ c_2 = \frac{6m+1}{4m+1}$$

(Ref. 1)

---

5. Edges supported. Central couple (trunnion loading)

(At $r = r_0$) Max $s_r = \frac{3M}{4\pi t^2r_0}\left[1 + \left(\frac{m+1}{m}\right)\log\frac{2(a-r_0)}{Ka}\right]$ $\quad$ where $K = \frac{0.49a^2}{(r_0+0.7a)^2}$

(Ref. 1)

(See also p. 242)

---

6. Edges fixed. Uniform load over entire surface

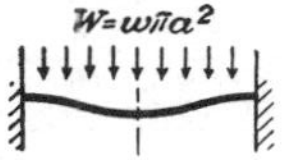

$W = w\pi a^2$

(At q) $s_r = \frac{3W}{8\pi mt^2}\left[(3m+1)\frac{r^2}{a^2} - (m+1)\right]$ $\quad s_t = \frac{3W}{8\pi mt^2}\left[(m+3)\frac{r^2}{a^2} - (m+1)\right]$ $\quad y = -\frac{3W(m^2-1)}{16\pi Em^2t^3}\left[\frac{(a^2-r^2)^2}{a^2}\right]$

(At edge) Max $s_r = \frac{3W}{4\pi t^2}$; $s_t = \frac{3W}{4\pi mt^2}$

(At center) $s_r = s_t = -\frac{3W(m+1)}{8\pi mt^2}$ $\quad$ Max $y = -\frac{3W(m^2-1)a^2}{16\pi Em^2t^3}$

TABLE X.—FORMULAS FOR FLAT PLATES.—(*Continued*)

Manner of loading and Case No.	Formulas for stress and deflection
7. Edges fixed Uniform load over concentric circular area of radius r_0 $W = w\pi r_0^2$	(At q, $r < r_0$) $s_r = -\frac{3W}{2\pi mt^2}\left[(m+1)\log\frac{a}{r_0} + (m+1)\frac{r_0^2}{4a^2} - (3m+1)\frac{r^2}{4r_0^2}\right]$ $\quad s_t = -\frac{3W}{2\pi mt^2}\left[(m+1)\log\frac{a}{r_0} + (m+1)\frac{r_0^2}{4a^2} - (m+3)\frac{r^2}{4r_0^2}\right]$ $y = -\frac{3W(m^2-1)}{16\pi Em^2t^3}\left[4a^2 - (8r^2+4r_0^2)\log\frac{a}{r_0} - \frac{2r^2r_0^2}{a^2} + \frac{r^4}{r_0^2} - 3r_0^2\right]$ (At q, $r > r_0$) $s_r = -\frac{3W}{2\pi mt^2}\left[(m+1)\log\frac{a}{r} + (m+1)\frac{r_0^2}{4a^2} + (m-1)\frac{r_0^2}{4r^2} - m\right]$ $\quad s_t = -\frac{3W}{2\pi mt^2}\left[(m+1)\log\frac{a}{r} + (m+1)\frac{r_0^2}{4a^2} - (m-1)\frac{r_0^2}{4r^2} - 1\right]$ $y = -\frac{3W(m^2-1)}{16\pi Em^2t^3}\left[4a^2 - (8r^2+4r_0^2)\log\frac{a}{r} - \frac{2r^2r_0^2}{a^2} - 4r^2 + 2r_0^2\right]$ (At edge) $s_r = \frac{3W}{2\pi t^2}\left(1 - \frac{r_0^2}{2a^2}\right) = \text{Max } s_r \text{ when } r_0 > 0.588a$ $\quad s_t = \frac{3W}{2\pi mt^2}\left(1 - \frac{r_0^2}{2a^2}\right)$ (At center) $s_r = s_t = -\frac{3W}{2\pi mt^2}\left[(m+1)\log\frac{a}{r_0} + (m+1)\frac{r_0^2}{4a^2}\right] = \text{Max } s_r \text{ when } r_0 < 0.588a$ $\text{Max } y = -\frac{3W(m^2-1)}{16\pi Em^2t^3}\left[4a^2 - 4r_0^2\log\frac{a}{r_0} - 3r_0^2\right]$ $\quad$ For r_0 very small (concentrated load): $\text{Max } y = -\frac{3W(m^2-1)a^2}{4\pi Em^2t^3}$
8. Edges fixed Uniform load on concentric circular ring of radius r_0 W	(At q, $r < r_0$) $s_r = s_t = -\frac{3W}{4\pi mt^2}\left[(m+1)\left(2\log\frac{a}{r_0} + \frac{r_0^2}{a^2} - 1\right)\right] = \text{Max } s \text{ when } r_0 < 0.31a$ $y = -\frac{3W(m^2-1)}{2\pi Em^2t^3}\left[\frac{1}{2}\left(1 + \frac{r_0^2}{a^2}\right)(a^2 - r^2) - (r^2 + r_0^2)\log\frac{a}{r_0} + (r^2 - r_0^2)\right]$ (At q, $r > r_0$) $s_r = -\frac{3W}{4\pi mt^2}\left[(m+1)\left(2\log\frac{a}{r} + \frac{r_0^2}{a^2}\right) + (m-1)\frac{r_0^2}{r^2} - 2m\right]$ $\quad s_t = -\frac{3W}{4\pi mt^2}\left[(m+1)\left(2\log\frac{a}{r} + \frac{r_0^2}{a^2}\right) - (m-1)\frac{r_0^2}{r^2} - 2\right]$ $y = -\frac{3W(m^2-1)}{2\pi Em^2t^3}\left[\frac{1}{2}\left(1 + \frac{r_0^2}{a^2}\right)(a^2 - r^2) - (r^2 + r_0^2)\log\frac{a}{r}\right]$ (At center) $\text{Max } y = \frac{-3W(m^2-1)}{2\pi Em^2t^3}\left[\frac{1}{2}(a^2 - r_0^2) - r_0^2\log\frac{a}{r_0}\right]$ (At edge) $s_r = \frac{3W}{2\pi t^2}\left(1 - \frac{r_0^2}{a^2}\right) = \text{max } s \text{ when } r_0 > 0.31a$ $\quad s_t = \frac{3W}{2\pi mt^2}\left(1 - \frac{r_0^2}{a^2}\right)$
9. Edges fixed Uniform load over small eccentric circular area of radius r_0 $2r_0$ W q r' r_1 f f'	(At point of load, f) $s_r = \frac{-3W}{2\pi mt^2}\left[(m+1)\log\frac{a-p}{r_0} + (m+1)\frac{r_0^2}{4(a-p)^2}\right] = \text{max } s \text{ when } r_0 < 0.6(a-p)$; $y = \frac{3W(m^2-1)}{4\pi Em^2t^3}\frac{(a^2-p^2)^2}{a^2}$ (At q) $y = -\frac{3W(m^2-1)}{2\pi Em^2t^3}\left[\frac{1}{2}\left(\frac{p^2r'^2}{a^2} - r_1^2\right) - r_1^2\log\frac{pr'}{ar_1}\right]$ (At edge) $s_r = \frac{3W}{2\pi t^2}\left[1 - \frac{r_0^2}{2(a-p)^2}\right] = \text{max } s \text{ when } r_0 > 0.6(a-p)$ $\quad p = \text{eccentricity of } W$

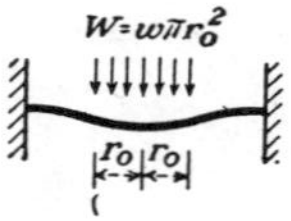

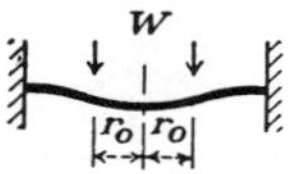

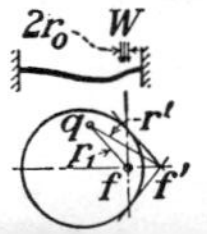

(Formulas due to Michell. Ref. 2)

Case	Formulas
10. Central couple (trunnion loading)	(At $r = r_0$) $\text{Max } s_r = \dfrac{3M}{4\pi t^2 r_0}\left[1 + \left(\dfrac{m+1}{m}\right)\log\dfrac{2(0.45a - r_0)}{0.45ka}\right]$ where $k = \dfrac{0.1a^2}{(r_0 + 0.28a)^2}$ (Ref. 1) (See also p. 242)
Supported by uniform pressure over entire lower surface **11.** Uniform load over concentric circular area of radius r_0	(At q, $r < r_0$) $s_r = -\dfrac{3W}{2\pi m t^2}\left\{(m+1)\log\dfrac{a}{r_0} + \dfrac{1}{4}\left(1 - \dfrac{r_0^2}{a^2}\right)\left[(m-1) - \dfrac{(3m+1)r^2}{r_0^2}\right]\right\}$ $s_t = -\dfrac{3W}{2\pi m t^2}\left\{(m+1)\log\dfrac{a}{r_0} + \dfrac{1}{4}\left(1 - \dfrac{r_0^2}{a^2}\right)\left[(m-1) - \dfrac{(m+3)r^2}{r_0^2}\right]\right\}$ $y = \dfrac{3W(m^2-1)}{16\pi E m^2 t^3}\left[(8r^2 + 4r_0^2)\log\dfrac{a}{r_0} + 2r^2\left(\dfrac{m-1}{m+1}\right)\left(1 - \dfrac{r_0^2}{a^2}\right) + 2r_0^2\left(\dfrac{3m+1}{m+1}\right) + \dfrac{r_0^4}{a^2} - a^2\left(\dfrac{7m+3}{m+1}\right) - \dfrac{(a^2 - r_0^2)(r^4 - r_0^4)}{a^2 r_0^2}\right]$ (At q, $r > r_0$) $s_r = -\dfrac{3W}{2\pi m t^2}\left\{(m+1)\log\dfrac{a}{r} + \dfrac{1}{4}(m-1)\left[1 - \dfrac{r_0^2}{a^2} + \dfrac{r_0^2}{r^2}\right] - m + \dfrac{(3m+1)r^2}{4a^2}\right\}$ $s_t = -\dfrac{3W}{2\pi m t^2}\left\{(m+1)\log\dfrac{a}{r} - \dfrac{1}{4}(m-1)\left[\dfrac{r_0^2}{a^2} + \dfrac{r_0^2}{r^2}\right] + \dfrac{1}{4}(m-5) + \dfrac{(m+3)r^2}{4a^2}\right\}$ $y = \dfrac{3W(m^2-1)}{16\pi E m^2 t^3}\left\{(8r^2 + 4r_0^2)\log\dfrac{a}{r} + 2r^2\left[\dfrac{3m+1}{m+1} - \dfrac{(m-1)r_0^2}{(m+1)a^2}\right] - \dfrac{r^4}{a^2} - a^2\left(\dfrac{7m+3}{m+1}\right) + \dfrac{2(m-1)r_0^2}{m+1}\right\}$ (At center) $\text{Max } s_r = s_t = -\dfrac{3W}{2\pi m t^2}\left[(m+1)\log\dfrac{a}{r_0} + \dfrac{1}{4}(m-1)\left(1 - \dfrac{r_0^2}{a^2}\right)\right]$ $\text{Max } y = +\dfrac{3W(m^2-1)}{16\pi E m^2 t^3}\left[4r_0^2\log\dfrac{a}{r_0} + 2r_0^2\left(\dfrac{3m+1}{m+1}\right) + \dfrac{r_0^4}{a^2} - a^2\left(\dfrac{7m+3}{m+1}\right) + \dfrac{(a^2 - r_0^2)r_0^4}{a^2 r_0^2}\right]$ For r_0 very small (concentrated load) $\text{Max } y = -\dfrac{3W(m-1)(7m+3)a^2}{16\pi E m^2 t^3}$
No support **12.** Uniform edge moment	(At any point) $s_r = s_t = -\dfrac{6M}{t^2}$ (At q) $y = -\dfrac{6(m-1)M(a^2 - r^2)}{Emt^3}$ (At center) $\text{Max } y = -\dfrac{6(m-1)Ma^2}{Emt^3}$ (At edge) $\theta = \dfrac{12(m-1)Ma}{Emt^3}$

TABLE X.—FORMULAS FOR FLAT PLATES.—(*Continued*)

Manner of loading and Case No.	Formulas for stress and deflection
	Circular, with concentric circular hole (circular flange) (B)
Outer edge supported 13. Uniform load over entire actual surface $W = w\pi(a^2 - b^2)$	(At inner edge) Max $s = s_t = -\frac{3w}{4mt^2(a^2-b^2)}\left[a^4(3m+1) + b^4(m-1) - 4ma^2b^2 - 4(m+1)a^2b^2 \log\frac{a}{b}\right]$ When b is very small, Max $s = s_t = -\frac{3wa^2(3m+1)}{4mt^2}$ Max $y = -\frac{3w(m^2-1)}{2m^2Et^3}\left[\frac{a^4(5m+1)}{8(m+1)} + \frac{b^4(7m+3)}{8(m+1)} - \frac{a^2b^2(3m+1)}{2(m+1)} + \frac{a^2b^2(3m+1)}{2(m-1)}\log\frac{a}{b} - \frac{2a^2b^4(m+1)}{(a^2-b^2)(m-1)}\left(\log\frac{a}{b}\right)^2\right]$
Outer edge supported 14. Uniform load along inner edge	(At inner edge) Max $s = s_t = -\frac{3W}{2\pi mt^2}\left[\frac{2a^2(m+1)}{a^2-b^2}\log\frac{a}{b} + (m-1)\right]$ Max $y = -\frac{3W(m^2-1)}{4\pi Em^2t^3}\left[\frac{(a^2-b^2)(3m+1)}{(m+1)} + \frac{4a^2b^2(m+1)}{(m-1)(a^2-b^2)}\left(\log\frac{a}{b}\right)^2\right]$
Supported along concentric circle near outer edge 15. Uniform load along concentric circle near inner edge.	(At inner edge) Max $s = s_t = -\frac{3W}{2\pi mt^2}\left[\frac{2a^2(m+1)}{a^2-b^2}\log\frac{c}{d} + (m-1)\frac{c^2-d^2}{a^2-b^2}\right]$

Case	Formulas
16. Uniform load over entire actual surface 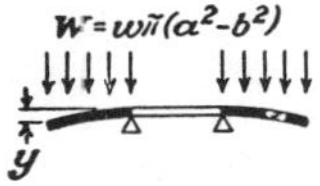 $W = w\pi(a^2 - b^2)$	(At inner edge) $\text{Max } s = s_t = \frac{3w}{4mt^2(a^2 - b^2)}\left[4a^4(m+1)\log\frac{a}{b} + 4a^2b^2 + b^4(m-1) - a^4(m+3)\right]$ (At outer edge) $\text{Max } y = \frac{3w(m-1)}{16Em^2t^3}\left[a^4(7m+3) + b^4(5m+1) - a^2b^2(12m+4) - \frac{4a^2b^2(3m+1)(m+1)}{(m-1)}\log\frac{a}{b} + \frac{16a^4b^2(m+1)^2}{(a^2-b^2)(m-1)}\left(\log\frac{a}{b}\right)^2\right]$
Outer edge fixed and supported 17. Uniform load over entire actual surface 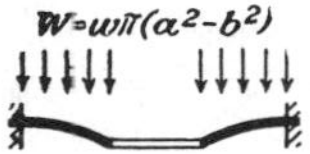 $W = w\pi(a^2 - b^2)$	(At outer edge) $\text{Max } s_r = \frac{3w}{4t^2}\left[a^2 - 2b^2 + \frac{b^4(m-1) - 4b^4(m+1)\log\frac{a}{b} + a^2b^2(m+1)}{a^2(m-1) + b^2(m+1)}\right] = \text{Max } s$ (At inner edge) $\text{Max } s_t = -\frac{3w(m^2-1)}{4mt^2}\left[\frac{a^4 - b^4 - 4a^2b^2\log\frac{a}{b}}{a^2(m-1) + b^2(m+1)}\right]$ $\text{Max } y = -\frac{3w(m^2-1)}{16m^2Et^3}$ $\left\{a^4 + 5b^4 - 6a^2b^2 + 8b^4\log\frac{a}{b} - \frac{[8b^6(m+1) - 4a^2b^4(3m+1) - 4a^4b^2(m+1)]\log\frac{a}{b} + 16a^2b^4(m+1)\left(\log\frac{a}{b}\right)^2 - 4a^2b^4 + 2a^4b^2(m+1) - 2b^6(m-1)}{a^2(m-1) + b^2(m+1)}\right\}$
Outer edge fixed and supported **18. Uniform load along inner edge**  W	(At outer edge) $\text{Max } s_r = \frac{3W}{2\pi t^2}\left[1 - \frac{2mb^2 - 2b^2(m+1)\log\frac{a}{b}}{a^2(m-1) + b^2(m+1)}\right] = \text{Max } s \text{ when } \frac{a}{b} < 2.4$ (At inner edge) $\text{Max } s_t = \frac{3W}{2\pi mt^2}\left[1 + \frac{ma^2(m-1) - mb^2(m+1) - 2(m^2-1)a^2\log\frac{a}{b}}{a^2(m-1) + b^2(m+1)}\right] = \text{Max } s \text{ when } \frac{a}{b} > 2.4$ $\text{Max } y = -\frac{3W(m^2-1)}{4\pi m^2Et^3}\left\{a^2 - b^2 + \frac{2mb^2(a^2-b^2) - 8ma^2b^2\log\frac{a}{b} + 4a^2b^2(m+1)\left(\log\frac{a}{b}\right)^2}{a^2(m-1) + b^2(m+1)}\right\}$

TABLE X.—FORMULAS FOR FLAT PLATES.—(*Continued*)

Manner of loading and Case No.	Formulas for stress and deflection
Outer edge fixed and supported. Inner edge fixed 19. Uniform load over entire actual surface 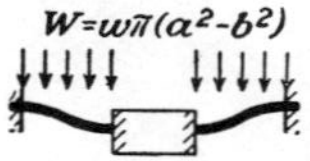 $W = w\pi(a^2 - b^2)$	(At outer edge) Max $s_r = \frac{3w}{4t^2}\left[(a^2 - 3b^2) + \frac{4b^4}{a^2 - b^2}\left(\log\frac{a}{b}\right)\right]$ (At inner edge) $s_r = -\frac{3w}{4t^2}\left[(a^2 + b^2) - \frac{4a^2b^2}{(a^2 - b^2)}\left(\log\frac{a}{b}\right)\right]$ Max $y = -\frac{3w(m^2 - 1)}{16m^2Et^3}\left[a^4 + 3b^4 - 4a^2b^2 - 4a^2b^2\log\frac{a}{b} + \frac{16a^2b^4}{a^2 - b^2}\left(\log\frac{a}{b}\right)^2\right]$
Outer edge fixed and supported. Inner edge fixed 20. Uniform load along inner edge 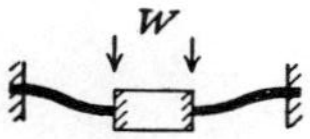 W	(At outer edge) $s_r = \frac{3W}{2\pi t^2}\left[1 - \frac{2b^2}{a^2 - b^2}\left(\log\frac{a}{b}\right)\right]$ (At inner edge) Max $s_r = \frac{3W}{2\pi t^2}\left[1 - \frac{2a^2}{a^2 - b^2}\left(\log\frac{a}{b}\right)\right]$ Max $y = -\frac{3W(m^2 - 1)}{4\pi m^2Et^3}\left[a^2 - b^2 - \frac{4a^2b^2}{a^2 - b^2}\left(\log\frac{a}{b}\right)^2\right]$
Inner edge fixed and supported 21. Uniform load over entire actual surface 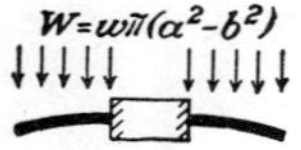 $W = w\pi(a^2 - b^2)$	(At inner edge) Max $s_r = \frac{3w}{4t^2}\left[\frac{4a^4(m + 1)\log\frac{a}{b} - a^4(m + 3) + b^4(m - 1) + 4a^2b^2}{a^2(m + 1) + b^2(m - 1)}\right]$ (At outer edge) Max $y = -\frac{3w(m^2 - 1)}{16m^2Et^3}\left\{\frac{a^6(7m + 3) + b^6(m - 1) - a^4b^2(m + 7) - a^2b^4(7m - 5) - 4a^2b^2[a^2(5m - 1) + b^2(m + 1)]\log\frac{a}{b} - 16a^4b^2(m + 1)\left(\log\frac{a}{b}\right)^2}{a^2(m + 1) + b^2(m - 1)}\right\}$

Case	Formulas
22. Uniform load along outer edge	(At inner edge) Max $s_r = \frac{3W}{2\pi t^2}\left[\frac{2a^2(m+1)\log\frac{a}{b} + a^2(m-1) - b^2(m-1)}{a^2(m+1) + b^2(m-1)}\right]$ (At outer edge) Max $y = -\frac{3W(m^2-1)}{4m^2\pi E t^3}\left[\frac{a^4(3m+1) - b^4(m-1) - 2a^2b^2(m+1) - 8ma^2b^2\log\frac{a}{b} - 4a^2b^2(m+1)\left(\log\frac{a}{b}\right)^2}{a^2(m+1) + b^2(m-1)}\right]$
Outer edge fixed 23. Uniform moment along inner edge 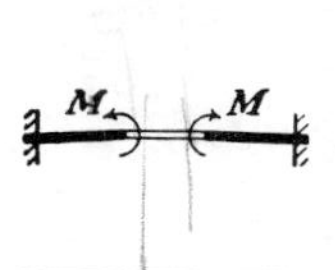	(At inner edge) Max $s_r = -\frac{6M}{t^2}$ Max $y = \frac{6M(m^2-1)}{mEt^3}\left[\frac{a^2b^2 - b^4 - 2a^2b^2\log\frac{a}{b}}{a^2(m-1) + b^2(m+1)}\right]$ (At outer edge) $s_r = -\frac{6M}{t^2}\left[\frac{2mb^2}{(m+1)b^2 + (m-1)a^2}\right]$
Inner edge fixed 24. Uniform moment along outer edge	(At inner edge) Max $s_r = -\frac{6M}{t^2}\left[\frac{2ma^2}{(m+1)a^2 + (m-1)b^2}\right]$ (At outer edge) $s_r = -\frac{6M}{t^2}$ Max $y = \frac{6M(m^2-1)}{mEt^3}\left[\frac{a^4 - a^2b^2 - 2a^2b^2\log\frac{a}{b}}{a^2(m+1) + b^2(m-1)}\right]$
Outer edge supported 25. Unequal uniform moments along edges	(At q) $s_r = -\frac{6}{t^2(a^2-b^2)}\left[a^2M_a - b^2M_b - \frac{a^2b^2}{r^2}(M_a - M_b)\right]$ $s_t = -\frac{6}{t^2(a^2-b^2)}\left[a^2M_a - b^2M_b + \frac{a^2b^2}{r^2}(M_a - M_b)\right]$ $y = -\frac{12(m^2-1)}{mEt^3(a^2-b^2)}\left\{\frac{a^2-r^2}{2}\left[\frac{a^2M_a - b^2M_b}{m+1}\right] + \log\frac{a}{r}\left[\frac{a^2b^2(M_a - M_b)}{m-1}\right]\right\}$ from outer edge level

TABLE X.—FORMULAS FOR FLAT PLATES.—(*Continued*)

Manner of loading and Case No.	Formulas for stress and deflection
	Elliptical, solid; $\frac{b}{a} = \alpha$ (C)
Edge supported **26.** Uniform load over entire surface	(At center) $s_b = -\frac{0.3125(2-\alpha)wb^2}{t^2} = \text{Max } s$ Max $y = \frac{(0.146 - 0.1\alpha)wb^4}{Et^3}\left(\text{for } \nu = \frac{1}{3}\right)$ (Approximate formula after Morley, Ref. 3)
Edge supported **27.** Uniform load over small concentric circular area of radius r_0	(At center) $s_b = -\frac{3W}{2\pi m t^2}\left[(m+1)\log\frac{b}{2r_0} + 6.57 - 2.57\alpha\right] = \text{Max } s$ Max $y = \frac{Wb^2}{Et^3}(0.19 - 0.045\alpha)\left(\text{for } \nu = \frac{1}{4}\right)$ (Approximate formulas by interpolation between cases of circular plate and infinitely long narrow strip, Ref. 4)
Edge fixed **28.** Uniform load over entire surface	(At edge) (Span a) $s_a = \frac{3wb^2\alpha^2}{2t^2(3 + 2\alpha^2 + 3\alpha^4)}$ (Span b) $s_b = \frac{3wb^2}{2t^2(3 + 2\alpha^2 + 3\alpha^4)} = \text{Max } s$ (At center) $s_a = -\frac{3wb^2(\alpha^2 m + 1)}{4t^2(3 + 2\alpha^2 + 3\alpha^4)m}$ $s_b = \frac{-3wb^2(m + \alpha^2)}{4t^2(3 + 2\alpha^2 + 3\alpha^4)m}$ Max $y = -\frac{3w(m^2 - 1)b^4}{16m^2Et^3(6 + 4\alpha^2 + 6\alpha^4)}$ (Formulas due to Prescott, Ref. 5)
Edge fixed **29.** Uniform load over small concentric circular area of radius r_0	(At center) $s_b = -\frac{3W(m+1)}{2\pi m t^2}\left[\log\frac{b}{r_0} - 0.317\alpha - 0.376\right]$ Max $y = -\frac{Wb^2(0.0815 - 0.026\alpha)}{Et^3}$ (Approximate formulas by interpolation between cases of circular plate and infinitely long narrow strip, Ref. 6. $\nu = 0.25$ for Max y)
	Square, solid; a (D)
Edges supported above and below. (Corners held down) **30.** Uniform load over entire surface	(At center) $s_a = -\frac{0.2208\, wa^2(m+1)}{mt^2} = \text{Max } s$ Max $y = -\frac{0.0487wa^4(m^2 - 1)}{m^2Et^3}$ (Formulas due to Prescott, Ref. 5)

held down)

31. Uniform load over small concentric circular area of radius r_0

(At center) $\text{Max } s = -\frac{3W}{2\pi m t^2}\left[(m+1)\log\frac{a}{2r_0} + 0.75m\right]$ $\text{Max } y = -\frac{0.1391 W a^2 (m^2-1)}{m^2 E t^3}$

Edges supported below only (corners free to rise)

32. Uniform load over entire surface

(At center, on diagonal section) $s = -\frac{0.2214 w a^2}{t^2}$ $\text{Max } y = -\frac{.0443 w a^4}{E t^3}$ $(\nu = 0.3)$

(At corners, on diagonal section) $s = -\frac{0.2778 w a^2}{t^2} = \text{Max } s$

Edges supported below only (corners free to rise)

33. Uniform load over small concentric circular area of radius r_0

Same as Case 31

All edges fixed

34. Uniform load over entire surface

(At center of each edge) $s_a = \frac{0.308 w a^2}{t^2} = \text{Max } s$

(At center) $s = -\frac{6w(m+1)a^2}{47 m t^2}$ (Ref. 5). $\text{Max } y = -\frac{0.0138 w a^4}{E t^3}$

(Other formulas based on coefficients given by Timoshenko, Ref. 7. $\nu = 0.3$)

---

35. Uniform load over small concentric circular area of radius r_0

(At center) $\text{Max } s = -\frac{3W}{2\pi m t^2}\left[(m+1)\log\frac{a}{2r_0}\right]$ $y = \frac{0.0624(m^2-1)Wa^2}{m^2 E t^3}$

(Ref. 6)

Rectangular solid

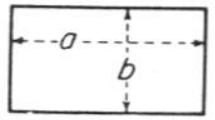

(E)

All edges supported

36. Uniform load over entire surface

(At center) $\text{Max } s = s_b = \beta\frac{wb^2}{t^2}$ $\text{Max } y = \alpha\frac{wb^4}{E t^3}$

$\frac{a}{b}$	1	1.2	1.4	1.6	1.8	2	3	4	5	∞
β	0.2874	0.3762	0.4530	0.5172	0.5688	0.6102	0.7134	0.7410	0.7476	0.750
α	0.0444	0.0616	0.0770	0.0906	0.1017	0.1110	0.1335	0.1400	0.1417	0.1421

(Ref. 21)

All edges supported

37. Uniform load over small concentric circular area of radius r_0

(At center) $\text{Max } s = \frac{3W}{2\pi m t^2}\left[(m+1)\log\frac{2b}{\pi r_0} + 1 - \beta m\right]$

$\text{Max } y = \alpha\frac{Wb^2}{E t^3}$

$\frac{a}{b}$	1	1.2	1.4	1.6	1.8	2
β	0.565	0.350	0.211	0.125	0.073	0.042
α	0.1267	0.1478	0.1581	0.1715	0.1770	0.1805

(Ref. 21)

TABLE X.—FORMULAS FOR FLAT PLATES.—(*Continued*)

Manner of loading and Case No.	Formulas for stress and deflection

38. All edges supported. Uniform load over central rectangular area shown shaded

(At center) Max $s = s_b = \beta \dfrac{W}{t^2}$, where β may be found from following table by interpolation:

$\frac{b_1}{b}$ \ $\frac{a_1}{b}$	$a = b$						$a = 1.4b$						$a = 2b$					
	0	0.2	0.4	0.6	0.8	1.0	0	0.2	0.4	0.8	1.2	1.4	0	0.4	0.8	1.2	1.6	2.0
0		1.82	1.38	1.12	0.93	0.76		2.0	1.55	1.12	0.84	0.75		1.64	1.20	0.97	0.78	0.64
0.2	1.82	1.28	1.08	0.90	0.76	0.63	1.78	1.43	1.23	0.95	0.74	0.64	1.73	1.31	1.03	0.84	0.68	0.57
0.4	1.39	1.07	0.84	0.72	0.62	0.52	1.39	1.13	1.00	0.80	0.62	0.55	1.32	1.08	0.88	0.74	0.60	0.50
0.6	1.12	0.90	0.72	0.60	0.52	0.43	1.10	0.91	0.82	0.68	0.53	0.47	1.04	0.90	0.76	0.64	0.54	0.44
0.8	0.92	0.76	0.62	0.51	0.42	0.36	0.90	0.76	0.68	0.57	0.45	0.40	0.87	0.76	0.63	0.54	0.44	0.38
1.0	0.76	0.63	0.52	0.42	0.35	0.30	0.75	0.62	0.57	0.47	0.38	0.33	0.71	0.61	0.53	0.45	0.38	0.30

(Values from charts of Ref. 8. $\nu = 0.3$)

39. All edges supported. Distributed load varying linearly along length

Max $s = \beta \dfrac{wb^2}{t^2}$ Max $y = \alpha \dfrac{wb^4}{Et^3}$, where β and α may be found from following table by interpolation:

$\frac{a}{b}$	1	1.5	2.0	2.5	3.0	3.5	4.0
β	0.16	0.26	0.34	0.38	0.43	0.47	0.49
α	0.022	0.043	0.060	0.070	0.078	0.086	0.091

(Values from charts of Ref. 8. $\nu = 0.3$)

40. All edges supported. Distributed load varying linearly along breadth

Max $s = \beta \dfrac{wb^2}{t^2}$ Max $y = \alpha \dfrac{wb^4}{Et^3}$, where β and α may be found from following table by interpolation:

$\frac{a}{b}$	1	1.5	2.0	2.5	3.0	3.5	4.0
β	0.16	0.26	0.32	0.35	0.37	0.38	0.38
α	0.022	0.042	0.056	0.063	0.067	0.069	0.070

(Values from charts of Ref. 8. $\nu = 0.3$)

All edges fixed
41. Uniform load over entire surface

(At centers of long edges) $s_b = \beta \frac{wb^2}{t^2} = \text{Max } s$ Max $y = \alpha \frac{wb^4}{Et^3}$
where β and α may be found from the following table:

$\frac{a}{b}$	1	1.2	1.4	1.6	1.8	2	∞
β	0.3078	0.3834	0.4356	0.4680	0.4872	0.4974	0.500
α	0.0138	0.0188	0.0226	0.0251	0.0267	0.0277	0.0284

(Ref. 21)

All edges fixed
42. Uniform load over small concentric circular area of radius r_0

(At center) $s_b = \beta \frac{W}{t^2} = \text{Max } s$ Max $y = \alpha \frac{Wb^2}{Et^3}$
where β and α may be found from the following table:

$\frac{a}{b}$	1	1.2	1.4	1.6	1.8	2	∞
β	0.7542	0.8940	0.9624	0.9906	1.000	1.004	1.008
α	0.0611	0.0705	0.0754	0.0777	0.0786	0.0788	0.0791

(Ref. 21)

Long edges fixed, short edges supported
43. Uniform load over entire surface

(At centers of long edges) $s_b = \beta \frac{wb^2}{t^2}$ Max $y = \alpha \frac{wb^4}{Et^3}$
where β and α may be found from the following table:

$\frac{a}{b}$	1	1.2	1.4	1.6	1.8	2	∞
β	0.4182	0.4626	0.4860	0.4968	0.4971	0.4973	0.500
α	0.0210	0.0243	0.0262	0.0273	0.0280	0.0283	0.0285

(Ref. 21)

Short edges fixed, long edges supported
44. Uniform load over entire surface

(At centers of short edges) $s_a = \beta \frac{wb^2}{t^2} = \text{Max } s$ Max $y = \alpha \frac{wb^4}{Et^3}$
where β and α may be found from the following table:

$\frac{a}{b}$	1	1.2	1.4	1.6	1.8	2	∞
β	0.4182	0.5208	0.5988	0.6540	0.6912	0.7146	0.750
α	0.0210	0.0349	0.0502	0.0658	0.0800	0.0922	

(Ref. 21)

One long edge fixed, others free; short edges supported
45. Uniform load over entire surface

(At center of fixed edge) $s_b = \beta \frac{wb^2}{t^2} = \text{Max } s$ Max $y = \alpha \frac{wb^4}{Et^3}$
where β and α may be found from the following table:

$\frac{a}{b}$	1	1.5	2	3	∞
β	0.714	1.362	1.914	2.568	3.00
α	0.1234	0.366	0.636	1.027	1.365

(Ref. 21)

One long edge clamped. Other three edges supported
46. Uniform load over entire surface

Max $s = \beta \frac{wb^2}{t^2}$ Max $y = \alpha \frac{wb^4}{Et^3}$, where β and α may be found from following table by interpolation:

$\frac{a}{b}$	1	1.5	2.0	2.5	3.0	3.5	4.0
β	0.50	0.66	0.73	0.74	0.74	0.75	0.75
α	0.030	0.046	0.054	0.056	0.057	0.058	0.058

(Values from charts of Ref. 8. $\nu = 0.3$)

TABLE X.—FORMULAS FOR FLAT PLATES.—(*Continued*)

Manner of loading and Case No.	Formulas for stress and deflection
One short edge clamped. Other three edges supported 47. Uniform load over entire surface	Max $s = \beta \frac{wb^2}{t^2}$, Max $y = \alpha \frac{wb^4}{Et^3}$, where β and α may be found from the following table by interpolation: (see table 47 below)
One short edge free. Other three edges supported 48. Uniform load over entire surface	Max $s = \beta \frac{wb^2}{t^2}$, Max $y = \alpha \frac{wb^4}{Et^3}$, where β and α may be found from the following table by interpolation: (see table 48 below)
One short edge free. Other three edges supported 49. Distributed load varying linearly along length	Max $s = \beta \frac{wb^2}{t^2}$, Max $y = \alpha \frac{wb^4}{Et^3}$, where β and α may be found from the following table by interpolation: (see table 49 below)
One long edge free. Other three edges supported 50. Uniform load over entire surface	Max $s = \beta \frac{wa^2}{t^2}$, Max $y = \alpha \frac{wa^4}{Et^3}$, where β and α may be found from the following table by interpolation: (see table 50 below)

Case 47:

$\frac{a}{b}$	1	1.5	2.0	2.5	3.0	3.5	4.0
β	0.50	0.67	0.73	0.74	0.75	0.75	0.75
α	0.030	0.071	0.101	0.122	0.132	0.137	0.139

(Values from charts of Ref. 8. $\nu = 0.3$)

Case 48:

$\frac{a}{b}$	1	1.5	2.0	4.0
β	0.67	0.77	0.79	0.80
α	0.140	0.160	0.165	0.167

(Values from charts of Ref. 8. $\nu = 0.3$)

Case 49:

$\frac{a}{b}$	1	1.5	2.0	2.5	3.0	3.5	4.0
β	0.2	0.28	0.32	0.35	0.36	0.37	0.37
α	0.040	0.050	0.058	0.064	0.067	0.069	0.070

(Values from charts of Ref. 8. $\nu = 0.3$)

Case 50:

$\frac{a}{b}$	1	1.5	2.0
β	0.67	0.45	0.36
α	0.140	0.106	0.080

Other three edges supported

51. Distributed load, varying linearly along breadth

Free edge w b

Max $s = \beta \frac{wa^2}{t^2}$, Max $y = \alpha \frac{wa^4}{Et^3}$, where β and α may be found from the following table by interpolation:

$\frac{a}{b}$	1	1.5	2.0
β	0.2	0.16	0.11
α	0.040	0.033	0.026

(Values from charts of Ref. 8. $\nu = 0.3$)

Semicircular pierced plate or flat ring

b a c c

(F)

52. Outer edge supported. Other edges free. Uniform load over entire actual surface

Simply supported edge

Free edges A B

(At A) $s_t = \frac{6wcb}{t^2}\left(\frac{b}{c} - \frac{1}{3}\right)\left[c_1\left(1 - \gamma_1^2\frac{c}{b}\right) + c_2\left(1 - \gamma_2^2\frac{c}{b}\right) + \frac{c}{b}\right]K$ (= Max stress)

(At B) $y = \frac{24wc^2b^2}{Et^3}\left(\frac{b}{c} - \frac{1}{3}\right)\left[c_1 \cosh\frac{\gamma_1\pi}{2} + c_2 \cosh\frac{\gamma_2\pi}{2} + \frac{c}{b}\right]$ (= Max deflection)

where

$$c_1 = \frac{1}{\left(\frac{b}{c} - \gamma_1^2\right)(\lambda - 1)\cosh\frac{\gamma_1\pi}{2}} \qquad c_2 = \frac{1}{\left(\frac{b}{c} - \gamma_2^2\right)\left(\frac{1}{\lambda} - 1\right)\cosh\frac{\gamma_2\pi}{2}}$$

$$\gamma_1 = \frac{\gamma}{\sqrt{2}}\sqrt{1 + \sqrt{1 - \frac{4b^2}{c^2\gamma^4}}}, \qquad \gamma_2 = \frac{\gamma}{\sqrt{2}}\sqrt{1 - \sqrt{1 - \frac{4b^2}{c^2\gamma^4}}}$$

$$\gamma = \sqrt{\frac{2b}{c} + 4\left(1 - \frac{0.625t}{2c}\right)\frac{G}{E}\left(1 + \frac{b}{c}\right)^2}, \quad \lambda = \frac{\gamma_1\left(\frac{b}{c} - \gamma_1^2 + \lambda_1\right)\left(\frac{b}{c} - \gamma_2^2\right)\tanh\frac{\gamma_1\pi}{2}}{\gamma_2\left(\frac{b}{c} - \gamma_2^2 + \lambda_1\right)\left(\frac{b}{c} - \gamma_1^2\right)\tanh\frac{\gamma_2\pi}{2}}, \quad \lambda_1 = 4\left(1 - \frac{0.625t}{2c}\right)\frac{G}{E}\left(1 + \frac{b}{c}\right)^2$$

K = function of $\frac{b-c}{b+c}$ and has values as follows:

$\frac{b-c}{b+c}$ =	0.05	0.10	0.2	0.3	0.4	0.5	0.6	0.7	0.8	0.9	1.0
K =	2.33	2.20	1.95	1.75	1.58	1.44	1.32	1.22	1.13	1.06	1.0

(Formulas due to Wahl, Ref. 10)

TABLE X.—FORMULAS FOR FLAT PLATES.—(*Continued*)

Manner of loading and Case No.	Formulas for stress and deflection
	Continuous solid plate
Supported at equal intervals a on circular supports of radius r_0 **53.** Uniform load over entire surface	(At edge of support) $s_a = \dfrac{0.15w\left(a - \frac{4}{3}r_0\right)^2\left(\frac{1}{n} + 4\right)}{t^2}$ when $n > 0.15 < 0.30$ $\left(n = \dfrac{2r_0}{a}\right)$ (Ref. 9) Or $s_a = \dfrac{3wa^2}{2\pi mt^2}\left[\log \dfrac{a}{r_0}(m + 1) - 21(m - 1)\dfrac{r_0^2}{a^2} - 0.55m - 1.50\right]$ when $n < 0.15$ (Ref. 11)
	Large rectangular plate (pavement slab)
Supported continuously on elastic foundation of modulus k (*i.e.*, the foundation deflects 1 in. for a pressure of k lb. per sq. in.) **54.** Load W on circular area of radius a, adjacent to a corner	Max $s = \dfrac{3W}{t^2}\left[1 - \left(\dfrac{a_1}{l}\right)^{0.6}\right]$, at distance $= 2\sqrt{a_1 l}$ from corner along diagonal Max $y = \dfrac{W}{kl^2}\left(1.1 - 0.88\dfrac{a_1}{l}\right)$, at corner $\left(\text{where } l = \sqrt[4]{\dfrac{Et^3}{12(1 - \nu^2)k}}\right)$ (Ref. 14)
Supported continuously on elastic foundation of modulus k **55.** Load W on circular area of radius a, remote from edges	Max $s = \dfrac{3(1 + \nu)W}{2\pi t^2}\left(\log \dfrac{l}{a} + 0.6159\right)$, under load Max $y = \dfrac{W}{8kl^2}$ Max. foundation pressure under load: $p_0 = \dfrac{1}{4} W \sqrt{3(1 - \nu^4)} \sqrt{\dfrac{k}{Et^3}}$ (l same as for case 54) (Ref. 14)

Case	Formulas
...on elastic foundation of modulus k. 56. Load W on circular area of radius a, adjacent to edge but remote from corner.	$\text{Max } s = \frac{0.863(1+\nu)W}{t^2}\left[\log\frac{l}{a} + 0.207\right]$, under load $\text{Max } y = \frac{1}{\sqrt{6}}(1+0.4\nu)\frac{W}{kl^2}$ (l same as for Case 54) (Ref. 14)
57. Outer edge supported. Inner edge fixed. Uniform load over entire actual surface. $W = w\pi(a^2 - b^2)$	Circular, with concentric circular hole (circular flange) (At inner edge) $\text{Max } s_r = \frac{3w}{4t^2}\left[\frac{4a^2b^2(m+1)\log\frac{a}{b} - a^4(3m+1) + a^2b^2(5m+1)}{a^2(m+1) + b^2(m-1)} - b^2\right] = \text{Max } s$ $\text{Max } y = -\frac{3w(m^2-1)}{16m^2Et^3}\left[a^4 - 3b^4 + 2a^2b^2 - 8a^2b^2\log\frac{a}{b} - \frac{16(m+1)a^2b^4\log^2\frac{a}{b} + [4(7m+3)a^2b^4 - 4(5m+3)a^4b^2]\log\frac{a}{b} + 4(4m+1)a^4b^2 - 2(3m+1)a^6 - 2(5m+1)a^2b^4}{a^2(m+1) + b^2(m-1)}\right]$
58. Both edges fixed. Balanced loading (piston). $W = w\pi(a^2 - b^2)$	(At inner edge) $\text{Max } s_r = \frac{3w}{4t^2}\left[\frac{4a^4}{a^2 - b^2}\log\frac{a}{b} - 3a^2 + b^2\right] = \text{Max } s$ $\text{Max } y = -\frac{3w(m^2-1)}{16Et^3m^2}\left[3a^4 - 4a^2b^2 + b^4 + 4a^2b^2\log\frac{a}{b} - \frac{16a^4b^2}{a^2-b^2}\left(\log\frac{a}{b}\right)^2\right]$

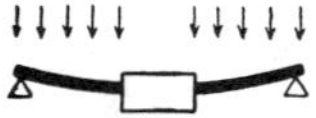

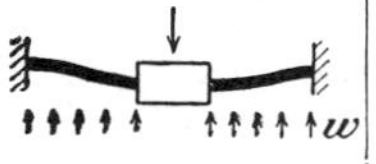

TABLE X.—FORMULAS FOR FLAT PLATES.—(*Continued*)

Manner of loading and Case No.	Formulas for stress and deflection
Outer edge supported Inner edge free 59. **Uniform** load on concentric circular ring of radius r_0 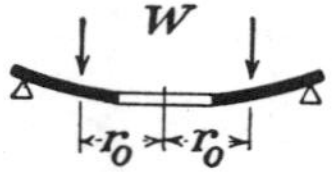	(At inner edge) $s_t = -\frac{3W}{2\pi m t^2}\left[\frac{1}{2}(m-1)+(m+1)\log\frac{a}{r_0}-(m-1)\frac{r_0^2}{2a^2}\right]-\frac{6M(a^2+b^2)}{(a^2-b^2)t^2}$ = Max s. $\text{Max } y = -\frac{3W(m^2-1)}{2\pi E m^2 t^3}\left[\frac{(a^2-b^2)(3m+1)}{2(m+1)}-(b^2+r_0^2)\log\frac{a}{r_0}+(b^2-r_0^2)-\frac{r_0^2(a^2-b^2)(m-1)}{2a^2(m+1)}\right]-\frac{6M(m^2-1)}{Emt^3}\left[\frac{b^2}{m+1}+\frac{2a^2b^2}{(a^2-b^2)(m-1)}\log\frac{a}{b}\right]$ where $M = \frac{W}{8\pi m}\left[(m-1)+2(m+1)\log\frac{a}{r_0}-(m-1)\frac{r_0^2}{a^2}\right]$
Outer edge fixed Inner edge free 60. Uniform load on concentric circular ring of radius r_0 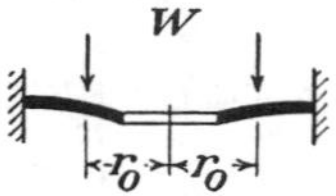	(At inner edge) $s_t = -\frac{3W}{4\pi m_t^2}\left[(m+1)\left(2\log\frac{a}{r_0}+\frac{r_0^2}{a^2}-1\right)\right]-\frac{6M}{t^2}\left[\frac{a^2(m-1)-b^2(m+1)}{a^2(m-1)+b^2(m+1)}\right]$ (At outer edge) $s_r = \frac{3W}{2\pi t^2}\left[1-\frac{r_0^2}{a^2}\right]+\frac{6mM}{t^2}\left[\frac{2b^2}{a^2(m-1)+b^2(m+1)}\right]$ $\text{Max } y = -\frac{3W(m^2-1)}{2\pi E m^2 t^3}\left[\frac{(a^2+r_0^2)(a^2-b^2)}{2a^2}-(b^2+r_0^2)\log\frac{a}{r_0}+(b^2-r_0^2)\right]-\frac{6M(m^2-1)}{Emt^3}\left[\frac{b^4+2a^2b^2\log\frac{a}{b}-a^2b^2}{b^2(m+1)+a^2(m-1)}\right]$ where $M = \frac{W}{8\pi m}\left[(m+1)\left(2\log\frac{a}{r_0}+\frac{r_0^2}{a^2}-1\right)\right]$
Edge supported 61. Linearly distributed load symmetrical about diameter 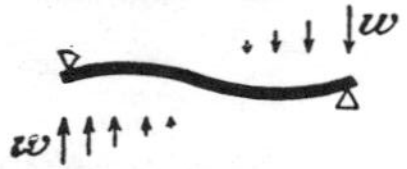	 Circular and solid Max $s_r = \frac{wa^2(5m+1)}{12\sqrt{3}\,t^2m}$ at $r = 0.577a$ Max $s_t = \frac{wa^2(5m+1)(m+3)}{12t^2(3m+1)m}$ at $r = 0.675a$ Max edge reaction per linear inch = $\frac{1}{4}wa$ Max $y = 0.042\frac{wa^4}{Et^3}$ at $r = 0.503a$ (values for $v = 0.3$) (Refs. 20, 21)

62. Central couple balanced by linearly distributed pressure (footing)

$w = \frac{4M}{\pi a^3}$

Circular and solid with central rigid portion

(At inner edge) Max $s_r = \beta \frac{M}{at^2}$ where β may be found from following table:

$\frac{a}{b}$	1.25	1.50	2	3	4	5
β	0.1625	0.4560	1.105	2.250	3.385	4.470

(values for $v = 0.3$) (Ref. 21)

63. Concentrated load applied at outer edge

(At inner edge) Max $s_r = \beta \frac{W}{t^2}$ where β may be found from following table:

$\frac{a}{b}$	1.25	1.50	2	3	4	5
β	3.7	4.25	5.2	6.7	7.9	8.8

(values for $v = 0.3$) (Refs. 22, 21)

Equilateral triangle, solid

64. Edges supported
Distributed load of intensity w over entire surface

Max $s_x = 0.1488 \frac{wa^2}{t^2}$ at $y = 0$, $x = -0.062a$ Max $s_y = 0.1554 \frac{wa^2}{t^2}$ at $y = 0$, $x = 0.129a$ (values for $v = 0.3$) (Refs. 23, 21)

Max $y = \frac{wa^4(m^2 - 1)}{81Et^3m^2}$ at 0.

TABLE X.—FORMULAS FOR FLAT PLATES.—(*Continued*)

Manner of loading and Case No.	Formulas for stress and deflection
Edges supported **65. Load** W concentrated at 0 on small circular area of radius r_0	$\text{Max } s_y = \frac{3(m+1)W}{2\pi m t^2}\left[\log \frac{.378a}{\sqrt{1.6r_0^2+t^2}-0.675t} - 0.379 + \frac{m-1}{2(m+1)}\right] = \text{Max } s$ $\text{Max } y = 0.06852 \frac{Pa^2(m^2-1)}{Et^3m^2}$ at 0
Edges supported **66. Distributed load of intensity** w **over entire surface**	Right angle isosceles triangle, solid $\text{Max } s_x = 0.131 \frac{wa^2}{t^2} = \text{Max } s \quad \text{Max } s_y = 0.1125 \frac{wa^2}{t^2}$ $\text{Max } y = 0.0095 \frac{wa^4}{Et^3}$ (values for $v = 0.3$) (Ref. 21)
Edges supported **67. Distributed load of intensity** w **over entire surface**	Circular sector, solid $\text{Max } s_r = \beta \frac{wa^2}{t^2} \quad \text{Max } s_t = \beta_1 \frac{wa^2}{t^2} \quad \text{Max } y = \alpha \frac{wa^4}{Et^3}$ (values for $v = 0.3$) (Ref. 21)

θ	45°	60°	90°	180°
β	0.102	0.147	0.240	0.522
β_1	0.114	0.155	0.216	0.312
α	0.0054	0.0105	0.0250	0.0870

68. All edges supported. Distributed load of intensity w over entire surface

Parallelepiped (skew slab)

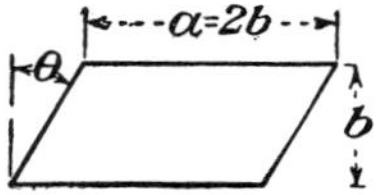

Max $s = s_b = \beta \frac{wb^2}{t^2}$ (at center) where β may be found from following table:

(values for $\nu = 0.2$) (Ref. 24)

θ	0	30°	45°	60°	75°
β	0.501	0.50	0.45	0.40	0.16

69. Edges b supported, Edges a free. Distributed load of intensity w over entire surface

Max $s = \beta \frac{wa^2}{t^2}$ (at center) where β may be found from following table:

(values for $\nu = 0.2$) (Ref. 24)

θ	0	30°	45°	60°
β	0.762	0.615	0.437	0.250

70. Like Case 39 but all edges fixed

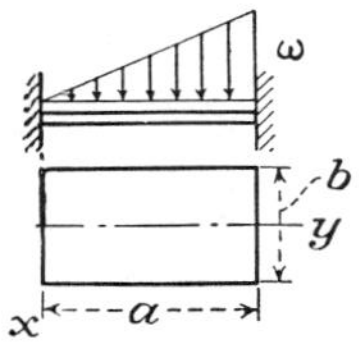

Max $s_b = \beta_1 \frac{wa^2}{t^2}$ at $x = \pm\frac{1}{2}b,\ y = 0.55a$

$s_b = \beta_2 \frac{wa^2}{t^2}$ at $x = 0,\ y = 0.6a$

Max $s_a = \beta_3 \frac{wa^2}{t^2}$ at $x = 0,\ y = a$

$s_a = \beta_4 \frac{wa^2}{t^2}$ at $x = 0,\ y = 0$

$s_a = \beta_5 \frac{wa^2}{t^2}$ at $x = 0,\ y = 0.6a$

Max $y = \alpha \frac{wa^4}{Et^3}$

(Ref. 28)

b/a	0.6	0.8	1	1.2	1.4	1.6	1.8	2
β_1	0.1308	0.1434	0.1686	0.1800	0.1842	0.1872	0.1902	0.1908
β_2	0.0636	0.0688	0.0762	0.0715	0.0612	0.0509	0.0415	0.0356
β_3	0.0832	0.1778	0.2365	0.2561	0.3004	0.3092	0.3100	0.3000
β_4	0.0206	0.0497	0.0898	0.1249	0.1482	0.1615	0.1680	0.1709
β_5	0.0410	0.0633	0.0869	0.1038	0.1128	0.1255	0.1157	0.1148
α	0.0016	0.0047	0.0074	0.0097	0.0113	0.0126	0.0133	0.0136

TABLE X.—FORMULAS FOR FLAT PLATES.—(Continued)

Manner of loading and Case No.	Formulas for stress and deflection
71. Like Case 67 but fixed along curved boundary	Max $s = s_r$ at curved boundary $= \beta \dfrac{wa^2}{t^2}$ Max $y = \dfrac{\alpha w a^4}{Et^3}$ (Ref. 21)
72. Solid sector of infinite radius, straight edges fixed, curved edge free, uniform load w	At q: $-s_r = \dfrac{1.125wr^2}{t^2}\left[\dfrac{4\cos\theta\cos 2\phi - (1-\nu)\cos 4\phi}{2\cos^2\theta + 1} - \dfrac{3+\nu}{3}\right]$; $-s_t = \dfrac{1.125wr^2}{t^2}\left[\dfrac{4\nu\cos\theta\cos 2\phi + (1-\nu)\cos 4\phi}{2\cos^2\theta + 1} - \dfrac{1+3\nu}{3}\right]$; $-y = \dfrac{3(1-\nu^2)wr^4}{16Et^3}\left(1 + \dfrac{\cos 4\phi - 4\cos\theta\cos 2\phi}{2\cos^2\theta + 1}\right)$ (Ref. 37)
73. Solid circular plate, uniform load w over shaded sector	Max $s = s_r$ at $p = \beta \dfrac{wa^2}{t^2}$ Max $y = \alpha \dfrac{wa^4}{t^3}$ (Ref. 38)
74. Solid semicircular plate, uniform load w, all edges fixed	Max $s = s_r$ at $A = \dfrac{0.42wa^2}{t^2}$; s_r at $B = \dfrac{0.36wa^2}{t^2}$; Max $s_t = \dfrac{0.21wa^2}{t^2}$ at C (Ref. 40)

Case 71:

θ	45°	60°	90°	180°
β	0.1500	0.2040	0.2928	0.4536
α	0.0035	0.0065	0.0144	0.0380

Case 73:

Edge	Coef.	θ						
		30°	60°	90°	120°	150°	180°	
Supported..........	α	0.061	0.121	0.179	0.235	0.289	0.340	at q, $r \approx 0.25a$
Fixed...............	α	0.0171	0.0342	0.0502	0.0642	0.077	0.0888	at q, $r \approx 0.25a$
	β	0.240	0.3714	0.4566	0.5178	0.5640	0.6018	at p

For supported edges s_r at center $= \theta/360 \times s_r$ at center for fully loaded plate.
For either edge condition y at center $= \theta/360 \times y$ at center for fully loaded plate.

75. Solid circular plate, uniform load w over shaded segment

Max s = max $s_r = \beta \frac{wa^2}{t^2}$ Max $y = \alpha \frac{wa^4}{Et^3}$, on symmetrical diameter at r given

Edge	Coef.	θ = 90°	θ = 120°	θ = 180°
Supported	α	0.0244, $r = 0.39a$	0.0844, $r = 0.30a$	0.345, $r = 0.15a$
	β	0.306, $r = 0.60a$		
Fixed	α	0.00368, $r = 0.50a$	0.0173, $r = 0.4a$	0.0905, $r = 0.20a$
	β	0.285, $r = a$		

Values for $\nu = \frac{1}{3}$

(Ref. 39)

76. Circular plate with circular hole, both edges supported, uniform load w over entire actual surface

$W = w\pi(a^2 - b^2)$

Max $s_r = \frac{\beta wa^2}{t^2}$ Edge shear per linear in. $= kwa$ Max $y = \frac{\alpha wa^4}{Et^3}$

a/b	1.25	1.5	2	3	4	5
β	0.03	0.0824	0.1815	0.3060	0.3666	0.3967
k (outer)	0.0943	0.1507	0.2135	0.2658	0.2866	0.2960
k (inner)	0.1071	0.1906	0.3230	0.5360	0.7297	0.9198
α	0.00017	0.0036	0.0088	0.0255	0.0393	0.0495

77. Circular plate with circular hole, both edges supported and fixed, uniform load w over entire actual surface

$W = w\pi(a^2 - b^2)$

Max $s_r = \beta \frac{wa^2}{t^2}$ Max $y = \alpha \frac{wa^4}{Et^3}$ Edge shear per linear in. $= kwa$

a/b	1.25	1.5	2	3	4	5
β (outer)	0.0195	0.0519	0.1119	0.1909	0.2360	0.2646
β (inner)	0.0205	0.0607	0.1482	0.2987	0.4136	0.5175
k (outer)	0.0959	0.1538	0.2208	0.2813	0.3090	0.3247
k (inner)	0.1051	0.1859	0.3084	0.4892	0.6391	0.7765
α	0.000051	0.000734	0.00187	0.0060	0.0094	0.01194

TABLE X.—FORMULAS FOR FLAT PLATES.—(*Continued*)

Manner of loading and Case No.	Formulas for stress and deflection
78. Rectangular solid plate, all edges supported, uniform load w, uniform tension or compression P lb. per linear in. applied to short edges	Max $y = \alpha \frac{wb^4}{Et^3}$ Max $s_x = \beta_x \frac{wb^2}{t^2}$ Max $s_y = \beta_y \frac{wb^2}{t^2}$. Here α, β_x, and β_y depend on ratios $\frac{a}{b}$ and $\frac{P}{P_E}$, where $P_E = \frac{\pi^2 E t^3}{3(1 - \nu^2)b^2}$, and have following values:

Coef.	a/b \ P/P_E	0	0.15	0.25	0.50	0.75	1	2	3	4	5
					P, Tension						
α	1	0.044	0.039	.....	0.030	.....	0.023	0.015	0.011	0.008	0.0075
	$1\frac{1}{2}$	0.084	0.075	.....	0.060	.....	0.045	0.0305	0.024	0.019	0.0170
	2	0.110	0.100	.....	0.084	.....	0.067	0.0475	0.0375	0.0300	0.0260
	3	0.1330	0.125	.....	0.1135	.....	0.100	0.081	0.066	0.0570	0.0490
	4	0.140	0.136	.....	0.1280	.....	0.118	0.102	0.089	0.080	0.072
β_y	1	0.287	.....	.....	......	.....	0.132	0.084	0.054	0.036	0.030
	$1\frac{1}{2}$	0.487	.....	.....	......	.....	0.240	0.156	0.114	0.090	0.072
	2	0.610	.....	.....	......	.....	0.360	0.258	0.198	0.162	0.138
	3	0.713	.....	.....	......	.....	0.510	0.414	0.348	0.294	0.258
	4	0.741	.....	.....	......	.....	0.624	0.540	0.480	0.420	0.372
β_x	1	0.287	.....	.....	......	.....	0.135	0.096	0.072	0.054	0.045
	$1\frac{1}{2}$	0.300	.....	.....	......	.....	0.150	0.105	0.078	0.066	0.048
	2	0.278	.....	.....	......	.....	0.162	0.117	0.093	0.075	0.069
	3	0.246	.....	.....	......	.....	0.180	0.150	0.126	0.105	0.093
	4	0.222	.....	.....	......	.....	0.192	0.168	0.156	0.138	0.124
					P, Compression						
α	1	0.044	.....	0.060	0.094	0.180					
	$1\frac{1}{2}$	0.084	.....	0.109	0.155	0.237					
	2	0.110	.....	0.139	0.161	0.181					
	3	0.1310	.....	0.145	0.150	0.150					
	4	0.140	.....	0.142	0.142	0.138					
β_x	1	0.287	.....	0.372	0.606	1.236					
	$1\frac{1}{2}$	0.300	.....	0.372	0.522	0.846					
	2	0.278	.....	0.330	0.390	0.450					
	3	0.246	.....	0.228	0.228	0.210					
	4	0.222	.....	0.225	0.225	0.225					
β_y	1	0.287	.....	0.420	0.600	1.260					
	$1\frac{1}{2}$	0.487	.....	0.624	0.786	1.380					
	2	0.610	.....	0.720	0.900	1.020					
	3	0.713	.....	0.750	0.792	0.750					
	4	0.741	.....	0.750	0.750	0.750					

(Ref. 41)

In above formulas s_x and s_y are stresses due to bending only; to s_x must be added direct stress P/t.

79. Rectangular solid plate, all edges supported, uniform load w, uniform tension P lb. per linear in. applied to all edges

Max $y = \alpha \frac{wb^4}{Et^3}$ Max $s_x = \beta_x \frac{wb^2}{t^2}$ Max $s_y = \beta_y \frac{wb^2}{t^2}$. Here α, β_x, and β_y depend on ratios $\frac{a}{b}$ and $\frac{P}{P_E}$, where $P_E = \frac{\pi^2 Et^3}{3(1-\nu^2)b^2}$, and have following values:

Coef.	a/b \ P/P_E	0	0.15	0.5	1	2	3	4	5
α	1	0.044	0.035	0.022	0.015	0.008	0.006	0.004	0.003
	$1\frac{1}{2}$	0.084	0.060	0.035	0.022	0.012	0.008	0.006	0.005
	2	0.110	0.075	0.042	0.025	0.014	0.010	0.007	0.006
	3	0.133	0.085	0.045	0.026	0.016	0.011	0.008	0.007
	4	0.140	0.088	0.046	0.026	0.016	0.011	0.008	0.007
β_x	1	0.287	0.216	0.132	0.084	0.048	0.033	0.026	0.021
	$1\frac{1}{2}$	0.300	0.204	0.117	0.075	0.045	0.031	0.024	0.020
	2	0.278	0.189	0.111	0.072	0.044	0.031	0.024	0.020
	3	0.246	0.183	0.108	0.070	0.043	0.031	0.025	0.020
	4	0.222	0.183	0.108	0.074	0.047	0.032	0.027	0.024
β_y	1	0.287	0.222	0.138	0.090	0.051	0.036	0.030	0.024
	$1\frac{1}{2}$	0.487	0.342	0.186	0.108	0.066	0.042	0.036	0.030
	2	0.610	0.302	0.216	0.132	0.072	0.051	0.042	0.036
	3	0.713	0.444	0.234	0.141	0.078	0.054	0.042	0.036
	4	0.741	0.456	0.240	0.144	0.078	0.054	0.042	0.036

In above formulas s_x and s_y are stresses due to bending only, to which direct stresses P/t must be added to obtain maximum resultant stresses. (Ref. 42)

80. Solid circular plate, concentric support, uniform load w over entire surface

$W = w\pi a^2$

(At center) $s_r = s_t = \frac{6W}{8\pi t^2 m}\left[(m-1)\frac{a^2-b^2}{a^2} - 2(m+1)\log\frac{b}{a} - \frac{1}{2}(3m+1)\right]$

$y = \frac{3W(m-1)b^2}{16\pi Em^2t^3}\left[(6m+2) - \frac{b^2}{a^2}(m+1) - 4(m-1)\frac{a^2-b^2}{a^2} + 8(m-1)\log\frac{b}{a}\right]$

(At support) $s_r = \frac{6W}{8\pi t^2 m}\left[(m-1)\frac{a^2-b^2}{a^2} - 2(m+1)\log\frac{b}{a} - \frac{1}{2}(3m+1)\left(1-\frac{b^2}{a^2}\right)\right]$

(At edge) $y = \frac{3W(m^2-1)}{2\pi Em^2t^3}\left[(a^2-b^2)\left(1+\frac{1}{2}\frac{m-1}{m+1}\frac{a^2-b^2}{a^2}\right) + 2b^2\log\frac{b}{a}\right] - \frac{3W}{8\pi Em^2t^3}\left[\frac{5m+1}{2}a^2 + \frac{m+1}{2}\frac{b^4}{a^2} - (3m+1)b^2\right]$

For minimum stress, $\frac{b}{a} = 0.71$

81. Square solid plate simply supported at all four corners; uniform load w

(At center) $y = 0.308(1-\nu^2)\frac{wa^4}{Et^3}$

$s_x = s_y = 0.6654\frac{wa^2}{t^2}$

(At middle of each side) $s = 0.9162\frac{wa^2}{t^2}$

In many of the formulas some terms become negligible and can be dropped when certain dimensions become small compared with others (*e.g.*, Cases 2 and 3 when r_0 is very small compared with a; Cases 13, 16, and others when b is very small compared with a). When this is the case, it is usually obvious on inspection, and the labor of using the formulas will be greatly reduced by taking full advantage of this fact. The procedure is illustrated in Example 3, p. 248.

When calculations of stress and deflection for any given case must be made frequently, much labor may be saved by using suitable graphs, or coefficients such as are given in Art. 57.

Deflection Due to Shear.—The formulas for deflection given in Table X take into account bending stresses only; there is, in every case, some additional deflection due to shear. Usually this is so slight as to be negligible, but in circular pierced plates with large openings the deflection due to shear may constitute a considerable proportion of the total deflection. Wahl (Ref. 19) suggests that this is the case when the thickness is greater than one-third the difference in inner and outer diameters for plates with simply supported edges, or greater than one-sixth this difference for plates with one or both edges fixed, and gives formulas which when F is taken equal to 1.2 as in Art. 35, become:

(For Cases 14, 20, and 22)

$$y_s = \frac{0.191W \log_e \alpha}{tG}$$

(For Case 13)

$$y_s = \frac{0.30wa^2}{tG}\left(1 - \frac{1}{\alpha^2} - \frac{2 \log_e \alpha}{\alpha^2}\right)$$

(For Cases 16 and 21)

$$y_s = \frac{0.30wa^2}{tG}\left(2 \log_e \alpha - 1 + \frac{1}{\alpha^2}\right)$$

Here y_s denotes the deflection due to shear, α the ratio of a to b, and G the modulus of rigidity.

57. Stress and Deflection Coefficients.—The maximum stresses, maximum deflections, and edge slopes for many of the cases represented in Table X can be conveniently expressed by simple formulas with numerical coefficients that depend upon the ratio of certain dimensions and upon the value chosen for ν.

Case No.	Coef.	a/b					
		1.25	1.5	2	3	4	5
13	β (for s_t)	0.592	0.976	1.44	1.88	2.08	2.19
	α	0.184	0.414	0.682	0.824	0.830	0.813
	λ (outer)	0.888	1.185	1.311	1.232	1.182	1.145
	λ (inner)	0.942	1.293	1.440	1.250	1.047	0.875
14	β (for s_t)	1.10	1.26	1.48	1.88	2.17	2.34
	α	0.341	0.519	0.672	0.734	0.724	0.704
	λ (outer)	1.646	1.470	1.237	1.006	0.895	0.832
	λ (inner)	1.758	1.650	1.475	1.238	1.082	0.932
16	β (for s_t)	0.660	1.19	2.04	3.34	4.30	5.10
	α	0.202	0.491	0.902	1.22	1.30	1.31
	λ (outer)	0.977	1.385	1.425	1.578	1.453	1.355
	λ (inner)	1.048	1.587	2.040	2.210	2.143	1.940
17	β (for s_r)	0.105	0.259	0.481	0.657	0.708	0.730
	β (for s_t)	0.0082	0.044	0.163	0.404	0.568	0.672
	α	0.0020	0.0149	0.0576	0.130	0.162	0.174
	λ	0.015	0.0607	0.163	0.269	0.283	0.269
18	β (for s_r)	0.195	0.320	0.455	0.539	0.538	0.532
	β (for s_t)	0.025	0.087	0.269	0.670	1.018	1.300
	α	0.00506	0.0242	0.0808	0.1714	0.215	0.237
	λ	0.045	0.115	0.269	0.448	0.510	0.522
19	β (s_r outer)	0.070	0.183	0.361	0.546	0.627	0.668
	β (s_r inner)	0.0412	0.114	0.245	0.422	0.520	0.579
	α	0.00068	0.0050	0.0229	0.0636	0.0926	0.112
20	β (s_r outer)	0.0984	0.1680	0.257	0.347	0.390	0.415
	β (s_r inner)	0.115	0.220	0.405	0.703	0.933	1.130
	α	0.0013	0.0064	0.0237	0.062	0.092	0.114
21	β (for s_r)	0.135	0.410	1.04	2.15	2.99	3.69
	α	0.0023	0.0183	0.0938	0.293	0.448	0.564
	λ	0.0142	0.0694	0.2273	0.495	0.659	0.762
22	β (for s_r)	0.227	0.428	0.753	1.205	1.514	1.745
	α	0.0051	0.0249	0.0877	0.209	0.293	0.350
	λ	0.046	0.1052	0.239	0.403	0.499	0.544
23	β (s_t inner)	0.366	0.863	2.44	4.10	4.84	5.11
	α	0.20	0.484	0.846	0.938	0.800	0.657
	λ	2.20	3.16	3.88	3.31	3.12	2.72
24	β (for s_r)	6.87	7.50	8.14	8.71	8.94	9.04
	α	0.233	0.660	1.493	2.552	3.105	3.415
	λ	2.30	3.84	5.67	6.94	7.82	8.17
25	β (s_t inner)	33.3	21.6	16.0	13.5	12.8	12.5
(M_a	α	10.37	9.23	7.80	6.31	5.62	5.23
only)	λ (outer)	51.0	28.0	16.4	11.6	10.23	9.61
	λ (inner)	53.3	27.8	15.6	8.78	6.24	4.86
(M_b	β (s_t inner)	27.36	15.60	10.0	7.50	6.80	6.50
only)	α	8.87	6.92	4.65	2.58	1.69	1.21
	λ (outer)	42.70	18.75	7.81	2.93	1.56	0.940
	λ (inner)	44.90	22.35	11.27	5.52	4.08	3.17
57	β (for s_r)	0.122	0.336	0.740	1.21	1.45	1.59
	α	0.0034	0.0313	0.125	0.291	0.417	0.492
	λ	0.1035	0.2141	0.4647	0.727	0.876	0.925
58	β (for s_t)	0.090	0.273	0.710	1.54	2.23	2.80
	α	0.0008	0.0062	0.0329	0.110	0.179	0.234

(For Cases 13, 16, 17, 19, 21, 57, 58)

$$\text{Max } s = \frac{\beta w a^2}{t^2}; \qquad \max y = \frac{\alpha w a^4}{E t^3}; \qquad \theta = \frac{\lambda w a^3}{E t^3}$$

(For Cases 14, 18, 20, 22)

$$\text{Max } s = \frac{\beta W}{t^2}; \qquad \max y = \frac{\alpha W a^2}{E t^3}; \qquad \theta = \frac{\lambda W a}{E t^3}$$

(For Cases 23, 24, 25)

$$\text{Max } s = \frac{\beta M}{t^2}; \qquad \max y = \frac{\alpha M a^2}{E t^3}; \qquad \theta = \frac{\lambda M a}{E t^3}$$

where β, α, and λ depend upon the ratio a/b and, for $\nu = 0.3$, have the values given in the table on page 241.

(For Cases 5 and 10)

$$\text{Max } s = \frac{\beta M}{a t^2}; \qquad \text{Max } \theta = \frac{M}{\alpha E t^3} \qquad \text{(at center)}$$

where β and α depend upon the ratio r_0/a and, for $\nu = 0.3$, have the values given in the following table:[1]

r_0/a	Case 5 (edges supported)			Case 10 (edges fixed)[2]		
	β (Table X)	β (Ref. 22)	α (Ref. 22)	β (Table X)	β (Ref. 21)	α (Ref. 21)
0.1	5.05	9.478	0.713	4.92	9.36	0.87
0.15	3.70	6.252	0.945	3.60	6.08	1.23
0.20	2.75	4.621	1.22	2.65	4.41	1.68
0.25	2.30	3.625	1.56	2.20	3.37	2.28
0.30	2.00	2.947	2.00	1.95	2.66	3.12
0.35	....	2.450	2.56	....	2.13	4.29
0.40	....	2.062	3.32	....	1.73	5.99
0.45	....	1.750	4.39	....	1.41	8.50
0.50	....	1.489	5.93	....	1.146	12.35
0.55	....	1.264	8.23	....	0.930	18.46
0.60	....	1.067	11.85	....	0.749	28.60
0.65	....	0.891	17.88	....	0.596	46.38
0.70	....	0.731	28.72	....	0.467	79.95
0.75	....	0.584	50.25	....	0.356	149.8
0.80	....	0.449	99.50	....	0.262	316.9

[1] The values of β and α given above were worked out from the basic equations by Professor Millard Johnson.

[2] For stress at outer edge multiply β by r_0/a.

58. Ultimate Strength.—Plates of brittle material fracture when the actual maximum tensile stress reaches the ultimate tensile strength of the material. A flat-plate modulus of rupture, analogous to the modulus of rupture of a beam, may be determined by calculating the (fictitious) maximum stress corresponding to the breaking load, using for this purpose the appropriate formula for elastic stress. This flat-plate modulus of rupture is usually greater than the modulus of rupture determined by testing a beam of rectangular section. In Table XVIII are given values of the ratio of plate modulus of rupture to beam modulus of rupture, and values of the rupture factor, for cast-iron and plaster plates of various forms.

Plates of ductile material fail, as do beams of similar material, by excessive plastic deflection. For a limited number of cases the load required to produce collapse has been determined analytically, and the results may be summarized as follows:

Circular plate, uniform load, edges simply supported:

$$W_u = s_y(\tfrac{3}{2}\pi t^2) \quad \text{(Ref. 43)}$$

Circular plate, uniform load, fixed edges:

$$W_u = s_y(2.814\pi t^2) \quad \text{(Ref. 43)}$$

Rectangular plate, length a, width b, uniform load, edges supported:

$$W_u = \beta s_y t^2$$

where β depends on the ratio of b to a and has values as follows (Ref. 44):

b/a = 1	0.9	0.8	0.7	0.6	0.5	0.4	0.3	0.2
β = 5.48	5.50	5.58	5.64	5.89	6.15	6.70	7.68	9.69

Plate of any shape and size, any type of edge support, concentrated load at any point:

$$W_u = s_y(\tfrac{1}{2}\pi t^2) \quad \text{(Ref. 45)}$$

In each of the above cases W_u denotes the total load in pounds required to collapse the plate, t the thickness of the plate in inches, and s_y the yield point of the material in pounds per square inch. Accurate prediction of W_u is hardly to be expected; the theoretical error in some of the formulas may range up to 30 per cent, and there seem to be few experimental data available.

59. Effect of Large Deflection; Diaphragm Stresses.—When, as may occur in thin plates, the deflection becomes larger than about one-half the thickness, the middle surface becomes appreciably strained and the stress in it cannot be ignored. This stress, called *diaphragm* stress or *direct* stress, enables the plate to carry part of the load as a diaphragm in direct tension. This tension may be balanced by radial tension at the edges if the edges are *held,* or by circumferential compression if the edges are not horizontally restrained. In thin plates this circumferential compression may cause buckling.

When this condition of large deflection obtains, the plate is stiffer than indicated by the ordinary theory, and the load-deflection and load-stress relations are nonlinear. Stresses for a given load are less, and stresses for a given deflection are generally greater, than the ordinary theory indicates.

Formulas for the stress and deflection when middle surface stresses are taken into account are given below for a number of cases of loading; these formulas should be used whenever the maximum deflection exceeds half the thickness, if accurate results are desired.

Let t = thickness of plate; a = radius of plate; w = unit load (pounds per square inch), assumed uniform over entire area; y = *maximum* deflection; s_b = bending stress; s_d = diaphragm stress; $s = s_b + s_d$ = maximum stress due to flexure and diaphragm tension combined. Then the following formulas apply:

Circular plate, uniform load, edges simply supported (neither fixed nor held):[1]

$$\frac{wa^4}{Et^4} = \frac{64}{63(1-\nu)}\left(\frac{y}{t}\right) + 0.376\left(\frac{y}{t}\right)^3 \tag{1}$$

(At center)

$$s = \frac{Et^2}{a^2}\left[\frac{1.238}{1-\nu}\left(\frac{y}{t}\right) + 0.294\left(\frac{y}{t}\right)^2\right] \tag{2}$$

Circular plate, uniform load, edges fixed but not held (no edge tension):

$$\frac{wa^4}{Et^4} = \frac{16}{3(1-\nu^2)}\left(\frac{y}{t}\right) + \frac{6}{7}\left(\frac{y}{t}\right)^3 \tag{3}$$

[1] Formulas 1 to 5 due to Prescott, Ref. 5.

(At edge)

$$s = s_b = \frac{Et^2}{a^2}\left[\frac{4}{1-\nu^2}\left(\frac{y}{t}\right)\right] \tag{4}$$

(At center)

$$s = \frac{Et^2}{a^2}\left[\frac{2}{1-\nu}\left(\frac{y}{t}\right) + \frac{1}{2}\left(\frac{y}{t}\right)^2\right] \tag{5}$$

Circular plate, uniform load, edges fixed and held:[1]

$$\frac{wa^4}{Et^4} = \frac{16}{3(1-\nu^2)}\left[\left(\frac{y}{t}\right) + 0.488\left(\frac{y}{t}\right)^3\right] \tag{6}$$

(At edge)

$$s = 4.40E\left(\frac{yt}{a^2}\right) + 0.476E\left(\frac{y}{a}\right)^2 \tag{7}$$

(At center)

$$s = 2.86E\left(\frac{yt}{a^2}\right) + 0.976E\left(\frac{y}{a}\right)^2 \tag{8}$$

In Eqs. 2, 5, 7, and 8, the first term represents the bending stress and the second term the membrane stress.

(These equations for stress are approximate. A more exact method of solution is given by Way, Ref. 16.)

Rectangular plate, uniform load:

Analytical solutions for uniformly loaded rectangular plates with large deflections are given in Refs. 30, 31, 32, 33, and 34, where the relations among load, deflection, and stress are expressed by numerical values of the dimensionless coefficients y/t, wb^4/Et^4, and sb^2/Et^2. The values of these coefficients given in the table on page 246 are taken from these references and are for $\nu = 0.316$. In this table, a, b, w, E, y, and t have the same meaning as in Table X; s_d is the diaphragm stress, and s is the total stress found by adding the diaphragm stress and the bending stress. In Ref. 35, experimentally determined deflections are given and compared with those predicted by theory.

Square plate, concentrated center load, edges supported or fixed:[2]

Let a = width of plate, P = load, K = fractional part of the load carried by bending, the remainder being carried by dia-

[1] Formula 6 due to Timoshenko, Ref. 15. Formulas 7 and 8 due to Waters; see Ref. 16.

[2] Formulas 9 and 11 are due to Sturm and Moore, Ref. 17, and Eq. 10 is an empirical formula that fits the result of their tests fairly closely.

RECTANGULAR PLATES UNDER UNIFORM LOAD PRODUCING LARGE DEFLECTION

a/b	Edges and point of max s	Coef.	wb^4/Et^4										
			0	12.5	25	50	75	100	125	150	175	200	250
1	Held; not fixed	y/t	0	0.430	0.650	0.930	1.13	1.26	1.37	1.47	1.56	1.63	1.77
	At center of plate	$s_d b^2/Et^2$	0	0.70	1.60	3.00	4.00	5.00	6.10	7.00	7.95	8.60	10.20
		sb^2/Et^2	0	3.80	5.80	8.70	10.90	12.80	14.30	15.60	17.00	18.20	20.50
1	Held; riveted	y/t	0	0.406	0.600	0.840	1.00	1.13	1.23	1.31	1.40	1.46	1.58
	At center of plate	$s_d b^2/Et^2$	0	0.609	1.380	2.68	3.80	4.78	5.75	6.54	7.55	8.10	9.53
		sb^2/Et^2	0	3.19	5.18	7.77	9.72	11.34	12.80	14.10	15.40	16.40	18.40
1	Held and fixed	y/t	0	0.165	0.25	0.59	0.80	0.95	1.08	1.19	1.28	1.38	1.54
	At center of long edges	$s_d b^2/Et^2$	0	0.070	0.22	0.75	1.35	2.00	2.70	3.30	4.00	4.60	5.90
		sb^2/Et^2	0	3.80	6.90	14.70	21.0	26.50	31.50	36.20	40.70	45.00	53.50
	At center of plate	$s_d b^2/Et^2$	0	0.075	0.30	0.95	1.65	2.40	3.10	3.80	4.50	5.20	6.50
		sb^2/Et^2	0	1.80	3.50	6.60	9.20	11.60	13.0	14.50	15.80	17.10	19.40
1.5	Held; not fixed	y/t	0	0.625	0.879	1.18	1.37	1.53	1.68	1.77	1.88	1.96	2.12
	At center of plate	$s_d b^2/Et^2$	0	1.06	2.11	3.78	5.18	6.41	7.65	8.60	9.55	10.60	12.30
		sb^2/Et^2	0	4.48	6.81	9.92	12.25	14.22	16.0	17.50	18.90	20.30	22.80
2 to ∞	Held; not fixed	y/t	0	0.696	0.946	1.24	1.44	1.60	1.72	1.84	1.94	2.03	2.20
	At center of plate	$s_d b^2/Et^2$	0	1.29	2.40	4.15	5.61	6.91	8.10	9.21	10.10	10.90	13.20
		sb^2/Et^2	0	4.87	7.16	10.30	12.60	14.60	16.40	18.00	19.40	20.90	23.60
1.5 to ∞	Held and fixed	y/t	0	0.28	0.51	0.825	1.07	1.24	1.40	1.50	1.63	1.72	1.86
	At center of long edges	$s_d b^2/Et^2$	0	0.20	0.66	1.90	3.20	4.35	5.40	6.50	7.50	8.50	10.30
		sb^2/Et^2	0	5.75	11.12	20.30	27.8	35.0	41.0	47.0	52.50	57.60	67.00

phragm action, y_0 = deflection produced by the concentrated load P; y_i = "initial deflection" or sag, produced by weight of plate or other loading, $y = y_0 + y_i$. Then

$$\frac{12Pa^2(1 - \nu^2)}{Et^3} = y_0\left[\phi_1 + \phi_2\left(\frac{y}{t}\right)^2\right] \tag{9}$$

where $\phi_1 = 87$ and $\phi_2 = 28$ for simply supported edges.
$\phi_1 = 192$ and $\phi_2 = 36$ for fixed edges.

$$K = \frac{1}{1 + 0.12(y/t)^2} \tag{10}$$

(At center of plate) $$s_d = \alpha E\left(\frac{y^2 - y_i^2}{a^2}\right) \tag{11}$$

where $\alpha = 1.60$ for simply supported edges.
$\alpha = 2.90$ for fixed edges.

To determine the bending stress s_b and the total stress s at the center of the plate, y_i is calculated by the appropriate formula from Table X (Cases 30, 32, 34); then y and y_0 are found by Eq. 9; K is found by Eq. 10; using KP as the load, s_b is found by the appropriate formula from Table X (Case 31 or 35); s is found by adding s_b and s_d.

Circular diaphragm without flexural stiffness, uniform load, edges held:[1]

(At center) $$\text{Max } y = 0.662a\sqrt[3]{\frac{wa}{Et}}$$

(At r from center)

$$y = \max y\left(1 - 0.9\frac{r^2}{a^2} - 0.1\frac{r^5}{a^5}\right)$$

(At center) $$s_d = 0.423\sqrt[3]{\frac{Ew^2a^2}{t^2}}$$

(At edge) $$s_d = 0.328\sqrt[3]{\frac{Ew^2a^2}{t^2}}$$

In most of the above cases, the maximum deflection y must first be determined, and this is perhaps most quickly done by solving for y/t, starting with a value of y somewhat less than

[1] Formulas due to Hencky, Ref. 18, and to Stevens, Ref. 29.

that given by the ordinary formula. When y is known, s may readily be calculated.

Examples

1. A circular steel plate, 0.2 in. thick and 20 in. in diameter, is supported along the edge and loaded with a uniformly distributed load of 3 lb. per sq. in. It is required to determine the deflection and the maximum stress.

Solution.—This comes under Case 1. Since the area of the plate is 314 sq. in., $W = 3 \times 314 = 942$ lb. Taking $1/m = \nu = 0.3$ and

$$E = 30{,}000{,}000$$

and substituting in the formulas,

$$\text{Max } y = (3)(942)(1 - 0.3)(5 + 0.3)(10^2) \div 16\pi(30{,}000{,}000)(0.2^3) = 0.087 \text{ in.}$$

$$\text{Max } s = [(3)(942)(3 + 0.3)] \div [8\pi(0.2^2)] = 9270 \text{ lb. per sq. in.}$$

2. For the plate of Example 1, it is required to determine the maximum deflection and maximum stress under a load of 10 lb. per sq. in.

If the ordinary theory held, the stress and deflection would be directly proportional to the load. But this would indicate a maximum deflection of $\frac{10}{3} \times 0.087 = 0.29$ in., which is much more than half the thickness. Therefore the ordinary theory does not apply with sufficient accuracy and we use the formulas that take into account diaphragm stress. The appropriate formulas are Eqs. 1 and 2. Equation 1 is solved by trial for y/t; since the deflection is known to be somewhat less than 0.29, trial is started with a "guessed" value for y/t of, say, 1.3, and it is soon found that the correct value is 1.09. Therefore the deflection is 0.218 in. Then by Eq. 2 the stress is found to be 27,400 lb. per sq. in. (By the ordinary theory, y would have been found to be 0.29 in. and s to be 30,900 lb. per sq. in.)

3. Suppose the plate of Example 1 is supported at the center by a $\frac{1}{4}$-in. diameter steel rod 20 in. long that passes through a $\frac{1}{2}$-in. diameter hole and has a spherical nut which bears against the lower edge of this hole. The plate is loaded as in Example 1. It is required to determine the maximum stress in the plate under these circumstances.

Solution.—This is a combination of Case 13 and Case 14, and is solved by superposition and the method of consistent deformations. For consistent deformations, the downward deflection y_1 due to the distributed load, minus the upward deflection y_2 due to the tension T in the rod, is equal to the stretch e of the rod. By the formula for Case 13 (in which, since b is very small, all terms in the brackets except the first and possibly the fourth can be dropped),

$$y_1 = (3)(3)(1 - 0.3^2)\left[\frac{10^4(5 + 0.3)}{8(1 + 0.3)} + 0 - 0 + \frac{10^2(0.25^2)(3 + 0.3)}{2(1 - 0.3)} \log_e 40 - 0\right] \div [2(30{,}000{,}000)(0.2^3)] = 0.088 \text{ in.}$$

By the formula for Case 14

$$y_2 = (3)(T)(1 - 0.3^2)\left[\frac{(10^2 - 0.25^2)(3 + 0.3)}{(1 + 0.3)} + \frac{(4)(10^2)(0.25^2)(1 + 0.3)}{(1 - 0.3)(10^2 - 0.25^2)}\right.$$
$$\left.(\log_e 40)^2\right] \div [4\pi(30{,}000{,}000)(0.2^3)] = 0.000233T$$

By Eq. 3, Art. 25,

$$e = (20T) \div [(30{,}000{,}000)(0.0491)] = 0.0000136T$$

Then

$$0.088 - 0.000233T = 0.0000136T$$

from which

$$T = 357 \text{ lb.}$$

The maximum stress will probably be at the edge of the hole, and is found by superposing the stress s_1 due to the downward load and the opposite stress s_2 due to the upward tension T. Using the formulas for Cases 13 and 14, and again noting that b is very small,

$$s_1 = [(3)(3)(10^2)(3 + 0.3)] \div [(4)(0.2^2)] = 18{,}600$$
$$s_2 = (3)(357)\left[\frac{2(10^2)(1 + 0.3)}{10^2 - 0.25^2}\log_e 40 + (1 - 0.3)\right] \div [2\pi(0.2^2)] = 44{,}000$$

The resultant stress at the edge of the hole is therefore

$$44{,}000 - 18{,}600 = 25{,}400 \text{ lb. per sq. in.}$$

In this case this is certainly the greatest stress, but obviously it would be possible to so adjust the bolt as to make the stress due to T just offset the stress due to w, in which case the maximum stress would occur at some point between the edge of the hole and the rim of the plate, and could most easily be found by plotting the two stress curves.

4. Assume the plate of Example 1 to have *fixed* edges, and to be loaded at the center by a load of 100 lb. applied through a steel sphere, the area of contact between this sphere and the plate being a circle with a radius $r_0 = 0.02$ in. It is required to determine the maximum bending stress produced.

Solution.—This is Case 7. Since r_0 is very small, the equivalent radius b is used. It is found to be

$$b = \sqrt{(1.6)(0.02^2) + 0.04} - 0.675(0.2) = 0.067 \text{ in.}$$

Using the formula for stress at the center and dropping negligibly small terms,

$$\text{Max } s = (3)(100)\left[(1 + 0.3)\log_e\left(\frac{10}{0.067}\right) + 0\right] \div [2\pi(0.2^2)]$$
$$= 7470 \text{ lb. per sq. in.}$$

The stress at the edge is only 1190 lb. per sq. in., and is practically independent of r_0 as long as r_0 is very small compared with a.

5. The plate of Example 1 is *partially* fixed at the edges, so that when the uniform load of 3 lb. per sq. in. is applied, the plate, instead of remaining

horizontal at the edges, assumes a slope there of 0.25 deg. It is required to determine the stress at the center and at the edge under these conditions.

Solution.—The principle of superposition is used. The stresses at the edge and at the center are first found on the assumption of true fixity. Then the uniform edge moment (Case 12) necessary to cause an edge slope of 0.25 deg, is found. Then the stresses produced by such an edge moment are superposed on the stresses formerly found; the results represent the true stresses.

For fixed edges (Case 6),

(At edge)

$$s = [(3)(942)] \div [4\pi(0.2^2)] = 5620$$

(At center)

$$s = [(3)(942)(1 + 0.3)] \div [8\pi(0.2^2)] = 3640$$

For $\theta = 0.25° = 0.00436$ radian (Case 12),

$$M = [(0.00436)(0.2^3)(30{,}000{,}000)] \div [(12)(10)(1 - 0.3)] = 12.45 \text{ in.-lb. per in.}$$

and

$$s = [(6)(12.45)] \div 0.2^2 = 1870$$

The resultant stress at the edge is

$$s = 5620 - 1870 = 3750 \text{ lb. per sq. in.}$$

The resultant stress at the center is

$$s = 3640 + 1870 = 5510 \text{ lb. per sq. in.}$$

60. Plates of Variable Thickness.—For any circular plate of variable thickness, loaded symmetrically with respect to the center, the stresses and deflections can be found as follows: The plate is divided into an arbitrary number of concentric rings, each of which is assumed to have a uniform thickness equal to its mean thickness. Each such ring is loaded by radial moments M_a, M_b at its outer and inner circumferences, respectively, by vertical shears at its inner and outer circumferences, and by whatever load is distributed over its surface. The shears are known, each being equal to the total load on the plate within the corresponding circumference. The problem is to determine the edge moments, and this is done by making use of the fact that the slope of each ring at its inner circumference is equal to the slope of the next inner ring at its outer circumference. This condition, together with the known slope (or moment) at the outer edge of the plate and the known slope (or moment) at the inside edge or center of the plate, enables as many equations to be written as there are unknown quantities, M. The edge moments having all been found, stresses and deflections can be calculated for each ring by the appropriate formulas of Table X and the deflections added to find the deflection of the plate. To carry out this procedure, it is necessary to determine the slope at the inner and outer edges of a ring due to edge moments (Case 25), edge shears (Case 14), and uniformly distributed loading (Case 13). This can be done by using the coefficients given in the table on page 241, or by using the formulas for slope given below.

For Case 25:

(At outer edge)

$$\theta = \frac{12a}{Et^3}\left\{M_a\left[\frac{(1-\nu)+(b/a)^2(1+\nu)}{1-(b/a)^2}\right] - 2M_b\left[\frac{(b/a)^2}{1-(b/a)^2}\right]\right\}$$

(At inner edge)

$$\theta = \frac{12a}{Et^3}\left\{2M_a\left[\frac{b/a}{1-(b/a)^2}\right] - M_b\left[\frac{(b/a)^3(1-\nu)+(b/a)(1+\nu)}{1-(b/a)^2}\right]\right\}$$

For Case 14:

(At outer edge)

$$\theta = \frac{3Wa(1-\nu^2)}{\pi Et^3}\left[\frac{1}{1+\nu} + \frac{2}{1-\nu}\,\frac{(b/a)^2}{1-(b/a)^2}\log\frac{a}{b}\right]$$

(At inner edge)

$$\theta = \frac{3Wa(1-\nu^2)}{\pi Et^3}\left[\frac{(b/a)}{1+\nu} + \frac{2}{1-\nu}\,\frac{(b/a)}{1-(b/a)^2}\log\frac{a}{b}\right]$$

For Case 13:

(At outer edge)

$$\theta = \frac{wa^3}{2Et^3}\left[3(1-\nu) + (3+9\nu)\left(\frac{b}{a}\right)^2 - 12(1+\nu)\frac{(b/a)^4}{1-(b/a)^2}\log\frac{a}{b}\right]$$

(At inner edge)

$$\theta = \frac{wa^3}{2Et^3}\left[3(3+\nu)\left(\frac{b}{a}\right) - 3(1-\nu)\left(\frac{b}{a}\right)^3 - 12(1+\nu)\frac{(b/a)^3}{1-(b/a)^2}\log\frac{a}{b}\right]$$

A more direct solution (Ref. 21) is available if the plate is of such form that the variation in thickness can be expressed fairly closely by the equation: $t = t_0(e^{\frac{-nx^2}{6}})$, where t is the thickness at any point distant r from the center, t_0 is the thickness at the center, e is the base for the Napierian system of logarithms (2.718), x is the ratio r/a, and n is a number chosen so as to make the equation agree with the actual variation in thickness. The constant n is positive for a plate that decreases in thickness towards the edge and negative for a plate that increases in thickness toward the edge. For a plate of uniform thickness, $n = 0$; for a plate twice as thick at the center as at the edge, $n = +4.16$. The maximum stress and deflection for a uniformly loaded circular plate are given by Max $s = \beta wa^2/t_0^2$, Max $y = \alpha wa^4/Et_0^3$, where β and α depend on n, and for values of n from 4 to -4 can be found by interpolation from the following table:

Edge conditions		n								
		+4	+3	+2	+1	0	−1	−2	−3	−4
Edges supported (Case 1)	β	1.63	1.55	1.45	1.39	1.24	1.16	1.04	0.945	0.855
	α	1.220	1.060	0.924	0.804	0.695	0.600	0.511	0.432	0.361
Edges fixed (Case 6)	β	2.14	1.63	1.31	0.985	0.75	0.55	0.43	0.32	0.26
	α	0.4375	0.3490	0.276	0.217	0.1707	0.1343	0.1048	0.0830	0.0653

For a circular pierced plate clamped at both edges, whose thickness increases linearly from the center outward (Fig. 33), the stress and deflection can be found from the following formulas and coefficients, taken from Ref. 36. The case numbers refer to the manner of loading and support represented in Table X.

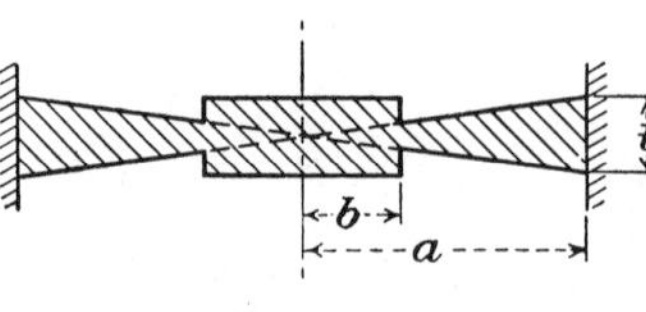

FIG. 33.

For Cases 19, 21, 57, *and* 58:

$$\text{Max } s = \frac{\beta w a^2}{t^2}; \qquad \max y = \frac{\alpha w a^4}{Et^3}$$

(Max stress at inner edge except for Case 19 when $a/b < 2$)

For Cases 20 *and* 22:

$$\text{Max } s = \frac{\beta W}{t^2}; \qquad \max y = \frac{\alpha W a^2}{Et^3}$$

(Max stress at inner edge)

Case No.	Coef.	a/b					
		1.25	1.5	2.0	3	4	5
19	β	0.0785	0.208	0.52	1.27	1.94	2.515
	α	0.00092	0.008	0.0496	0.193	0.346	0.482
20	β	0.159	0.396	1.091	3.306	6.549	10.78
	α	0.00174	0.0112	0.0606	0.261	0.546	0.876
21	β	0.249	0.638	3.96	13.64	26.00	40.63
	α	0.00372	0.0453	0.401	2.119	4.245	6.283
22	β	0.353	0.933	2.626	6.877	11.47	16.51
	α	0.00816	0.0583	0.3448	1.358	2.387	3.268
57	β	0.149	0.991	2.23	5.57	7.78	9.16
	α	0.0055	0.0564	0.412	1.673	2.786	3.573
58	β	0.1275	0.5145	2.051	7.965	17.35	30.00
	α	0.00105	0.01145	0.0934	0.537	1.261	2.16

61. Nonuniform Loading.—The case of a circular plate under a nonuniformly distributed loading symmetrical about the center can be solved by treating the load as a series of elementary ring loadings and summing up the stresses and deflections produced by such loadings. For solid plates the formulas of Cases 3 and 8 are appropriate, and for pierced plates the formulas of Cases 59 and 60 are appropriate. The number of ring loadings into which the actual load should be resolved depends upon the rate at which the distributed load varies along the radius and upon the accuracy desired. In general, a division of the load into rings each having a width equal to one-fifth the loaded length of the radius should be sufficient.

62. Disk Springs.—The conical disk or Belleville spring (Fig. 34) is, of course, not a flat plate, but it may appropriately be considered in this chapter because it bears a superficial resemblance to a flat ring and is sometimes erroneously analyzed by the formulas for Case 14.

The stress and deflection produced in a spring of this type are not proportional to the applied load, because the change in form consequent upon deflection markedly changes the load-deflection and load-stress relationships. This is indeed the peculiar advantage of this form of spring, because it makes it possible to secure almost any desired variation of "spring rate" and to obtain a considerable range of deflection under almost constant load.

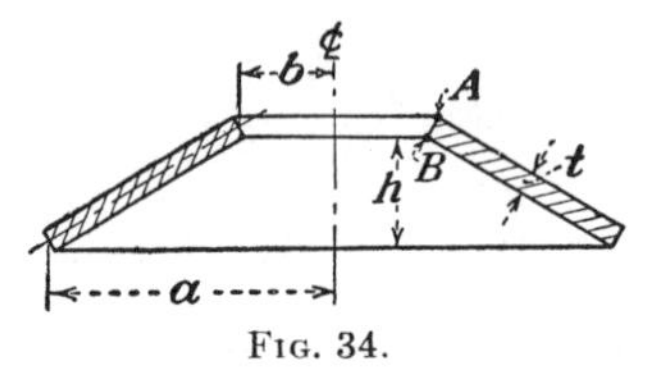

FIG. 34.

Formulas for deflection and stress (Ref. 27) are

$$P = \frac{E\delta}{(1 - \nu^2)Ma^2}\left[(h - \delta)\left(h - \frac{\delta}{2}\right)t + t^3\right]$$

$$\text{Max stress at } A = \frac{E\delta}{(1 - \nu^2)Ma^2}\left[C_1\left(h - \frac{\delta}{2}\right) + C_2 t\right]$$

$$\text{Max stress at } B = \frac{E\delta}{(1 - \nu^2)Ma^2}\left[C_1\left(h - \frac{\delta}{2}\right) - C_2 t\right]$$

where P = total applied load, E = modulus of elasticity, δ = deflection, h = cone height of either inner or outer surface, t = thickness, a and b are the outer and inner radii of the middle surface, and M, C_1, and C_2 are constants whose values are functions of a/b and are given in the following table:

a/b	M	C_1	C_2
1.0	0		
1.2	0.31	1.02	1.05
1.4	0.46	1.07	1.14
1.6	0.57	1.14	1.23
1.8	0.64	1.18	1.30
2.0	0.70	1.23	1.39
2.2	0.73	1.27	1.46
2.6	0.76	1.35	1.60
3.0	0.78	1.43	1.74
3.4	0.80	1.50	1.88
3.8	0.80	1.57	2.00
4.2	0.80	1.64	2.14
4.6	0.80	1.71	2.26
5.0	0.79	1.77	2.38

The formulas for stress may give either positive or negative results, depending upon δ; a positive result indicates compressive stress, a negative result a tensile stress. It is to be noted that P also may become negative.

63. Narrow Ring under Distributed Torque about Its Axis.—When the inner radius b is almost as great as the outer radius a, the loading for Cases 13, 14, 15, and 16 becomes almost equivalent to that shown in Fig. 35, which represents a ring subjected to a uniformly distributed moment of M in.-lb. per linear in. acting about its axis. An approximation to this type of loading also occurs in clamping or "follower" rings used for joining pipe; here the bolt pulls and balancing gasket or flange pressure produce the distributed moment, which obviously tends to "roll" the ring or turn it inside out, so to speak.

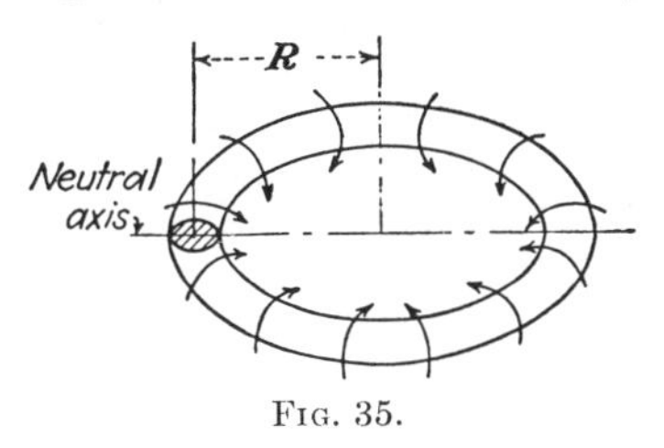

FIG. 35.

Under this loading the ring, whatever the shape of its cross section (so long as this is reasonably compact) is subjected to a bending moment at every section equal to MR, the neutral axis being the central axis of the cross section in the plane of the ring. The maximum resulting stress occurs at the extreme fiber and is given by Eq. 12 of Art. 32, *i.e.*,

$$s = \frac{MR}{I/c}$$

The ring does not bend, and there is no twisting, but every section rotates in its own plane about its centroid through an angle

$$\theta = \frac{MR^2}{EI} = \frac{sR}{Ec}$$

These formulas may be used to obtain approximate results for the cases of flat-plate loading listed above when the difference between a and b is small, as well as for pipe flanges, etc.

References

1. ROARK, R. J.: Stresses Produced in a Circular Plate by Eccentric Loading and by a Transverse Couple, *Univ. Wis. Eng. Exp. Sta., Bull.* 74, 1932. The deflection formulas are due to Föppl. See Die Biegung einer kreisförmigen Platte, *Sitzungsber. mathem.-physik. Klasse K. B. Akademie Wissensch. München,* p. 155, 1912.

2. MICHELL, J. H.: The Flexure of Circular Plates, *Proc. Math. Soc. London*, p. 223, 1901.
3. MORLEY, A.: "Strength of Materials," Longmans, Green & Company, 1919.
4. TIMOSHENKO, S.: Über die Biegung der allseitig unterstützten rechteckigen Platte unter Wirkung einer Einzellast, *Der Bauingenieur*, Vol. 3, Jan. 31, 1922.
5. PRESCOTT, J.: "Applied Elasticity," Longmans, Green & Company, 1924.
6. NADAI, A.: Über die Spannungsverteilung in einer durch eine Einzelkraft belasteten rechteckigen Platte, *Der Bauingenieur*, Vol. 2, Jan. 15, 1921.
7. TIMOSHENKO, S., and J. M. LESSELLS: "Applied Elasticity," Westinghouse Technical Night School Press, 1925.
8. WOJTASZAK, I. A.: Stress and Deflection of Rectangular Plates, *Am. Soc. Mech. Eng. Paper* A-71, *Jour. Appl. Mech.*, Vol. 3, No. 2, 1936.
9. WESTERGAARD, H. M., and A. SLATER: Moments and Stresses in Slabs, *Proc. Am. Concrete Inst.*, Vol. 17, 1921.
10. WAHL, A. M.: Strength of Semicircular Plates and Rings under Uniform External Pressure, *Trans. Am. Soc. Mech. Eng.*, Vol. 54, No. 23, 1932.
11. NADAI, A.: Die Formänderungen und die Spannungen von durchlaufenden Platten, *Der Bauingenieur*, Vol. 5, p. 102, 1924.
12. NADAI, A.: "Elastische Platten," Berlin, 1925.
13. HOLL, D. L.: Analysis of Thin Rectangular Plates Supported on Opposite Edges, *Iowa Eng. Exp. Sta., Iowa State College, Bull.* 129, 1936.
14. WESTERGAARD, H. M.: Stresses in Concrete Pavements Computed by Theoretical Analysis, *Public Roads*, U.S. Dept. of Agriculture, Bureau of Public Roads, Vol. 7, No. 2, 1926.
15. TIMOSHENKO, S.: "Vibration Problems in Engineering," p. 319, D. Van Nostrand Company, Inc., 1928.
16. WAY, S.: Bending of Circular Plates with Large Deflection, *Trans. Am. Soc. Mech. Eng.*, Vol. 56, No. 8, 1934 (see also discussion by E. O. Waters).
17. STURM, R. G., and R. L. MOORE: The Behavior of Rectangular Plates under Concentrated Load, *Am. Soc. Mech. Eng., Paper* A-75, *Jour. Appl. Mech.*, Vol. 4, No. 2, 1937.
18. HENCKY, H.: "Über den Spannungszustand in kreisrunder Platten mit verschwindender Biegungssteifigkeit," *Zeits. Math. Phys.*, Vol. 63, p. 311, 1915.
19. WAHL, A. M.: Stresses and Deflections in Flat Circular Plates with Central Holes, *Trans. Am. Soc. Mech. Eng., Paper* APM-52-3, Vol. 52(1), p. 29, 1930.
20. FLÜGGE, W.: Kreisplatten mit linear veränderlichen Belastungen, *Bauingenieur*, Vol. 10, No. 13, p. 221, 1929.
21. TIMOSHENKO, S., and S. WOINOWSKY-KRIEGER: "Theory of Plates and Shells," 2nd ed., McGraw-Hill Book Company, 1959.
22. REISSNER, H.: Über die unsymmetrische Biegung dünner Kreisringplatte, *Ing.-Archiv*, Vol. 1, p. 72, 1929.

23. Woinowsky-Krieger, S.: Berechnung der ringsum frei aufliegenden gleichseitigen Dreiecksplatte, *Ing.-Archiv*, Vol. 4, p. 254, 1933.
24. Jensen, V. P.: Analysis of Skew Slabs, *Eng. Exp. Sta. Univ. Ill., Bull.* 332, 1941.
25. Evans, T. H.: Tables of Moments and Deflections for a Rectangular Plate Fixed at All Edges and Carrying a Uniformly Distributed Load, *Am. Soc. Mech. Eng., Jour. Appl. Mech.*, Vol. 6, No. 1, March, 1939.
26. Young, D.: Clamped Rectangular Plates with a Central Concentrated Load, *Am. Soc. Mech. Eng., Paper* A-114, *Jour. Appl. Mech.*, Vol. 6, No. 3, 1939.
27. Almen, J. O., and A. Laszlo: The Uniform-section Disc Spring, *Trans. Am. Soc. Mech. Eng.*, Vol. 58, p. 305, 1936.
28. Odley, E. G.: Deflections and Moments of a Rectangular Plate Clamped on all Edges and under Hydrostatic Pressure, *Am. Soc. Mech. Eng., Jour. Appl. Mech.*, Vol. 14, No. 4, December, 1947.
29. Stevens, H. H.: Behavior of Circular Membranes Stretched above the Elastic Limit by Air Pressure, *Exp. Stress Analysis*, Vol. II, No. 1, 1944.
30. Levy, S.: Bending of Rectangular Plates with Large Deflections, *Nat. Adv. Comm. Aeron., Tech. Note* 846, 1942.
31. Levy, S.: Square Plate with Clamped Edges under Normal Pressure Producing Large Deflections, *Nat. Adv. Comm. Aeron., Tech. Note* 847, 1942.
32. Levy, S., and S. Greenman: Bending with Large Deflection of a Clamped Rectangular Plate with Length-width Ratio of 1.5 under Normal Pressure, *Nat. Adv. Comm. Aeron., Tech. Note* 853, 1942.
33. Chi-Teh Wang: Nonlinear Large Deflection Boundary-value Problems of Rectangular Plates, *Nat. Adv. Comm. Aeron., Tech. Note* 1425, 1948.
34. Chi-Teh Wang: Bending of Rectangular Plates with Large Deflections, *Nat. Adv. Comm. Aeron., Tech. Note* 1462, 1948.
35. Ramberg, W., A. E. McPherson, and S. Levy: Normal Pressure Tests of Rectangular Plates, *Nat. Adv. Comm. Aeron., Rept.* 748, 1942.
36. Conway, H. D.: The Bending of Symmetrically Loaded Circular Plates of Variable Thickness, *Am. Soc. Mech. Eng., Jour. Appl. Mech.*, Vol. 15 No. 1, March, 1948.
37. Reissmann, Herbert: Bending of Clamped Wedge Plates, *Am. Soc. Mech. Eng., Jour. Appl. Mech.*, Vol. 20, March, 1953.
38. Bassali, W. A., and R. H. Dawoud: Bending of an Elastically Restrained Circular Plate under Normal Loading on a Sector, *Am. Soc. Mech. Eng., Jour. Appl. Mech.*, Vol. 25, No. 1, March, 1958.
39. Bassali, W. A., and M. Nassif: Stresses and Deflections in Circular Plate Loaded over a Segment, *Am. Soc. Mech. Eng., Jour. Appl. Mech.*, Vol. 26, No. 1, March, 1959.
40. Jurney, W. H.: Displacements and Stresses of a Laterally Loaded Semicircular Plate with Clamped Edges, *Am. Soc. Mech. Eng., Jour. Appl. Mech.*, Vol. 26, No. 2, June 1959.
41. Conway, H. D.: Bending of Rectangular Plates Subjected to a Uniformly Distributed Lateral Load and to Tensile or Compressive Forces

in the Plane of the Plate, *Am. Soc. Mech. Eng., Jour. Appl. Mech.*, Vol. 16, No. 3, September, 1949.

42. MORSE, R. F., and H. D. CONWAY: The Rectangular Plate Subjected to Hydrostatic Tension and to Uniformly Distributed Lateral Load, *Am. Soc. Mech. Eng., Jour. Appl. Mech.*, Vol. 18, No. 2, June, 1951.
43. HODGE, P. G., JR.: "Plastic Analysis of Structures," McGraw-Hill Book Company, 1959.
44. SHULL, H. E., and L. W. HU: Load-carrying Capacities of Simply Supported Rectangular Plates, *Am. Soc. Mech. Eng., Jour. Appl. Mech.*, Vol. 30, No. 4, December, 1963.
45. ZAID, M.: Carrying Capacity of Plates of Arbitrary Shape, *Am. Soc. Mech. Eng., Jour. Appl. Mech.*, Vol. 25, No. 4, December, 1958.

CHAPTER 11

COLUMNS AND OTHER COMPRESSION MEMBERS

64. Columns; Common Case.—The formulas and discussion of this article are based on the following assumptions: (1) The column is nominally straight and is subjected only to nominally concentric and axial end loads; such crookedness and eccentricity as may occur are accidental, and not greater than is consistent with standard methods of fabrication and ordinary conditions of service. (2) The column is homogeneous and of uniform cross section. (3) If the column is made up of several longitudinal elements, these elements are so connected as to act integrally. (4) There are no parts so thin as to fail by local buckling before the column as a whole has developed its full strength.

End Conditions.—The strength of a column is in part dependent on the *end conditions*, by which is meant the degree of end fixity or constraint. A column the ends of which are supported and fixed, so that there can be neither lateral displacement nor change in slope at either end, is called *fixed-ended*. A column the ends of which are supported against lateral displacement but not constrained against change in slope is called *round-ended*. A column one end of which is fixed and the other end neither laterally supported nor otherwise constrained is called *free-ended*. A column both end-surfaces of which are flat and normal to the axis, and bear evenly against rigid loading surfaces, is called *flat-ended*. A column, the ends of which bear against transverse pins, is called *pin-ended*.

Truly fixed-ended and truly round-ended columns practically never occur in practice; the actual conditions are almost always intermediate. The greatest degree of fixity is found in columns the ends of which are riveted or welded to relatively rigid parts that are themselves fixed. Theoretically a flat-ended column is equivalent to a fixed-ended column until the load reaches a certain critical value at which the column "kicks out" and bears only on one edge of each end surface instead of on the whole surface. Actually, flat-ended columns have a degree of end constraint considerably less than that required to produce fixity. The nearest approach to round-ended conditions is found in pin-ended columns subject to vibration or other imposed motion. The degree of end fixity may be expressed by the "coefficient of constraint" (explained below), or by the "free" or "effective" length, which is the length measured between points of counterflexure, or length of a round-ended column of equal strength.

Behavior.—If sufficiently slender, a column will fail by elastic instability (see Chap. 14). In this case the maximum unit load sustained is less than the proportional limit of the material; it depends on the modulus of elasticity, on the slenderness ratio (ratio of the length of the column to the least radius of gyration of the section), and on the end conditions, and is independent of the strength of the material. Columns which fail in this way are called *long columns.*

Columns too short to fail by elastic instability are called *short columns;* such a column will fail when the maximum fiber stress due to direct compression and to the bending that results from accidental crookedness and eccentricity reaches a certain value. This value is about equal to the tensile yield point for structural steel, is about equal to the compressive yield strength for light alloys, and lies between the flexural elastic limit and the modulus of rupture in the case of wood.

For a given material and given end conditions, there is a certain slenderness ratio which marks the dividing point between long and short columns; this is called the *critical* slenderness ratio.

Formulas for Long Columns.—The unit load at which a long column fails by elastic instability is given by the Euler formula

$$\frac{P}{A} = \frac{C\pi^2 E}{(L/r)^2} \tag{1}$$

where P = total load, A = area of section, E = modulus of elasticity, L/r = slenderness ratio, and C is the coefficient of constraint, which depends on end conditions. For round ends, $C = 1$; for fixed ends, $C = 4$; for the end conditions that obtain in practice C can rarely be assumed greater than 2. It is generally not considered good practice to employ long columns in building and bridge construction, but they are used in aircraft, and in Table XI the Euler equations used in aeronautical design are given for a number of materials and end conditions. (Formulas for the loads producing elastic instability of uniform and tapered bars, under a wide variety of conditions of loading and support, are given in Table XV.)

Formulas for Short Columns.—It is not possible to calculate with accuracy the maximum stress produced in a short column by a nominally concentric load, because of the large influence of the indeterminate crookedness and eccentricity. The maximum unit load that a column will sustain, however, can be expressed by any of a number of formulas, in each of which one or more terms are empirically adjusted to secure conformity with test results. Of such formulas, those given below are the best known and provide the basis for most of the design formulas used in American practice. In these equations P denotes the load at failure, A the cross-sectional area, L the length, and r the least radius of gyration of the section; the meaning of other symbols used is explained in the discussion of each formula.

$$\text{(Secant formula)} \qquad \frac{P}{A} = \frac{s}{1 + \frac{ec}{r^2} \sec\left[\frac{KL}{2r}\sqrt{\frac{P}{AE}}\right]} \qquad (2)$$

This is adapted from the formula for stress due to eccentric loading (Eq. 27, Art. 67). Here s denotes the maximum fiber stress at failure (usually taken as the yield point for steel and as the yield strength for light alloys); e denotes the *equivalent eccentricity* (that eccentricity which in a perfectly straight column would cause the same amount of bending as do the actual eccentricity and crookedness); c denotes the distance from the central axis about which bending occurs to the extreme fiber on the concave or compression side of the bent column, and K is a numerical coefficient, dependent on end conditions, such that KL is the effective length of the column, or distance between points of inflection. The term ec/r^2 is called the *eccentric ratio*, and a value is assumed for this ratio which makes the formula agree with the results of tests on columns of the type under consideration. For example, tests on structural steel columns of conventional design indicate that the average value of the eccentric ratio is 0.25. In using the secant formula, P/A must be solved for by trial, or by the use of prepared charts.

$$\text{(Parabolic formula)} \qquad \frac{P}{A} = s - k\left(\frac{L}{r}\right)^2 \qquad (3)$$

TABLE XI.—STANDARD COLUMN FORMULAS

Notation: Q = allowable load (lb.); P = ultimate load (lb.); A = section area of column (sq. in.); L = length of column (in.); r = least radius of gyration of column section (in.); S_u = ultimate strength and S_y = yield point or yield strength of material (lb. per sq. in.); E = modulus of elasticity of material (lb. per sq. in.); m = factor of safety; $(L/r)'$ = critical slenderness ratio.

Material	Service	Type of section	End conditions assumed	Formulas for: Allowable unit load Q/A	Formulas for: Ultimate unit load P/A
Structural steel	Buildings	Structural shapes or fabricated	Ends riveted or welded, or columns continuous	$\frac{Q}{A} = \frac{\left[1 - \frac{(L/r)^2}{2C_c^2}\right]}{m} s_y$ for $\frac{L}{r} < C_c$ $\frac{Q}{A} = \frac{149{,}000{,}000}{(L/r)^2}$ for $\frac{L}{r} > C_c < 200$ Here: $C_c = \sqrt{\frac{2\pi^2 E}{S_y}}$ (Ref. 1) $m = \frac{5}{3} + \frac{3(L/r)}{8C_c} - \frac{(L/r)^3}{8C_c^3}$ For s_y = 33,000 36,000 42,000 46,000 50,000 C_c = 131.7 126.1 116.7 111.6 107.0	$\frac{P}{A} = \frac{Q}{A} \times m$
Structural carbon steel s_y = 33,000	Bridges	Structural shapes or fabricated	Ends riveted	$\frac{Q}{A} = \frac{S_y/m}{1 + 0.25 \sec\left(\frac{0.75L}{2r}\sqrt{\frac{mQ}{EA}}\right)}$ (Ref. 4) Suggested S_y = 32,000; suggested m = 1.7	$\frac{P}{A} = \frac{S_y}{1 + 0.25 \sec\left(\frac{0.75L}{2r}\sqrt{\frac{P}{EA}}\right)}$ or (Ref. 4) $\frac{P}{A} = 25{,}600 - 0.425\left(\frac{L}{r}\right)^2$ up to $\frac{L}{r} = 160$
				$\frac{Q}{A} = 15{,}000 - \frac{1}{4}\left(\frac{L}{r}\right)^2$ up to $\frac{L}{r} = 140$ (Refs. 3, 4)	
				$\frac{Q}{A} = \frac{18{,}750}{1 + 0.25 \sec \frac{0.75L}{2r}\sqrt{\frac{1.76Q}{EA}}}$ for $\frac{L}{r} > 140$ (Ref. 3)	

			Ends pinned	$\frac{Q}{A} = 15{,}000 - \frac{1}{3}\left(\frac{L}{r}\right)^2$ up to $\frac{L}{r} = 140$ (Refs. 3, 4) $\frac{Q}{A} = \frac{18{,}750}{1 + 0.25 \sec\left(\frac{0.875L}{2r}\sqrt{\frac{1.76Q}{EA}}\right)}$ for $\frac{L}{r} > 140$ (Ref. 3)	$\frac{P}{A} = \frac{[illegible]}{1 + 0.25 \sec\left(\frac{0.85L}{2r}\sqrt{\frac{P}{EA}}\right)}$ or $\frac{P}{A} = 25{,}600 - 0.566\left(\frac{L}{r}\right)^2$ up to $\frac{L}{r} = 140$ (Ref. 4)
Structural silicon steel $S_u = 80{,}000$ $S_y = 45{,}000$	Bridges, and general structural use	Structural shapes or fabricated	Ends riveted	$\frac{Q}{A} = 20{,}000 - 0.46\left(\frac{L}{r}\right)^2$ up to $\frac{L}{r} = 130$ (Ref. 3) $\frac{Q}{A} = \frac{25{,}000}{1 + 0.25 \sec\left(\frac{0.75L}{2r}\sqrt{\frac{1.8Q}{EA}}\right)}$ for $\frac{L}{r} > 130$	$\frac{P}{A} = 1.8\frac{Q}{A}$
				$\frac{Q}{A} = 27{,}000 - 80\frac{L}{r}$, max $\frac{Q}{A} = 23{,}000$ (Ref. 5)	
			Ends pinned	$\frac{Q}{A} = 20{,}000 - 0.61\left(\frac{L}{r}\right)^2$ up to $\frac{L}{r} = 130$ $\frac{Q}{A} = \frac{25{,}000}{1 + 0.25 \sec\left(\frac{0.875L}{2r}\sqrt{\frac{1.8Q}{EA}}\right)}$ for $\frac{L}{r} > 130$ (Ref. 3)	$\frac{P}{A} = 1.8\frac{Q}{A}$
Structural nickel steel $S_y = 55{,}000$	Bridges and general structural use	Structural shapes or fabricated	Ends riveted	$\frac{Q}{A} = 24{,}000 - 0.66\left(\frac{L}{r}\right)^2$ up to $\frac{L}{r} = 120$ $\frac{Q}{A} = \frac{30{,}000}{1 + 0.25 \sec\left(\frac{0.75L}{2r}\sqrt{\frac{1.83Q}{EA}}\right)}$ for $\frac{L}{r} > 120$ (Ref. 3)	$\frac{P}{A} = 1.83\frac{Q}{A}$
				$\frac{Q}{A} = 24{,}000 - 98\frac{L}{r}$ (Ref. 6)	
			Ends pinned	$\frac{Q}{A} = 24{,}000 - 0.86\left(\frac{L}{r}\right)^2$ up to $\frac{L}{r} = 120$ $\frac{Q}{A} = \frac{30{,}000}{1 + 0.25 \sec\left(\frac{0.875L}{2r}\sqrt{\frac{1.83Q}{EA}}\right)}$ for $\frac{L}{r} > 120$ (Ref. 3)	$\frac{P}{A} = 1.83\frac{Q}{A}$

TABLE XI.—STANDARD COLUMN FORMULAS.—(*Continued*)

Material	Service	Type of section	End conditions assumed	Formulas for: Allowable unit load Q/A — s_y	Q/A	L/r	Ultimate unit load P/A
High-strength steel	General	Structural shapes and fabricated	Finned	33,000	$15{,}000 - 0.325\left(\frac{L}{r}\right)^2$	0–140	$\frac{P}{A} = 1.8\frac{Q}{A}$
					$\frac{15{,}000}{0.5 + \frac{1}{15{,}860}\left(\frac{L}{r}\right)^2}$	140–200	
				45,000	$20{,}500 - 0.605\left(\frac{L}{r}\right)^2$	0–120	
					$\frac{20{,}500}{0.5 + \frac{1}{11{,}630}\left(\frac{L}{r}\right)^2}$	120–200	
				50,000	$22{,}500 - 0.738\left(\frac{L}{r}\right)^2$	0–110	
					$\frac{22{,}500}{0.5 + \frac{1}{10{,}460}\left(\frac{L}{r}\right)^2}$	110–200	
				55,000	$25{,}000 - 0.902\left(\frac{L}{r}\right)^2$	0–105	
					$\frac{25{,}000}{0.5 + \frac{1}{9510}\left(\frac{L}{r}\right)^2}$	105–200	(From "Design Manual for High Strength Steels," copyright U.S. Steel Corp., Ref. 28)
Low-carbon and alloy steel	Airplanes	Tubular, circular, or noncrippling shapes	Represented by C	$\frac{Q}{A} = \frac{P}{A} \div m$ m is usually taken as 1.5 in aircraft design			See below

Ultimate unit load P/A (Low-carbon and alloy steel, Airplanes):

s_y	P/A	$\left(\frac{L'}{r}\right)_{cr}$
36,000	$36{,}000 - 1.172\left(\frac{L'}{r}\right)^2$	122
75,000	$79{,}500 - 51.9\left(\frac{L'}{r}\right)^{1.5}$	91
103,000	$113{,}000 - 11.15\left(\frac{L'}{r}\right)^2$	73
132,000	$145{,}000 - 18.36\left(\frac{L'}{r}\right)^2$	63
163,000	$179{,}000 - 27.95\left(\frac{L'}{r}\right)^2$	56

					Here s_y is tensile yield strength for 0.002 offset. Column yield strength is higher, and is the first term in the formula. $L' = L/C$, where C is usually taken as 1.5 for riveted ends and as 2 for welded ends. For $L'/r > (L'/r)_{cr}$, $P/A = 286{,}000{,}000/(L'/r)^2$ (Ref. 9)
Cast iron	Buildings	Hollow, round	Flat	$\frac{Q}{A} = 12{,}000 - 60\frac{L}{r}$ Max $\frac{Q}{A} = 10{,}000$; max $\frac{L}{r} = 100$ (Ref. 3)	$\frac{P}{A} = 34{,}000 - 88\frac{L}{r}$
				$\frac{Q}{A} = 9000 - 40\frac{L}{r}$ Max $\frac{L}{r} = 70$ Min diameter = 6 in.; min thickness = $\frac{1}{2}$ in. (Ref. 7)	
Structural aluminum: 6061-T6, 6062-T6 $s_y = 35{,}000$ $s_u = 38{,}000$ $E = 10{,}000{,}000$	Building structures (nonwelded)	Structural shapes or fabricated	Partial constraint	$\frac{L}{r} < 10$ $\frac{Q}{A} = 19{,}000$ $\frac{L}{r} > 10 < 67$ $\frac{Q}{A} = 20{,}400\text{–}135\frac{L}{r}$ $\frac{L}{r} > 67$ $\frac{Q}{A} = \frac{51{,}000{,}000}{(L/r)^2}$ (Ref. 30, spec. A-7b, p. 42)	$\frac{P}{A} = 1.95\frac{Q}{A}$
	Bridge structures (nonwelded)	Structural shapes or fabricated	Partial constraint	$\frac{L}{r} < 9.2$ $\frac{Q}{A} = 17{,}000$ $\frac{L}{r} > 9.2 < 67$ $\frac{Q}{A} = 18{,}100 - 120\frac{L}{r}$ $\frac{L}{r} > 67$ $\frac{Q}{A} = \frac{45{,}000{,}000}{(L/r)^2}$ (Ref. 30, spec. A-7a, p. 6)	$\frac{P}{A} = 2.20\frac{Q}{A}$

TABLE XI.—STANDARD COLUMN FORMULAS.—(*Continued*)

Material	Service	Type of section	End conditions assumed	Formulas for: Allowable unit load Q/A	Formulas for: Ultimate unit load P/A
Structural aluminum: 2014-T4 $F_{cy} = 35,000$; 2024-T3 $F_{cy} = 42,000$; 2024-T4 $F_{cy} = 40,000$; 6061-T6 $F_{cy} = 35,000$	Airplanes	Tubular, circular, or noncrippling shapes	Represented by $c = 1.5$ (riveted ends) to 2 (welded ends)	$\frac{Q}{A} = \frac{P}{A} \div m$ m is usually taken as 1.5 in aircraft design	$\frac{P}{A} = F_{co}\left(1 - 0.385\frac{L'/r}{\pi\sqrt{E/F_{co}}}\right)$ up to $\left(\frac{L'}{r}\right)_{cr} = 1.732\pi\sqrt{\frac{E}{F_{co}}}$ $\frac{P}{A} = \frac{\pi^2 E}{(L'/r)^2}$ for $\frac{L'}{r} > \left(\frac{L'}{r}\right)_{cr}$ Here $L' = L/\sqrt{c}$ F_{co} = column yield stress $= F_{cy}\left(1 + \frac{F_{cy}}{200,000}\right)$ where F_{cy} = comp. yield strength at 0.2% offset (Ref. 9)
7075-T6 $F_{cy} = 66,000$	Airplanes	Tubular, circular, or noncrippling shapes	Represented by c (as above)		$\frac{P}{A} = F_{co}\left[1 - F_{co}\frac{(L'/r)^2}{4\pi^2 E}\right]$ up to $\left(\frac{L'}{r}\right)_{cr} = 1.414\pi\sqrt{\frac{E}{F_{co}}}$ $F_{co} = 1.075F_{cy}$ (Ref. 9)
Structural magnesium alloy (see Ref. 10)	General structural use	Structural shapes or fabricated	Ends riveted or with equivalent constraint	$\frac{Q}{A} = \frac{1}{2}\frac{P}{A}$ or less	$\frac{P}{A} = \frac{S}{1 + f\left(\frac{kL}{r}\right)^2}$, not to exceed S' Alloy / S / f / S': AMC 58S-T51 / 160,900 / 0.00249 / 36,000 AMC 58S / 46,000 / 0.00072 / 22,000 AMC 57S / 34,300 / 0.00053 / 19,000 AMC 52S / 25,500 / 0.00040 / 16,000 AM 3S / 16,750 / 0.00026 / 11,000 Here $k = 0.5$
			Ends pinned	$\frac{Q}{A} = \frac{1}{2}\frac{P}{A}$ or less	Same as for riveted ends except $k = 1$
Wood (values are for timber of select structural grade)	General structural use under continuously dry conditions	Solid square or rectangular	Ends flat	$\frac{Q}{A} = S\left[1 - \frac{1}{3}\left(\frac{L}{Kd}\right)^4\right]$ up to $\frac{L}{d} = K = 0.64\sqrt{\frac{E}{S}}$ $\frac{Q}{A} = \frac{0.274E}{\left(\frac{L}{d}\right)^2}$ for $\frac{L}{d} > K$	$\frac{P}{A} = 4\frac{Q}{A}$

Hemlock $S = 700$ $E = 1{,}100{,}000$ Longleaf yellow pine $S = 1450$ $E = 1{,}600{,}000$ Southern cypress $S = 1100$ $E = 1{,}200{,}000$ Douglas fir $S = 1200$ $E = 1{,}600{,}000$				Here S = allowable compressive stress; d = least dimension of cross section $\frac{Q}{A} = 700\left[1 - 0.00000097\left(\frac{L}{d}\right)^4\right]$, $K = 24.2$ $\frac{Q}{A} = 1450\left[1 - 0.00000162\left(\frac{L}{d}\right)^4\right]$, $K = 21.23$ $\frac{Q}{A} = 1100\left[1 - 0.00000168\left(\frac{L}{d}\right)^4\right]$, $K = 21.10$ $\frac{Q}{A} = 1200\left[1 - 0.00000112\left(\frac{L}{d}\right)^4\right]$, $K = 23.35$ (Ref. 11)	
	General structural use under continuously dry conditions	Laminated with cover plates or boxed around solid core; square or rectangular	Ends flat	Ratio of $\frac{Q}{A}$ to $\frac{Q}{A}$ for solid column of same dimensions depends on $\frac{L}{d}$ and is as follows $\frac{L}{d}$ = 6 10 14 18 22 26 Ratio = 0.82 0.77 0.71 0.65 0.74 0.82 (Ref. 11)	
		Solid, circular	Ends flat	$\frac{Q}{A}$ is same as for square column of equal area. For tapered round column, d and A are taken as for section distant $\frac{1}{3}L$ from smaller end. $\frac{Q}{A}$ at small end must not exceed S (Ref. 11)	
	Airplanes	Solid	Represented by c taken as 1 to 1.5	$\frac{Q}{A} = \frac{P}{A} \div m$	$\frac{P}{A} = F_{cu}\left[1 - \frac{1}{3}\left(\frac{L'}{r(L'/r)_{cr}}\right)^4\right]$ up to $\left(\frac{L'}{r}\right)_{cr}$ $\frac{P}{A} = \frac{10E_L}{(L'/r)^2}$ for $\left(\frac{L'}{r}\right) > \left(\frac{L'}{r}\right)_{cr}$ $\left(\frac{L'}{r}\right)_{cr} = \sqrt{\frac{15E_L}{F_{cu}}}$ Here: F_{cu} = ultimate compressive strength E_L = modulus of elasticity from static bending test $L' = L/\sqrt{c}$ (Ref. 25)

This is an empirical formula. The value of s is taken as for the secant formula; the value of the coefficient k is adjusted so as to make the curve agree with the results of tests through the L/r range of most importance, or to make it tangent to the Euler curve for the material and end conditions in question.

$$\text{(Straight-line formula)} \qquad \frac{P}{A} = s - k\left(\frac{L}{r}\right) \tag{4}$$

This also is an empirical formula. The value of s is sometimes taken as the ultimate compressive strength of the material when tested in the form of a short prism, k then being taken so as to make the straight-line tangent to the corresponding Euler curve. But more frequently both s and k are empirically adjusted to make the straight line agree with the results of tests through the L/r range of most importance.

$$\text{(Rankine formula)} \qquad \frac{P}{A} = \frac{s}{1 + \phi(L/r)^2} \tag{5}$$

This is a semirational formula. The value of s is sometimes taken as the ultimate strength of the material and the value of ϕ as $s/C\pi^2E$, thus making the formula agree with the results of tests on short prisms when L/r is very small, and making it agree with Euler's equation when L/r is very large. More often s and ϕ are empirically adjusted to make the equation agree with the results of tests through the L/r range of most importance.

By applying a proper safety factor, a formula for the *safe* unit load Q/A may be derived from any one of the above formulas for ultimate unit load. In Table XI are given a number of the ultimate strength and working formulas most commonly used in American practice, together with specified restrictions as to the permissible slenderness ratio, and values of the critical slenderness ratio $(L/r)'$ which marks the transition point between long and short columns. The use of the formulas is illustrated in Examples 1 and 2 below.

Calculation of Stress.—The best way to compute the probable value of the maximum fiber stress in a short column, caused by the imposition of a nominally concentric load less than the ultimate, is to use the secant formula (Eq. 2) with an assumed value of e or ec/r^2. However, any one of the Eqs. 3, 4, or 5 can, by transposing terms, be written so as to give the maximum stress s

in terms of the load P. Such procedure is logical only when s is the fiber stress at failure and P the ultimate load, but if the maximum stress due to some load less than the ultimate is thus computed, the result, while probably considerably in error, is almost sure to be greater than the true stress, and hence the method errs on the side of safety. The stress in a transmission shaft due to a longitudinal compressive load is sometimes computed in this way, a straight-line formula being written in the form

$$s = \frac{P/A}{\left(1 - 0.0044\frac{L}{r}\right)} \quad \text{(Ref. 12)}$$

Examples

1. Figure 36 represents the cross section of a structural steel column composed of two 10-in. 35-lb. channels, placed 12 in. back to back and latticed together. The length of the column is 349.3 in. It is required to determine the maximum load this column will carry and the safe load (assuming riveted ends and using appropriate formulas from Table XI). (This column is one the test of which is reported in Ref. 4; it is there designated as No. 27, Series D.)

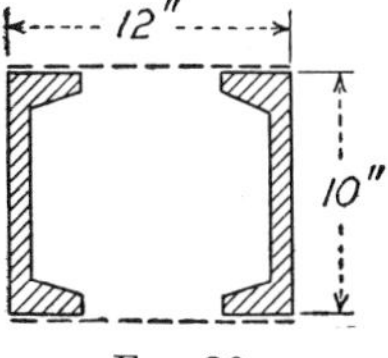

FIG. 36.

Solution.—The actual area of the section is 20.13 sq. in.; the least radius of gyration is that for axis 2, and is 3.34 in.; the slenderness ratio $L/r = 349.3/3.34 = 104.5$. The maximum unit load is first found by the parabolic formula to be $P/A = 25{,}600 - 0.425(104.5)^2 = 25{,}600 - 4650 = 20{,}950$ lb. per square inch. The maximum total load is therefore $P = 20.13 \times 20{,}950 = 421{,}500$ lb. Solution will also be effected by the secant formula. This involves successive trial, and since the parabolic and secant formulas are known to be in close agreement, trial will be commenced with 21,000. We have

$$\frac{P}{A} = \frac{32{,}000}{1 + 0.25 \sec\left[\frac{(0.75)(349.3)}{(2)(3.34)}\sqrt{\frac{21{,}000}{30{,}000{,}000}}\right]} = 21{,}400$$

Evidently 21,000 is too small; we try with slightly higher assumed values of P/A, and after one or two trials find that $P/A = 21{,}300$, or $P = 429{,}000$ lb.

The safe unit load is given by

$$\frac{Q}{A} = 15{,}000 - \frac{1}{4}(104.5)^2 = 12{,}270 \text{ lb. per sq. in.}$$

Hence the safe load

$$Q = 20.13 \times 12{,}270 = 247{,}000 \text{ lb.}$$

2. A piece of cypress piling, 18 ft. long, is to be used as a flat-ended column. The section is circular, the diameter being 18 in. at one end and 15 in. at the other. It is required to find the safe load.

Solution.—Assuming a uniform taper, the diameter at a distance from the smaller end equal to one-third the length is 16 in.; the section area at that point is therefore 201 sq. in., and a square column of equal area would have $d = 14.2$ in. L/d is therefore $(18 \times 12)/14.2 = 15.2$, and since this is greater than 11 and less than K, the allowable unit load is calculated as follows:

$$\frac{Q}{A} = 1100[1 - 0.00000168(15.2)^4] = 1100[1 - 0.09] = 1{,}000$$

The safe load is therefore

$$201 \times 1000 = 201{,}000 \text{ lb.}$$

65. Local Buckling.—If a column is composed wholly or in part of thin material, local buckling may occur at a unit load less than that required to cause failure of the column as a whole. When such local buckling occurs at a unit stress less than the proportional limit, it represents elastic instability; the critical stress at which this occurs can be determined by mathematical analysis. Formulas for the critical stress at which bars and thin plates exhibit elastic instability, under various conditions of loading and support, are given in Tables XV and XVI of Chap. 13. All such formulas are based upon assumptions as to homogeneity of material, regularity of form, and boundary conditions that are never realized in practice; the critical stress to be expected under any actual set of circumstances is nearly always less than that indicated by the corresponding theoretical formula, and can only be determined with certainty by test. This is also true of the ultimate load that will be carried by such parts as buckle, since elastic buckling is not necessarily attended by failure, and thin flanges and webs may, by virtue of the support afforded by attached parts, carry a load considerably in excess of that at which buckling occurs (see Art. 69).

In the following paragraphs, the more important facts and relations that have been established concerning local buckling are stated, in so far as they apply to columns of more or less conventional design. In the formulas given, b represents the unsupported width of the part under consideration, t its thickness, s_y the yield point or yield strength, and E and ν have their usual meanings.

Outstanding Flanges.—For a long flange having one edge fixed and the other edge free, the theoretical formula for buckling stress is

$$s' = \frac{1.09E}{1 - \nu^2}\left(\frac{t}{b}\right)^2 \qquad (6)$$

and for a flange having one edge simply supported and the other edge free the corresponding formula is

$$s' = \frac{0.416E}{1 - \nu^2}\left(\frac{t}{b}\right)^2 \qquad (7)$$

(See Table XVI.)

For the outstanding flange of a column the edge condition is intermediate, the degree of constraint depending upon the torsional rigidity of the main member and on the way in which the flange is attached. The conclusions of the A.S.C.E. Column Research Committee (Ref. 4) on this point may be summed up as follows: For columns of structural steel having a proportional limit of 30,000 lb. per sq. in., an outstanding flange riveted between two angles, each having a thickness equal to that of the flange will not fail by elastic buckling if b/t is less than 15, b being measured from the free edge of the flange to the first row of rivets. For wider flanges, the buckling stress is given by the formula

$$s' = 0.4E\left(\frac{t}{b}\right)^2 \qquad (8)$$

If the thickness of each supporting angle is twice that of the flange, elastic buckling will not occur if b/t is less than 20, b in this case being measured from the free edge of the flange to the toe of angle. For wider flanges the buckling stress is given by the formula

$$s' = 0.6E\left(\frac{t}{b}\right)^2 \qquad (9)$$

The ultimate strength of an outstanding flange is practically equal to the area times the yield point up to a b/t ratio of 15; for wider flanges the ultimate load is not appreciably greater, and so there is no substantial gain in load-carrying capacity when the width of a flange is increased to more than 15 times the thickness. In Ref. 1 are given recommended limiting values of width-to-thickness ratios in terms of s_y for webs, flanges, and other parts subject to buckling.

In the case of aluminum, the *allowable* unit stress on an outstanding flange may be found by the formula

(Allowable) $$s = 15{,}000 - 123\left(k\frac{b}{t}\right) \quad \text{when} \quad k\frac{b}{t} < 81 \qquad (10)$$

and by the formula

(Allowable) $$s = \frac{33{,}000{,}000}{\left(k\frac{b}{t}\right)^2} \quad \text{when} \quad k\frac{b}{t} > 81 \qquad (11)$$

Here k is to be taken as 4 when the outstanding flange is one leg of an angle, T, or other section having relatively little torsional rigidity, and may be taken as 3 when the flange is part of, or firmly attached to, a heavy web or other part that offers relatively great edge constraint. A formula (Ref. 13) for the ultimate strength of short compression members consisting of single angles, which takes into account both local and general buckling, is

$$\frac{P}{A} = s \tanh \left[K\left(\frac{t}{b}\right)^2\right] \qquad (12)$$

where $K = 149.1 + 0.1\left(\frac{L}{r} - 47\right)^2$ and s, which depends on $\frac{L}{r}$, has values as follows

$\frac{L}{r}$	0	20	40	60	80
s	40,000	38,000	34,000	27,000	18,000

The formula is for an alloy (24ST) having a yield strength of 43,000 lb. per sq. in. and a modulus of elasticity of 10,500,000 lb. per sq. in., and is for round-ended columns ($c = 1$). A more general formula, for thin sections other than angles, is

$$\frac{P}{A} = s \tanh (Kt) \qquad (12a)$$

Here $s = s_y(1 + B)/(1 + B + B^2)$, where $B = [s_y(L/r)^2]/(c\pi^2E)$, and $K = K_0(s_y/s)^{\frac{1}{2}}$, where K_0 is a "shape factor" the value of which is found from Eq. 12a, P/A being experimentally determined by testing columns of the section in question that have a slenderness ratio of about 20. For a closed box or "hat" section, $K_0 = 15.6$; for a section with flat flanges whose width is not over 25 times the thickness, $K_0 = 10.8$; for sections of oval form, or sections having wholly or partially curved flanges, K_0 ranges from 12 to 32 (Ref. 13). An extensive discussion of design procedures and of buckling formulas for aluminum columns and other structural elements is to be found in Ref. 8.

For spruce and other wood of similar properties, Trayer and March (Ref. 3, Chap. 14) give as the formula for buckling stress

$$s' = 0.07E\left(\frac{t}{b}\right)^2 \tag{13}$$

when the edge constraint is as great as can normally be expected in all-wood construction, and

$$s' = 0.044E\left(\frac{t}{b}\right)^2 \tag{14}$$

when conditions are such as to make the edge constraint negligible.

Thin Webs.—For a long thin web fixed along each edge the theoretical formula for buckling stress is

$$s' = \frac{5.73E}{1 - \nu^2}\left(\frac{t}{b}\right)^2 \tag{15}$$

and for a web simply supported along each edge the corresponding formula is

$$s' = \frac{3.29E}{1 - \nu^2}\left(\frac{t}{b}\right)^2 \tag{16}$$

(See Table XVI.)

For structural steel columns, the conclusion of the A.S.C.E. Column Research Committee (Ref. 4) is that elastic buckling will not occur at b/t ratios less than 30. Tests made by the Bureau of Standards (Ref. 15), on steel members consisting of wide webs riveted between edge angles, indicate that this conclusion is conservative, and that b/t may safely be as great as 35 if b is taken as the width between rivet lines.

For aluminum columns, the same formulas for allowable stress on a thin web are suggested as those given above for the outstanding flange (Eqs. 10 and 11) but with $k = 1.2$.

(For discussion of the ultimate strength developed by a thin web, see Art. 69.)

Thin Cylindrical Tubes.—For a thin cylindrical tube the theoretical formula for the critical stress at which buckling occurs is

$$s' = \frac{E}{\sqrt{3}\sqrt{1 - \nu^2}}\frac{t}{R} \tag{17}$$

where R denotes the mean radius of the tube (see Table XVI). Tests indicate that the critical stress actually developed is usually only 40 to 60 per cent of this theoretical value. Lundquist (Ref. 12, Chap. 14) suggests the use of the formula

$$s' = KE \tag{18}$$

where the nondimensional coefficient K, which depends on the ratio R/t and on the imperfections of the cylinder, is to be based on tests. From the data available, it would appear that even for very carefully prepared cylinders K should not be taken as more than 50 per cent of the theoretical value (given by Eq. 17) when R/t is about 200, and not more than 30 per cent for values of R/t around 1000. Younger (Ref. 15) suggests as a conservative formula $s' = 0.12Et/R$. Wilson and Newmark (Ref. 16; Ref. 13, Chap. 14), on the basis of extensive tests, suggest as safe *design* formulas for steel columns

$$\text{(Allowable)} \qquad s = 2{,}000{,}000\frac{t}{R}\left(\lesseqqgtr \frac{1}{2} \text{ proportional limit}\right) \tag{19}$$

for cold-drawn or machined tubes, and

$$\text{(Allowable)} \qquad s = 1{,}600{,}000\frac{t}{R}\left(\lesseqqgtr \frac{1}{3} \text{ yield point}\right) \tag{20}$$

for fabricated columns without local indentations or lap girth seams. Wilson concludes that when $t/R \gtreqqless 0.015$, the full yield point of the steel will be developed before wrinkling occurs, assuming this yield point to be 33,000 lb. per sq. in. or less. These experiments, and others on very thin tubes, indicate that for a constant t/R ratio the wrinkling stress is less for a thin plate than for a thick plate, owing to the fact that form irregularities occur on a relatively greater scale in the thinner material.

The Chicago Bridge and Iron Company has used, for the design of large fabricated tubular columns of structural steel, a formula which takes into account both local and general buckling. It is

$$\text{(Allowable)} \qquad \frac{Q}{A} = XY \tag{21}$$

where $Y = 1$ for $L/r \lesseqqgtr 60$

$$Y = \frac{21{,}600}{18{,}000 + (L/r)^2} \text{ for } \frac{L}{r} > 60$$

$$X = \left[1{,}000{,}000\frac{t}{R}\right]\left[2 - \frac{2}{3}\left(100\frac{t}{R}\right)\right] \text{ for } \frac{t}{R} \lesseqqgtr 0.015$$

$$X = 15{,}000 \text{ for } t/R \gtreqqless 0.015$$

Min $t = \frac{1}{4}$ in.

This formula is based on tests made by Wilson and Newmark at University of Illinois (Ref. 16; Ref. 13, Chap. 14). Transverse bulkheads have no appreciable effect upon the critical stress at which buckling occurs unless they are very closely spaced. The same statement holds true of longitudinal stiffeners, but these may greatly increase the *ultimate strength* of a column (see Art. 69).

Attached Plates.—When the flanges or web of a column are formed by riveting a number of plates placed flat against one another, there is a possibility of the outer plate or plates buckling between points of attachment if the unsupported length is too great compared with the thickness. If the full yield strength, s_y, of an outer plate is to be developed, the ratio of unsupported length a to thickness t should not exceed the value indicated by the formula

$$\frac{a}{t} = 0.52\sqrt{\frac{E}{s_y}} \tag{22}$$

(Ref. 17). Some specifications (Ref. 3) guard against the possibility of such buckling by limiting the maximum distance between rivets (in the direction of the stress) to 16 times the thickness of the thinnest outside plate, and to 20 times the thickness of the thinnest inside plate. The ratio 16 is in line with Eq. 22.

Local Buckling of Latticed Column.—To guard against the possibility of longitudinal elements of a latticed-column buckling individually between points of support, some specifications (Ref. 3) limit the slenderness ratio of such parts, between points of attachment of lacing bars, to 40, or to two-third the slenderness ratio of the column as a whole, whichever is less.

Lacing Bars.—In a column composed of channels or other structural shapes connected by lacing bars, the function of the latter is to resist the transverse shear due to initial obliquity and that consequent upon such bending as may occur under load. The amount of this shear is conjectural since the obliquity is accidental and indeterminate.

Salmon (Ref. 17) shows that with the imperfections usually to be expected, the transverse shear will be at least 1 per cent of the axial load. Moore and Talbot (Ref. 18) found that for certain experimental columns the shear amounted to from 1 to 3 per cent of the axial load. Some specifications require that in buildings the lacing be designed to resist a shear equal to 2 per cent of the axial load (Ref. 1), and that in bridges it be designed to resist a shear V given by the equation

$$V = \frac{P}{100}\left[\frac{100}{(L/r) + 10} + \frac{(L/r)}{100}\right]$$

where P is the allowable axial load and r is the radius of gyration of the column section with respect to the central axis perpendicular to the plane of the lacing (Ref. 3).

The strength of individual lacing bars as columns has been investigated experimentally. For a bar of rectangular section with a single rivet at each end, the ultimate strength is given by

$$\frac{P}{A} = 25{,}000 - 50\frac{L}{r} \text{ (Ref. 4)} \qquad \text{or} \qquad \frac{P}{A} = 21{,}400 - 45\frac{L}{r} \text{ (Ref. 18)}$$

For bars of angle or channel section these formulas are conservative. For flat bars used as double lacing, the crossed bars being riveted together, tests show that the effective L is about half the actual distance between end rivets. Some specifications (Refs. 1, 3) require lacing bars of any section to be designed by the regular column formula, L being taken as the distance between end rivets for single lacing, and as 70 per cent of that distance for double lacing. There are additional limitations as to slope of lacing, minimum section, and method of riveting.

66. Strength of Latticed Columns.—While it is customary to assume that a latticed column acts integrally and develops the full strength of the nominal section, tests show that when bending occurs in the plane of the lacing the column is less stiff than would be the case if this assumption were valid. For a column so designed that buckling occurs in a plane normal to that of the lacing, this fact is unimportant, but in long open columns laced on all sides, such as are often used for derrick booms and other light construction, it may be necessary to take it into account.

For any assumed transverse loading, it is easy to calculate that part of the deflection of a latticed member which is due to strains in the lacing bars, and thus to derive a value for what may be called the reduced modulus of elasticity, KE. Such calculations agree reasonably well with the results of tests (see Ref. 4), but K, of course, varies with the nature of the assumed transverse loading, or, what amounts to the same thing, with the form of the assumed elastic curve. For uniformly distributed loading and end support, and for the type of lacing shown in Fig. 37*a*, K is given by the equation

$$K = \frac{1}{1 + \dfrac{4.8I}{AL^2 \cos^2 \theta \sin \theta}} \tag{23}$$

Here L = length of the column, I = moment of inertia of the column section with reference to the axis of bending, and A = cross-sectional area of a single lacing bar. For double lacing, 2.4 should be used in place of 4.8. If KE is used in place of E, the effect of reduced stiffness on the strength of a long column will be approximately allowed for. The method is theoretically inexact, mainly because the form of elastic curve assumed is not

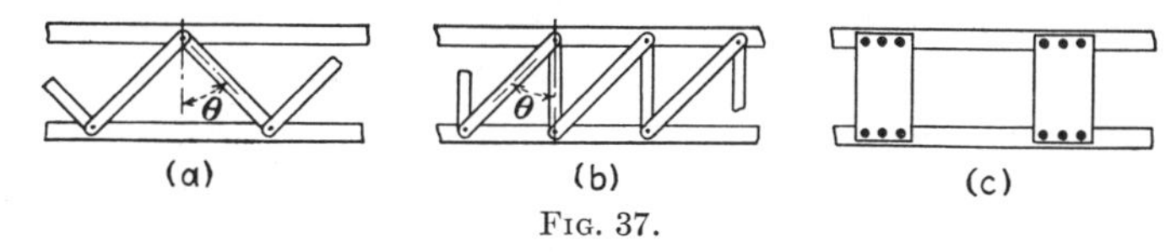

FIG. 37.

identical with that taken by the column, but the error due to this is small.

Timoshenko (Ref. 19) gives formulas, based upon the assumption that the elastic curve of the column is a sinusoid, from which the following expressions for K may be derived:
For the arrangement shown in Fig. 37*a*,

$$K = \frac{1}{1 + \dfrac{4.93I}{AL^2 \cos^2 \theta \sin \theta}} \tag{24}$$

For the arrangement shown in Fig. 37*b*,

$$K = \frac{1}{1 + \dfrac{4.93I}{A_1L^2 \cos^2 \theta \sin \theta} + \dfrac{4.93I}{A_2L^2 \tan \theta}} \tag{25}$$

where A_1 = cross-sectional area of the diagonal bars and A_2 = cross-sectional area of the transverse bars.

For the channel and batten-plate arrangement shown in Fig. 37*c*.

$$K = \frac{1}{1 + \dfrac{\pi^2 I}{L^2}\left(\dfrac{ab}{12I_2} + \dfrac{a^2}{24I_1}\right)} \tag{26}$$

where a = distance center to center of battens, b = horizontal length of a batten between rivets, I_1 = moment of inertia of a channel section about a horizontal central axis parallel to the web, and I_2 = moment of inertia of a vertical batten-plate section about its horizontal central axis (*i.e.*, I_1 has reference to bending of the channel perpendicular to its own plane and I_2 has reference to vertical bending of the batten plate in its own plane).

In all of the above expressions for K, it is assumed that all parts have the same modulus of elasticity, and only the additional deflection due to longitudinal strain in the lacing bars, and to secondary flexure of channels and batten plates, is taken into account. For fairly long columns laced over practically the entire length, the values of K given by Eqs. 23, 24, and 25 are probably sufficiently accurate. More elaborate formulas for shear deflection, in which direct shear stress in the channels, bending of the end portions of channels between stay plates, and rivet deformation, as well as longitudinal strains in lacing bars, are taken into account, are given in Ref. 4. These should be used when the deflection of a short latticed column under direct transverse loading is to be calculated.

The use of K as a correction factor for obtaining a reduced value of E is convenient in designing long latticed columns; for short columns the correction is best made by replacing L, in whatever column formula is selected, by $\sqrt{(1/K)}L$.

67. Eccentric Loading; Initial Curvature.—When a round-ended column is loaded eccentrically with respect to one of the principal axes of the section (here called axis 1) the maximum stress produced is given by the formula

$$s = \frac{P}{A}\left\{1 + \frac{ec}{r^2} \sec\left[\frac{P}{4EA}\left(\frac{L}{r}\right)^2\right]^{\frac{1}{2}}\right\} \tag{27}$$

where e = eccentricity, c = distance from axis 1 to the extreme fiber on the side nearest the load, and r = radius of gyration of the section with respect to axis 1. (The above equation may be derived from the formula for Case 7, Table VI, by putting $M_1 = Pe$.)

If a column with fixed ends is eccentrically loaded as here assumed, the effect of the eccentricity is merely to increase the constraining moments at the ends; the moment at mid-length and the buckling load are not affected. If the ends are *partially* constrained, as by a frictional moment M, this constraint may be taken into account by considering the actual eccentricity e reduced to $e - (M/P)$. If a free-ended column is eccentrically loaded as here assumed, the maximum stress is given by

$$s = \frac{P}{A}\left\{1 + \frac{ec}{r^2}\sec\left[\frac{P}{EA}\left(\frac{L}{r}\right)^2\right]^{\frac{1}{2}}\right\} \tag{28}$$

where the notation is the same as for Eq. 27.

When a round-ended column is loaded eccentrically with respect to *both* principal axes of the section (here called axes 1 and 2), the maximum stress is given by

$$s = \frac{P}{A}\left\{1 + \frac{e_1c_1}{r_1^2}\sec\left[\frac{P}{4EA}\left(\frac{L}{r_1}\right)^2\right]^{\frac{1}{2}} + \frac{e_2c_2}{r_2^2}\sec\left[\frac{P}{4EA}\left(\frac{L}{r_2}\right)^2\right]^{\frac{1}{2}}\right\} \tag{29}$$

where the subscripts 1 and 2 have reference to axes 1 and 2, the notation otherwise being the same as for Eq. 27.

The use of Eq. 27 is illustrated in the example below, which also shows the use of Eq. 23 in obtaining a reduced modulus of elasticity to use with a latticed column.

If a round-ended column is initially curved in a plane perpendicular to principal axis 1 of the section, the maximum stress produced by concentric end loading is given by

$$s = \frac{P}{A}\left\{1 + \frac{dc}{r^2}\frac{8EA}{P(L/r)^2}\left[\sec\left(\frac{P}{4EA}\left(\frac{L}{r}\right)^2\right)^{\frac{1}{2}} - 1\right]\right\} \tag{30}$$

where d = maximum initial deflection, c = distance from axis 1 to the extreme fiber on the concave side of the column, and r = radius of gyration of the section with respect to axis 1.

If the column is initially curved in a plane which is not the plane of either of the principal axes 1 and 2 of the section, the maximum stress is given by

$$s = \frac{P}{A}\left\{1 + \frac{d_1c_1}{r_1^2}\frac{8EA}{P(L/r_1)^2}\left[\sec\left(\frac{P}{4EA}\left(\frac{L}{r_1}\right)^2\right)^{\frac{1}{2}} - 1\right] + \frac{d_2c_2}{r_2^2}\frac{8EA}{P(L/r_2)^2}\left[\sec\left(\frac{P}{4EA}\left(\frac{L}{r_2}\right)^2\right)^{\frac{1}{2}} - 1\right]\right\} \tag{31}$$

where d_1 = the component of the initial deflection perpendicular to the plane of axis 1, d_2 = the component of the initial deflection perpendicular to the plane of axis 2, and c_1, c_2, r_1, and r_2 each has reference to the axis indicated by the subscript.

Eccentrically loaded columns and columns with initial curvature can also be designed by the interaction formulas given in Art. 68.

Example

The column described in Example 1, Art. 64, has single lacing, the bars being of rectangular section, $2\frac{1}{2}$ by $\frac{1}{4}$ in., and being inclined at 45 deg. This column is loaded eccentrically, the load being applied on axis 2 but 2.40 in. from axis 1. With respect to bending in the plane of the eccentricity, the column is round-ended. It is required to calculate the maximum fiber stress in the column when a load of 299,000 lb., or 14,850 lb. per sq. in., is thus applied.

Solution.—For axis 1, $r = 5.38$ in., $c = 6.03$ in. (measured), and $e = 2.40$ in. Since the bending due to the eccentricity is in the plane of the lacing, a reduced E is used. K is calculated by Eq. 23, where $I = 583$, $A = 2\frac{1}{2} \times \frac{1}{4} = 0.625$ sq. in., $L = 349.3$ in., and $\theta = 45°$. Therefore

$$K = \frac{1}{1 + \dfrac{(4.8)(583)}{(0.625)(349.3^2)(0.707^2)(0.707)}} = 0.94$$

and using the secant formula (Eq. 27), we have

$$s = 14{,}850 \left\{1 + \frac{(2.40)(6.03)}{5.38^2} \sec\left[\frac{14{,}850}{(4)(0.94)(30{,}000{,}000)}\left(\frac{349.3}{5.38}\right)^2\right]^{\frac{1}{2}}\right\} = 25{,}300 \text{ lb. per sq. in.}$$

(This column was actually tested under the above described loading, and the maximum stress, as determined by strain-gauge measurements, was found to be 25, 250 lb. per sq. in. Such close agreement between measured and calculated stress must, however, be regarded as fortuitous.)

68. Column under Combined Compression and Bending.—A column bent by lateral forces or by couples presents essentially the same problem as a beam under axial compression, and the stresses produced can be found by the formulas of Table VI, provided the end conditions are determinable. Because these and other uncertainties generally preclude precise solution, it is common practice to rely upon some interaction formula, such as one of those given below. The column may be considered safe for the given loading when the relevant equations are satisfied.

The following notation is common to all the equations; other terms are defined as introduced:

F_a = allowable value of P/A for the member considered as a concentrically loaded column.

F_b = allowable value of compressive fiber stress for the member considered as a beam under bending only.

$f_a = P/A$ = average axial compressive stress due to the axial load P.

f_b = computed maximum bending stress due to the trans-v[illegible]ads, or to applied couples, or to a combination [illegible]

[illegible]length in plane of bending.

[illegible]ratio for buckling in that plane.

[illegible]*teel:*

[illegible] ≤ 1 when $\dfrac{f_a}{F_a} > 0.15$ [illegible] F_b

[illegible] $+ \dfrac{f_b}{F_b} \leq 1$ when $\dfrac{f_a}{F_a} < 0.15$

[illegible]n braced points, and

$$\frac{f_a}{0.6F_y} + \frac{f_b}{F_b} \leq 1$$

for sections at braced points only.

Here $F_e = \dfrac{149{,}000{,}000}{(L/r)^2}$, F_y = yield point of steel. $C_m = 0.85$ except that for restrained compression members in frames braced against joint translation and without transverse loading between joints, $C_m = 0.6 + 0.4(M_1/M_2)$, where M_1 is the smaller and M_2 the larger of the moments at the ends of the critical unbraced length of the member. M_1/M_2 is positive when the unbraced length is bent in single curvature and negative when it is bent in reverse curvature. For such members with transverse loading between joints, C_m may be determined by rational analysis, or the appropriate formula from Table VI may be used. (Formulas adapted from Ref. 1.)

For structural aluminum:

$$f_b \gtreqless F_b\left(1 - \frac{f_a}{F_a}\right)\left(1 - \frac{f_a}{F_e}\right)\frac{f_a}{F_a} + \frac{f_b}{F_b\left(1 - \dfrac{f_a}{F_e}\right)} \leqq 1$$

Here $F_e = \dfrac{51{,}000{,}000}{(L/r)^2}$ for building structures and $\dfrac{45{,}000{,}000}{(L/r)^2}$ for bridge structures. (Formulas from Ref. 30 with some changes of notation.)

For wood (solid rectangular):

$$\frac{f_b}{F_b} + \frac{f_a}{F_a} \leq 1 \qquad \text{when} \qquad \frac{L}{d} \lesseqqgtr \sqrt{\frac{0.3E}{F_a}}$$

For columns having $L/d > \sqrt{0.3E/F_a}$:

1. Concentric end loads plus lateral loads,

$$\frac{f_b}{F_b - f_a} + \frac{f_a}{F_a} \leq 1$$

2. Eccentric end load,

$$\frac{1.25 f_b}{F_b - f_a} + \frac{f_a}{F_a} \leq 1$$

3. Eccentric end load plus lateral loads,

$$\frac{f_{bl} + 1.25 f_{be}}{F_b - f_a} + \frac{f_a}{F_a} \leq 1$$

Here d = dimension of the section in the plane of bending.
f_{bl} = computed bending stress due to lateral loads.
f_{be} = computed bending stress due to the eccentric moment.

(Formulas from Ref. 26 with some changes of notation.)

69. Thin Plate with Stiffeners.—Compression members and compression flanges of flexural members are sometimes made of a very thin sheet reinforced with attached stiffeners; this construction is especially common in airplanes, where both wings and fuselage are often of the "skin-stressed" type.

When a load is applied to such a combination, the portions of the plate not very close to the stiffeners buckle elastically at a very low unit stress, but those portions immediately adjacent to the stiffeners develop the same stress as do the latter, and portions a short distance from the stiffeners develop an intermediate stress. In calculating the part of any applied load that will be carried by the plate, or in calculating the strength of the combination, it is convenient to make use of the concept of "effective" or "apparent" width, *i.e.*, the width of that portion of the sheet which, if it developed the same stress as the stiffener, would carry the same load as is actually carried by the entire sheet. For a flat, rectangular plate, supported but not fixed along each of two opposite edges and subjected to a uniform shortening parallel to those edges, the theoretical expression (Ref. 20) for the effective width is

$$w = \frac{\pi t}{2\sqrt{3(1-\nu^2)}}\sqrt{\frac{E}{s}} \tag{32}$$

where w denotes the effective width along each supported edge, t = the thickness of the plate, and s = unit stress at the supported edge. Since the maximum value of s is s_y (the yield point or yield strength) the maximum load that can be carried by the effective strip, or, what amounts to the same thing, by the whole plate, is

$$P = \frac{\pi t^2}{\sqrt{3(1-\nu^2)}}\sqrt{Es_y} \tag{33}$$

This formula can be written

$$P = Ct^2\sqrt{Es_y} \tag{34}$$

where C is an empirical constant to be determined experimentally for any given material and manner of support. Tests (Ref. 21) made on single plates of various metals, supported at the edges, gave values for C ranging from 1.18 to 1.67; its theoretical value from Eq. 33, taking $\nu = 0.25$, is 1.87.

Sechler (Ref. 22) represents C as a function of $\lambda = (t/b)\sqrt{E/s_y}$, where b is the panel width, and gives a curve showing experimentally determined values of C plotted against λ. The following table of corresponding values is taken from Sechler's corrected graph:

λ	0.02	0.05	0.1	0.15	0.2	0.3	0.4	0.5	0.6	0.8
C	2.0	1.76	1.62	1.50	1.40	1.28	1.24	1.20	1.15	1.10

The effective width at failure can be calculated by the relation

$$w = \frac{1}{2}Ct\sqrt{\frac{E}{s_y}} = \frac{1}{2}Cb\lambda$$

In the case of a cylindrical panel loaded parallel to the axis, the effective width at failure can be taken as approximately equal to that for a flat sheet, but the increase in the buckling stress in the central portion of the panel, due to curvature, must be taken into account. Sechler shows that the contribution of this central portion to the strength of the panel may be allowed for by using for C in the formula $P = Ct^2 \sqrt{Es_y}$, a value given by

$$C = C_f - 0.3C_f\lambda\eta + 0.3\eta$$

where $\lambda = \frac{t}{b}\sqrt{\frac{E}{s_y}}$, $\eta = \frac{b}{r}\sqrt{\frac{E}{s_y}}$, and C_f is the value of C for a flat sheet, as given by the above table.

The above formulas and experimental data refer to single sheets supported along each edge. In calculating the load carried by a flat sheet with longitudinal stiffeners, at any given stiffener stress s_s, the effective width corresponding to that stress is found by the equation $w = b[0.25 + 0.91\lambda^2]$, where $\lambda = (t/b)\sqrt{E/s_s}$ and b = distance between the stiffeners (Ref. 23). The total load carried by n stiffeners and the supported plate is then $P = n(A_s + 2wt)s_s$, where A_s is the section area of one stiffener. When s_s is the maximum unit load the stiffener can carry as a column, P becomes the ultimate load for the reinforced sheet.

In calculating the ultimate load on a curved sheet with stiffeners, the strength of each unit or panel may be found by adding, to the buckling strength of the central portion of the panel, the strength of a column made up of the stiffener and the effective width of the attached sheet, this effective width being found by the equation $w = \frac{1}{2}C_f t \sqrt{E/s_c}$, where C_f is the flat sheet coefficient corresponding to $\lambda = (t/b)\sqrt{Es_c}$ and s_c is the unit load that the stiffener-and-sheet column will carry before failure, determined by an appropriate column formula. (For the type of thin section often used for stiffeners in airplane construction, S_c may be found by Eq. 12 or 12*a*.) Since the unit load s_c and the effective width w are interdependent (because of the effect of w on the column radius of gyration), it is necessary to assume a value of s_c, to then calculate the corresponding w, and to then ascertain if the value of s_c is consistent (according to the column formula used) with this w. This procedure may have to be repeated several times before agreement is reached. Then, s_c and w being known, the strength of the stiffener-and-sheet combination is calculated as

$$P = n[s_c(A_s + 2wt) + (b - 2w)ts']$$

where n is the number of stiffeners, A_s is the section area of one stiffener, b is the distance between stiffeners (rivet line to rivet line) and s' is the critical buckling stress for the central portion of the sheet, taken as $s' = 0.3ET/r$, r being the radius of curvature of the sheet.

Methods of calculating the strength of stiffened panels and of thin columns subject to local and torsional buckling are being continually modified in the light of current study and experimentation. A more extensive discussion than is appropriate here can be found in books on airplane stress analysis, in Refs. 8 and 9, and in the book "Light Gage Cold-formed Steel Design Manual" (and Commentary) published by the American Iron and Steel Institute.

70. Short Prisms under Eccentric Loading.—When a compressive or tensile load is applied eccentrically to a short prism (*i.e.*, one so short that the effect of deflection is negligible), the resulting stresses are readily found by superposition. The eccentric load P is replaced by an equal axial load P' and by couples Pe_1 and Pe_2, where e_1 and e_2 denote the eccentricities of P with respect to the principal axes 1 and 2, respectively. The stress at any point, or the maximum stress, is then found by superposing the direct stress P'/A due to the axial load and the bending stresses due to the couples Pe_1 and Pe_2, these being found by the ordinary flexure formula (Art. 32).

If, however, the prism is composed of a material that can withstand compression only (masonry) or tension only (very thin shell), this method cannot be employed when the load acts *outside the kern*, because the reversal of stress implied by the flexure formula cannot occur. By assuming a linear stress distribution, and making use of the facts that the volume of the stress solid must equal the applied load P and that the center of gravity of the stress solid must lie on the line of action of P, formulas can be derived for the position of the neutral axis (line of zero stress) and for the maximum fiber stress in a prism of any given cross section. A number of such formulas are given in Table XII, together with the dimensions of the kern for each of the sections considered. For any section that is symmetrical about the axis of eccentricity, the maximum stress $K(P/A)$ is just twice the average stress P/A when the load is applied at the edge of the kern, and increases as the eccentricity increases, becoming (theoretically)

TABLE XII.—FORMULAS FOR SHORT PRISMS ECCENTRICALLY LOADED; STRESS REVERSAL IMPOSSIBLE

Notation: m and n are dimensions of the kern, shown shaded; x is the distance from the most stressed fiber to the neutral axis, A is the net area of the section. Formulas for x and for maximum stress assume the prism to be subjected to longitudinal load P acting outside the kern, on one principal axis of the section and at a distance e from the other principal axis

Form of section, form of kern, and Case No.	Formulas for m, n, x, and Max. stress
1. Solid rectangular section	$m = \frac{1}{6}d \qquad n = \frac{1}{6}b$ $x = 3(\frac{1}{2}d - e)$ $\text{Max } s = \frac{P}{A}\left(\frac{4d}{3d - 6e}\right)$
2. Hollow rectangular section	$m = \frac{1}{6}\frac{bd^3 - ca^3}{d(db - ac)} \qquad n = \frac{1}{6}\frac{db^3 - ac^3}{b(db - ac)}$ x satisfies the eq.: $\frac{e}{d} = \frac{1}{2} - \left\{\frac{\frac{1}{6}bx^3 - \frac{1}{2}a^2c(\frac{1}{2}d - \frac{1}{6}a) - \frac{1}{2}acd(x - \frac{1}{2}a - \frac{1}{2}d)}{d[\frac{1}{2}bx^2 - ac(x - \frac{1}{2}d)]}\right\}$ if $x > \frac{1}{2}(a + d)$ x satisfies the eq.: $\frac{e}{d} = \frac{1}{2} - \left\{\frac{\frac{1}{6}bx^3 - \frac{1}{2}c(x - \frac{1}{2}d - \frac{1}{2}a)^2(\frac{1}{3}x + \frac{1}{6}d - \frac{1}{6}a)}{d[\frac{1}{2}bx^2 - \frac{1}{2}c(x - \frac{1}{2}d - \frac{1}{2}a)^2]}\right\}$ if $x < \frac{1}{2}(a + d)$ $\text{Max } s = \frac{P}{\left[\frac{1}{2}bx - \frac{ac(x - \frac{1}{2}d)}{x}\right]}$ if $x > \frac{1}{2}(a + d)$ $\text{Max } s = \frac{P}{\left[\frac{1}{2}bx - \frac{(x - \frac{1}{2}d + \frac{1}{2}a)^2}{2x}\right]}$ if $x < \frac{1}{2}(a + d)$
3. Thin-walled rectangular shell	$m = \frac{1}{6}d\left(\frac{dt_1 + 3bt_2}{dt_1 + bt_2}\right) \qquad n = \frac{1}{6}b\left(\frac{bt_2 + 3dt_1}{dt_1 + bt_2}\right)$ $x = \frac{1}{2}\left(\frac{3}{2}d - 3e\right) + \sqrt{b\left(\frac{3}{2}d\frac{t_2}{t_1} - 3e\frac{t_2}{t_1}\right) + \frac{1}{4}\left(\frac{3}{2}d - 3e\right)^2}$ $\text{Max } s = \frac{P}{(xt_1 + bt_2)}$

$x = r(1 - \sin\phi)$, where ϕ satisfies the eq.: $\dfrac{e}{r} = \dfrac{\frac{1}{8}\pi - \frac{1}{4}\phi - \frac{5}{12}\sin\phi\cos\phi + \frac{1}{6}\sin^3\phi\cos\phi}{\cos\phi - \frac{1}{3}\cos^3\phi - \frac{1}{2}\pi\sin\phi + \phi\sin\phi}$

Max $s = \dfrac{P}{A}\left[\dfrac{\pi(1 - \sin\phi)}{\cos\phi - \frac{1}{3}\cos^3\phi - \frac{1}{2}\pi\sin\phi + \phi\sin\phi}\right]$ or Max $s = \dfrac{P}{A}K$, where K is given by following table:

$\frac{e}{r}$ =	0.25	0.30	0.35	0.40	0.45	0.50	0.55	0.60	0.65	0.70	0.75	0.80	0.90
K =	2	2.20	2.43	2.70	3.10	3.55	4.20	4.92	5.90	7.20	9.20	13	80

5. Hollow circular section

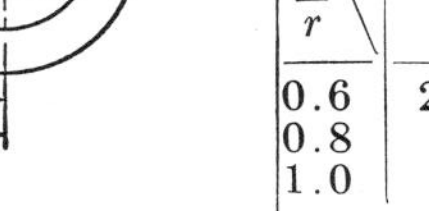

$m = \dfrac{\frac{1}{4}(r^2 + r_1^2)}{r}$

Max $s = \dfrac{P}{A}K$, where K is given by following table:

$\frac{r_1}{r}$ \ $\frac{e}{r}$	0.34	0.35	0.40	0.41	0.45	0.50	0.55	0.60	0.65	0.70	0.75	0.80	0.85	0.90	0.95
0.6	2.00		2.15		2.35	2.60	2.90	3.30	3.80	4.60	5.80	8.00			
0.8				2.00	2.10	2.25	2.40	2.64	2.90	3.35	4.00	5.00	8.00		
1.0						2.00	2.08	2.23	2.40	2.65	2.90	3.25	3.80	4.60	6.70

6. Thin-walled circular shell

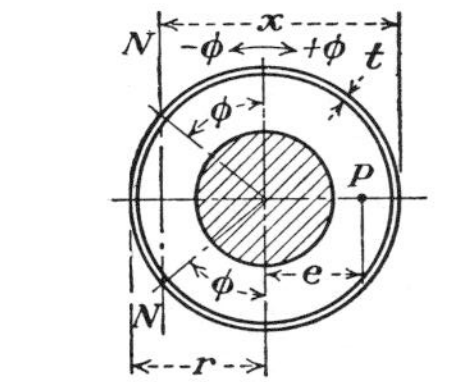

$m = \frac{1}{2}r$

$x = r(1 - \sin\phi)$, where ϕ satisfies the eq.: $\dfrac{e}{r} = \dfrac{\frac{1}{2}\pi - \phi - \sin\phi\cos\phi}{2\cos\phi - \pi\sin\phi + 2\phi\sin\phi}$

Max $s = \dfrac{P}{tr}\left[\dfrac{1 - \sin\phi}{2\cos\phi - \pi\sin\phi + 2\phi\sin\phi}\right]$ or Max $s = \dfrac{P}{A}K$, where K is given by the above table (Case 5) for $\dfrac{r_1}{r} = 1$

infinite when the load is applied at the extreme fiber. A prism made of material incapable of sustaining both tension and compression will fail completely when the resultant of the loads falls outside the boundary of any cross section, and will crack (under tension) or buckle (under compression) part way across any section through which the resultant of the loads passes at a point lying outside the kern.

For any section not shown in Table XII, a chart may be constructed showing the relation between e and x; this is done by assuming successive positions of the neutral axis (parallel to one principal axis) and solving for the corresponding eccentricity by the relation: $b = I/M$, where b = distance from the neutral axis to the point of application of the load (assumed to be on the other principal axis), I = the moment of inertia, and M = the statical moment, about the neutral axis, of that part of the section carrying stress. The position of the neutral axis for any given eccentricity being known, the maximum stress can be found by the relation: Max $s = Px/M$. These equations simply express the facts stated above—that the center of gravity of the stress solid lies on the line of action of P, and that the volume of the stress solid is equal to P. The procedure outlined is simple in principle, but rather laborious when applied to any except the simpler type of section, since both M and I may have to be determined by graphical integration.

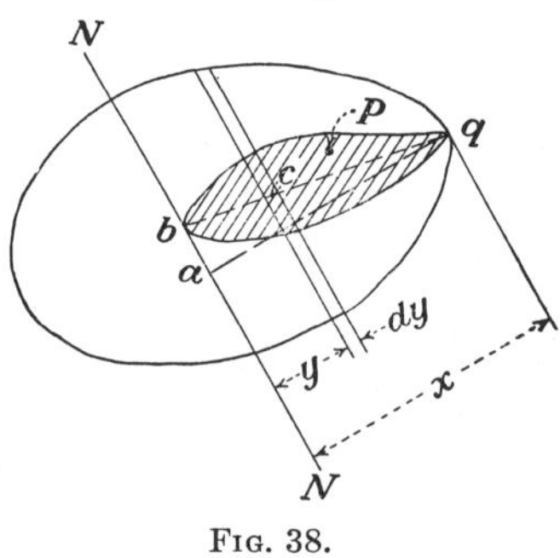

FIG. 38.

The method of solution outlined above, and all the formulas of Table XII, are based on the assumption that the load is applied on one of the principal axes of the section. If the load is applied outside the kern and on neither principal axis, solution is more difficult, because neither the position nor direction of the neutral axis, corresponding to a given position of the load, is known. The following graphical method, which involves successive trial, may be used for a section of any form.

Let a prism of any section (Fig. 38) be loaded at any point P. Guess the position of the neutral axis NN. Draw from NN to the most remote fiber q the perpendicular aq. That part of the section on the load side of NN is under compression, and the intensity of stress varies linearly from 0 at NN to s at q. Divide the stressed area into narrow strips of uniform width dy, running parallel to NN. The total stress on any strip acts at the center of that strip, and is proportional to the area of the strip $w\,dy$ and to its distance y from NN. The locus of the centers of the strips, bcq, is drawn, and a length of strip extending $\frac{1}{2}(y/x)w$ to each side of this locus is marked off. This portion of the strip, if it sustained a unit stress s, would carry the same total load as does the whole strip when sustaining the actual unit stress $(y/x)s$, and may be called the *effective portion* of the strip. The effective portions of all strips combine to form the *effective area*, shown shaded in the figure. Now if the assumed position of NN is correct, the centroid of this effective area will coincide with the point P, and the maximum stress s will then be equal to the load P divided by the effective area. To ascertain whether or not the centroid of the effective area does coincide with P, its outline is traced on stiff cardboard; the piece so outlined is then cut out, and balanced on a pin thrust through at P. If the piece balances in any position, P is of course the centroid. Obviously the chance of guessing the position of NN correctly at the first attempt is remote, and a number of trials are likely to be necessary. Each trial, however, enables the position of NN to be estimated more closely, and the method is less tedious than might be supposed.

$\frac{e_2}{b}$ \ $\frac{e_1}{d}$	0	0.05	0.10	0.15	0.175	0.200	0.225	0.250	0.275	0.300	0.325	0.350	0.375	0.400
0	1.0	1.30	1.60	1.90	2.05	2.22	2.43	2.67	2.96	3.33	3.87	4.44	5.33	6.67
0.05	1.30	1.60	1.90	2.21	2.38	2.58	2.81	3.09	3.43	3.87	4.41	5.16	6.17	7.73
0.10	1.60	1.90	2.20	2.56	2.76	2.99	3.27	3.60	3.99	4.48	5.14	5.99	7.16	9.00
0.15	1.90	2.21	2.56	2.96	3.22	3.51	3.84	4.22	4.66	5.28	6.03	7.04	8.45	10.60
0.175	2.05	2.38	2.76	3.22	3.50	3.81	4.16	4.55	5.08	5.73	6.55	7.66	9.17	11.50
0.200	2.22	2.58	2.99	3.51	3.81	4.13	4.50	4.97	5.54	6.24	7.12	8.33	9.98	
0.225	2.43	2.81	3.27	3.84	4.16	4.50	4.93	5.48	6.05	6.83	7.82	9.13	10.90	
0.250	2.67	3.09	3.60	4.22	4.55	4.97	5.48	6.00	6.67	7.50	8.57	10.0	12.00	
0.275	2.96	3.43	3.99	4.66	5.08	5.54	6.05	6.67	7.41	8.37	9.55	11.1		
0.300	3.33	3.87	4.48	5.28	5.73	6.24	6.83	7.50	8.37	9.37	10.80			
0.325	3.87	4.41	5.14	6.03	6.55	7.12	7.82	8.57	9.55	10.80				
0.350	4.44	5.16	5.99	7.04	7.66	8.33	9.13	10.00	11.10					
0.375	5.33	6.17	7.16	8.45	9.17	9.98	10.90	12.00						
0.400	6.67	7.73	9.00	10.60	11.50									

By double linear interpolation, the value of K for any eccentricity within the limits of the table may readily be found.

For a solid rectangular section, Esling (Ref. 24) explains a special method of analysis and gives tabulated constants which greatly facilitate solution for this particular case. The coefficient K, by which the average stress P/A is multiplied to give the maximum stress s, is given as a function of the eccentric ratios e_1/d and e_2/b, where the terms have the meaning shown by Fig. 39.

The values of K, taken from Esling's paper, are as shown in the preceding table.

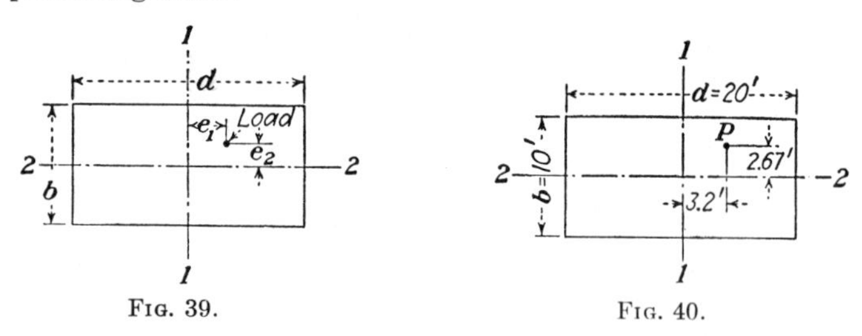

FIG. 39. FIG. 40.

Example

A bridge pier of masonry, 80 ft. high, is rectangular in section, measuring at the base 20 by 10 ft., the longer dimension being parallel to the track. This pier is subjected to a vertical load P (including its own weight) of 1500 tons, a horizontal braking load (parallel to the track) of 60 tons, and a horizontal wind load P_z (transverse to the track) of 50 tons. It is required to determine the maximum compressive stress at the base of the pier, first assuming that the masonry can sustain tension, second, that it cannot.

Solution.—For convenience in numerical work, the ton will be retained as the unit of force and the foot as the unit of distance.

(*a*) Masonry takes tension. Take $d = 20$ ft., $b = 10$ ft., and take axes 1 and 2 as shown in Fig. 40. Then with respect to axis 1, the bending moment $M_1 = 60 \times 80 = 4800$ ft.-tons, and the section modulus

$$(I/c)_1 = \tfrac{1}{6}(10)(20^2) = 667 \text{ ft.}^3$$

With respect to axis 2 the bending moment $M_2 = 50 \times 80 = 4000$ ft.-tons, and the section modulus $(I/c)_2 = \frac{1}{6}(20)(10^2) = 333$ ft.^{3} The section area is $10 \times 20 = 200$ sq. ft. The maximum stress obviously occurs at the corner where both bending moments cause compression, and is

$$s = \frac{1500}{200} + \frac{4800}{667} + \frac{4000}{333} = 7.5 + 7.2 + 12 = 26.7 \text{ tons per sq. ft.}$$

(*b*) Masonry cannot take tension. The resultant of the loads pierces the base section of the pier at point P, distant $e_1 = (60 \times 80)/1500 = 3.2$ ft. from axis 1 and $e_2 = (50 \times 80)/1500 = 2.67$ ft. from axis 2. This resultant is resolved at point P into rectangular components, the only one of which causing compression is the vertical component, equal to 1500, with eccentricities e_1 and e_2. The eccentric ratios are $e_1/d = 0.16$ and $e_2/b = 0.267$. Referring to the tabulated values of K, linear interpolation between $e_1/d = 0.15$ and 0.175 at $e_2/b = 0.250$ gives $K = 4.35$. Similar interpolation at $e_2/b = 0.275$ gives $K = 4.83$. Linear interpolation between these values gives, as the true value at $e_2/b = 0.267$, $K = 4.68$. The maximum stress is therefore $s = KP/A = 4.68 \times 1500/200 = 35.1$ tons per sq. ft.

References

1. Specification for the Design, Fabrication and Erection of Structural Steel for Buildings, American Institute of Steel Construction, 1961.
2. Recommended Building Code for Working Stresses in Building Materials, U.S. Bureau of Standards, 1926.
3. Specifications for Steel Railway Bridges, American Railway Association, 1950.
4. Final Report of the Special Committee on Steel Column Research, *Trans. Am. Soc. Civil Eng.*, Vol. 98, p. 1376, 1933.
5. Specifications for George Washington Bridge, *Trans. Am. Soc. Civil Eng.*, Vol. 97, p. 105, 1933.
6. Quebec Bridge Specifications, Board of Engineers.
7. New York City Building Code, 1937.
8. "Alcoa Structural Handbook," Aluminum Co. of America, 1960.
9. ANC Mil-Hdbk-5, Strength of Metal Aircraft Elements, Armed Forces Supply Support Center, March, 1959.
10. "Designing with Magnesium," Aluminum Co. of America, 1951.
11. "Wood Handbook," U.S. Dept. of Agriculture, 1935.
12. Standard Formulas for Use in Determining the Size of Transmission Shafting, *Am. Soc. Mech. Eng. Code.*
13. Kilpatrick, S. A., and O. U. Schaefer: Stress Calculations for Thin Aluminum Alloy Sections, *Product Eng.*, February, March, April, May, 1936.
14. Johnston, R. S.: Compressive Strength of Column Web Plates and Wide Web Columns, *Tech. Paper Bur. Standards* 327, 1926.
15. Younger, J. E.: "Structural Design of Metal Airplanes," McGraw-Hill Book Company, 1935.
16. Wilson, W. M.: Tests of Steel Columns, *Univ. Ill. Eng. Exp. Sta., Bull.* 292, 1937.
17. Salmon, E. H.: "Columns," Oxford Technical Publications, Henry Frowde and Hodder & Stoughton, London, 1921.
18. Talbot, A. N., and H. F. Moore: Tests of Built-up Steel and Wrought Iron Compression Pieces, *Trans. Am. Soc. Civil Eng.*, Vol. 65, p. 202, 1909. (Also *Univ. Ill. Eng. Exp. Sta., Bull.* 44.)
19. Timoshenko, S.: "Strength of Materials," D. Van Nostrand Company, Inc., 1930.
20. von Kármán, Th., E. E. Sechler, and L. H. Donnell: The Strength of Thin Plates in Compression, *Am. Soc. Mech. Eng., Jour. Appl. Mech.*, Vol. 54, No. 2, p. 53, 1932.

21. SCHUMAN, L., and G. BLACK: Strength of Rectangular Flat Plates under Edge Compression, *Nat. Adv. Comm. Aeron.*, *Report* 356, 1930.
22. SECHLER, E. E.: A Preliminary Report on the Ultimate Compressive Strength of Curved Sheet Panels, *Guggenheim Aeron. Lab.*, *Calif. Inst. Tech.*, *Pub.* 36, 1937.
23. SECHLER, E. E.: Stress Distribution in Stiffened Panels under Compression, *Jour. Aeron. Sci.*, Vol. 4, No. 8, p. 320, 1937.
24. ESLING, K. E.: A Problem Relating to Railway-bridge Piers of Masonry or Brickwork, *Proc. Inst. Civil Eng.*, Vol. 165, p. 219, 1905–1906.
25. ANC 18 Bulletin, Design of Wood Aircraft Structures, Munitions Board Aircraft Committee, June, 1951.
26. National Design Specification for Stress-grade Lumber and Its Fastenings, National Lumber Manufacturers Association, 1960.
27. Standard Specifications for Highway Bridges, 7th ed., American Association of State Highway Officials, 1957.
28. PRIEST, H. MALCOLM: "Design Manual for High Strength Steels," U.S. Steel Corp. 1954.
29. National Building Code of Canada, 1953.
30. Suggested Specifications for Structures of Aluminum Alloys 6061-T6 and 6062-T6, *Proc. Am. Soc. Civil Eng.*, Vol. 88, ST6, *Paper* 3341, December, 1962.

CHAPTER 12

PRESSURE VESSELS; PIPES

71. Circumstances and General State of Stress.—The discussion and formulas of this section apply to any vessel that is a figure of revolution. For convenience of reference, a line that represents the intersection of the wall and a plane containing the axis of the vessel is called a *meridian*, and a line representing the intersection of the wall and a plane normal to the axis of the vessel is called a *circumference*. Obviously the meridian through any point is perpendicular to the circumference through that point.

When a vessel of the kind under consideration is subjected to uniform internal or external pressure, stresses are set up in the walls. The state of stress is triaxial; at any point there is a *meridional stress* s_1 acting parallel to the meridian, a circumferential or *hoop stress* s_2 acting parallel to the circumference, and a radial stress s_3. There may in addition be bending stresses and shear stresses. In consequence of these stresses, there will be meridional, circumferential, and radial strains, and there may be a change in meridional slope. Because of symmetry about the axis, there will be no tendency for any circumference to depart from the circular form.

72. Thin Vessel under Various Loadings.—If the walls of the vessel are relatively thin (less than about one-tenth the radius) and have no abrupt changes in thickness, slope, or curvature, then under uniform pressure and at points remote from the ends, the stresses s_1 and s_2 are practically uniform throughout the thickness of the wall and are the only stresses of importance present, the radial stress s_3 and such bending stresses as occur being negligibly small. For any vessel which is a figure of revolution, the stresses s_1 and s_2, called *membrane* or *diaphragm* stresses, are readily found by the general formulas for Case 6 in Table XIII. If there is any circumference an abrupt change in thickness or in meridional slope or curvature, such change will cause bending and shear along that and adjacent circumferences. The stresses due to this bending and shear are called *discontinuity stresses.* They are superposed upon the membrane stresses and comprise (1) a meridional bending stress s_1', which varies linearly throughout the thickness of the wall; (2) a circumferential bending stress s_2', which varies linearly throughout the thickness of the wall; (3) an additional hoop stress s_2'', uniform throughout the thickness of the wall; (4) a shear stress s_s on circumferential sections, assumed uniform throughout the thickness of the wall.

In Table XIII formulas are given for membrane and discontinuity stresses and for the accompanying deformations, and in some cases for the bursting pressure and for the pressure causing yield. Formulas are also given for the stresses and deformations caused by various localized loadings and constraint forces, such as are exerted by heads and supports.

The formulas for membrane stresses due to uniform pressure are accurate provided the conditions of relative thinness and geometrical regularity are satisfied; the formulas for stresses and deflections due to localized loading are much more difficult to derive and entail various approximations, so that they are in general less accurate. Formulas for the effects of edge shears and moments, used in finding the discontinuity stresses at the junction of two vessels as illustrated in the example below, are accurate for vessels of conventional proportions, but become inaccurate for forms approaching that of a flat plate and for forms that have a rapidly changing meridional curvature. Discontinuity stresses fade out very rapidly, becoming negligibly small at a short distance from the circumference where the discontinuity occurs, and over that short distance the quantities λ and β may usually be considered constant. If the thickness or meridional curvature changes very rapidly, however, this assumption cannot be made, and λ and β must be treated as variables. This can be done as explained in Refs. 5 and 6, by replacing the term λx by $\Sigma\lambda\, dx$, where dx denotes a very short zone over which λ may be considered constant. The use of the formulas for thin vessels and the way in which they may be combined to determine, by superposition, the stresses caused by a discontinuity are illustrated in the following example.

Example

The vessel shown in quarter longitudinal section in Fig. 41*a* consists of a cylindrical shell ($R = 24$ in., $t = 0.633$ in.) with conical ends ($\phi = 45°$, $t = 0.755$ in.). The parts are welded together. The material is steel. It is required to determine the maximum stresses at the junction of the cylinder and cone due to an internal pressure of 300 lb. per sq. in. (This vessel corresponds to one for which the results of a supposedly precise analysis, and also experimentally determined stress values, are available. See Ref. 17.)

Solution.—Taking $E = 30{,}000{,}000$ and $\nu = 0.25$, we have for the cone

$\phi = 45°$; $\omega = 0$; $R_2 = 24 \div 0.707 = 33.9$; $\beta = 8.65$; $K_1 = 0.9734$; $K_2 = 0.911$

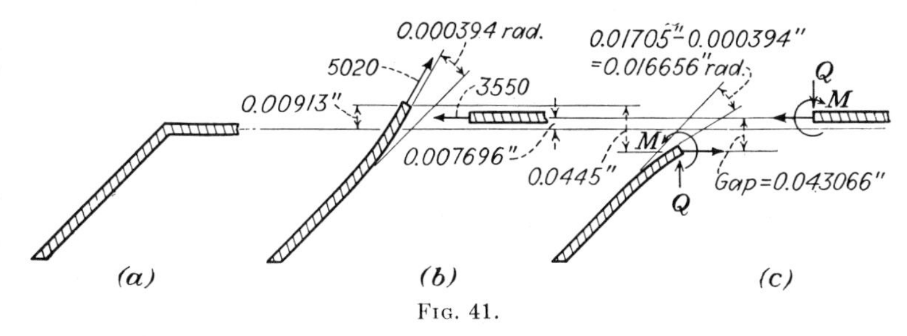

FIG. 41.

and for the cylinder

$$R = 24; \qquad \lambda = 0.334; \qquad D = 687{,}000$$

Solving for the membrane stresses, radial displacement, and angular displacement of each part as though the discontinuity (joint) were not present, we have

For the cone (Case 3) $s_1 = 6650$
$s_2 = 13{,}300$
Radial displacement $= +0.00913$ in.
Angular displacement $= 0.000394$ rad., outward
and for the cylinder (Case 1) $s_1 = 5610$
$s_2 = 11{,}220$
Radial displacement $= +0.007696$ in.
Angular displacement $= 0$

Figure 41*b* shows the relative positions of head and cylinder after the above displacements have occurred, and shows also the external edge forces (found for each part by multiplying the meridional stress s_1 by the wall thickness) required to maintain the membrane stresses. We now find the dimensions the cone would assume if held by the horizontal component only of the edge force. To do this, the radial component of the edge force is eliminated by superposing an equal inward radial force amounting to $5020 \times \cos 45° = 3550$ lb. per linear in. This inward radial force would produce a radial displacement ΔR and an angular displacement θ, both inward. Using the appropriate formulas of Case 10, we have

$$\Delta R = \frac{(3550)(8.65)(33.9)(0.5)(1.938)}{(30{,}000{,}000)(0.755)} = 0.0445 \text{ in.}$$

$$\theta = \frac{(3550)(2)(8.65^2)(0.707)(1.027)}{(30{,}000{,}000)(0.755)} = 0.01705 \text{ rad.}$$

Eliminating the radial component of the membrane stress therefore leaves the cone and cylinder in the relative positions shown in Fig. 41*c*.

We now conceive the edges to be brought together and given a common slope by the reciprocally exerted radial forces Q and moments M, and solve for the values of Q and M by equating: (1) the outward deflection of the cone plus the inward deflection of the cylinder, produced by Q and M, to the present gap of 0.043066 in., and (2) the angular displacement of the cone minus the present disparity of 0.016656 rad. to the angular displacement of the cylinder. Expressing conditions (1) and (2) by the appropriate formulas for Cases 14, 15, 16, and 17, we have

$$\frac{Q}{(30{,}000{,}000)(0.755)}\left[(8.65)(33.9)(0.5)\left(.911+\frac{1}{.9734}\right)\right] + \frac{M}{(30{,}000{,}000)(0.755)}\left[\frac{(2)(74.9)(0.707)}{0.9734}\right] + \frac{Q}{(2)(687{,}000)(0.334^3)} - \frac{M}{(2)(687{,}000)(0.334^2)} = 0.043066 \quad (1)$$

$$\frac{Q}{(30{,}000{,}000)(0.755)}\left[(2)(8.65^2)(0.707)\left(\frac{1}{0.9734}\right)\right] + \frac{M}{(30{,}000{,}000)(0.755)}\left[\frac{(4)(0.865^3)}{(33.9)(0.9734)}\right] - 0.016656 = \frac{Q}{(2)(687{,}000)(0.334^2)} - \frac{M}{(687{,}000)(0.334)} \quad (2)$$

Solving (Eqs. 1 and 2) for M and Q, we find

$$M = 2450, \qquad Q = 1470$$

The discontinuity and combined stresses in each part can now readily be calculated. Thus, for the cylinder:

Meridional bending stress $s_1' = \frac{(6)(2450)}{0.633^2} = 36{,}650$, tensile at inner surface.

Max combined meridional stress $s_1' + s_1 = 36{,}650 + 5610$
$= 42{,}260$ lb. per sq. in., tensile at inner surface.

Direct hoop stress due to $Q = \frac{(2)(1470)}{0.633}(0.334)(24) = 37{,}300$, compressive.

Direct hoop stress due to $M = \frac{(2)(2450)}{0.633}(0.334^2)(24) = 20{,}360$, tensile.

Hoop bending stress due to $M = (0.25)(36{,}650)$
$= 9160$, compressive at outer surface, tensile at inner surface.

Membrane hoop stress due to pressure $= 11{,}220$ tensile.

Max combined compressive hoop stress $= 37{,}300 - 20{,}360 + 9160$
$- 11{,}220 = 15{,}000$ lb. per sq. in., at outer surface.

Max combined tensile hoop stress $= 20{,}360 + 9160 + 11{,}220 - 37{,}300$
$= 3440$ lb. per sq. in., at inner surface.

The stresses in the cone can readily be found in the same way. It is to be noted that in calculating the hoop stress in the cone the effect of the inward radial force of 3550 lb. per in. must be taken into account, as well as the effects of Q and M and the membrane stress due to the internal pressure.

The stress values calculated above are in substantial agreement with the computed and experimental values cited in Refs. 17 and 26, showing that the formulas for Cases 16 and 17 are applicable to a conical as well as to a spherical shell. However, solution of this problem can be carried out more expeditiously by using the formulas for Cases 23, 24, and 25.

The question as to how important discontinuity stresses such as these are, with respect to the safety of a structure, depends upon the nature of the required service. Under essentially static loading, such stresses undoubtedly often exceed the elastic limit without any apparent deleterious effect, and reported tests on a pressure vessel that had given satisfactory service for many years showed that, at working pressure, the maximum measured strains corresponded to stresses well beyond the yield point (Ref. 18). On the other hand, under cyclic or fluctuating loading, such high discontinuity strains might cause failure before the end of the normal service life of the vessel, or under certain conditions might lead to brittle fracture.

Both analytical and experimental work in pressure vessel analysis and design have been greatly stimulated by developments in the field of nuclear energy, and the designer should keep himself familiar with the current literature.

Short Cylinders.—The formulas given in Table XIII for Cases 11, 14, and 15 are for long cylinders, having length $L > (6/\lambda)$. For shorter cylinders the maximum moment, radial deflection, and angular displacement can be found by multiplying the corresponding quantity as found for a long cylinder by the appropriate coefficient as defined and tabulated below:

Case 11: For max M, use C_1
For radial deflection, use C_2

Case 14: For radial deflection at loaded end, use C_3
For radial deflection at other end, use C_3'
For θ at loaded end, use C_4
For θ at other end, use C_4'

Case 15: For radial deflection at loaded end, use C_5
For radial deflection at other end, use C_5'
For θ at loaded end, use C_6
For θ at other end, use C_6'

λL	C_1	C_2	C_3	$-C_3'$	C_4, C_5	C_4', $-C_5'$	C_6	C_6'
0.4	0.3986	1.6014	4.990	2.472	18.696	18.663	46.906	46.733
0.6	0.5945	1.4055	3.310	1.639	8.285	8.223	13.936	13.632
0.8	0.7722	1.2278	2.507	1.241	4.749	4.641	6.150	5.751
1.0	0.9211	1.0789	2.019	0.986	3.105	2.940	3.371	2.879
1.2	1.0248	0.9752	1.699	0.809	2.233	1.996	2.179	1.586
1.4	1.0790	0.9210	1.479	0.676	1.732	1.414	1.605	0.919
1.7	1.0850	0.9150	1.265	0.523	1.327	0.872	1.223	0.410
2.0	1.0540	0.9461	1.137	0.400	1.134	0.535	1.076	0.155
3.0	1.0000	1.0000	1.007	0.139	1.005	0.080	1.005	0.002
6.0	1.0000	1.0000	1.000	0.003	1.000	−0.002	1.000	0.000

TABLE XIII.—FORMULAS FOR STRESSES AND DEFORMATIONS IN PRESSURE VESSELS

Notation for thin vessels: p = unit pressure (lb. per sq. in.); s_1 = meridional membrane stress, positive when tensile (lb. per sq. in.); s_2 = hoop membrane stress, positive when tensile (lb. per sq. in.); s_1' = meridional bending stress, positive when tensile on convex surface (lb. per sq. in.); s_2' = hoop bending stress, positive when tensile at convex surface (lb. per sq. in.); s_2'' = hoop stress due to discontinuity, positive when tensile (lb. per sq. in.); s_s = shear stress (lb. per sq. in.); V_o, V_x = transverse shear normal to wall, positive when acting as shown (lb. per linear in.); M_o, M_x = bending moment, uniform along circumference, positive when acting as shown (in.-lb. per linear in.); x = distance measured along meridian from edge of vessel or from discontinuity (in.); R_1 = mean radius of curvature of wall along meridian (in.); R_2 = mean radius of curvature of wall normal to meridian (in.); R = mean radius of circumference (in.); t = wall thickness (in.); E = modulus of elasticity (lb. per sq. in.); ν = Poisson's ratio; $D = \frac{Et^3}{12(1-\nu^2)}$; $\lambda = \sqrt[4]{\frac{3(1-\nu^2)}{R_2^2t^2}}$; radial displacement positive when outward (in.); θ = change in slope of wall at edge of vessel or at discontinuity, positive when outward (radians); y = vertical deflection, positive when downward (in.). Subscripts 1 and 2 refer to parts into which vessel may be imagined as divided, *e.g.*, cylindrical shell and hemispherical head. General relations: $s_1' = \frac{6M}{t^2}$ at surface; $s_s = \frac{V}{t}$.

Notation for thick vessels: s_1 = meridional wall stress, positive when acting as shown (lb. per sq. in.); s_2 = hoop wall stress, positive when acting as shown (lb. per sq. in.); s_3 = radial wall stress, positive when acting as shown (lb. per sq. in.); a = inner radius of vessel (in.); b = outer radius of vessel (in.); r = radius from axis to point where stress is to be found (in.); Δa = change in inner radius due to pressure, positive when representing an increase (in.); Δb = change in outer radius due to pressure, positive when representing an increase (in.). Other notation same as that used for thin vessels

Form of vessel	Manner of loading and Case No.	Formulas
		Thin vessels—membrane stresses s_1 (meridional) and s_2 (hoop)
Cylindrical	1. Uniform internal (or external) pressure p, lb. per sq. in.	$s_1 = \frac{pR}{2t}$ $s_2 = \frac{pR}{t}$ Radial displacement $= \frac{R}{E}(s_2 - \nu s_1)$. Internal bursting pressure $p_u = 2s_u \frac{b-a}{b+a}$ (Here s_u = ultimate tensile strength, a = inner radius, b = outer radius) External collapsing pressure $p' = \frac{t}{R}\left(\frac{s_y}{1 + 4\frac{s_y}{E}\left(\frac{R}{t}\right)^2}\right)$, where s_y = compressive yield point of material (Ref. 1). This formula is for *nonelastic* failure, and holds only when $\frac{p'R}{t}$ > proportional limit. For critical stress producing *elastic* instability in very thin cylinder, see Table XVI

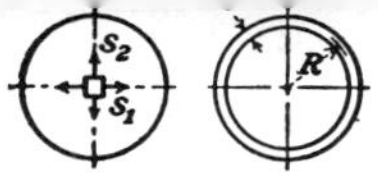 Spherical		Radial displacement $= \frac{Rs}{E}(1 - \nu)$
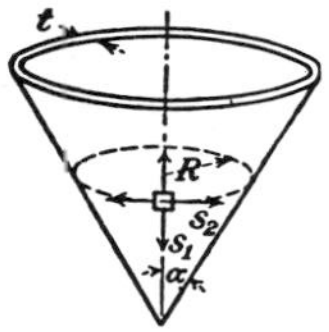	3. Uniform internal (or external) pressure p, lb. per sq. in., tangential edge support	$s_1 = \frac{pR}{2t \cos \alpha}$ Change in side slope $\Delta\alpha = \frac{3pR \sin \alpha}{2Et \cos^2 \alpha}$ $s_2 = \frac{pR}{t \cos \alpha}$
	4. Same as Case 3 but vertical edge support	At supported edge $s_1 = \frac{pR}{2t} \cos \alpha$ $s_2 = p\left[-U\sqrt{\frac{R^3 \sin^2 \alpha}{2t^3 \cos \alpha}} + \frac{(1 - \nu/2)R}{t \cos \alpha}\right] + \nu s_1$ Radial displacement $\Delta R_0 = \frac{p}{E}\left[-U\sqrt{\frac{R^5 \sin^2 \alpha}{2t^3 \cos \alpha}} + \frac{(1 - \frac{1}{2}\nu)R^2}{t \cos \alpha}\right]$ Rotation $\theta = \frac{p}{E}\left[-\frac{U^2}{2}\frac{R^2 \tan \alpha}{t^2} + \frac{3R \tan \alpha}{2t \cos \alpha}\right]$ $(U = \sqrt[4]{12(1 - \nu^2)}$. Signs here are for internal pressure) (Ref. 30)
Conical	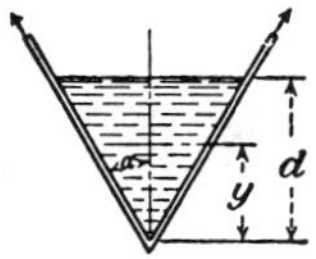 5. Filled to depth d with liquid of sp. wt. γ lb. per cu. in., tangential edge support	At any level y above bottom $s_1 = \frac{\gamma y \tan \alpha}{2t \cos \alpha}\left(d - \frac{2}{3}y\right)$, Max $s_1 = \frac{3\gamma d^2 \tan \alpha}{16t \cos \alpha}$ when $y = \frac{3}{4}d$ $s_2 = \frac{(d - y)\gamma \cdot y \tan \alpha}{t \cos \alpha}$, Max $s_2 = \frac{\gamma d^2 \tan \alpha}{4t \cos \alpha}$ when $y = \frac{1}{2}d$

TABLE XIII.—FORMULAS FOR STRESSES AND DEFORMATIONS IN PRESSURE VESSELS.—(*Continued*)

Form of vessel	Manner of loading and Case No.	Formulas
Any figure of revolution, tangential edge support	6. Uniform internal (or external) pressure p, lb. per sq. in.	$s_1 = \frac{pR_2}{2t}$ $s_2 = \frac{pR_2}{2t}\left(2 - \frac{R_2}{R_1}\right)$ Radial displacement $= \frac{R}{E}(s_2 - \nu s_1)$ $p = \frac{s_1 t}{R_1} + \frac{s_2 t}{R_2}$

Thin vessels—local and discontinuity stresses s_1' (meridional bending stress), s_2' (circumferential bending stress), s_2'' (membrane hoop stress)

7. Radial load P uniformly distributed over small area A, approximately square or round, located near mid-span

Max. stresses are circumferential stresses at center of loaded area and can be found from following table. Values given are for $L/R = 8$ but may be used for L/R ratios between 3 and 40. (Coefficients adapted from Bijlaard, Refs. 22, 23, 28)

R/t \ A/R^2	0.0004	0.0016	0.0036	0.0064	0.010	0.0144	0.0196	0.0256	0.0324	0.040	0.0576	0.090	0.160	0.25
	Values of $s_2'(t^2/P)$													
300	1.475	1.11	0.906	0.780	0.678	0.600	0.522	0.450	0.390	0.348	0.264	0.186	0.120	0.078
100	......	1.44	1.20	1.044	0.918	0.840	0.750	0.666	0.600	0.540	0.444	0.342	0.240	0.180
50	......	......	1.44	1.254	1.11	1.005	0.900	0.840	0.756	0.720	0.600	0.480	0.360	0.264
15	......	......	......	......	......	......	......	......	......	0.990	0.888	0.780	0.600	0.468
	Values of $s_2(Rt/P)$													
300	58	53.5	49	44.5	40	35.5	32	28	24	21	16	11	6	4
100	......	33.5	30.5	27.6	25	22.5	20	17.5	15	13	10	7	4.2	3.6
50	......	......	......	......	9.6	9	8.5	8.0	7.7	7.5	6.5	5.6	4.1	3.1
15	......	......	......	......	......	......	......	......	......	3.25	3.0	2.4	2.0	1.56

For A very small (nominal point loading) at point of load

$$s_2 = \frac{0.4P}{t^2},\quad s_2' = \frac{2.4P}{t^2},\quad y = \frac{P}{Et}\left[0.48\left(\frac{L}{R}\right)^{\frac{1}{2}}\left(\frac{R}{t}\right)^{1.22}\right]$$

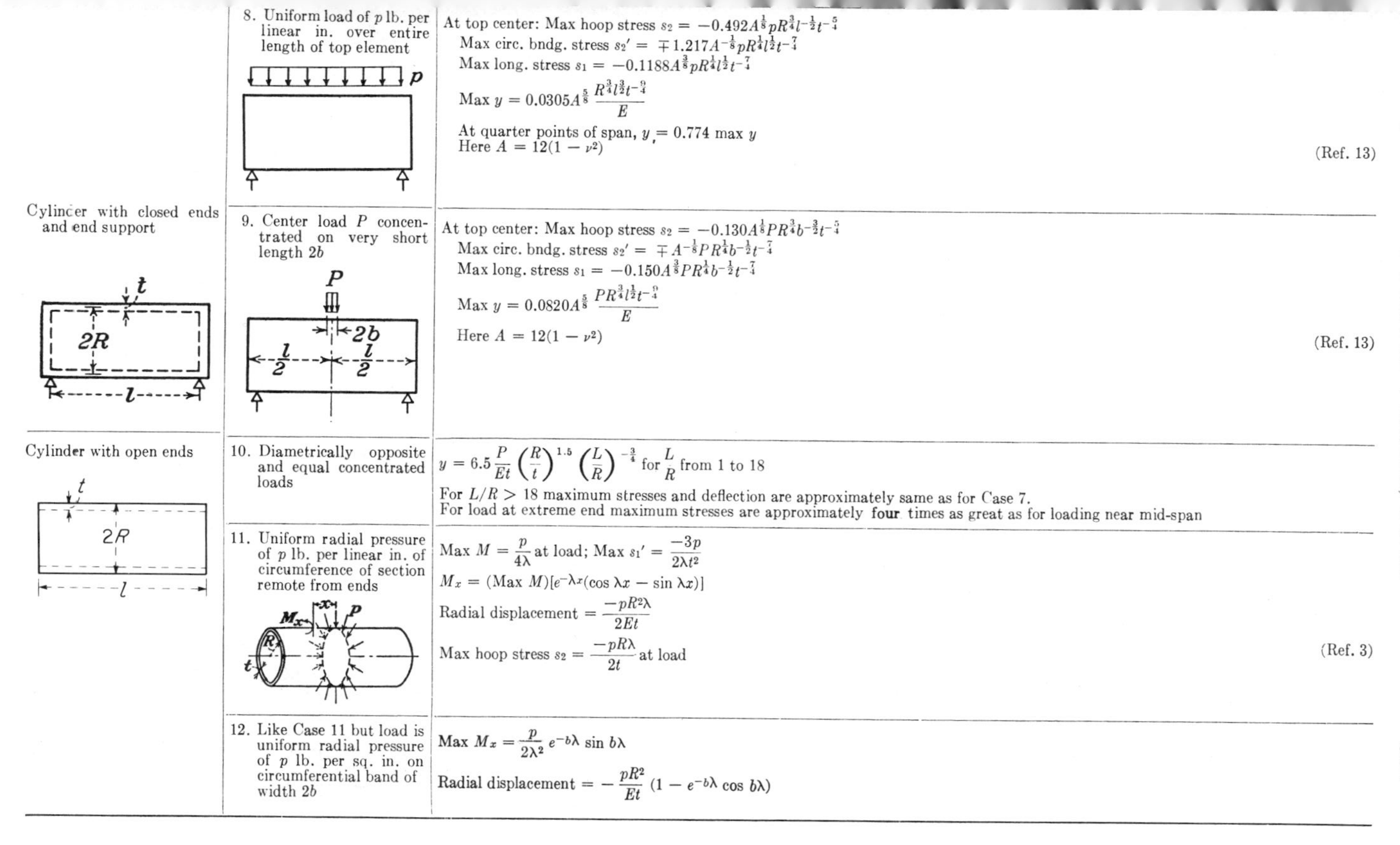

	8. Uniform load of p lb. per linear in. over entire length of top element	At top center: Max hoop stress $s_2 = -0.492A^{\frac{1}{8}}pR^{\frac{3}{4}}l^{-\frac{1}{2}}t^{-\frac{5}{4}}$ Max circ. bndg. stress $s_2' = \mp 1.217A^{-\frac{1}{8}}pR^{\frac{1}{4}}l^{\frac{1}{2}}t^{-\frac{7}{4}}$ Max long. stress $s_1 = -0.1188A^{\frac{3}{8}}pR^{\frac{1}{4}}l^{\frac{1}{2}}t^{-\frac{7}{4}}$ Max $y = 0.0305A^{\frac{5}{8}}\frac{R^{\frac{3}{4}}l^{\frac{3}{2}}t^{-\frac{9}{4}}}{E}$ At quarter points of span, $y' = 0.774$ max y Here $A = 12(1 - \nu^2)$ (Ref. 13)
Cylinder with closed ends and end support	9. Center load P concentrated on very short length $2b$	At top center: Max hoop stress $s_2 = -0.130A^{\frac{1}{8}}PR^{\frac{3}{4}}b^{-\frac{3}{2}}t^{-\frac{5}{4}}$ Max circ. bndg. stress $s_2' = \mp A^{-\frac{1}{8}}PR^{\frac{1}{4}}b^{-\frac{1}{2}}t^{-\frac{7}{4}}$ Max long. stress $s_1 = -0.150A^{\frac{3}{8}}PR^{\frac{1}{4}}b^{-\frac{1}{2}}t^{-\frac{7}{4}}$ Max $y = 0.0820A^{\frac{5}{8}}\frac{PR^{\frac{3}{4}}l^{\frac{3}{2}}t^{-\frac{9}{4}}}{E}$ Here $A = 12(1 - \nu^2)$ (Ref. 13)
Cylinder with open ends	10. Diametrically opposite and equal concentrated loads	$y = 6.5\frac{P}{Et}\left(\frac{R}{t}\right)^{1.5}\left(\frac{L}{R}\right)^{-\frac{3}{4}}$ for $\frac{L}{R}$ from 1 to 18 For $L/R > 18$ maximum stresses and deflection are approximately same as for Case 7. For load at extreme end maximum stresses are approximately **four** times as great as for loading near mid-span
	11. Uniform radial pressure of p lb. per linear in. of circumference of section remote from ends	Max $M = \frac{p}{4\lambda}$ at load; Max $s_1' = \frac{-3p}{2\lambda t^2}$ $M_x = (\text{Max } M)[e^{-\lambda x}(\cos \lambda x - \sin \lambda x)]$ Radial displacement $= \frac{-pR^2\lambda}{2Et}$ Max hoop stress $s_2 = \frac{-pR\lambda}{2t}$ at load (Ref. 3)
	12. Like Case 11 but load is uniform radial pressure of p lb. per sq. in. on circumferential band of width $2b$	Max $M_x = \frac{p}{2\lambda^2}e^{-b\lambda}\sin b\lambda$ Radial displacement $= -\frac{pR^2}{Et}(1 - e^{-b\lambda}\cos b\lambda)$

TABLE XIII.—FORMULAS FOR STRESSES AND DEFORMATIONS IN PRESSURE VESSELS.—(*Continued*)

Form of vessel	Manner of loading and Case No.	Formulas
Cylindrical, with reinforcing ring of cross-sectional area A	13. Uniform internal (or external) pressure of p lb. per sq. in.	$M_0 = \left(\frac{p}{2\lambda^2}\right)\left(\frac{A}{A + tc + 2t/\lambda}\right)$ ($M_0 = p/2\lambda^2$ for rigid ring or disk) $V_0 = 2M_0\lambda$ ($V_0 = p/\lambda$ for rigid ring or disk) Max long. bending stress $= \frac{-6M_0}{t^2}$ at edge of ring. Formulas for Cases 14 and 15 may be used to find M_x, s_1' and V_x at other sections. Ring pressure per linear in. of circumference $= 2V_0$. The above formulas are valid if rings are spaced so far apart that the influence of one does not extend to the next. This spacing $\geqq \frac{4}{\lambda}$. The sum of the direct and bending longitudinal stresses $s_1 + s_1'$ exceeds the normal hoop stress s_2 unless the ring spacing $< \frac{\pi}{2}\sqrt{Rt}$ (Refs. 4, 5)
Cylindrical (Long)	14. Uniform radial shear or pressure V_0 lb. per linear in. of circumference at end	$M_x = \frac{1}{\lambda} V_0 e^{-\lambda x} \sin \lambda x$ Max $M = 0.322 \frac{V_0}{\lambda}$ at $x = \frac{\pi}{4\lambda}$ $V_x = V_0 e^{-\lambda x}(\cos \lambda x - \sin \lambda x)$ $s_1' = \frac{6M_x}{t^2}$; Max $s_1' = \frac{1.932\ V_0}{\lambda t^2}$; $s_2' = \nu s_1'$ $s_s = \frac{V}{t}$ Hoop stress $s_2 = \frac{-2V_0}{t}(\lambda R e^{-\lambda x} \cos \lambda x)$; Max $s_2 = \frac{-2V_0}{t}\lambda R$ at end Radial displacement $= \frac{-V_0}{2D\lambda^3}$ $\theta = \frac{-V_0}{2D\lambda^2}$ (For short cylinder see p. 297) (Refs. 5, 6)
	15. Uniform radial moment M_0 in.-lb. per linear in. of circumference at end 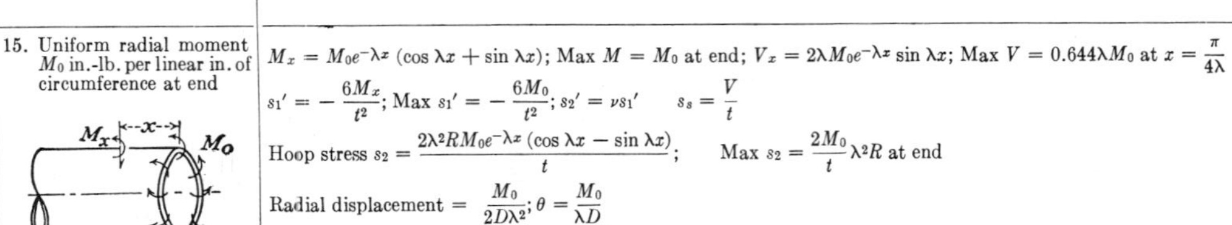	$M_x = M_0 e^{-\lambda x}(\cos \lambda x + \sin \lambda x)$; Max $M = M_0$ at end; $V_x = 2\lambda M_0 e^{-\lambda x} \sin \lambda x$; Max $V = 0.644\lambda M_0$ at $x = \frac{\pi}{4\lambda}$ $s_1' = -\frac{6M_x}{t^2}$; Max $s_1' = -\frac{6M_0}{t^2}$; $s_2' = \nu s_1'$ $s_s = \frac{V}{t}$ Hoop stress $s_2 = \frac{2\lambda^2 R M_0 e^{-\lambda x}(\cos \lambda x - \sin \lambda x)}{t}$; Max $s_2 = \frac{2M_0}{t}\lambda^2 R$ at end Radial displacement $= \frac{M_0}{2D\lambda^2}$; $\theta = \frac{M_0}{\lambda D}$ (For short cylinder see p. 297) (Refs. 5, 6)

for Cases 16 and 17 are approximate for cone or other shell of revolution M_ω, t, h, ω, ϕ, $R_2 = R_1$, R	lb. per linear in. at edge Q Q	$M_\omega = \ldots \frac{\ldots}{2\beta\sqrt{\sin(\phi-\omega)}}[K_1 \cos(\beta\omega+\psi) + \sin(\beta\omega+\psi)]$ Max M at $\omega = \frac{\pi}{4\lambda R_2}$ $s_1 = \frac{C}{t}\cot(\phi-\omega)\frac{e^{-\beta\omega}}{\sqrt{\sin(\phi-\omega)}}\sin(\beta\omega+\psi)$ Max $s_1 = -\frac{Q\cos\phi}{t}$ at edge $s_2 = -\frac{C}{t}\frac{\beta e^{-\beta\omega}}{2\sqrt{\sin(\phi-\omega)}}[2\cos(\beta\omega+\psi) - (K_1+K_2)\sin(\beta\omega+\psi)]$ Max $s_2 = -\frac{Q}{t}\left(\frac{1}{K_1}+\frac{K_1+K_2}{2}\right)\beta\sin\phi$, at edge Radial displacement $= -\frac{Q}{Et}(\beta R_2\sin^2\phi)\left(K_2+\frac{1}{K_1}\right)$ $\theta = -\frac{Q}{Et}(2\beta^2\sin\phi)\left(\frac{1}{K_1}\right)$ Here $\beta = \sqrt[4]{3(1-\nu^2)\left(\frac{R_2}{t}\right)^2}$; $K_1 = 1 - \frac{1-2\nu}{2\beta}\cot(\phi-\omega)$; $K_2 = 1 - \frac{1+2\nu}{2\beta}\cot(\phi-\omega)$ $C = Q(\sin\phi)^{\frac{3}{2}}\left(\frac{\sqrt{1+K_1^2}}{K_1}\right)$; $\psi = \tan^{-1}(-K_1)$ (Ref. 14; see also Ref. 42)
	17. Uniform radial moment M_0 in.-lb. per linear in. at edge M_0 M_0	M_ω, s_1, and s_2 as for Case 16 except $C = -\frac{2M_0\beta(\sin\phi)^{\frac{1}{2}}}{R_2K_1}$ and $\psi = 0$ Max $M = M_0$; max $s_2 = \frac{M_0}{tR_2}\left(\frac{2\beta^2}{K_1}\right)$ at edge Radial displacement $= \frac{M_0}{Et}\left(\frac{2\beta^2\sin\phi}{K_1}\right)$ $\theta = \frac{M_0}{Et}\left(\frac{4\beta^3}{R_2K_1}\right)$ Here β, K_1, and K_2 are same as for Case 16 (Ref. 14; see also Ref. 42)
	18. Loaded by own weight of w lb. per sq. in. of surface area. Tangential support θ	$s_1 = -\frac{Rw}{t(1+\cos\theta)}$ Max $s_1 = -\frac{Rw}{t(1+\cos\phi)}$ at edge $(\theta = \phi)$ $s_2 = \frac{Rw}{t}\left(\frac{1}{1+\cos\theta} - \cos\theta\right)$ Max compressive $s_2 = \frac{Rw}{2t}$ at $\theta = 0$ Max tensile $s_2 = \frac{Rw}{t}\left(\frac{1}{1+\cos\phi} - \cos\phi\right)$ when $\phi > 51.83°$ (Ref. 3)

TABLE XIII.—FORMULAS FOR STRESSES AND DEFORMATIONS IN PRESSURE VESSELS.—(*Continued*)

Form of vessel	Manner of loading and Case No.	Formulas
	19. Like Case 18, but load is w lb. per sq. in. of horizontal projected area	$s_1 = \frac{wR}{2t}$ $s_2 = \frac{wR \cos 2\theta}{2t}$
	20. Load P concentrated on small circular area of radius r_0 at pole. Vertical support, edge neither held nor fixed	Max deflection $y = A\frac{PR_2}{Et^2}$ Max membrane stress $s_1 = s_2 = B\frac{P}{t^2}$ at pole Max bending stress $s_1' = s_2' = C\frac{P}{t^2}$ at pole Here A, B, and C are numerical coefficients that depend on $\mu = \sqrt[4]{12(1-\nu^2)}\left(\frac{r_0}{\sqrt{R_2 t}}\right)$ and have values as tabulated below (Ref. 15)
	21. Point load at pole, edge fixed but not held	Max deflection $y = A\frac{PR^2}{16\pi D}$ Edge moment $M_0 = B\frac{P}{4\pi}$ Here A and B are numerical coefficients that depend on $\alpha = 2\sqrt[4]{3(1-\nu^2)}\sqrt{\frac{h}{t}}$ and have values as tabulated below (Ref. 15)
	22. Load as for Case 21; edge fixed and held	Formulas for y and M_0 same as for Case 18 but A and B have values as tabulated below (Ref. 15)

Case 20:

μ	0	0.1	0.2	0.4	0.6	0.8	1.0	1.2	1.4
A	0.424	0.418	0.410	0.405	0.381	0.354	0.330	0.305	0.280
B	0.212	0.209	0.205	0.202	0.190	0.177	0.165	0.152	0.140
C	∞	1.74	1.33	0.923	0.693	0.536	0 421	0.332	0.263

(Ref. 15)

Case 21:

α	0	1	2	3	4	5	6	7	8	9	10
A	1	0.996	0.935	0.754	0.406	0.321	0.210	0.148	0.111	0.085	0.069
B	1	0.995	0.932	0.746	0.498	0.324	0.234	0.192	0.168	0.153	0.140

(Ref. 15)

Case 22:

α	0	1	2	3	4	5	6	7	8	9	10
A	1	0.985	0.817	0.515	0.320	0.220	0.161	0.122	0.095	0.075	0.061
B	1	0.975	0.690	0.191	−0.080	−0.140	−0.117	−0.080	−0.059	−0.034	−0.026

(Ref. 15)

Conical shell

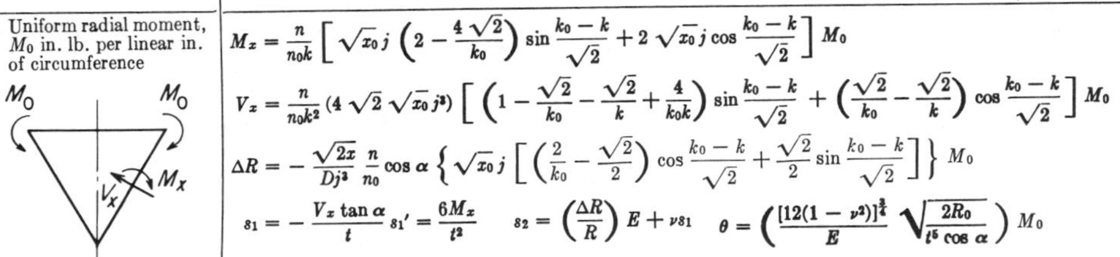

23. Uniform internal (or external) pressure, p lb. per sq. in. Vertical edge support

$$M_x = \left(\frac{n}{n_0 k}\sqrt{2}\,x_0^2 \sin^2\alpha\right)\left(\sin\frac{k_0 - k}{\sqrt{2}}\right) p$$

$$V_x = \frac{n}{n_0 k^2}(2j^2 x_0^2 \sin^2\alpha)\left[\cos\frac{k_0 - k}{\sqrt{2}} + \left(\frac{2\sqrt{2}}{k} - 1\right)\sin\frac{k_0 - k}{\sqrt{2}}\right] p$$

$$s_1 = -\frac{V_x \tan\alpha}{t} + \frac{px}{2t}\tan\alpha \qquad \Delta R = \left[-\frac{\sqrt{2x}}{Dj^3}\frac{n}{n_0}\left(\frac{x_0^2 \sin^2\alpha\cos\alpha}{2}\right)\left(\cos\frac{k_0 - k}{\sqrt{2}}\right) + \frac{(1 - \nu/2)R^2}{Et\cos\alpha}\right] p$$

$$s_1' = \frac{6M_x}{t^2} \qquad s_2 = \left(\frac{\Delta R}{R}\right)E + \nu s_1$$

$$j = \sqrt[4]{\frac{12(1 - \nu^2)}{t^2 \tan^2\alpha}} \qquad k = 2j\sqrt{x} \qquad n = \frac{e^{k/\sqrt{2}}}{\sqrt{2\pi k}} \qquad \theta = \left(\frac{-tR_0\tan\alpha}{2D\sqrt{12(1 - \nu^2)}} + \frac{3R_0\tan\alpha}{2Et\cos\alpha}\right) p$$

(Subscript 0 denotes that the term in question has value corresponding to $x = x_0$) (Ref. 30)

24. Uniform outward (or inward) radial force, H lb. per linear in. of circumference at edge

$$M_x = \frac{n}{n_0 k}(2\sqrt{2}\,x_0\cos\alpha)\left(\sin\frac{k_0 - k}{\sqrt{2}}\right) H$$

$$V_x = \frac{n}{n_0 k^2}(2x_0\cos\alpha)\left[\cos\frac{k_0 - k}{\sqrt{2}} + \left(\frac{2\sqrt{2}}{k} - 1\right)\sin\frac{k_0 - k}{\sqrt{2}}\right](2j^2) H$$

$$\Delta R = \frac{\sqrt{2x}}{Dj^3}\frac{n}{n_0}(x_0\cos^2\alpha)\left(\cos\frac{k_0 - k}{\sqrt{2}}\right) H$$

$$s_1 = \frac{V_x\tan\alpha}{t} \qquad s_1' = \frac{6M_x}{t^2} \qquad s_2 = \left(\frac{\Delta R}{R}\right)E + \nu s_1 \qquad \theta = \left(\frac{\sqrt{12(1 - \nu^2)}}{E}\frac{R_0}{t^2}\right) H$$

(Ref. 30)

25. Uniform radial moment, M_0 in. lb. per linear in. of circumference

$$M_x = \frac{n}{n_0 k}\left[\sqrt{x_0}\,j\left(2 - \frac{4\sqrt{2}}{k_0}\right)\sin\frac{k_0 - k}{\sqrt{2}} + 2\sqrt{x_0}\,j\cos\frac{k_0 - k}{\sqrt{2}}\right] M_0$$

$$V_x = \frac{n}{n_0 k^2}(4\sqrt{2}\sqrt{x_0}\,j^3)\left[\left(1 - \frac{\sqrt{2}}{k_0} - \frac{\sqrt{2}}{k} + \frac{4}{k_0 k}\right)\sin\frac{k_0 - k}{\sqrt{2}} + \left(\frac{\sqrt{2}}{k_0} - \frac{\sqrt{2}}{k}\right)\cos\frac{k_0 - k}{\sqrt{2}}\right] M_0$$

$$\Delta R = -\frac{\sqrt{2x}}{Dj^3}\frac{n}{n_0}\cos\alpha\left\{\sqrt{x_0}\,j\left[\left(\frac{2}{k_0} - \frac{\sqrt{2}}{2}\right)\cos\frac{k_0 - k}{\sqrt{2}} + \frac{\sqrt{2}}{2}\sin\frac{k_0 - k}{\sqrt{2}}\right]\right\} M_0$$

$$s_1 = -\frac{V_x\tan\alpha}{t} \quad s_1' = \frac{6M_x}{t^2} \qquad s_2 = \left(\frac{\Delta R}{R}\right)E + \nu s_1 \qquad \theta = \left(\frac{[12(1 - \nu^2)]^{\frac{3}{4}}}{E}\sqrt{\frac{2R_0}{t^5\cos\alpha}}\right) M_0$$

(Ref. 30)

TABLE XIII.—FORMULAS FOR STRESSES AND DEFORMATIONS IN PRESSURE VESSELS.—(*Continued*)

Form of vessel	Manner of loading and Case No.	Formulas
Torus	26. Complete torus under uniform internal pressure p lb. per sq. in.	$s_1 = \frac{pb}{t}\left(\frac{r+a}{2r}\right)$ Max $s_1 = \frac{pb}{t}\left(\frac{2a-b}{2a-2b}\right)$ at 0 $s_2 = \frac{pb}{2t}$ (uniform throughout)
	27. Split torus under axial load P (omega joint)	Stretch $= \frac{10.88Pb\sqrt{1-\nu^2}}{\pi E t^2}$ Max merid. bndg. stress $s_1' = \frac{2.99P}{2\pi ta\sqrt[6]{1-\nu^2}}\sqrt[3]{\frac{ab}{t^2}}$ (near 0) Max circ. mem. stress $s_2 = \frac{2.15P\sqrt[3]{1-\nu^2}}{2\pi ta}\sqrt[3]{\frac{ab}{t^2}}$ (tensile, at 0) } for $4 < \mu < 40$ where $\mu = \frac{b^2}{at}\sqrt{12(1-\nu^2)}$ (Refs. 16, 40)
	28. Corrugated tube under axial load P	Stretch $= \frac{1.813Pbn\sqrt{1-\nu^2}}{\pi E t^2}$ Max merid. bndg. stress $s_1' = \frac{1.63P}{2\pi ta\sqrt[6]{1-\nu^2}}\sqrt[3]{\frac{ab}{t^2}}$ Max circ. mem. stress $s_2 = \frac{0.925P\sqrt[3]{1-\nu^2}}{2\pi ta}\sqrt[3]{\frac{ab}{t^2}}$ (compressive) } for $4 < \mu < 40$ Here n = number of semicircular corrugations (5 in figure shown) (For U-shaped corrugations, see Ref. 41) (Ref. 16)
	29. Same as Case 28 except loaded only by uniform internal pressure, p lb. per sq. in.	Stretch = 0 Max merid. bndg. stress $s_1' = \frac{0.955p}{\sqrt[3]{1-\nu^2}}\sqrt[3]{\left(\frac{ab}{t^2}\right)^2}$ Max. circ. mem. stress. $s_2 = 0.955p\sqrt[6]{1-\nu^2}\sqrt[3]{\left(\frac{ab}{t^2}\right)^2}$ (Ref. 16) (For U-shaped corrugations, see Ref. 41)

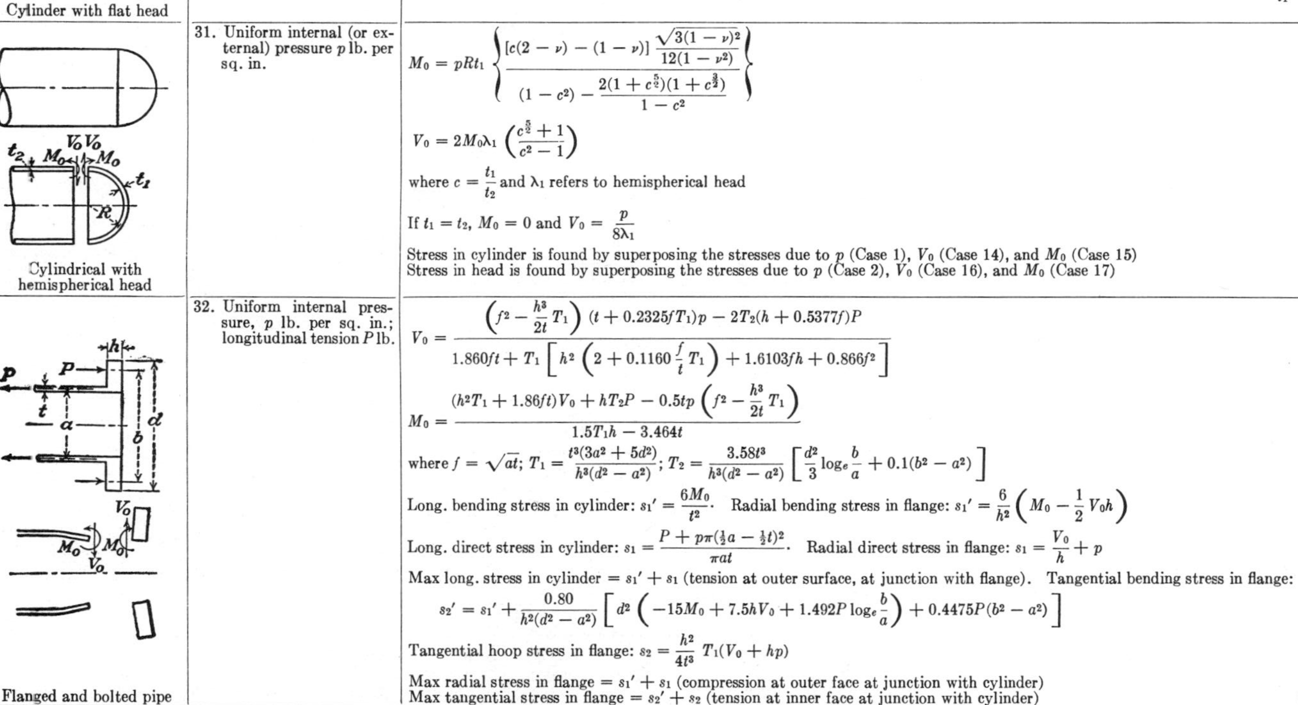

Cylinder with flat head		$2\lambda_2 + \frac{\quad}{D_1(1+\nu)} - \frac{\quad}{Et_1 + 2D_2\lambda_2^3R(1-\nu)}$ $V_0 = M_0\left(2\lambda_2 + \frac{2R\lambda_2^2D_2}{D_1(1+\nu)}\right) - \frac{pR^3\lambda_2^2D_2}{4D_1(1+\nu)}$ Here D_1 refers to flat head; D_2 and λ_2 refer to cylinder Stress in cylinder is found by superposing the stresses due to p (Case 1), V_0 (Case 14), and M_0 (Case 15) Stress in head is found by superposing the stresses due to p (Case 1, Table X), M_0 (Case 12, Table X), and the radial stress $\frac{V_0}{t_1}$ due to V_0
Cylindrical with hemispherical head	31. Uniform internal (or external) pressure p lb. per sq. in.	$M_0 = pRt_1\left\{\frac{[c(2-\nu)-(1-\nu)]\frac{\sqrt{3(1-\nu)^2}}{12(1-\nu^2)}}{(1-c^2) - \frac{2(1+c^{\frac{5}{2}})(1+c^{\frac{3}{2}})}{1-c^2}}\right\}$ $V_0 = 2M_0\lambda_1\left(\frac{c^{\frac{5}{2}}+1}{c^2-1}\right)$ where $c = \frac{t_1}{t_2}$ and λ_1 refers to hemispherical head If $t_1 = t_2$, $M_0 = 0$ and $V_0 = \frac{p}{8\lambda_1}$ Stress in cylinder is found by superposing the stresses due to p (Case 1), V_0 (Case 14), and M_0 (Case 15) Stress in head is found by superposing the stresses due to p (Case 2), V_0 (Case 16), and M_0 (Case 17)
Flanged and bolted pipe	32. Uniform internal pressure, p lb. per sq. in.; longitudinal tension P lb.	$V_0 = \frac{\left(f^2 - \frac{h^3}{2t}T_1\right)(t + 0.2325fT_1)p - 2T_2(h + 0.5377f)P}{1.860ft + T_1\left[h^2\left(2 + 0.1160\frac{f}{t}T_1\right) + 1.6103fh + 0.866f^2\right]}$ $M_0 = \frac{(h^2T_1 + 1.86ft)V_0 + hT_2P - 0.5tp\left(f^2 - \frac{h^3}{2t}T_1\right)}{1.5T_1h - 3.464t}$ where $f = \sqrt{at}$; $T_1 = \frac{t^3(3a^2+5d^2)}{h^3(d^2-a^2)}$; $T_2 = \frac{3.58t^3}{h^3(d^2-a^2)}\left[\frac{d^2}{3}\log_e\frac{b}{a} + 0.1(b^2-a^2)\right]$ Long. bending stress in cylinder: $s_1' = \frac{6M_0}{t^2}$. Radial bending stress in flange: $s_1' = \frac{6}{h^2}\left(M_0 - \frac{1}{2}V_0h\right)$ Long. direct stress in cylinder: $s_1 = \frac{P + p\pi(\frac{1}{2}a - \frac{1}{2}t)^2}{\pi at}$. Radial direct stress in flange: $s_1 = \frac{V_0}{h} + p$ Max long. stress in cylinder $= s_1' + s_1$ (tension at outer surface, at junction with flange). Tangential bending stress in flange: $s_2' = s_1' + \frac{0.80}{h^2(d^2-a^2)}\left[d^2\left(-15M_0 + 7.5hV_0 + 1.492P\log_e\frac{b}{a}\right) + 0.4475P(b^2-a^2)\right]$ Tangential hoop stress in flange: $s_2 = \frac{h^2}{4t^3}T_1(V_0 + hp)$ Max radial stress in flange $= s_1' + s_1$ (compression at outer face at junction with cylinder) Max tangential stress in flange $= s_2' + s_2$ (tension at inner face at junction with cylinder) (Ref. 10)

TABLE XIII.—FORMULAS FOR STRESSES AND DEFORMATIONS IN PRESSURE VESSELS.—(*Continued*)

Form of vessel	Manner of loading and Case No.	Formulas
		Thick vessels—wall stresses s_1 (longitudinal), s_2 (circumferential) and s_3 (radial)
	33. Uniform internal radial pressure p lb. per sq. in. (longitudinal pressure zero or externally balanced)	$s_1 = 0$ $\quad s_2 = p\dfrac{a^2(b^2+r^2)}{r^2(b^2-a^2)}$. Max $s_2 = p\dfrac{b^2+a^2}{b^2-a^2}$ at inner surface $s_3 = p\dfrac{a^2(b^2-r^2)}{r^2(b^2-a^2)}$. Max $s_3 = p$ at inner surface; max $s_s = p\dfrac{b^2}{b^2-a^2}$ at inner surface $\Delta a = p\dfrac{a}{E}\left(\dfrac{b^2+a^2}{b^2-a^2}+\nu\right)$; $\Delta b = p\dfrac{b}{E}\left(\dfrac{2a^2}{b^2-a^2}\right)$
	34. Uniform external radial pressure p lb. per sq. in.	$s_1 = 0$ $\quad s_2 = -p\dfrac{b^2(a^2+r^2)}{r^2(b^2-a^2)}$. Max $s_2 = -p\dfrac{2b^2}{b^2-a^2}$ at inner surface $s_3 = p\dfrac{b^2(r^2-a^2)}{r^2(b^2-a^2)}$. Max $s_3 = p$ at outer surface; max $s_s = \frac{1}{2}$ max s_2 at inner surface $\Delta a = -p\dfrac{a}{E}\left(\dfrac{2b^2}{b^2-a^2}\right)$; $\Delta b = -p\dfrac{b}{E}\left(\dfrac{a^2+b^2}{b^2-a^2}-\nu\right)$
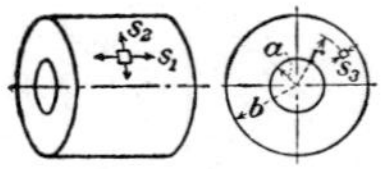 Cylindrical	35. Uniform internal pressure p lb. per sq. in. in all directions	$s_1 = p\dfrac{a^2}{b^2-a^2}$. s_2 and s_3 same as for Case 33 $\Delta a = p\dfrac{a}{E}\left[\dfrac{b^2+a^2}{b^2-a^2}-\nu\left(\dfrac{a^2}{b^2-a^2}-1\right)\right]$; $\Delta b = p\dfrac{b}{E}\left[\dfrac{a^2}{b^2-a^2}(2-\nu)\right]$; $p_u = s_u \log_e \dfrac{b}{a}$
	36. Uniform internal pressure p lb. per sq. in.	$s_1 = s_2 = p\dfrac{a^3(b^3+2r^3)}{2r^3(b^3-a^3)}$. Max $s_1 = \max s_2 = p\dfrac{b^3+2a^3}{2(b^3-a^3)}$ at inner surface $s_3 = p\dfrac{a^3(b^3-r^3)}{r^3(b^3-a^3)}$. Max $s_3 = p$ at inner surface; max $s_s = p\dfrac{3b^3}{4(b^3-a^3)}$ at inner surface (Ref. 3) $\Delta a = p\dfrac{a}{E}\left[\dfrac{b^3+2a^3}{2(b^3-a^3)}(1-\nu)+\nu\right]$; $\Delta b = p\dfrac{b}{E}\left[\dfrac{3a^3}{2(b^3-a^3)}(1-\nu)\right]$. Yield pressure $p_y = \dfrac{2s_y}{3}\left(1-\dfrac{a^3}{b^3}\right)$ (Ref. 20)
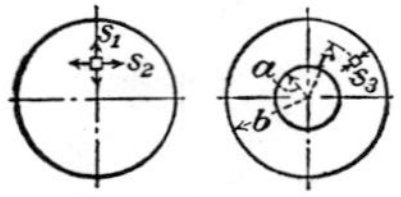	37. Uniform external pressure p lb. per sq. in.	$s_1 = s_2 = -p\dfrac{b^3(a^3+2r^3)}{2r^3(b^3-a^3)}$. Max $s_1 = \max s_2 = -p\dfrac{3b^3}{2(b^3-a^3)}$ at inner surface $s_3 = p\dfrac{b^3(r^3-a^3)}{r^3(b^3-a^3)}$. Max $s_3 = p$ at outer surface $\Delta a = -p\dfrac{a}{E}\left[\dfrac{3b^3}{2(b^3-a^3)}(1-\nu)\right]$; $\Delta b = -p\dfrac{b}{E}\left[\dfrac{a^3+2b^3}{2(b^3-a^3)}(1-\nu)-\nu\right]$

73. Thin Vessels under External Pressure.—All formulas given in Table XIII for thin vessels under uniform pressure are for internal pressure. They will apply equally to cases of external pressure if p is given a negative sign, but the stresses so found are significant only when the pressure is insufficient to cause failure through *elastic instability*, that is, through buckling that starts at stresses within the proportional limit. This type of failure is not considered here; it is discussed in Chap. 14, and formulas for the critical pressures or stresses producing it are given in Table XVI.

A vessel of moderate thickness may collapse under external pressure at stresses above the proportional limit but below the yield point, its behavior being comparable to that of a short column. The problem of ascertaining the pressure that produces failure of this kind is of special interest in connection with cylindrical vessels and pipes, and under Case 1 a formula is given that is applicable to this problem. In Ref. 8 charts are given that provide a solution to this same problem.

74. Thick Vessels under Internal or External Pressure.—If the wall thickness of a vessel is more than about one-tenth the radius, the meridional and hoop stresses cannot be considered uniform throughout the thickness of the wall, and the radial stress cannot be considered negligible. These stresses in thick vessels, here called *wall stresses*, must be found by formulas that are quite different from those used in finding membrane stresses in thin vessels.

It can be seen from the formulas for Cases 33 and 35 that the stress s_2 at the inner surface of a thick cylinder approaches p as the ratio of outer to inner radius approaches infinity. It is, therefore, apparent that if the stress is to be limited to some specified value s, the pressure must never exceed $p = s$, no matter how thick the wall is made. To overcome this limitation, the material at and near the inner surface must be put into a state of initial compression; this can be done by shrinking on one or more jackets (as explained in Art. 11 and in the examples below), or by subjecting the vessel to a high internal pressure that stresses the inner part into the plastic range and, when removed, leaves residual compression there and residual tension in the outer part. This procedure is called *autofrettage*, or self-hooping. If many successive jackets are superimposed on the original tube by shrinking or wrapping, the resulting structure is called a *multilayer* vessel. Such construction has certain advantages, but it should be noted that the formulas for hoop stresses are based on the assumption of an isotropic material; in a multilayered vessel the effective radial modulus of elasticity is less than the tangential modulus, and in consequence the hoop stress at and near the outer wall is less than the formula would indicate. Consequently, the outer layers of material contribute less to the strength of the vessel than might be supposed.

The tabulated formulas for elastic membrane stresses are accurate for both thin and thick vessels, but the formulas for predicted yield and bursting pressures, especially the former, do not always agree closely with experimental results (Refs. 21, 34, 35, 37, 39). The expressions for p_y given in the table are based on the minimum strain-energy theory of elastic failure. The expression for bursting pressure $p_u = 2s_u\left(\frac{b-a}{b+a}\right)$, commonly known as the "mean diameter" formula, is essentially empirical, but is given because it agrees reasonably well with experiment for both thin and thick vessels and is convenient to use. For very thick vessels the formula $p_u = s_u \log_e (b/a)$ is preferable. Greater accuracy can be obtained by using with this formula a multiplying factor that takes into account the strain-hardening properties of the material (Refs. 20, 37). With the same objective, Faupel (Ref. 39) proposed (with different notation) the formula $p_u = \frac{2s_y}{\sqrt{3}} \log_e \frac{b}{a}\left(2 - \frac{s_y}{s_u}\right)$. A rather extensive discussion of bursting pressure is given in Ref. 38, which presents a tabulated comparison between bursting pressures as calculated by a number of different formulas and as determined by actual experiment.

Example

At the powder chamber, the inner radius of a 3-in. gun tube is 1.605 in., the outer radius is 2.425 in. It is desired to shrink a jacket on this tube so as to produce a radial pressure between tube and jacket of 7600 lb. per sq. in. The outer radius of this jacket is 3.850 in. It is required to determine the difference between the inner radius of the jacket and the outer radius of the tube in order to produce the desired pressure, to calculate the stresses in each part when assembled, and to calculate the stresses in each part when the gun is fired, generating a powder pressure of 32,000 lb. per sq. in.

Solution.—Using the formulas for Case 34, it is found that for an external pressure of 7600 the stress s_2 at the outer surface of the tube is $-19{,}430$, the stress s_2 at the inner surface is $-27{,}050$, and the change in outer radius $\Delta b = -0.001385$. It is found that for an internal pressure of 7600 the stress s_2 at the inner surface of the jacket is $+17{,}630$, the stress s_2 at the outer surface is $+10{,}050$, and the change in inner radius $\Delta a = +0.001615$. (In making these calculations the inner radius of the jacket is assumed to be 2.425 in.) The initial difference between the inner radius of the jacket and outer radius of the tube must be equal to the sum of the radial deformations they suffer, or $0.001385 + 0.001615 = 0.0030$. Therefore the initial radius of the jacket should be $2.425 - 0.0030 = 2.422$ in.

The stresses produced by the powder pressure are calculated at the inner surface of the tube, at the common surface of tube and jacket ($r = 2.425$) and at the outer surface of the jacket. These stresses are then superposed on those found above. The calculations are as follows:

For the tube:

$$s_2 = +32{,}000\left(\frac{3.85^2 + 1.605^2}{3.82^2 - 1.605^2}\right) = +45{,}450$$

$$s_3 = +32{,}000$$

For tube and jacket:

$$s_2 = +32{,}000\left(\frac{1.605^2}{2.425^2}\right)\left(\frac{3.85^2 + 2.425^2}{3.85^2 - 1.605^2}\right) = +23{,}500$$

$$s_3 = +32{,}000\left(\frac{1.605^2}{2.425^2}\right)\left(\frac{3.85^2 - 2.425^2}{3.85^2 - 1.605^2}\right) = +10{,}200$$

For the jacket:

$$s_2 = +32{,}000\left(\frac{1.605^2}{3.85^2}\right)\left(\frac{3.85^2 + 3.85^2}{3.85^2 - 1.605^2}\right) = +13{,}500$$

These are the stresses due to the powder pressure. Superposing the stresses due to the shrinkage, we have as the resultant stresses:

At inner surface of tube,

$$s_2 = -27{,}050 + 45{,}450 = +18{,}400 \text{ lb. per sq. in.}$$
$$s_3 = 0 + 32{,}000 = +32{,}000 \text{ lb. per sq. in.}$$

At outer surface of tube,

$$s_2 = -19{,}430 + 23{,}500 = +4070 \text{ lb. per sq. in.}$$
$$s_3 = +7600 + 10{,}200 = +17{,}800 \text{ lb. per sq. in.}$$

At inner surface of jacket,

$$s_2 = +17{,}630 + 23{,}500 = +41{,}130 \text{ lb. per sq. in.}$$
$$s_3 = +7600 + 10{,}200 = +17{,}800 \text{ lb. per sq. in.}$$

75. Design Formulas for Conventional Pressure Vessels.—As can be seen from the example of Art. 72, the discontinuity stresses at the junction of a cylindrical shell and its head may greatly exceed the membrane stresses in either part. This is also true of the local stresses at the junction of shells of different thickness, at reducing sections, at openings, and at the connections of nozzles and other attachments. The A.S.M.E Code for Unfired Pressure Vessels (Ref. 9) does not require that such stresses be calculated, but does prescribe measures to be taken to minimize them. For example, the interposition of a toroidal knuckle between a cylindrical vessel and conical head is required if the cone half-angle is greater than 30 deg.; the use of such a knuckle in the vessel of the above example reduced the discontinuity stresses by more than 50 per cent. When such a knuckle is employed, the stresses can be calculated by using the influence coefficients for a torus given in Ref. 29. The opinion has been advanced that, even when designed in accordance with the code, a pressure vessel of the torispherical or toriconical type may have unconservatively high discontinuity stresses (Refs. 31, 32). To avoid stresses due to form irregularity, out-of-roundness is limited by the rule that the maximum difference between two inside diameters at any cross section shall not exceed 1 per cent of the nominal diameter.

The tentative code for reactor pressure vessels (Ref. 27) also prescribes the acceptable form and proportions of heads and attachments, and requires a detailed stress analysis, analytical or experimental, of stresses in flanges and reducers. Both these codes, and others, give basic formulas for computing the thickness of shell and head when the vessel is subjected to internal pressure; several of the more important of these, taken from Ref. 9, are given below. No corresponding formulas are available for designing against external pressure; charts for this purpose are provided in the code.

Notation:

t = required thickness (inches).
p = pressure (pounds per square inch).
s = allowable stress (pounds per square inch).
R = inside radius of shell or hemispherical head (inches).
L = inside radius of dished head (inches).
D = inside diameter of conical head (inches).
α = half the apex angle of conical head.
E = joint efficiency

$$Z = \frac{sE + p}{sE - p}$$

$$Y = \frac{2(sE + p)}{2sE - p}$$

For cylindrical shell:

$$t = \frac{pR}{sE - 0.6p} \qquad \text{when} \qquad t < \tfrac{1}{2}R \text{ or } p < 0.385sE$$

$$t = R(Z^{\frac{1}{2}} - 1) \qquad \text{when} \qquad t > \tfrac{1}{2}R \text{ or } p > 0.385sE$$

For spherical shell or hemispherical head:

$$t = \frac{pR}{2sE - 0.2p} \qquad \text{when} \qquad t < 0.356R \text{ or } p < 0.665sE$$

$$t = R(Y^{\frac{1}{3}} - 1) \qquad \text{when} \qquad t > 0.356R \text{ or } p > 0.665sE$$

For conical head without transition knuckle, $\alpha < 30°$

$$t = \frac{pD}{2 \cos \alpha(sE - 0.6p)}$$

The pressure vessel designer will, of course, usually be obligated to conform with some specified code, but it is interesting to note that the provisions of the several authorized and widely accepted codes are by no means uniform. In Ref. 33 a comparison is made of the regulations of 13 different countries, and it is shown that the required wall thickness of a cylindrical vessel as determined by the several codes may differ by as much as 100 per cent, mainly because of differences in the basic allowable design stresses. Some codes go into greater detail than others; for example, in Ref. 27 much attention is devoted to fatigue and to stress concentration, and the possibility of brittle fracture is guarded against by specifying that if the temperature of the steel is expected to be less than 60° above the transition temperature, the allowable stresses must be reduced to 20 per cent of their normal value.

76. Pipe on Supports at Intervals.—The stress analysis of a pipe or cylindrical tank supported at intervals on saddles or pedestals and filled or partly filled with liquid is difficult, and the results are rendered uncertain by doubtful boundary conditions. Certain conclusions arrived at from a study of tests (Refs. 11, 12) may be helpful in guiding design:

1. For a circular pipe or tank supported at intervals and held circular at the supports by rings or bulkheads, the ordinary theory of flexure is applicable if the pipe is completely filled.

2. If the pipe is only partially filled, the cross section at points between supports becomes out of round, and the distribution of longitudinal fiber stress is neither linear nor symmetrical across the section. The highest stresses occur for the half-full condition; then the maximum longitudinal compressive stress and the maximum circumferential bending stresses occur at the ends of the horizontal diameter, the maximum longitudinal tensile stress occurs at the bottom, and the longitudinal stress at the top is practically zero. According to theory (Ref. 4), the greatest of these stresses is the longitudinal compression, which is equal to the maximum longitudinal stress for the full condition divided by $K^{\frac{1}{4}} = \left(\frac{L}{R}\sqrt{\frac{t}{R}}\right)^{\frac{1}{2}}$, where R = the pipe radius, t = the thickness, and L = the span. The maximum circumferential stress is about one-third of this. Tests (Ref. 11) on a pipe having $K = 1.36$ showed a longitudinal stress somewhat less, and a circumferential stress considerably greater, than indicated by this theory.

3. For an unstiffened pipe resting in saddle supports, there are high local stresses, both longitudinal and circumferential, adjacent to the tips of the saddles. These stresses are less for a large saddle angle β (total angle subtended by arc of contact between pipe and saddle) than for a small angle and for the ordinary range of dimensions are practically independent of the thickness of the saddle, *i.e.*, its dimension parallel to the pipe axis. The maximum value of these localized stresses, for a pipe that fits the saddle well, will probably not exceed that indicated by the formula

$$s_{\max} = k\frac{P}{t^2}\log_e\left(\frac{R}{t}\right)$$

where P = the total saddle reaction, R = the pipe radius, t = pipe thickness, and k = a coefficient given by

$$k = 0.02 - 0.00012(\beta - 90)$$

where β is in degrees. This stress is almost wholly due to circumferential bending, and occurs at points about 15 deg. above the saddle tips.

4. The maximum value of P the pipe can sustain is about 2.25 times the value that, according to the formula given above, will produce a maximum stress equal to the yield point of the pipe material.

5. For a pipe supported in flexible slings instead of on rigid saddles, the maximum local stresses occur at the points of tangency of sling and pipe section; they are in general less than the corresponding stresses in the saddle supported pipe, but are of the same order of magnitude.

References

1. SOUTHWELL, R. V.: On the Collapse of Tubes by External Pressure, *Philos. Mag.*, Vol. 29, p. 67, 1915.
2. ROARK, R. J.: The Strength and Stiffness of Cylindrical Shells under Concentrated Loading, *Am. Soc. Mech. Eng., Jour. Appl. Mech.*, Vol. 2, No. 4, p. A-147, 1935.
3. TIMOSHENKO, S.: "Theory of Plates and Shells," Engineering Societies Monograph, McGraw-Hill Book Company, 1940.
4. SCHORER, H.: Design of Large Pipe Lines, *Trans. Am. Soc. Civil Eng.*, Vol. 98, p. 101, 1933.
5. MAULBETSCH, J. L., and M. HETENYI: Stresses in Pressure Vessels, *Am. Soc. Mech. Eng., Jour. Appl. Mech.*, Vol. 3, No. 3, p. A-107, 1936.
6. COATES, W. M.: The State of Stress in Full Heads of Pressure Vessels, *Trans. Am. Soc. Mech. Eng.*, Vol. 52, p. 117, 1930.
7. SAUNDERS, H. E., and D. F. WINDENBURG: Strength of Thin Cylindrical Shells Under External Pressure, *Trans. Am. Soc. Mech. Eng.*, Vol. 53, p. 207, 1931.
8. JASPER, T. M., and J. W. W. SULLIVAN: The Collapsing Strength of Steel Tubes, *Trans. Am. Soc. Mech. Eng.*, Vol. 53, p. 219, 1931.
9. AMERICAN SOCIETY OF MECHANICAL ENGINEERS: Rules for Construction of Unfired Pressure Vessels, Sec. VIII, A.S.M.E. Boiler Construction Code, 1949.
10. HOLMBERG, E. O., and KARL AXELSON: Analysis of Stresses in Circular Plates and Rings, *Am. Soc. Mech. Eng., Jour. Appl. Mech.*, Vol. 54, No. 2, p. 13, 1932.
11. HARTENBERG, R. S.: The Strength and Stiffness of Thin Cylindrical Shells on Saddle Supports, doctor's dissertation, University of Wisconsin, 1941.
12. WILSON, W. M., and E. D. OLSON: Tests on Cylindrical Shells, *Eng. Exp. Sta., Univ. Ill. Bull.* 331, 1941.
13. ODQVIST, F. K. G.: Om Barverkan Vid Tunna Cylindriska Skal Ock Karlvaggar, *Proc. Roy. Swedish Inst. for Eng. Research,* No. 164, 1942.
14. HETÉNYI, M.: Spherical Shells Subjected to Axial Symmetrical Bending, Int. Assn. for Bridge and Structural Eng., fifth volume of the "Publications," 1938.

15. REISSNER, E.: Stresses and Small Displacements of Shallow Spherical Shells, II, *Jour. Math. and Phys.*, Vol. 25, No. 4, 1947.
16. CLARK, R. A.: On the Theory of Thin Elastic Toroidal Shells, *Jour. Math. and Phys.*, Vol. 29, No. 3, 1950.
17. O'BRIEN, G. J., E. WETTERSTROM, M. G. DYKHUIZEN, and R. G. STURM: Design Correlations for Cylindrical Pressure Vessels with Conical or Toriconical Heads, *Welding Research Supplement*, Vol. 15, No. 7, p. 336, 1950.
18. SCHOESSOW, G. J., and E. A. BROOKS: Analysis of Experimental Data Regarding Certain Design Features of Pressure Vessels, *Trans. Am. Soc. Mech. Eng.*, Vol. 72, p. 567, 1950.
19. ROARK, R. J.: Stresses and Deflections in Thin Shells and Curved Plates due to Concentrated and Variously Distributed Loading, *Nat. Adv. Comm. Aeron.*, *Tech. Note* 806, 1941.
20. SVENSSON, N. L.: The Bursting Pressure of Cylindrical and Spherical Vessels, *Am. Soc. Mech. Eng.*, *Jour. Appl. Mech.*, Vol. 25, No. 1, March, 1958.
21. DURELLI, A. J., J. W. DALLY, and S. MORSE: Experimental Study of Thin-wall Pressure Vessels, *Proc. Soc. Exp. Stress Anal.*, Vol. 18, No. 1, 1961.
22. BJILAARD, P. P.: Stresses from Local Loadings in Cylindrical Pressure Vessels, *Am. Soc. Mech. Eng. Trans.*, Vol. 77, No. 6, August, 1955 (also in Ref. 28).
23. BJILAARD, P. P.: Stresses from Radial Loads in Cylindrical Pressure Vessels, *Welding Jour.*, Vol. 33, December, 1954 (also in Ref. 28).
24. YUAN, S. W., and L. TING: On Radial Deflections of a Cylinder Subjected to Equal and Opposite Concentrated Radial Loads, *Am. Soc. Mech. Eng.*, *Jour. Appl. Mech.*, Vol. 24, No. 6, June, 1957.
25. TING, L., and S. W. YUAN: On Radial Deflection of a Cylinder of Finite Length with Various End Conditions, *Jour. Aeron. Sci.*, Vol. 25, 1958.
26. Final Report, Purdue University Project, Design Division, Pressure Vessel Research Committee, Welding Research Council, 1952.
27. Tentative Structural Design Basis for Reactor Pressure Vessels and Directly Associated Components (Pressurized Water Cooled Systems), U.S. Dept. of Commerce, Office of Technical Services.
28. VON KÁRMÁN, TH., and HSUE-SHEN TSIEN: Pressure Vessel and Piping Design, *Am. Soc. Mech. Eng.*, *Collected Papers* 1927–1959.
29. GALLETLY, G. D.: Edge Influence Coefficients for Toroidal Shells of Positive; Also Negative Gaussian Curvature, *Am. Soc. Mech. Eng.*, *Jour. Eng. for Industry*, Vol. 82, February, 1960.
30. WENK, EDWARD, JR., and C. E. TAYLOR: "Analysis of Stresses at the Reinforced Intersection of Conical and Cylindrical Shells," Report 826, Navy Dept., David W. Taylor Model Basin, March, 1953.
31. GALLETLY, G. D.: Torispherical Heads: Caution to Designers (in Ref. 28).
32. SHIELD, R. T., and D. C. DRUCKER: Limit Strength of Thin Walled Pressure Vessels with ASME Standard Torispherical Head, *Proc. 3d U.S. Nat. Congr. of Appl. Mech.*, 1958.

33. LANCASTER, J. F.: A Comparison of United States, European and British Commonwealth Codes for the Construction of Welded Boilers and Pressure Vessels, *Am. Soc. Mech. Eng. Paper* 61-SA-40, 1961.
34. NARDRUZZI, E. D., and GEORGE WELTER: High-pressure Vessels Subjected to Static and Dynamic Loads, *Welding Jour. Research Supplement* 1954.
35. DUBUC, J., and GEORGE WELTER: Investigation of Static and Fatigue Resistance of Model Pressure Vessels, *Welding Jour. Research Supplement,* July, 1956.
36. KOOISTRA, L. F., and M. M. LEMCOE: Low Cycle Fatigue Research on Full-size Pressure Vessels, *Welding Jour.,* July, 1962.
37. WEIL, N. A.: Bursting Pressure and Safety Factors for Thin-walled Vessels, *Jour. Franklin Inst.,* February, 1958.
38. BROWNELL, L. E., and E. H. YOUNG: "Process Equipment Design: Vessel Design," John Wiley & Sons, Inc., 1959.
39. FAUPEL, J. H.: Yield and Bursting Characteristics of Heavy-wall Cylinders, *Trans. Am. Soc. Mech. Eng.,* Vol. 78, No. 5, 1956.
40. DAHL, N. C.: Toroidal-shell Expansion Joints, *Am. Soc. Mech. Eng., Jour. Appl. Mech.,* Vol. 20, 1953.
41. LAUPA, A., and N. A. WEIL: Analysis of U-shaped Expansion Joints, *Am. Soc. Mech. Eng., Jour. Appl. Mech.,* Vol. 29, No. 1, March, 1962.
42. BAKER, B. R., and G. B. CLINE, JR.: Influence Coefficients for Thin Smooth Shells of Revolution Subjected to Symmetric Loads, *Am. Soc. Mech. Eng., Jour. Appl. Mech.,* Vol. 29, No. 2, June, 1962.

CHAPTER 13

BODIES UNDER DIRECT BEARING AND SHEAR STRESS

77. Stress Due to Pressure between Elastic Bodies.—The stresses caused by the pressure between elastic bodies are of importance in connection with the design or investigation of ball and roller bearings, trunnions, expansion rollers, track stresses, etc. Hertz (Ref. 1) developed the mathematical theory for the surface stresses and the deformations produced by pressure between curved bodies, and the results of his analysis are supported by experiment. Formulas based on this theory give the maximum compressive stresses, which occur at the center of the surfaces of contact, but not the maximum shear stresses, which occur in the interiors of the compressed parts, nor the maximum tensile stress, which occurs at the boundary of the contact area and is normal thereto.

Both surface and subsurface stresses were studied by Belajef (Ref. 28, 29), and some of his results are cited in Ref. 6. A tabulated summary of surface and subsurface stresses, greatly facilitating calculation, is given in Ref. 33. For a cylinder on a plane and for crossed cylinders Thomas and Hoersch (Ref. 2) investigated mathematically surface compression and internal shear, and checked the calculated value of the latter experimentally. The stresses due to the pressure of a sphere on a plate (Ref. 3) and of a cylinder on a plate (Ref. 4) have also been investigated by photoelasticity. The deformation and contact area for a ball in a race were measured by Whittemore and Petrenko (Ref. 8) and compared with the theoretical values. Some recent investigations have considered the influence of tangential combined with normal loading (Ref. 35).

In Table XIV are given formulas for the elastic stress and deformation produced by pressure between bodies of various forms, and for the dimensions of the circular, elliptical, or rectangular area of contact formed by the compressed surfaces. Except where otherwise indicated, these equations are based on Hertz's theory, which assumes the length of the cylinder and

TABLE XIV.—FORMULAS FOR STRESS AND STRAIN DUE TO PRESSURE ON OR BETWEEN ELASTIC BODIES

Notation: s_c = unit compressive stress; s_s = unit shear stress; s_t = unit tensile stress; a = radius of circular contact area for cases 1, 2, and 3; b = width of rectangular contact area for cases 4, 5, and 6; c = major semiaxis and d = minor semiaxis of elliptical contact area for cases 7 and 8; y = combined deformation of both bodies at each contact, along axis of load; ν = Poisson's ratio; E = modulus of elasticity. Subscripts 1 and 2 refer to bodies 1 and 2, respectively. All dimensions in inches, all forces in pounds

Conditions and Case No.	Formulas for dimensions of contact area and for a maximum stress
1. Sphere on a flat plate. P = total load	$a = 0.721\sqrt[3]{PD\left[\frac{1-\nu_1^2}{E_1}+\frac{1-\nu_2^2}{E_2}\right]}$ Max $s_c = 0.918\sqrt[3]{\frac{P}{D^2\left[\frac{1-\nu_1^2}{E_1}+\frac{1-\nu_2^2}{E_2}\right]^2}}$ If $E_1 = E_2 = E$ and $\nu_1 = \nu_2 = 0.3$, $a = 0.881\sqrt[3]{\frac{PD}{E}}$, Max $s_c = 0.616\sqrt[3]{\frac{PE^2}{D^2}}$, Max $s_t = 0.133$ (Max s_c), $y = 1.55\sqrt[3]{\frac{P^2}{E^2D}}$ (Ref. 6) Max $s_s = \frac{1}{3}$(Max s_c), at depth $\frac{1}{2}a$ below surface of plate (approximate values, from Refs. 3 and 6)
2. Sphere on a sphere. P = total load	$a = 0.721\sqrt[3]{P\left(\frac{D_1D_2}{D_1+D_2}\right)\left[\frac{1-\nu_1^2}{E_1}+\frac{1-\nu_2^2}{E_2}\right]}$ Max $s_c = 0.918\sqrt[3]{P\frac{\left(\frac{D_1+D_2}{D_1D_2}\right)^2}{\left[\frac{1-\nu_1^2}{E_1}+\frac{1-\nu_2^2}{E_2}\right]^2}}$, $y = 1.04\sqrt[3]{\frac{P^2(D_1+D_2)}{D_1D_2}\left(\frac{1-\nu_1^2}{E_1}+\frac{1-\nu_2^2}{E_2}\right)^2}$ If $E_1 = E_2 = E$ and $\nu_1 = \nu_2 = 0.3$, $a = 0.881\sqrt[3]{\frac{P}{E}\frac{D_1D_2}{D_1+D_2}}$, Max $s_c = 0.616\sqrt[3]{PE^2\left(\frac{D_1+D_2}{D_1D_2}\right)^2}$, Max $s_s = \frac{1}{3}$ (Max s_c), Max $s_t = 0.133$ (Max s_c), $y = 1.55\sqrt[3]{\frac{P^2}{E^2}\frac{(D_1+D_2)}{D_1D_2}}$ (Ref. 6)
3. Sphere in spherical socket. P = total load	$a = 0.721\sqrt[3]{P\frac{D_1D_2}{D_1-D_2}\left[\frac{1-\nu_1^2}{E_1}+\frac{1-\nu_2^2}{E_2}\right]}$ Max $s_c = 0.918\sqrt[3]{P\frac{\left(\frac{D_1-D_2}{D_1D_2}\right)^2}{\left[\frac{1-\nu_1^2}{E_1}+\frac{1-\nu_2^2}{E_2}\right]^2}}$ If $E_1 = E_2 = E$ and $\nu_1 = \nu_2 = 0.3$, $a = 0.881\sqrt[3]{\frac{P}{E}\frac{D_1D_2}{D_1-D_2}}$, Max $s_c = 0.616\sqrt[3]{PE^2\left(\frac{D_1-D_2}{D_1D_2}\right)^2}$, Max $s_s = \frac{1}{3}$ (Max s_c), Max $s_t = 0.133$ (Max s_c), $y = 1.55\sqrt[3]{\frac{P^2}{E^2}\frac{(D_1-D_2)}{D_1D_2}}$

TABLE XIV.—FORMULAS FOR STRESS AND STRAIN DUE TO PRESSURE ON OR BETWEEN ELASTIC BODIES.—(*Continued*)

Conditions and Case No.	Formulas for dimensions of contact area and for a maximum stress
4. Cylinder between flat plates p = load per linear in. $= P/L$	$b = 1.6\sqrt{pD\left[\frac{1-\nu_1^2}{E_1}+\frac{1-\nu_2^2}{E_2}\right]}$ Max $s_c = 0.798\sqrt{\frac{p}{D\left[\frac{1-\nu_1^2}{E_1}+\frac{1-\nu_2^2}{E_2}\right]}}$ Total compression of cylinder between two plates is: $\Delta D = 4p\left(\frac{1-\nu^2}{\pi E}\right)\left(\frac{1}{3}+\log_e\frac{2D}{b}\right)$ (Ref. 5) If $E_1 = E_2 = E$ and $\nu_1 = \nu_2 = 0.3$, $b = 2.15\sqrt{\frac{pD}{E}}$, Max $s_c = 0.591\sqrt{\frac{pE}{D}}$ For $E = 30{,}000{,}000$, $\nu_1 = \nu_2 = 0.25$, $b = 0.0004\sqrt{pD}$, Max $s_c = 3190\sqrt{\frac{p}{D}}$, Max $s_s = 958\sqrt{\frac{p}{D}}$ at depth $0.393b$ below surface of plane (Approximate formula, from Ref. 2) Mutual approach of remote points in two plates $= 4p\frac{1-\nu^2}{\pi E}\log_e\frac{\pi EL}{p(1-\nu^2)}$ (Ref. 44)
5. Cylinder on cylinder. Axes parallel. p = load per linear in.	$b = 1.6\sqrt{p\frac{D_1D_2}{D_1+D_2}\left[\frac{1-\nu_1^2}{E_1}+\frac{1-\nu_2^2}{E_2}\right]}$ Max $s_c = 0.798\sqrt{\frac{p\frac{D_1+D_2}{D_1D_2}}{\left[\frac{1-\nu_1^2}{E_1}+\frac{1-\nu_2^2}{E_2}\right]}}$ If $E_1 = E_2 = E$ and $\nu_1 = \nu_2 = 0.3$, $b = 2.15\sqrt{\frac{p}{E}\frac{D_1D_2}{D_1+D_2}}$, Max $s_c = 0.591\sqrt{pE\frac{D_1+D_2}{D_1D_2}}$, $y = \frac{2(1-\nu^2)}{E}\frac{p}{\pi}\left(\frac{2}{3}+\log_e\frac{2D_1}{b}+\log_e\frac{2D_2}{b}\right)$ (Ref. 31)
6. Cylinder in circular groove. p = load per linear in.	$b = 1.6\sqrt{p\frac{D_1D_2}{D_1-D_2}\left[\frac{1-\nu_1^2}{E_1}+\frac{1-\nu_2^2}{E_2}\right]}$ Max $s_c = 0.798\sqrt{\frac{p\frac{D_1-D_2}{D_1D_2}}{\left[\frac{1-\nu_1^2}{E_1}+\frac{1-\nu_2^2}{E_2}\right]}}$ If $E_1 = E_2 = E$ and $\nu_1 = \nu_2 = 0.3$, $b = 2.15\sqrt{\frac{p}{E}\frac{D_1D_2}{D_1-D_2}}$, Max $s_c = 0.591\sqrt{pE\frac{D_1-D_2}{D_1D_2}}$

7. Cylinder on cylinder. Axes at right angles. P = total load

$$c = \alpha \sqrt[3]{P\frac{D_1 D_2}{D_1 + D_2}\left[\frac{1-\nu_1^2}{E_1} + \frac{1-\nu_2^2}{E_2}\right]},\quad d = \beta c,\quad \text{Max } s_c = \frac{1.5P}{\pi c d}\qquad y = \lambda \sqrt[3]{\frac{P^2}{\left(\frac{E_1}{1-\nu_1^2} + \frac{E_2}{1-\nu_2^2}\right)^2}\,\frac{(D_1 + D_2)}{D_1 D_2}}$$

where α and β and λ depend on ratio $\frac{D_1}{D_2}$ and have values as follows:

$\frac{D_1}{D_2}$	1	$1\frac{1}{2}$	2	3	4	6	10
α	0.908	1.045	1.158	1.350	1.505	1.767	2.175
β	1	0.765	0.632	0.482	0.400	0.308	0.221
λ	2.080	2.060	2.025	1.950	1.875	1.770	1.613

If $E_1 = E_2 = 30{,}000{,}000$, $\nu_1 = \nu_2 = 0.25$, $c = 0.00397\alpha \sqrt[3]{P\frac{D_1 D_2}{D_1 + D_2}}$

For these values of E and ν and for values of $\frac{D_1}{D_2}$ between 1 and 8, Max $s_s = \frac{11{,}750}{\left(\frac{R_1}{R_2}\right)^{0.271}} \sqrt[3]{\frac{P}{R_2^2}}$, where $R_1 = \frac{1}{2}D_1$, $R_2 = \frac{1}{2}D_2$

(Approximate formula, from Ref. 2)

8. General case of two bodies in contact. P = total pressure

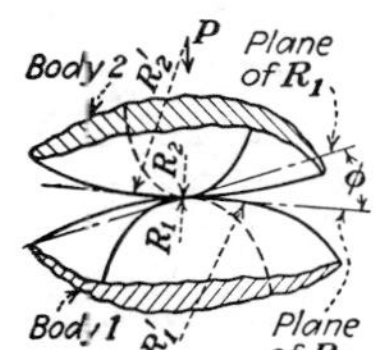

At point of contact minimum and maximum radii of curvature are R_1 and R_1' for Body 1, R_2 and R_2' for Body 2. Then $\frac{1}{R_1}$ and $\frac{1}{R_1'}$ are *principal curvatures* of Body 1, and $\frac{1}{R_2}$ and $\frac{1}{R_2'}$ of Body 2, and in each body the principal curvatures are mutually perpendicular. The plane containing curvature $\frac{1}{R_1}$ in Body 1 makes with the plane containing curvature $\frac{1}{R_2}$ in Body 2 the angle ϕ. Then:

$$\text{Max } s_c = \frac{1.5P}{\pi c d},\quad c = \alpha\sqrt[3]{\frac{P\delta}{K}},\quad d = \beta\sqrt[3]{\frac{P\delta}{K}},\ \text{and}\ y = \lambda\sqrt[3]{\frac{P^2}{K^2\delta}},\ \text{where}\ \delta = \frac{4}{\frac{1}{R_1} + \frac{1}{R_2} + \frac{1}{R_1'} + \frac{1}{R_2'}}\ \text{and}\ K = \frac{8}{3}\frac{E_1 E_2}{E_2(1-\nu_1^2) + E_1(1-\nu_2^2)}$$

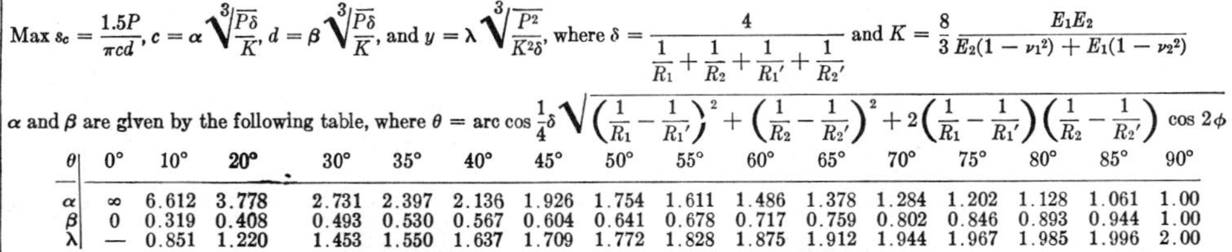

α and β are given by the following table, where $\theta = \text{arc cos } \frac{1}{4}\delta \sqrt{\left(\frac{1}{R_1} - \frac{1}{R_1'}\right)^2 + \left(\frac{1}{R_2} - \frac{1}{R_2'}\right)^2 + 2\left(\frac{1}{R_1} - \frac{1}{R_1'}\right)\left(\frac{1}{R_2} - \frac{1}{R_2'}\right)\cos 2\phi}$

θ	0°	10°	20°	30°	35°	40°	45°	50°	55°	60°	65°	70°	75°	80°	85°	90°
α	∞	6.612	3.778	2.731	2.397	2.136	1.926	1.754	1.611	1.486	1.378	1.284	1.202	1.128	1.061	1.00
β	0	0.319	0.408	0.493	0.530	0.567	0.604	0.641	0.678	0.717	0.759	0.802	0.846	0.893	0.944	1.00
λ	—	0.851	1.220	1.453	1.550	1.637	1.709	1.772	1.828	1.875	1.912	1.944	1.967	1.985	1.996	2.00

(Values from Ref. 8)

TABLE XIV.—FORMULAS FOR STRESS AND STRAIN DUE TO PRESSURE ON OR BETWEEN ELASTIC BODIES.—(Continued)

Conditions and Case No.	Formulas for dimensions of contact area and for a maximum stress
9. Rigid knife-edge across edge of semi-infinite plate. Load p lb. per linear in.	At any point Q, $s_c = \dfrac{2p\cos\theta}{\pi r}$ (Ref. 3)
10. Rigid block of width $2b$ across edge of semi-infinite plate. Load p lb. per linear in.	At any point Q on surface of contact, $s_c = \dfrac{p}{\pi\sqrt{b^2 - x^2}}$ (Ref. 6) (For loading on block of finite width and influence of distance of load from corner see Ref. 45)
11. Uniform pressure p lb. per sq. in. over length L across edge of semi-infinite plate	At any point O_1 outside loaded area, $y = \dfrac{2p}{\pi E}\left[(L + x_1)\log_e \dfrac{d}{L + x_1} - x_1 \log_e \dfrac{d}{x_1}\right] + pL\left(\dfrac{1-\nu}{\pi E}\right)$ At any point O_2 inside loaded area $y = \dfrac{2p}{\pi E}\left[(L - x_2)\log_e \dfrac{d}{L - x_2} + x_2 \log_e \dfrac{d}{x_2}\right] + pL\left(\dfrac{1-\nu}{\pi E}\right)$ Where y = deflection relative to a remote point A distant d from edge of loaded area At any point Q, $S_c = 0.318\,p(\alpha + \sin\alpha)$ $S_s = 0.318\,p\sin\alpha$ (Ref. 6)
12. Rigid cylindrical die of radius R on surface of semi-infinite body, total load P lb.	$y = \dfrac{P(1-\nu^2)}{2RE}$ At any point Q on surface of contact $s_c = \dfrac{P}{2\pi R\sqrt{R^2 - r^2}}$ Max $s_c = \infty$ at edge Min $s_c = \dfrac{P}{2\pi R^2}$ at center (Ref. 6)

Manner of loading	Formulas
13. Uniform pressure p lb. per sq. in. over circular area of radius R on surface of semi-infinite body 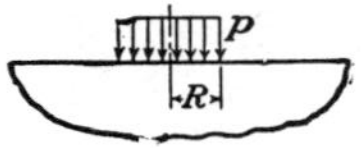	Max $y = \dfrac{2pR(1-\nu^2)}{E}$ at center y at edge $= \dfrac{4pR(1-\nu^2)}{\pi E}$ Max $s_s = 0.33\,p$ at point $0.638R$ below center of loaded area
14. Uniform pressure p lb. per sq. in. over square area of sides $2b$ on surface of semi-infinite body 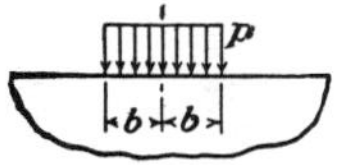	Max $y = \dfrac{2.24pb(1-\nu^2)}{E}$ at center $y = \dfrac{1.12pb(1-\nu^2)}{E}$ at corners Average $y = \dfrac{1.90pb(1-\nu^2)}{E}$ (Ref. 6)

dimensions of the plate to be infinite. For a very short cylinder and for a plate having a width less than five or six times that of the contact area, or a thickness less than five or six times the depth to the point of maximum shear stress, the actual stresses may vary considerably from the values indicated by the theory (see Ref. 4). The use of the formulas of Table XIV is illustrated in the example below. The general formula for Case 8 can be used, as in the example, for any contact-stress problems involving any geometrically regular bodies except parallel cylinders, but for bearing calculations use should be made of charts such as those given in Ref. 33 and 34, which not only greatly facilitate calculations but provide for influences not taken into account in the formulas.

Because of the very small area involved in what initially approximates a point or line contact, contact stresses for even light loads are very high, but as the formulas show, the stresses do not increase in proportion to the loading. Furthermore, because of the facts that the stress is highly localized and triaxial, the actual stress intensity can be very high without producing apparent damage. In order to make use of the Hertz formulas for purposes of design or safe load determination, it is necessary to know the relationship between theoretical stresses and likelihood of failure, whether from excessive deformation or fracture. In discussing this relationship, it is convenient to refer to the computed stress as the Hertz stress, whether the elastic range has been exceeded or not. Some of the available information showing the Hertz stress corresponding to loadings found to be safe and to loadings that produced excessive deformations or fracture may be summarized as follows.

Static or Near Static Conditions.—

CYLINDER.—The American Railway Engineering Association gives as the allowable loading for a steel cylinder on a flat steel plate the formulas

$$p = \left(\frac{s_y - 13{,}000}{20{,}000}\right) 600d \qquad \text{for } d < 25 \text{ in.}$$

and

$$p = \left(\frac{s_y - 13{,}000}{20{,}000}\right) 3000\sqrt{d} \qquad \text{for } d > 25 < 125 \text{ in.}$$

Here (and in subsequent equations) p is the load per linear inch in pounds, d is the diameter of the cylinder in inches, and s_y is the tensile yield point of the steel in the roller or in the plate, whichever is lower. If s_y is taken as 32,000 lb. per sq. in., the Hertz stress corresponding to this loading is constant at 76,200 lb. per sq. in. for any diameter up to 25 in., and decreases as $d^{-\frac{1}{4}}$ to 50,900 at $d = 125$ in.

Wilson (Refs. 7, 11, 32) carried out several series of static and slow-rolling tests on large rollers. From static tests on rollers of medium-grade cast steel having diameters of 120 to 720 in., he concluded that the load per linear inch required to produce appreciable permanent set could be represented by the empirical formula $p = 500 + 110d$, provided the bearing plates were 3 in. or more thick. He found that p increased with the axial length of the roller up to a length of 6 in., after which it remained practically constant (Ref. 32). Slow-rolling tests (Ref. 11) undertaken to determine the load required to produce a permanent elongation or spread of 0.001 in. per in. in the bearing plate led to the empirical formula

$$p = (18{,}000 + 120d)\,\frac{s_y - 13{,}000}{23{,}000}$$

for rollers with $d > 120$ in. Wilson's tests indicated that the average pressure on the area of contact required to produce set was greater for small rollers than for large rollers, and that there was little difference in bearing capacity under static and slow-rolling conditions, though the latter showed more tendency to produce surface deterioration.

Jensen (Ref. 4), making use of Wilson's test results and taking into account the three-dimensional aspect of the problem, proposed for the load-producing set the formula

$$p = 1 + \left(\frac{1.78}{1 + d^2/800L^2}\right)\frac{s_y{}^2 d}{E}$$

where L is the length of the cylinder in inches, and E is the modulus of elasticity in pounds per square inch. For values of the ratio d/L from 0.1 to 10 the corresponding Hertz stress ranges from $1.66s_y$ to $1.72s_y$.

Whittemore (Ref. 8) found that the elastic limit load for a flexible roller of hardened steel (tensile strength about 265,000 lb.

per sq. in.) tested between slightly hardened races corresponded to a Hertz stress of about 436,000 lb. per sq. in. The roller failed before the races.

SPHERE.—Tests reported in Ref. 8 gave, for balls 1, $1\frac{1}{4}$, and $1\frac{1}{2}$ in. in diameter, tested between straight races, Hertz stresses of 239,000, 232,000, and 212,000 lb. per sq. in. at loads producing a permanent strain of 0.001. The balls were of steel having sclerescope hardness of 60 to 68, and the races were of approximately the same hardness. The critical strain usually occurred first in the races.

From the results of crushing tests of a sphere between two similar spheres, SKF derived the empirical formula $P = 1960(8d)^{1.75}$, where P is the crushing load in pounds, and d the diameter of the sphere in inches. The test spheres were made of steel believed to be of hardness 64 to 66 Rockwell C, and the formula corresponds to a Hertz stress of about $4{,}000{,}000 \times d^{-\frac{1}{12}}$.

KNIFE-EDGE.—Knife-edge pivots are widely used in scales and balances, and if accuracy is to be maintained, the bearing loads must not cause excessive deformation. It is impossible for a truly sharp edge to bear against a flat plane without suffering plastic deformation, and so pivots are not designed on the supposition that the contact stresses will be elastic; instead, the maximum load per inch consistent with the requisite degree of accuracy in weighing is determined by experience or by testing. In Ref. 9, the National Bureau of Standards is quoted as recommending that for heavy service the load per linear inch should not exceed 5000 lb. per in. for high-carbon steels nor 6000 for special alloy steels; for light service the values can be increased to 6000 and 7000, respectively. In the tests described in Ref. 9, the maximum load that could be sustained without damage—the so-called "critical load"—was defined as the load per linear inch that produced (1) an increase in the edge width of 0.0005 in., or (2) a sudden increase in the load rate of vertical deformation. The two methods gave about the same results when the bearing was harder than the pivot, as it should be for good operation. The conclusions drawn from the reported tests may be summarized as follows:

The bearing value of a knife-edge or pivot varies approximately with the wedge angle for angles of 30 to 120 deg., the bearing value of a flat pivot varies approximately with the width of the edge for widths of 0.004 to 0.04 in., and the bearing value of pivots increases with the hardness for variations in hardness of 45 to 60 on the Rockwell C scale. Successive applications of a load less than the critical load will cause no plastic flow; the edge of a pivot originally sharp will increase in width with the load, but no further plastic deformation is produced by successive applications of the same or smaller loads. The application of a load greater than the critical load will widen the edge at the first application, but additional applications of the same load will not cause additional flow; the average unit pressure on 90-deg. pivots having a hardness represented by Rockwell C numbers of 50 to 60 is about 400,000 to 500,000 lb. per sq. in. at the critical load. This critical unit pressure appears to be independent of the width of the edge, but increases with the pivot angle and the hardness of the material (Ref. 9).

These tests and the quoted recommendations relate to applications involving heavy loads (thousands of pounds) and reasonable accuracy. For light loads and extreme accuracy, as in analytical balances—the pressures are limited to much smaller values. Thus, in Ref. 39, on the assumption that an originally sharp edge indents the bearing and that the common surface becomes cylindrical, it is stated that the radius of the loaded edge must not exceed 0.25 micron (approximately 0.00001 in.) if satisfactory accuracy is to be attained, and that the corresponding loading would be about 35,000 lb. per sq. in. of contact area.

Dynamic Conditions.—If the motion involved is a true rolling motion without any slip, then under conditions of slow motion—expansion rollers, bascules, etc.—the stress conditions are comparable with those produced by static loading. This is indicated by a comparison of the conclusions reached in Ref. 7, where the conditions were truly static, with those reached in Ref. 11, where there was a slow-rolling action. If there is even a slight amount of slip, however, the conditions are very much more severe, and failure is likely to occur through mechanical wear. The only guide to proper design against wear is real or simulated service testing (Refs. 24, 41).

When the motion involved is at high speed and produces cyclic loading, as in ball and roller bearings, fatigue is an important consideration. A great many tests have been made to determine the fatigue properties of bearings, especially ball bearings, and such tests have been carried out to as many as a billion cycles and with Hertz stresses up to 750,000 lb. per sq. in. (Ref. 37). The number of cycles-to-damage (either spalling or excessive deformation) has been found to be inversely proportional to the cube of the load for point contact (balls) and to the fourth power for line contact; this would be inversely proportional to the ninth and eighth powers, respectively, of the Hertz stress. Styri (Ref. 40) found the cycles to failure to vary as the ninth power of the Hertz stress, and was unable to establish a true endurance limit. Some of these tests show that ball bearings can run for a great number of cycles at very high stresses; for example, $\frac{1}{2}$-in. balls of S.A.E. 52,100 steel (RC 63 to 64) withstood 17,500,000 cycles at a stress of 174,000 lb. per sq. in. before 10 per cent failures occurred, and withstood 700,000,000 cycles at that stress before 90 per cent failures occurred. One difficulty in correlating different tests on bearings is the difference in criteria for judging damage; some experimenters have defined failure as a certain permanent deformation; others as visible surface damage through spalling. Palmgren (Ref. 36) states that a permanent deformation at any one contact point of rolling element and bearing ring combined equal to 0.0001 times the diameter of the rolling element has no significant influence on the functioning of the bearing. In the tests of Ref. 37, spalling of the surface was taken as the sign of failure; this spalling generally originated on planes of maximum shear stress below the surface.

It is apparent, from the foregoing discussion, that the practical design of parts that sustain direct bearing must be based largely on experience, since this alone affords a guide as to whether, at any given load and number of stress cycles, there is enough deformation or surface damage to interfere with proper functioning. The rated capacities of bearings and gears are furnished by the manufacturers, with proper allowance indicated for the conditions of service and recommendations as to proper lubrication. Valid and helpful conclusions, however, can often be drawn from a comparison of service records with calculated stresses.

Example

A ball 1.50 in. in diameter, in a race which has a diameter of 10 in. and a groove radius of 0.80 in., is subjected to a load of 2000 lb. It is required to find the dimensions of the contact area, the combined deformation of ball and race at the contact, and the maximum compressive stress.

Solution.—The formulas and table of Case 8 are used. The race is taken as body 1, the ball as body 2, hence $R_1 = -0.80$, $R_1' = -5$, $R_2 = R_2' = 0.75$ in. Taking $E_1 = E_2 = 30{,}000{,}000$ and $\nu_1 = \nu_2 = 0.3$, we have

$$K = \frac{8}{3}\left(\frac{30{,}000{,}000}{2(1 - 0.09)}\right) = 44{,}000{,}000$$

$$\delta = \frac{4}{-1.25 + 1.33 - 0.20 + 1.33} = 3.29$$

$$\theta = \text{arc cos } \tfrac{1}{4}(3.29)\sqrt{(-1.25 + 0.2)^2 + 0 + 0} = \text{arc cos } 0.864 = 30.3°$$

From the table, by interpolation,

$$\alpha = 2.710; \qquad \beta = 0.495; \qquad \lambda = 1.458$$

Then

$$c = 2.710\sqrt[3]{\frac{(2000)(3.29)}{44{,}000{,}000}} = 0.144 \text{ in.}$$

$$d = 0.495\sqrt[3]{\frac{(2000)(3.29)}{44{,}000{,}000}} = 0.0262 \text{ in.}$$

Therefore the contact area is an ellipse with a major axis of 0.288 in. and a minor axis of 0.0524 in.

$$y = 1.458\sqrt[3]{\frac{2000^2}{(44{,}000{,}000)^2(3.29)}} = 0.00125 \text{ in.}$$

$$\text{Max } s_c = \frac{1.5(2000)}{\pi(0.144)(0.0262)} = 253{,}000 \text{ lb. per sq. in.}$$

78. Rivets and Riveted Joints.—Although the actual state of stress in a riveted joint is complex, it is customary—and experience shows it is permissible—to ignore such considerations as stress concentration at the edges of rivet holes, unequal division of load among rivets, and nonuniform distribution of shear stress across the section of the rivet and of the bearing stress between rivet and plate. Simplifying assumptions are made, which may be summarized as follows: (1) The applied load is assumed to be transmitted entirely by the rivets, friction between the connected plates being ignored. (2) When the center of gravity of the rivets is on the line of action of the load, the rivets of the joint are all assumed to carry equal parts of the load if of the same size, or to be loaded proportionally to their respective section areas if of different sizes. (3) The shear stress is assumed to be uniformly distributed across the rivet section. (4) The bearing stress between plate and rivet is assumed to be uniformly distributed over an area equal to the rivet diameter times the plate thickness. (5) The stress in a tension member is assumed to be uniformly distributed over the net area. (6) The stress in a compression member is assumed to be uniformly distributed over the gross area.

The design of riveted joints on the basis of these assumptions is the accepted practice, although none of them is strictly correct, and methods of stress calculation that are supposedly more accurate have been proposed (Ref. 12).

Details of Design and Limitations.—The possibility of secondary failure due to secondary causes, such as the shearing or tearing out of a plate between rivet and edge of plate or between adjacent rivets, the bending or insufficient upsetting of long rivets, or tensile failure along a zigzag line when rivets are staggered, is guarded against in standard specifications (Ref. 13) by detailed rules for edge clearance, maximum grip of rivets, maximum pitch, and for computing the net width of riveted parts. Provision is made for the use of high-strength bolts in place of rivets under certain circumstances (Ref. 42). Joints may be made by welding instead of riveting, but the use of welding in conjunction with riveting is not approved on new work; the division of the load as between the welds and the rivets would be indeterminate.

Tests on Riveted Joints.—In general, tests on riveted joints show that while under working loads the stress conditions may be considerably at variance with the usual assumptions, the ultimate strength may be closely predicted by calculations based thereon. Some of the other conclusions drawn from such tests may be summarized as follows:

In either lap or double-strap butt joints in very wide plates, the unit tensile strength developed by the net section is greater than that developed by the plate itself when tested in full width, and practically equal to that developed by narrow tension specimens cut from the plate. The rivets in lap joints are as strong, relative to undriven rivets tested in shear, as are the rivets in butt joints. Lap joints bend sufficiently at stresses below the usual design stresses to cause opening of caulked joints (Ref. 14).

Although it is frequently specified that rivets shall not be used in tension, tests show that buttonhead rivets hot-driven develop a strength in direct tension greater than the strength of the rod from which they are made, and that they may be relied upon to develop this strength in every instance. Although the initial tension in such rivets, due to cooling, usually amounts to 70 per cent or more of the yield strength, this initial tension does not reduce the ability of the rivets to resist an applied tensile load (see also Art. 11). Unless a joint is subjected to reversals of primary load the use of rivets in tension appears to be justified, but when the primary load, producing shear in the rivets, is reversed, the reduction in friction due to simultaneous rivet tension may permit slip to occur, with possible deleterious effects (Ref. 15).

With respect to the form of rivet head, the rounded or buttonhead type is standard, but countersunk rivets are often used, and tests show that these develop the same ultimate strength, although they permit much more slip and deformation at working loads than do the buttonhead rivets (Ref. 16).

In designing riveted joints in very thin metal, especially the light alloys, factors not usually considered in ordinary structural-steel work, such as the radial stresses caused at the hole edges by closing pressure, and the buckling of the plates under rivet pressure, may have to be taken into account (Ref. 17).

Eccentric Loading.—When the rivets of a joint are so arranged that the center of gravity G of the group lies not on the line of action of the load but at a distance e therefrom, the load P can be replaced by an equal and parallel load P' acting through G and a couple Pe. The load on any one of the n rivets is then found by *vectorially* adding the load P/n due to P' and the load Q due to the couple Pe. This load Q acts normal to the line from G to the rivet, and is given by the equation: $Q = PeA_1r_1/J$, where A_1 is the area of the rivet in question, r_1 its distance from G, and $J = \Sigma Ar^2$ for all the rivets of the group. When all rivets are of the same size, as is usually the case, the formula becomes $Q = Per_1/\Sigma r^2$. Charts and tables are available which greatly facilitate the labor of the calculation involved, and which make possible direct design of the joint without recourse to trial and error (Ref. 18). The direct procedure, as outlined above, is illustrated in the example below.

The stiffness or resistance to angular displacement of a riveted joint determines the degree of fixity that should be assumed in the analysis of beams with riveted ends, or of rectangular frames. Tests (Ref. 19) have shown that while joints made with wide gusset plates are practically rigid, joints made by simply riveting through clip angles are not even approximately so. A method of calculating the elastic constraint afforded by riveted joints of different types, based on an extensive series of tests, has been proposed by Rathbun (Ref. 20).

Example

Figure 42 represents a lap joint in which three 1-in. rivets are used to connect a 15-in. channel to a plate. The channel is eccentrically loaded as shown. It is required to determine the maximum shear stress in the rivets. (This is not, of course, a properly designed joint intended to develop the

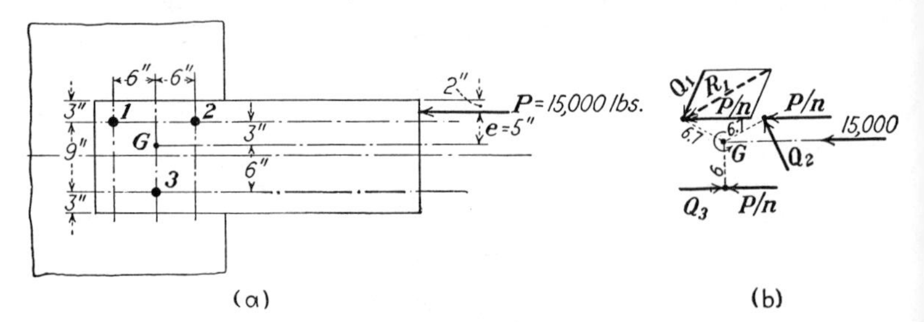

FIG. 42.

full strength of the channel. It represents a simple arrangement of rivets assumed for the purpose of illustrating the calculation of rivet stress due to a moment.)

The center of gravity of the rivet group is found to be at G. The applied load is replaced by an equal load through G and a couple equal to

$$15{,}000 \times 5 = 75{,}000 \text{ in.-lb.}$$

as shown in (b). The distances r_1, r_2, and r_3 of rivets 1, 2, and 3, respectively, from G are as shown. The value of Σr^2 is 126. The loads on the rivets due to the couple of 75,000 lb. are therefore

$$Q_1 = Q_2 = \frac{(75{,}000)(6.7)}{126} = 3990 \text{ lb.}$$

$$Q_3 = \frac{(75{,}000)(6)}{126} = 3570 \text{ lb.}$$

These loads act on the rivets in the directions shown. In addition, each rivet is subjected to a load in the direction of P' of $P/n = 5000$ lb. The resultant load on each rivet is then found by graphically (or algebraically) solving for the resultant of Q and P/n as shown. These resultant loads are $R_1 = R_2 = 8750$ lb.; $R_3 = 1430$ lb. The maximum shear stress occurs in rivets 1 and 2 and is $s_s = 8750/0.785 = 11{,}150$ lb. per sq. in.

79. Miscellaneous Cases.—In most instances, the stress in bodies subjected to direct shear or pressure is calculated on the basis of simplifying assumptions such as are made in analyzing a riveted joint. Design is based on rules justified by experience rather than exact theory, and a full discussion does not properly come within the scope of this book. A brief consideration is here given to a number of cases, a more complete treatment of which may be found in books on machine and structural design, and in the references cited.

Pins and *bolts* are designed on the basis of shear and bearing stress calculated in the same way as for rivets. In the case of pins bearing on wood, the allowable bearing stress must be reduced to provide for nonuniformity of pressure when the length of bolt is more than five or six times its diameter. When the pressure is inclined to the grain, the safe load is found by the formula: $N = \frac{PQ}{P \sin^2 \theta + Q \cos^2 \theta}$, where N is the safe load for the case in question, P is the safe load applied parallel to the grain, Q the safe load applied transverse to the grain, and θ is the angle N makes with the direction of the grain (Ref. 21).

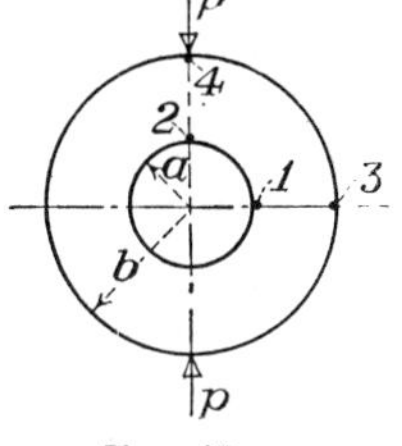

FIG. 43.

Hollow pins and rollers are usually much too thick walled to be analyzed as circular rings by the formulas of Table VIII. The loading is essentially as shown in Fig. 43, and the greatest circumferential stresses, which occur at points 1, 2, 3, and 4, may be found by the formula: $s = K \frac{2p}{\pi b}$, where the numerical coefficient K depends on the ratio a/b and has values as tabulated below. A plus sign for K indicates tensile stress and a minus sign compressive stress (Ref. 30).

Point	a/b							
	0	0.1	0.2	0.3	0.4	0.5	0.6	0.7
1	−5.0	−5.05	−5.30	−5.80	−7.00	−9.00	−12.9	−21.4
2	+3.0	+3.30	+3.80	+4.90	+7.00	+10.1	+16.0	+31.0
3	0	+0.06	+0.20	+1.0	+1.60	+3.0	+5.8	+13.1
4	+0.5	+0.40	0	−0.50	−1.60	−3.8	−8.4	−19.0

Gear teeth are investigated by considering the tooth as a cantilever beam, the critical stress being the tensile bending stress at the base. This stress can be calculated by the modified Heywood formula for a very short cantilever beam (Art. 35) or by a combination of the modified Lewis formula and stress concentration factor given for Case 18 in Table XVII (see also Refs. 22, 23, 24). The allowable stress is reduced according to speed of operation by one of several empirical formulas (Ref. 24). Under certain conditions the bearing stress between teeth may become important, especially as this stress affects wear, and this stress may be calculated by the formula for Case 5, Table XIV. The total deformation of the tooth, the result of direct compression at the point of contact and of beam deflection and shear, may be calculated by the formula of Case 5 and the methods of Art. 32 (Ref. 23).

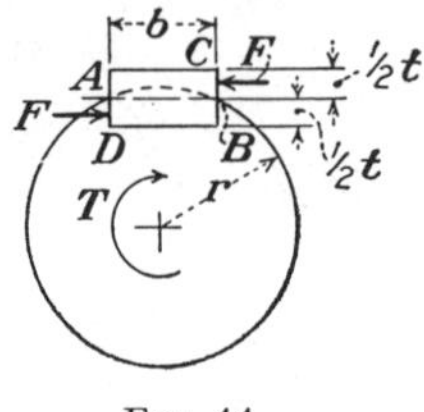

FIG. 44.

Keys are designed for a total shearing force $F = T/r$ (Fig. 44), where T represents the torque transmitted. The shear stress is assumed to be uniformly distributed over the horizontal section AB, and the bearing stress to be uniformly distributed over half the face. These assumptions lead to the formulas: $S_s = F/Lb$; $s_b = 2F/tL$ on the sides; $s_b = 2Ft/b^2L$ on top and bottom. Here L is the length of the key; in conventional design $4b < L < 16b$. As usually made, $b \gtreqless t$, hence the bearing stress on the sides is greater than that on the top and bottom. Photoelastic analysis of the stresses in square keys shows that the shear stress is not uniform across the breadth b, but is greatest at A and B, where it may reach a value of from two to four times the average value (Ref. 25). Undoubtedly the shear stress also varies in intensity along the length of the key. The bearing stresses on the surfaces of the key are also nonuniform, that on the sides being greatest near the common surface of shaft and hub and that on the top and bottom being greatest near the corners, C, D. When conservative working stresses are used, however, and the proportions of the key are such as have been found satisfactory in practice, the approximate methods of stress calculation that have been indicated result in satisfactory design.

Fillet welds are successfully designed on the basis of uniform distribution of shear stress on the longitudinal section of least area, although analysis and tests show that there is considerable variation in the intensity of shear stress along the length of the fillet (Refs. 26, 27).

Detailed recommendations for the design of welded structural joints are given in Ref. 13.

Screw Threads.—The strength of screw threads is of great importance in the design of joints, where the load is transferred to a bolt or stud by a nut. Here the problem is two-fold. In the first place the load is not transferred uniformly along the engaged thread length; both mathematical analysis and tests show that the maximum load per linear inch of thread, which occurs near the loaded face of the nut is several times as great as the average over the engaged length. This ratio, called the thread-load concentration factor and denoted by H, is often 2, 3, or even 4 (Ref. 43). The maximum load per linear inch on a screw thread is, therefore, the total load divided by the helical length of engaged screw thread, times H. The maximum stress due to this loading can be computed by the Heywood-Kelley-Pedersen formula for a short cantilever as given on p. 132. It is important to note that the values of k_f given in Table XVII are in some cases for loading through a nut, and so include H, while in other cases, as in rotating beam tests, this influence is absent. Because of the combined effects of reduced area, nonuniform load distribution, and stress concentration, the efficiency of a bolted joint under reversed repeated loading is likely to be quite small. In Ref. 49 of Chap. 3, values from 18% (for a 60,000-psi steel with rolled threads) to 6.6% (for a 200,000-psi steel with machine-cut threads) are cited.

The design of bolted connections has received much study, and an extensive discussion and bibliography are given by Heywood (Ref. 49 of Chap. 3) and in some of the papers of Ref. 54 of Chap. 3.

References

1. HERTZ, H.: "Gesammelte Werke," Vol. I, Leigzig, 1895.
2. THOMAS, H. R., and V. A. HOERSCH: Stresses Due to the Pressure of One Elastic Solid Upon Another, *Eng. Exp. Sta. Univ. Ill., Bull.* 212, 1930.
3. OPPEL, G.: The Photoelastic Investigation of Three-Dimensional Stress and Strain Conditions, *Nat. Adv. Comm. Aeron., Tech. Memo.* 824, 1937.
4. JENSEN, V. P.: Stress Analysis by Means of Polarized Light with Special Reference to Bridge Rollers, *Bull. Assoc. State Eng. Soc.*, October, 1936.
5. FÖPPL, A.: "Technische Mechanik," 4th ed., Vol. 5, p. 350.

6. TIMOSHENKO, S., and J. N. GOODIER: "Theory of Elasticity," 2d. ed., Engineering Societies Monograph, McGraw-Hill Book Company, 1951.
7. WILSON, W. M.: The Bearing Value of Rollers, *Eng. Exp. Sta. Univ. Ill., Bull.* 263, 1934.
8. WHITTEMORE, H. L., and S. N. PETRENKO: Friction and Carrying Capacity of Ball and Roller Bearings, *Tech. Paper Bur. Standards,* No. 201, 1921.
9. WILSON, W. M., R. L. MOORE, and F. P. THOMAS: Bearing Value of Pivots for Scales, *Eng. Exp. Sta. Univ. Ill., Bull.* 242, 1932.
10. Manual of the American Railway Engineering Association, 1936.
11. WILSON, W. M.: Rolling Tests of Plates, *Eng. Exp. Sta. Univ. Ill., Bull.* 191, 1929.
12. HRENIKOFF, A.: Work of Rivets in Riveted Joints, *Trans. Am. Soc. Civil Eng.,* Vol. 99, p. 437, 1934.
13. American Institute of Steel Construction, Specifications for the Design, Fabrication and Erection of Structural Steel for Buildings, and Commentary, 1963.
14. WILSON, W. M., J. MATHER, and C. O. HARRIS: Tests of Joints in Wide Plates, *Eng. Exp. Sta. Univ. Ill., Bull.* 239, 1931.
15. WILSON, W. M., and W. A. OLIVER: Tension Tests of Rivets, *Eng. Exp. Sta. Univ. Ill., Bull.* 210, 1930.
16. KOMMERS, J. B.: Comparative Tests of Button Head and Countersunk Riveted Joints, *Bull. of Eng. Exp. Sta. Univ. Wis.,* Vol. 9, No. 5, 1925.
17. HILBES, W.: Riveted Joints in Thin Plates, *Nat. Adv. Comm. Aeron., Tech. Memo.* 590.
18. DUBIN, E. A.: Eccentric Riveted Connections, *Trans. Am. Soc. Civil Eng.,* Vol. 100, p. 1086, 1935.
19. WILSON, W. M., and H. F. MOORE: Tests to Determine the Rigidity of Riveted Joints of Steel Structures, *Eng. Exp. Sta. Univ. Ill., Bull.* 104, 1917.
20. RATHBUN, J. C.: Elastic Properties of Riveted Connections, *Trans. Am. Soc. Civil Eng.,* Vol. 101, p. 524, 1936.
21. "Wood Handbook," U.S. Dept. of Agriculture.
22. BAUD, R. V., and R. E. PETERSON: Loads and Stress Cycles in Gear Teeth, *Mech. Eng.,* Vol. 51, p. 653, 1929.
23. TIMOSHENKO, S., and R. V. BAUD: The Strength of Gear Teeth, *Mech. Eng.,* Vol. 48, p. 1108, 1926.
24. Dynamic Loads on Gear Teeth, *Am. Soc. Mech. Eng., Research Pub.,* 1931.
25. SOLAKIAN, A. G., and G. B. KARELITZ: Photoelastic Study of Shearing Stress in Keys and Keyways, *Am. Soc. Mech. Eng., Jour. Appl. Mech.,* Vol. 54, No. 11, p. 97, 1932.
26. TROELSCH, H. W.: Distributions of Shear in Welded Connections, *Trans. Am. Soc. Civil Eng.,* Vol. 99, p. 409, 1934.
27. Report of Structural Steel Welding Committeee of the American Bureau of Welding, 1931.
28. BELAJEF, N. M.: On the Problem of Contact Stresses, *Bull. of Eng. of Ways of Communication,* St. Petersburg, 1917.

29. Belajef, N. M.: Computation of Maximal Stresses Obtained from Formulas for Pressure in Bodies in Contact, *Bull. of Eng. of Ways of Communication*, Leningrad, 1929.
30. Horger, O. J.: Fatigue Tests of Some Manufactured Parts, *Proc. Soc. Exp. Stress Anal.*, Vol. 3, No. 2, p. 135, 1946.
31. Radzimovsky, E. I.: Stress Distribution and Strength Conditions of Two Rolling Cylinders Pressed Together, *Eng. Exp. Sta. Univ. Ill., Bull.* 408, 1953.
32. Wilson, W. M.: Tests on the Bearing Value of Large Rollers, *Univ. Ill., Eng. Exp. Sta., Bull.* 162, 1927.
33. New Departure, Division of General Motors Corp., Analysis of Stresses and Deflections, Bristol, Conn., 1946.
34. Lundberg, G., and H. Sjovall: Stress and Deformation in Elastic Contacts, Institution of Theory of Elasticity and Strength of Materials, Chalmers University of Technology, Gothenburg, 1958.
35. Smith, J. O., and C. K. Lin: Stresses Due to Tangential and Normal Loads on an Elastic Solid with Application to Some Contact Stress Problems, *Jour. Appl. Mech.*, June, 1953.
36. Palmgren, Arvid: "Ball and Roller Bearing Engineering," 3d ed., SKF Industries Inc., 1959.
37. Butler, R. H., H. R. Bear, and T. L. Carter: Effect of Fiber Orientation on Ball Failure, *Nat. Adv. Comm. Aeron., Tech. Note* 3933 (also *Tech. Note* 3930).
38. Selection of Bearings, Timken Roller Bearing Co.
39. Corwin, A. H.: "Techniques of Organic Chemistry," 3d ed., Vol. 1, Part 1, Interscience Publishers, Inc., 1959.
40. Styri, Haakon: Fatigue Strength of Ball Bearing Races and Heat Treated Steel Specimens, *Proc. Am. Soc. Testing Materials*, Vol. 51, 1951.
41. Burwell, J. T., Jr. (ed.): "Mechanical Wear," American Society for Metals, 1950.
42. Specifications for Assembly of Structural Joints Using High Strength Steel Bolts, distributed by American Institute of Steel Construction; approved by Research Council on Riveted and Bolted Structural Joints of the Engineering Foundation; endorsed by American Institute of Steel Construction and Industrial Fasteners Institute.
43. Sopwith, D. G.: The Distribution of Load in Screw Threads, *Proc. Inst. Mech. Eng.*, Vol. 159, 1948.
44. Lundberg, Gustaf: Cylinder Compressed between Two Plane Bodies, reprint courtesy of SKF Industries Inc., 1949.
45. Hiltscher, R., and G. Florin: Spalt- und Abreisszugspannungen in rechteckingen Scheiben, die durch eine Last in verschiedenem Abstand von einer Scheibenecke belastet sind, *Die Bautechnik*, Vol. 12, 1963.
46. MacGregor, C. W. (ed.): "Handbook of Analytical Design for Wear," I.B.M. Corp., Plenum Press, 1964.

CHAPTER 14

ELASTIC STABILITY

80. General Considerations.—Failure through elastic instability has been discussed briefly in Art. 12, where it was pointed out that it may occur when the bending or twisting effect of an applied load is proportional to the deformation it produces. In this chapter, formulas for the critical load or critical unit stress at which such failure occurs are given for a wide variety of members and conditions of loading.

Such formulas can be derived mathematically by integrating the differential equation of the elastic curve, or by equating the strain energy of bending to the work done by the applied load in the corresponding displacement of its point of application, the form of the elastic curve being assumed when unknown. Of all possible forms of the curve, that which makes the critical load a minimum is the correct one, but almost any reasonable assumption (consistent with the boundary conditions) can be made without gross error resulting, and for this reason the strain-energy method is especially adapted to the approximate solution of difficult cases.

A very thorough discussion of the general problem, with detailed solutions of many specified cases, is given in Timoshenko's "Theory of Elastic Stability" (Ref. 1), from which book many of the formulas in this chapter are taken. Formulas for many cases are also given in Refs. 35 and 36.

At one time, most of the problems involving elastic stability were of academic interest only, since engineers were reluctant to use compression members so slender as to fail by buckling at elastic stresses, and danger of corrosion interdicted the use of very thin material in exposed structures. The development of the metal airplane, however, has given great impetus to the theoretical and experimental investigation of elastic stability, and to the use of parts in the design of which it is a governing consideration. Furthermore, the use of nonrusting and high-strength metals tends to encourage "light" design in other structures than aircraft. Certain definite advantages of light construction, in which stability determines strength, are to be noted. One is that since elastic buckling may occur without damage, part of a structure—such as the skin of an airplane wing or web of a deep beam—may be safely used at loads that cause local buckling, and under these circumstances the resistance afforded by the buckled part is definitely known. Again, members such as Euler columns may be loaded experimentally to their maximum capacity, and subsequently incorporated in a structure.

81. Buckling of Bars.—In Table XV are given formulas for the critical loads on columns, beams, and shafts. In general, the theoretical values are in good agreement with test results so long as the assumed conditions are reasonably well satisfied. It is to be noted that even slight changes in the amount of end constraint have a marked effect on the critical loads, and therefore it is important that such constraint be closely estimated. Slight irregularities in form and small accidental eccentricities are less likely to be important in the case of columns than in the case of thin plates. For latticed columns, or columns with tie plates, a reduced value of E may be used, calculated as shown in Art. 66. Formulas for the elastic buckling of bars may be applied to conditions under which the proportional limit is exceeded if a reduced value of E corresponding to the actual stress is used (Ref. 1) but the procedure requires a stress-strain diagram for the material and is not, in general, practical.

82. Buckling of Flat and Curved Plates.—In Table XVI are given formulas for the critical loads and critical stresses on plates and thin-walled members. Because of the greater likelihood of serious geometrical irregularities, and their greater relative effect, the critical stresses actually developed by such members usually fall short of the theoretical values by a wider margin than in the case of bars. The discrepancy is generally greater for pure compression (thin tubes under longitudinal compression or external pressure) than for tension and compression combined (thin tubes under torsion, or flat plates under edge shear), and increases with the thinness of the material. The critical stress or load indicated by any one of the theoretical formulas should therefore be regarded as an upper limit, approached more or less closely according to the closeness with which the actual shape of the member approximates the geometrical form assumed. In

TABLE XV.—FORMULAS FOR ELASTIC STABILITY OF BARS AND RINGS

E = modulus of elasticity, I = moment of inertia of cross section about central axis perpendicular to plane of buckling. All dimensions are in inches, all forces in pounds, all angles in radians

Form of bar, manner of loading and support	Formulas for critical load P', critical unit load p', critical torque T', critical bending moment M', or critical combination of loads at which elastic buckling occurs
1. Uniform straight bar under end load. One end free, other end fixed 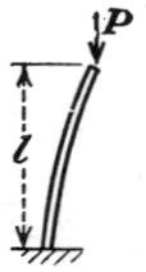	$P' = \frac{\pi^2 EI}{4l^2}$
2. Uniform straight bar under end load. Both ends hinged 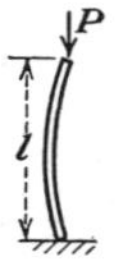	$P' = \frac{\pi^2 EI}{l^2}$
3. Uniform straight bar under end load. One end fixed, other end hinged and horizontally constrained over fixed end 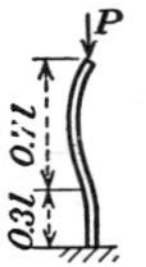	$P' = \frac{\pi^2 EI}{(0.7l)^2}$

4. Uniform straight bar under end load. One end fixed, other end hinged and aligned with point of inflection	$P' = \frac{9\pi^2 EI}{4l^2}$
5. Uniform straight bar under end load. Both ends fixed	$P' = \frac{4\pi^2 EI}{l^2}$
6. Uniform straight bar under end load P_1, and intermediate load P_2, applied at mid-length. Both ends hinged	$(P_1 + P_2)' = \frac{\pi^2 EI}{(kl)^2}$, where k depends on the ratio: $c = \frac{P_1}{P_1 + P_2}$. (Ref. 1) Approximately, $k = \frac{1}{2 - c^{\frac{1}{4}}}$
7. Uniform straight bar under load p lb. per in. uniformly distributed along its length. One end free, other end fixed	$p'l = \frac{\pi^2 EI}{(1.122l)^2}$ (Ref. 1)

TABLE XV.—FORMULAS FOR ELASTIC STABILITY OF BARS AND RINGS.—(*Continued*)

Form of bar, manner of loading and support	Formulas for critical load P', critical unit load p', critical torque T', critical bending moment M', or critical combination of loads at which elastic buckling occurs
8. Uniform straight bar under end load P and uniformly distributed load p lb. per in. One end free, other end fixed 	$P' = \frac{\pi^2 EI}{4l^2} - 0.3pl$ (Ref. 1) (Closely approximate formula. If this gives negative value for P', it represents the tension required to prevent buckling under load pl)
9. Uniform straight bar under end load P and uniformly distributed load p lb. per in. Both ends hinged 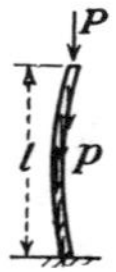	$P' = \frac{\pi^2 EI}{l^2} - 0.5\,pl$ (Ref. 1) (Closely approximate formula. If this gives negative value for P', it represents the tension required to prevent buckling under load pl)
10. Uniform straight bar under end load P, both ends hinged and bar elastically supported by lateral pressure p, proportional to deflection ($p = \beta y$, where β = lateral force in lb. per in. per in. of deflection) 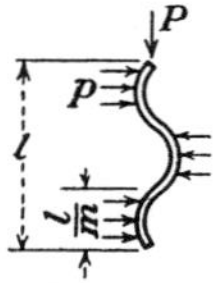	$P' = \frac{\pi^2 EI}{l^2}\left(m^2 + \frac{\beta l^4}{m^2 \pi^4 EI}\right)$, (Ref. 1) where m represents the number of half-waves in which the bar buckles and is equal to the lowest integer greater than: $\frac{1}{2}\left[\sqrt{1 + \frac{4l^2}{\pi^2}\sqrt{\frac{\beta}{EI}}} - 1\right]$

Case	Formula
end twisting couples T; cross section of bar has same I for all central axes. Both ends hinged	$\ldots 4(EI)^2 \ldots EI \ldots l^2$ If $P = 0$, formula gives critical twisting moment T' which, acting alone, would cause buckling If for a given value of T, the formula gives a negative value for P, $T > T'$ and P represents tensile load required to prevent buckling For thin circular tube of diameter D and thickness t under torsion only, critical shear stress $s_s = \frac{\pi ED}{l(1-\nu)}\left(1 - \frac{t}{D} + \frac{1}{3}\frac{t^2}{D^2}\right)$ for helical buckling (Ref. 2)
12. Uniform circular ring under uniform radial pressure p lb. per in. Mean radius of ring r	$p' = \frac{3EI}{r^3}$ (Ref. 1)
13. Uniform circular arch under uniform radial pressure p lb. per in. Mean radius r. Ends hinged	$p' = \frac{EI}{r^3}\left(\frac{\pi^2}{\alpha^2} - 1\right)$ (Ref. 1) (For symmetrical arch of any form under central concentrated loading see Ref. 40)
14. Uniform circular arch under uniform radial pressure p lb. per in. Mean radius r. Ends fixed	$p' = \frac{EI}{r^3}(k^2 - 1)$ (Ref. 1) where k depends on α and is found by trial from the equation: $k \tan \alpha \cot k\alpha = 1$ or from the following table: α = 15° 30° 45° 60° 75° 90° 120° 180° k = 17.2 8.62 5.80 4.37 3.50 3.00 2.36 2.00

TABLE XV.—FORMULAS FOR ELASTIC STABILITY OF BARS AND RINGS.—(*Continued*)

Form of bar, manner of loading and support	Formulas for critical load P', critical unit load p', critical torque T', critical bending moment M', or critical combination of loads at which elastic buckling occurs
15. Straight uniform beam of narrow rectangular section under pure bending 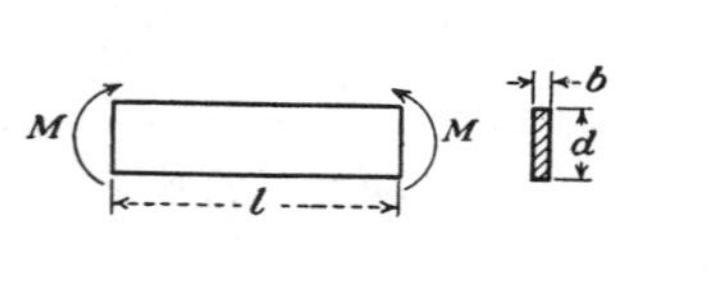	For ends held vertical but not fixed in horizontal plane: **(Refs. 1, 3, 4)** $M' = \dfrac{\pi b^3 d \sqrt{EG\left(1 - 0.63\frac{b}{d}\right)}}{6l}$ For ends held vertical and fixed in horizontal plane: $M' = \dfrac{2\pi b^3 d \sqrt{EG\left(1 - 0.63\frac{b}{d}\right)}}{6l}$
16. Straight uniform cantilever beam of narrow rectangular section under end load applied at a point distant a above (a positive) or below (a negative) centroid of section 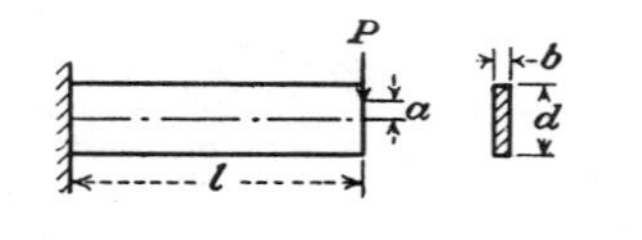	$P' = \dfrac{0.669 b^3 d \sqrt{\left(1 - 0.63\frac{b}{d}\right)EG}}{l^2}\left[1 - \dfrac{a}{2l}\sqrt{\dfrac{E}{G\left(1 - 0.63\frac{b}{d}\right)}}\right]$ (Refs. 1, 3, 4) For a load W uniformly distributed along the beam the critical load $W' = 3P'$ (approximately)
17. Straight uniform beam of narrow rectangular section under center load applied at a point distant a above (a positive) or below (a negative) centroid of section. Ends of beam simply supported and constrained against twisting 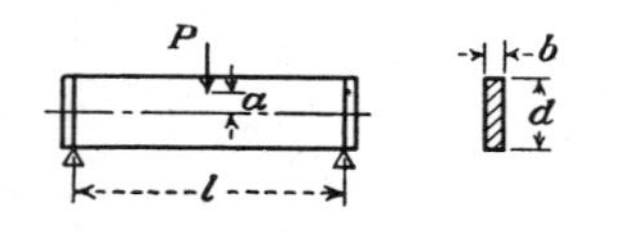	$P' = \dfrac{2.82 b^3 d \sqrt{\left(1 - 0.63\frac{b}{d}\right)EG}}{l^2}\left[1 - \dfrac{1.74a}{l}\sqrt{\dfrac{E}{G\left(1 - 0.63\frac{b}{d}\right)}}\right]$ For a uniformly distributed load the critical load $W' = 1.67P'$, approximately. If P is applied at an intermediate point, distant C from one end, its critical value is practically the same as for central loading if $C > 0.4l < 0.5l$; if $C < 0.4l$, the critical load is given approximately by multiplying the P' for central loading by: $0.36 + 0.28\frac{l}{C}$. If the ends of the beam are fixed and the load P is applied at the centroid of the middle cross section, $P' = \dfrac{4.43 b^3 d}{l^2}\sqrt{\left(1 - 0.63\frac{b}{d}\right)EG}$ (Refs. 1, 3, 4)

18. Straight uniform I-beam under pure bending d = depth center to center of flange. Ends constrained against twisting 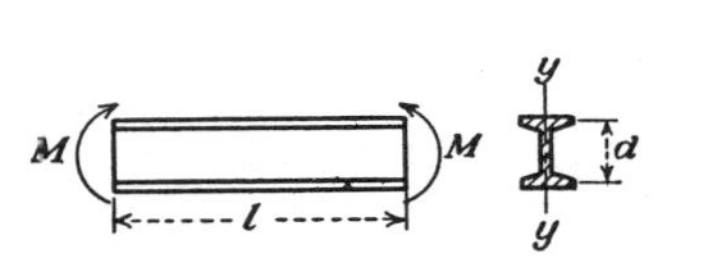	$M' = \frac{\pi\sqrt{(EI_y)(KG)}}{l}\sqrt{1 + \pi^2\frac{I_f Ed^2}{2KGl^2}}$, where I_y is the moment of inertia of the cross section about its vertical axis of symmetry, I_f is the moment of inertia of one flange about this axis, and KG represents the torsional rigidity of the section (see Table IX, Case 17) (Refs. 1, 3)
19. Straight uniform cantilever beam of I section under end load applied at centroid of cross section, d = depth center to center of flanges 	$P' = \frac{m\sqrt{(EI_y)(KG)}}{l^2}$, where m is approximately equal to $4.01 + 11.7\sqrt{\frac{I_f Ed^2}{2KGl^2}}$ and I_y, I_f, and KG have the same significance as in Case 18. (Refs. 1, 3)
20. Straight uniform I-beam loaded at centroid of middle section. Ends simply supported and constrained against twisting 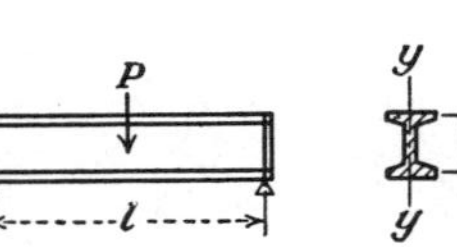	$P' = \frac{m\sqrt{(EI_y)(KG)}}{l^2}$, where m is approximately equal to $16.93 + 45\left(\frac{I_f Ed^2}{2KGl^2}\right)^{0.8}$ and I_y, I_f, and KG have same significance as in Case 18 (Refs. 1, 3)

TABLE XV.—FORMULAS FOR ELASTIC STABILITY OF BARS AND RINGS.—(*Continued*)

Form of bar, manner of loading and support		Formulas for critical load P', critical unit load p', critical torque T', critical bending moment M', or critical combination of loads at which elastic buckling occurs
21. Straight bar, middle portion uniform, end portions tapered and alike. End load. I = moment of inertia of cross section of middle portion, I_0 = moment of inertia of end cross sections, I_x = moment of inertia of section x	21. $I_x = I\left(\frac{x}{b}\right)$ *e.g.*, rectangular section tapering uniformly in width	$P' = \frac{KEI}{l^2}$, where K depends on $\frac{I_0}{I}$ and $\frac{a}{l}$ and may be found from the following table: (Ref. 4)
	22. $I_x = I\left(\frac{x}{b}\right)^2$ *e.g.*, section of four slender members latticed together	$P' = \frac{KEI}{l^2}$, where K may be found from the following table: (Ref. 4)
	23. $I_x = I\left(\frac{x}{b}\right)^3$ *e.g.*, rectangular section tapering uniformly in thickness	$P' = \frac{KEI}{l^2}$, where K may be found from the following table: (Ref. 4)
	24. $I_x = I\left(\frac{x}{b}\right)^4$ *e.g.*, end portions pyramidal or conical	$P' = \frac{KEI}{l^2}$, where K may be found from the following table:

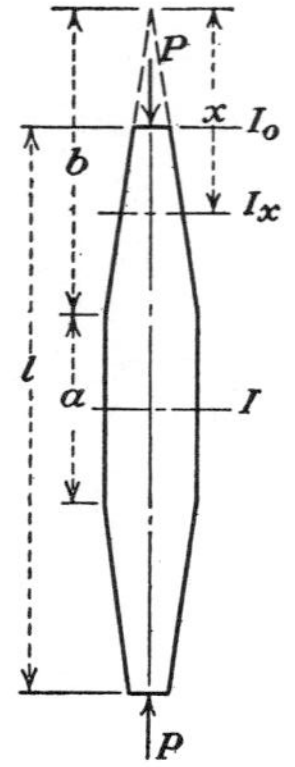

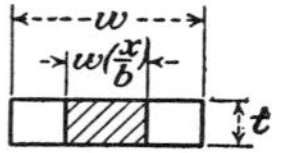

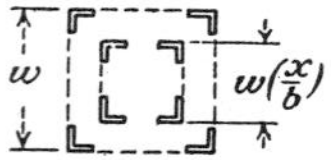

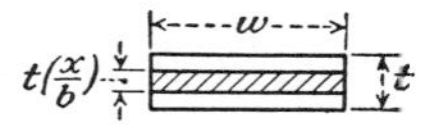

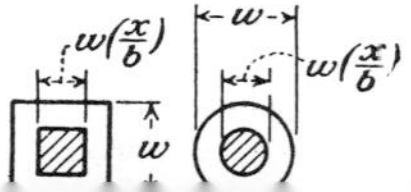

Case 21:

$\frac{a}{l}$ \ $\frac{I_0}{I}$	K for ends hinged							K for ends fixed			
	0	0.01	0.10	0.2	0.4	0.6	0.8	0.2	0.4	0.6	0.8
0	5.78	5.87	6.48	7.01	7.86	8.61	9.27	20.36	26.16	31.04	35.40
0.2	7.04	7.11	7.58	7.99	8.59	9.12	9.53	22.36	27.80	32.20	36.00
0.4	8.35	8.40	8.63	8.90	9.19	9.55	9.68	23.42	28.96	32.92	36.36
0.6	9.36	9.40	9.46	9.73	9.70	9.76	9.82	25.44	30.20	33.80	36.84
0.8	9.80	9.80	9.82	9.82	9.83	9.85	9.86	29.00	33.08	35.80	37.84

Case 22:

$\frac{a}{l}$ \ $\frac{I_0}{I}$	K for ends hinged							K for ends fixed			
	0	0.01	0.10	0.2	0.4	0.6	0.8	0.2	0.4	0.6	0.8
0	1.00	3.45	5.40	6.37	7.61	8.51	9.24	18.94	25.54	30.79	35.35
0.2	1.56	4.73	6.67	7.49	8.42	9.04	9.50	21.25	27.35	32.02	35.97
0.4	2.78	6.58	8.08	8.61	9.15	9.48	9.70	22.91	28.52	32.77	36.34
0.6	6.25	8.62	9.25	9.44	9.63	9.74	9.82	24.29	29.69	33.63	36.80
0.8	9.57	9.71	9.79	9.81	9.84	9.85	9.86	27.67	32.59	35.64	37.81

Case 23:

$\frac{a}{l}$ \ $\frac{I_0}{I}$	K for ends hinged							K for ends fixed			
	0	0.01	0.10	0.2	0.4	0.6	0.8	0.2	0.4	0.6	0.8
0	0	2.55	5.01	6.14	7.52	8.50	9.23	18.48	25.32	30.72	35.32
0.2	0	3.65	6.32	7.31	8.38	9.02	9.50	20.88	27.20	31.96	35.96
0.4	0	5.42	7.84	8.49	9.10	9.46	9.69	22.64	28.40	32.72	36.32
0.6	0	7.99	9.14	9.39	9.62	9.74	9.81	23.96	29.52	33.56	36.80
0.8	0	9.63	9.77	9.81	9.84	9.85	9.86	27.24	32.44	35.60	37.80

Case 24:

$\frac{a}{l}$ \ $\frac{I_0}{I}$	K for ends hinged							K for ends fixed			
	0	0.01	0.10	0.2	0.4	0.6	0.8	0.2	0.4	0.6	0.8
0	0	2.15	4.81	6.02	7.48	8.47	9.23	18.23	25.23	30.68	35.33
0.2	0	3.13	6.11	7.20	8.33	9.01	9.49	20.71	27.13	31.94	35.96
0.4	0	4.84	7.68	8.42	9.10	9.45	9.69	22.49	28.33	32.69	36.32
0.6	0	7.53	9.08	9.38	9.62	9.74	9.81	23.80	29.46	33.54	36.78

the table the approximate discrepancy to be expected between theory and experiment has been indicated wherever the data available have made this possible.

The formulas given in Table XVI are based on information available in 1942. Much work, both experimental and analytical, has been done on plate and shell buckling since that time, and as the problem is of especial importance in airplane design, the results of a considerable number of recent investigations have been published by the National Advisory Committee for Aeronautics. Since the data are usually presented in the form of extensive charts and tables which cannot be reproduced in the limited space here available, the interested reader is referred to Refs. 22 to 36 at the end of this chapter. These are cited under the appropriate cases in Table XVI. Because of the importance of the subject in airframe and missile design, the bending and buckling strength of structural components of sandwich and laminated construction has been extensively investigated in recent years. Reference 38 and the publications listed in Ref. 39 will serve to introduce the interested reader to the literature.

TABLE XVI.—FORMULAS FOR ELASTIC STABILITY OF PLATES AND SHELLS

E = modulus of elasticity; ν = Poisson's ratio, a = longer dimension, b = shorter dimension for all rectangular plates. t = thickness for all plates and shells. All dimensions in inches, all forces in pounds, all angles in radians. Compression positive; tension negative.

Form of plate or shell and manner of loading	Manner of support	Formulas for critical unit compressive stress s', unit shear stress s_s', load P', bending moment M', or unit external pressure p' at which elastic buckling occurs
A. Rectangular plate under equal uniform compression on two opposite edges b	1. All edges simply supported	$s' = K\frac{E}{1-\nu^2}\left(\frac{t}{b}\right)^2$ Here K depends on ratio $\frac{a}{b}$ and may be found from the following table: $\frac{a}{b}$ = 0.2 0.3 0.4 0.6 0.8 1.0 1.2 1.4 1.6 1.8 2.0 2.2 2.4 2.7 3 ∞ K = 22.2 10.9 6.92 4.23 3.45 3.29 3.40 3.68 3.45 3.32 3.29 3.32 3.40 3.32 3.29 3.29 (For unequal end compressions, see Ref. 33) (Refs. 1, 6)
	2. All edges clamped	$s' = K\frac{E}{1-\nu^2}\left(\frac{t}{b}\right)^2$ $\frac{a}{b}$ = 1 2 3 ∞ K = 7.7 6.7 6.4 5.73 (Refs. 1, 6, 7)
	3. Edges b simply supported, edges a clamped	$s' = K\frac{E}{1-\nu^2}\left(\frac{t}{b}\right)^2$ $\frac{a}{b}$ = 0.4 0.5 0.6 0.7 0.8 1.0 1.2 1.4 1.6 1.8 2.1 ∞ K = 7.76 6.32 5.80 5.76 6.00 6.32 5.80 5.76 6.00 5.80 5.76 5.73 (Refs. 1, 6)
	4. Edges b simply supported, one edge a simply supported, other edge a free	$s' = K\frac{E}{1-\nu^2}\left(\frac{t}{b}\right)^2$ $\frac{a}{b}$ = 0.5 1.0 1.2 1.4 1.6 1.8 2.0 2.5 3.0 4.0 5.0 K = 3.62 1.18 0.934 0.784 0.687 0.622 0.574 0.502 0.464 0.425 0.416 (Ref. 1)
	5. Edges b simply supported, one edge a clamped, other edge a free	$s' = K\frac{E}{1-\nu^2}\left(\frac{t}{b}\right)^2$ $\frac{a}{b}$ = 1 1.1 1.2 1.3 1.4 1.5 1.6 1.7 1.8 1.9 2.0 2.2 2.4 K = 1.40 1.28 1.21 1.16 1.12 1.10 1.09 1.09 1.10 1.12 1.14 1.19 1.21 (Ref. 1)
	6. Edges b clamped, edges a simply supported	$s' = K\frac{E}{1-\nu^2}\left(\frac{t}{b}\right)^2$ $\frac{a}{b}$ = 0.6 0.8 1.0 1.2 1.4 1.6 1.7 1.8 2.0 2.5 3.0 K = 11.0 7.18 5.54 4.80 4.48 [illegible] [illegible] [illegible] [illegible] [illegible] [illegible] (Ref. 1)

B. Rectangular plate under uniform compression (or tension) s_x on edges b and uniform compression (or tension) s_y on edges a

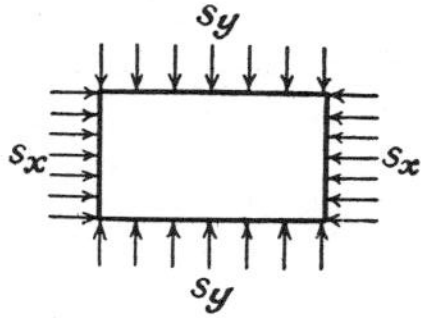

7. All edges simply supported

$$s_x'\frac{m^2}{a^2} + s_y'\frac{n^2}{b^2} = 0.823\frac{E}{1-\nu^2}t^2\left(\frac{m^2}{a^2}+\frac{n^2}{b^2}\right)$$

Here m and n signify the number of half-waves in the buckled plate in the x and y directions, respectively. To find s_y' for a given s_x', take $m = 1$, $n = 1$ if $C\left(1 - 4\frac{a^4}{b^4}\right) < s_x < C\left(5 + 2\frac{a^2}{b^2}\right)$, where $C = \frac{0.823Et^2}{(1-\nu^2)a^2}$. If s_x is too large to satisfy this inequality, take $n = 1$ and m to satisfy: $C\left(2m^2 - 2m + 1 + 2\frac{a^2}{b^2}\right) < s_x < C\left(2m^2 + 2m + 1 + 2\frac{a^2}{b^2}\right)$. If s_x is too small to satisfy this inequality, take $m = 1$ and n to satisfy: $C\left[1 - n^2(n-1)^2\frac{a^4}{b^4}\right] > s_x > C\left[1 - n^2(n+1)^2\frac{a^4}{b^4}\right]$ (Refs. 1, 6)

8. All edges clamped

$$s_x + \frac{a^2}{b^2}s_y = 1.1\frac{Et^2a^2}{1-\nu^2}\left(\frac{3}{a^4} + \frac{3}{b^4} + \frac{2}{a^2b^2}\right)$$

(This equation is approximate and is most accurate when the plate is nearly square and s_x and s_y nearly equal (Ref. 1)

C. Rectangular plate under linearly varying stress on edges b (bending or bending combined with tension or compression)

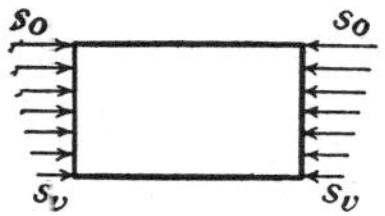

9. All edges simply supported

$$s_o' = K\frac{E}{1-\nu^2}\left(\frac{t}{b}\right)^2$$

Here K depends on $\frac{a}{b}$ and on $\alpha = \frac{s_v}{s_o - s_v}$ and may be found from the following table:

α \ $\frac{a}{b}$ =	0.4	0.5	0.6	0.667	0.75	0.8	0.9	1.0	1.5
$\alpha = 0.5$ ($K =$)	23.9	21.1	19.8	19.7	19.8	20.1	21.1	21.1	19.8
0.75	15.4		10.6		9.5	9.2		9.1	9.5
1.00	12.4		8.0		6.9	6.7		6.4	6.9
1.25	10.95		6.8		5.8	5.7		5.4	5.8
1.50	8.9		5.3		5.0	4.9		4.8	5.0
∞ (Pure Comp.)	6.92		4.25			3.45		3.29	3.57

(Refs. 1, 6)

D. Rectangular plate under uniform shear on all edges

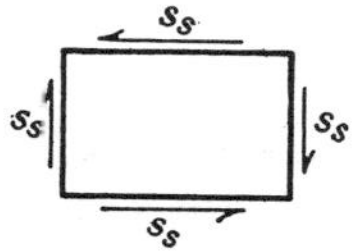

10. All edges simply supported

$$s_s' = K\frac{E}{1-\nu^2}\left(\frac{t}{b}\right)^2$$

$\frac{a}{b}$ =	1.0	1.2	1.4	1.5	1.6	1.8	2.0	2.5	3.0	∞
K =	7.75	6.58	6.00	5.84	5.76	5.59	5.43	5.18	5.02	4.40

(Refs. 1, 6, 8, 22)

11. All edges clamped

$$s_s' = K\frac{E}{1-\nu^2}\left(\frac{t}{b}\right)^2$$

$\frac{a}{b}$ =	1	2	∞
K =	12.7	9.5	7.38

Test results indicate a value for K of about 4.1 for very large values of $\frac{a}{b}$ (Ref. 9)

(For continuous panels, see Ref. 30)

TABLE XVI.—FORMULAS FOR ELASTIC STABILITY OF PLATES AND SHELLS.—(*Continued*)

Form of plate or shell and manner of loading	Manner of support	Formulas for critical unit compressive stress s', unit shear stress s_s', load P', bending moment M', or unit external pressure p' at which elastic buckling occurs
E. Rectangular plate under uniform shear on all edges. Compression (or tension) s_x on edges *b*. Compression (or tension) s_y on edges *a*. a/b very large	12. All edges simply supported	$s_s' = \sqrt{C^2\left(2\sqrt{1-\frac{s_y}{C}}+2-\frac{s_x}{C}\right)\left(2\sqrt{1-\frac{s_y}{C}}+6-\frac{s_x}{C}\right)}$ where $C = \frac{0.823}{1-\nu^2}\left(\frac{t}{b}\right)^2$ (Refs. 1, 6, 23, 31)
	13. All edges clamped	$s' = \sqrt{C^2\left(2.31\sqrt{4-\frac{s_y}{C}}+\frac{4}{3}-\frac{s_x}{C}\right)\left(2.31\sqrt{4-\frac{s_y}{C}}+8-\frac{s_x}{C}\right)}$ where $C = \frac{0.823}{1-\nu^2}\left(\frac{t}{b}\right)^2$ (s_x and s_y are negative when tensile) (Ref. 6)
F. Rectangular plate under uniform shear on all edges and bending stresses on edges *b*	14. All edges simply supported	$s' = K\frac{E}{1-\nu^2}\left(\frac{t}{b}\right)^2$ Here *K* depends on $\frac{s_s}{s_s'}$ (ratio of actual shear stress to shear stress that, acting alone, would be critical), and on $\frac{a}{b}$. *K* varies less than 10 per cent for values of $\frac{a}{b}$ from 0.5 to 1, and for $\frac{a}{b} = 1$ is approximately as follows: $\frac{s_s}{s_s'}$ = 0 0.2 0.3 0.4 0.5 0.6 0.7 0.8 0.9 1.0 K = 21.1 20.4 19.6 18.5 17.7 16.0 14.0 11.9 8.20 0 (Refs. 1, 10)
G. Rectangular plate under concentrated center loads on two opposite edges	15. All edges simply supported	$P = \frac{\pi}{3}\frac{Et^3}{(1-\nu^2)b}\left(\text{for } \frac{a}{b} > 2\right)$ (Ref. 1)
	16. Edges *b* simply supported edges *a* clamped	$P = \frac{2\pi}{3}\frac{Et^3}{(1-\nu^2)b}\left(\text{for } \frac{a}{b} > 2\right)$ (Ref. 1)

Form of plate and manner of loading	Manner of support	Formula for critical unit compressive stress s'
H. Isotropic circular plate under uniform radial edge compression	17. Edges simply supported	$s' = 0.35\frac{E}{1-\nu^2}\left(\frac{t}{a}\right)^2$ (Ref. 1)
	18. Edges clamped	$s' = 1.22\frac{E}{1-\nu^2}\left(\frac{t}{a}\right)^2$ (Ref. 1) For elliptical plate with major semiaxis a, minor semiaxis b, $s' = K\frac{E}{1-\nu^2}\left(\frac{t}{b}\right)^2$, where K has values as follows: $\frac{a}{b} = 1.0$ 1.1 1.2 1.3 2.0 5.0 $K = 1.22$ 1.13 1.06 1.01 0.92 0.94 (Ref. 21)
I. Circular plate with concentric hole under uniform radial compression on outer edge	19. Outer edge simply supported, inner edge free	$s' = K\frac{E}{1-\nu^2}\left(\frac{t}{a}\right)^2$ Here K depends on $\frac{b}{a}$ and is given approximately by following table: $\frac{b}{a} = 0$ .1 .2 .3 .4 .5 .6 .7 .8 .9 $K = 0.35$ 0.33 0.30 0.27 0.23 0.21 0.19 0.18 0.17 0.16 (Ref. 1)
	20. Outer edge clamped, inner edge free	$s' = K\frac{E}{1-\nu^2}\left(\frac{t}{a}\right)^2$ Here K depends on $\frac{b}{a}$ and is given approximately by following table: $\frac{b}{a} = 0$ 0.1 0.2 0.3 0.4 0.5 $K = 1.22$ 1.17 1.11 1.21 1.48 2.07 (Ref. 1)
J. Isometric plate in form of equilateral triangle under equal uniform compressive stress on all edges	21. All edges simply supported	$s' = 3.29\frac{E}{1-\nu^2}\left(\frac{t}{a}\right)^2$ (Ref. 1)
K. Curved panel under uniform compression on curved edges b. (b = width of panel measured on arc, r = radius of curvature)	22. All edges simply supported	$s' = \frac{1}{6}\frac{E}{1-\nu^2}\left[\sqrt{12(1-\nu^2)\left(\frac{t}{r}\right)^2 + \left(\frac{\pi t}{b}\right)^4} + \left(\frac{\pi t}{b}\right)^2\right]$ or $s' = 0.6E\left(\frac{t}{r}\right)$ if $\frac{b}{r}$ (central angle of curve) is less than $\frac{1}{2}$ and b and a are nearly equal (Refs. 1, 6) (For compression combined with shear, see Refs. 28, 34)

TABLE XVI.—FORMULAS FOR ELASTIC STABILITY OF PLATES AND SHELLS.—(*Continued*)

Form of plate or shell and manner of loading	Manner of support	Formulas for critical unit compressive stress s', unit shear stress s_s', load P', bending moment M', or unit external pressure p' at which elastic buckling occurs
L. Curved panel under uniform shear on all edges	23. All edges simply supported	$s_s' = 0.1E\frac{t}{r} + 5E\left(\frac{t}{b}\right)^2$ (Refs. 6, 27, 29)
	24. All edges clamped	$s_s' = 0.1E\frac{t}{r} + 7.5E\left(\frac{t}{b}\right)^2$ (Ref. 6) Tests show $s' = 0.075E\frac{t}{r}$ for panels curved to form quadrant of a circle (Ref. 11) (See also Refs. 27, 29)
M. Thin-walled circular tube under uniform longitudinal compression. (Radius of tube $= r$)	25. Ends not constrained	$s' = \frac{1}{\sqrt{3}} \frac{E}{\sqrt{1-\nu^2}} \frac{t}{r}$ (Refs. 6, 12, 13, 24) Most accurate for very long tubes, but applicable if length is several times as great as $1.72\sqrt{rt}$, which is the length of a half-wave of buckling. Tests indicate an actual buckling strength of from 40 to 60 per cent of this theoretical value, or $s' = 0.3E\frac{t}{r}$, approximately
N. Thin-walled circular tube under a transverse bending moment *M*. (Radius of tube $= r$)	26. No constraint	$M' = K\frac{E}{1-\nu^2}rt^2$ Here theoretical value of K, for pure bending and long tubes, is 0.99. The average value of K determined by tests is 1.14 and the minimum value is 0.72. Except for very short tubes, length effect is negligible, and a small transverse shear produces no appreciable reduction in M'. A very short cylinder under transverse (beam) shear may fail by buckling at neutral axis when shear stress there reaches a value of about 1.25 s' for Case 27 (Refs. 6, 14, 15)

O. Thin-walled circular tube under a twisting moment T that produces a uniform circumferential shear stress:

$$s_s = \frac{T}{2\pi r^2 t}$$

(Length of tube $= l$, radius of tube $= r$)

27. Ends hinged, *i.e.*, wall free to change angle with cross section, but circular section maintained

$$s_s' = \frac{E}{1-\nu^2}\left(\frac{t}{l}\right)^2\left[2.8 + \sqrt{2.6 + 0.494H^{\frac{3}{2}}}\right]$$

Here $H = \sqrt{1-\nu^2}\,\dfrac{l^2}{tr}$ (Refs. 6, 16)

Tests indicate that the actual buckling stress is from 60 to 75 per cent of this theoretical value and the recommended formula for design is: $s_s' = E\left(\frac{t}{l}\right)^2\left[1.8 + \sqrt{1.2+0.201\left(\frac{l}{\sqrt{tr}}\right)^3}\right]$, derived from above by taking $\nu = 0.3$ and multiplying the theoretical value of s_s' by 0.6. These equations apply only if: $\frac{l}{r} < 6.6\sqrt[4]{1-\nu^2}\sqrt{\frac{r}{t}}$; for greater values of $\frac{l}{r}$, $s_s' = 0.272\dfrac{E}{(1-\nu^2)^{\frac{3}{4}}}\left(\frac{t}{r}\right)^{\frac{3}{2}}$.

For $\frac{l}{r} < 5$, the eq. $s_s' = 0.1E\frac{t}{r} + 5E\left(\frac{t}{l}\right)^2$ is in accord with tests (Ref. 18) (See also Ref. 25)

28. Ends clamped, *i.e.*, wall held perpendicular to cross section and circular section maintained

$$s_s' = \frac{E}{1-\nu^2}\left(\frac{t}{l}\right)^2\left[4.6 + \sqrt{7.8 + 0.590H^{\frac{3}{2}}}\right]$$ (Refs. 6, 16, 25)

Here $H = \sqrt{1-\nu^2}\,\dfrac{l^2}{tr}$

The remarks made relative to Case 27 apply to this case also, and the recommended formula is:

$$s_s' = E\left(\frac{t}{l}\right)^2\left[3.0 + \sqrt{3.4 + 0.240\left(\frac{l}{\sqrt{tr}}\right)^3}\right].$$

These equations apply only if: $\frac{l}{r} < 7.9\sqrt[4]{1-\nu^2}\sqrt{\frac{r}{t}}$

For greater values of $\frac{l}{r}$, $s_s' = 0.272\dfrac{E}{(1-\nu^2)^{\frac{3}{4}}}\left(\frac{t}{r}\right)^{\frac{3}{2}}$

For $\frac{l}{r} < 5$ the eq. $s_s' = 0.1E\frac{t}{r} + 9.1E\left(\frac{t}{l}\right)^2$ is in accord with tests (Ref. 18)

Tests also support the empirical formula $s_s = KE\left(\frac{t}{r}\right)^{1.35}$ where K depends on $\frac{l}{r}$ and has values as follows:

$\frac{l}{r}$ =	0.2	0.25	0.30	0.40	0.50	0.75	1.0	1.5	2.0	3	4	5
K =	3.30	2.75	2.45	2.02	1.78	1.45	1.27	1.06	0.94	0.78	0.68	0.61

(Ref. 17)

P. Thin-walled circular tube under uniform longitudinal compression s and uniform circumferential shear s_s due to torsion (Case 25 combined with 27 or 28)

29. Edges hinged (as in Case 27) or clamped (as in Case 28)

The equation: $1 - \frac{s'}{s_0'} = \left(\frac{s_s'}{s_{s_0}'}\right)^n$ holds, where s' and s_s' are the critical compressive and shear stresses for the combined loading, s_0' is the critical compressive stress for the cylinder under compression alone (Case 25) and s_{s_0}' is the critical shear stress for the cylinder under torsion alone (Case 27 or Case 28, according to end conditions). Tests indicate that n is approximately 3. If s is tensile, then s' should be considered negative (Ref. 6)

(See also Ref. 26. For square tube, see Ref. 32)

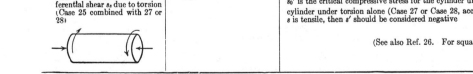

TABLE XVI.—FORMULAS FOR ELASTIC STABILITY OF PLATES AND SHELLS.—(*Continued*)

Form of plate or shell and manner of loading	Manner of support	Formulas for critical unit compressive stress s', unit shear stress s_s', load P', bending moment M', or unit external pressure p' at which elastic buckling occurs
Q. Thin tube under uniform lateral external pressure. Radius of tube $= r$	30. Very long tube with free ends; length l	$p' = \frac{1}{4}\frac{E}{1-\nu^2}\frac{t^3}{r^3}$ Applicable when $l > 4.90r\sqrt{\frac{r}{t}}$ (Ref. 19)
	31. Short tube, of length l, ends held circular, but not otherwise constrained, or long tube held circular at intervals l	Approximate formula $p' = 0.807\frac{Et^2}{lr}\sqrt[4]{\left(\frac{1}{1-\nu^2}\right)^3\frac{t^2}{r^2}}$ (Ref. 19)
R. Thin tube with closed ends under uniform external pressure, lateral and longitudinal. Length of tube $= l$, radius of tube $= r$	32. Ends held circular	$p' = \frac{E\left(\frac{t}{r}\right)}{1+\frac{1}{2}\left(\frac{\pi r}{nl}\right)^2}\left\{\frac{1}{n^2\left[1+\left(\frac{nl}{\pi r}\right)^2\right]^2} + \frac{n^2t^2}{12r^2(1-\nu^2)}\left[1+\left(\frac{\pi r}{nl}\right)^2\right]^2\right\}$ (Refs. 19, 20) where n = number of lobes formed by the tube in buckling. To determine p' for tubes of a given $\frac{t}{r}$, plot a group of curves, one curve for each integral value of n of 2 or over, with $\frac{l}{r}$ as ordinates and p' as abscissa. That curve of the group which gives the least value of p' is then used to find the p' corresponding to a given $\frac{l}{r}$
S. Curved panel under uniform radial pressure. (Radius of curvature r, central angle 2α, when 2α = arc $AB \div r$	33. Curved edges free, straight edges at A and B simply supported (*i.e.*, hinged)	$p' = \frac{Et^3\left(\frac{\pi^2}{\alpha^2}-1\right)}{12r^3(1-\nu^2)}$ (Ref. 1)
	34. Curved edges free, straight edges at A and B clamped	$p' = \frac{Et^3(k^2-1)}{12r^3(1-\nu^2)}$ Here k is found from the equation: $k \tan \alpha \cot k\alpha = 1$ and has values as follows: $\alpha =$ 15° 30° 60° 90° 120° 150° 180° $k =$ 17.2 8.62 4.37 3.0 2.36 2.07 2.0 (Ref. 1)
T. Thin sphere under uniform external pressure. Radius of sphere $= r$	35. No constraint	$p' = \frac{2Et^2}{r^2\sqrt{3(1-\nu^2)}}$ (For ideal case) (Refs. 1, 37) $p' = \frac{0.365Et^2}{r^2}$ (Probable actual minimum p') For spherical cap, half-central angle ϕ between 20° and 60°, R/t between 400 and 2000, $p' = [1 - .00875(\phi° - 20°)](1 - .000175\ R/t)(.3E)(t/R)^2$ (Empirical formula, Ref. 44)

References

1. Timoshenko, S.: "Theory of Elastic Stability," Engineering Societies Monograph, McGraw-Hill Book Company, 1936.
2. Schwerin, E.: "Die Torsionstabilität des dünnwandigen Rohres, *Zeits. angew. Math. Mech.*, Vol. 5, No. 3, p. 235, 1925.
3. Trayer, G. W., and H. W. March: Elastic Instability of Members Having Sections Common in Aircraft Construction, *Nat. Adv. Comm. Aeron., Rept.* 382, 1931.
4. Dumont, C., and H. N. Hill: The Lateral Instability of Deep Rectangular Beams, *Nat. Adv. Comm. Aeron., Tech. Note* 601, 1937.
5. Dinnik, A.: Design of Columns of Varying Cross-section, *Trans. Am. Soc. Mech. Eng.*, Vol. 54, No. 18, p. 165, 1932.
6. Heck, O. S., and H. Ebner: Methods and Formulas for Calculating the Strength of Plate and Shell Construction as Used in Airplane Design, *Nat. Adv. Comm. Aeron., Tech. Memo.* 785, 1936.
7. Maulbetsch, J. L.: Buckling of Compressed Rectangular Plates with Built-in Edges, *Am. Soc. Mech. Eng., Jour. Appl. Mech.*, Vol. 4, No. 2, June, 1937.
8. Southwell, R. V., and S. W. Skan: On the Stability under Shearing Forces of a Flat Elastic Strip, *Proc. Royal Soc. London*, Series *A*, Vol. 105, p. 582, 1924.
9. Bollenrath, F.: Wrinkling Phenomena of Thin Flat Plates Subjected to Shear Stresses, *Nat. Adv. Comm. Aeron., Tech. Memo.* 601, 1931.
10. Way, S.: Stability of Rectangular Plates under Shear and Bending Forces, *Am. Soc. Mech. Eng., Jour. Appl. Mech.*, Vol. 3, No. 4, Dec., 1936.
11. Smith, G. M.: Strength in Shear of Thin Curved Sheets of Alclad, *Nat. Adv. Comm. Aeron., Tech. Note* 343, 1930.
12. Lundquist, E. E.: Strength Tests of Thin-walled Duralumin Cylinders in Compression, *Nat. Adv. Comm. Aeron., Rept.* 473, 1933.
13. Wilson, W. M., and N. M. Newmark: The Strength of Thin Cylindrical Shells as Columns, *Eng. Exp. Sta. Univ. Ill., Bull.* 255, 1933.
14. Lundquist, E. E.: Strength Tests of Thin-walled Duralumin Cylinders in Pure Bending, *Nat. Adv. Comm. Aeron., Tech. Note* 479, 1933.
15. Lundquist, E. E.: Strength Tests of Thin-walled Duralumin Cylinders in Combined Transverse Shear and Bending, *Nat. Adv. Comm. Aeron., Tech. Note* 523, 1935.
16. Donnell, L. H.: Stability of Thin-walled Tubes under Torsion, *Nat. Adv. Comm. Aeron., Tech. Rept.* 479, 1933.
17. Lundquist, E. E.: Strength Tests of Thin-walled Duralumin Cylinders in Torsion, *Nat. Adv. Comm. Aeron., Tech. Note* 427, 1932.
18. Ebner, H.: Strength of Shell Bodies—Theory and Practice, *Nat. Adv. Comm. Aeron., Tech. Memo.* 838, 1937.
19. Saunders, H. E., and D. F. Windenberg: Strength of Thin Cylindrical Shells under External Pressure, *Trans. Am. Soc. Mech. Eng.*, Vol. 53, No. 15, p. 207, 1931.

20. VON MISES, R.: Der kritische Aussendruck zylindrischer Rohre, *Zeits. Vereine deutscher Ing.*, Vol. 58, p. 750, 1914.
21. VOINOVSKY-KRIEGER, S.: The Stability of a Clamped Elliptic Plate under Uniform Compression, *Am. Soc. Mech. Eng., Jour. Appl. Mech.*, Vol. 4, No. 4, December, 1937.
22. STEIN, M., and J. NEFF: Buckling Stresses in Simply Supported Rectangular Flat Plates in Shear, *Nat. Adv. Comm. Aeron., Tech. Note* 1222, 1947.
23. BATDORF, S. B., and M. STEIN: Critical Combinations of Shear and Direct Stress for Simply Supported Rectangular Flat Plates, *Nat. Adv. Comm. Aeron., Tech. Note* 1223, 1947.
24. BATDORF, S. B., M. SCHILDCROUT, and M. STEIN: Critical Stress of Thin-walled Cylinders in Axial Compression, *Nat. Adv. Comm. Aeron., Tech. Note* 1343, 1947.
25. BATDORF, S. B., M. STEIN, and M. SCHILDCROUT: Critical Stress of Thin-walled Cylinders in Torsion, *Nat. Adv. Comm. Aeron., Tech. Note* 1344, 1947.
26. BATDORF, S. B., M. STEIN, and M. SCHILDCROUT: Critical Combinations of Torsion and Direct Axial Stress for Thin-walled Cylinders, *Nat. Adv. Comm. Aeron., Tech. Note* 1345, 1947.
27. BATDORF, S. B., M. SCHILDCROUT, and M. STEIN: Critical Shear Stress of Long Plates with Transverse Curvature, *Nat. Adv. Comm. Aeron., Tech. Note* 1346, 1947.
28. BATDORF, S. B., M. SCHILDCROUT, and M. STEIN, Critical Combinations of Shear and Longitudinal Direct Stress for Long Plates with Transverse Curvature, *Nat. Adv. Comm. Aeron., Tech. Note* 1347, 1947.
29. BATDORF, S. B., M. STEIN, and M. SCHILDCROUT: Critical Shear Stress of Curved Rectangular Panels, *Nat. Adv. Comm. Aeron., Tech. Note* 1348, 1947.
30. BUDIANSKY, B., R. W. CONNOR, and M. STEIN: Buckling in Shear of Continuous Flat Plates, *Nat. Adv. Comm. Aeron., Tech. Note* 1565, 1948.
31. PETERS, R. W.: Buckling Tests of Flat Rectangular Plates under Combined Shear and Longitudinal Compression, *Nat. Adv. Comm. Aeron., Tech. Note* 1750, 1948.
32. BUDIANSKY, B., M. STEIN, and A. C. GILBERT: Buckling of a Long Square Tube in Torsion and Compression, *Nat. Adv. Comm. Aeron., Tech. Note* 1751, 1948.
33. LIBOVE, C., S. FERDMAN, and J. G. REUSCH: Elastic Buckling of a Simply Supported Plate under a Compressive Stress that Varies Linearly in the Direction of Loading, *Nat. Adv. Comm. Aeron., Tech. Note* 1891, 1949.
34. SCHILDCROUT, M., and M. STEIN: Critical Combinations of Shear and Direct Axial Stress for Curved Rectangular Panels, *Nat. Adv. Comm. Aeron., Tech. Note* 1928, 1949.
35. PFLUGER, A.: "Stabilitätsprobleme der Elastostatik," Springer-Verlag, 1964.
36. GERARD, G., and HERBERT BECKER: Handbook of Structural Stability, *Nat. Adv. Comm. Aeron., Tech. Notes* 3781–3786 inclusive, and D163, 1957–1959.

37. VON KÁRMÁN, TH., and HSUE-SHEN TSIEN: The Buckling of Spherical Shells by External Pressure, Pressure Vessel and Piping Design, *Am. Soc. Mech. Eng., Collected Papers* 1927–1959.
38. CHENG, SHUN: On the Theory of Bending of Sandwich Plates, *Proc. 4th U.S. Nat. Congr. Appl. Mech.*, 1962.
39. U.S. Forest Products Laboratory, List of Publications on Structural Sandwich, Plastic Laminates, and Wood-base Aircraft Components, 1962.
40. LIND, N. C.: Elastic Buckling of Symmetrical Arches, *Univ. Ill., Eng. Exp. Sta. Tech. Report* 3, 1962.
41. GOODIER, J. N., and N. J. HOFF (eds.): "Structural Mechanics," Proc. 1st Symp. on Naval Structural Mechanics, Pergamon Press, 1960.
42. Collected Papers on Instability of Shell Structures, *Nat. Aeron. Space Admin., Tech. Note D*-1510, 1962.
43. POGORODOV, A. V.: Post Buckling Behavior of Cylindrical Shells, *Nat. Aeron. Space Admin., Tech. Transl. F*-90, 1964.
44. KLOPPEL, K., and O. JUNGBLUTH: Beitrag zum Durchschlagproblem dünnwandiger Kugelschalen, *Der Stahlbau*, 1953.

CHAPTER 15

DYNAMIC AND TEMPERATURE STRESSES

83. Dynamic Stress; General Conditions.—Dynamic loading was defined in Art. 1 as any loading during which the parts of the body could not be considered in equilibrium. It was further pointed out that two kinds of dynamic loading could conveniently be distinguished, *viz.*, (1) that in which the body has imposed upon it a particular kind of motion involving known accelerations, and (2) impact, of which sudden loading may be considered a special case. In the following articles, specific cases of each kind of dynamic loading will be considered.

84. Body in a Known State of Motion.—The acceleration a of each particle of mass dm being known, the effective force on each particle is $dm \times a$, directed like a. If to each particle a force equal and opposite to the effective force were applied, equilibrium would result. If then such reversed effective forces are assumed to be applied to all the constituent particles of the body, the body may be regarded as in equilibrium under these forces and the actual forces (loads and reactions) that act upon it, and the resulting stresses can then be found exactly as for a body at rest. The reversed effective forces are *imaginary* forces exerted *on* the particles, but are equal to and directed like the actual reactions the particles exert on whatever gives them their acceleration, *i.e.*, in general, on the rest of the body. Since these reactions are due to the inertia of the particles, they are called *inertia forces*, and the body may be thought of as loaded by these inertia forces. Similarly, any attached mass will exert on a body inertia forces equal and opposite to the forces which the body has to exert on the attached mass to accelerate it.

The results of applying this method of analysis to a number of more or less typical problems are given below. In all cases it has been assumed, in finding the accelerations of the particles, that the effect of deformation could be ignored; *i.e.*, the acceleration of each particle has been found as though the body were rigid. For convenience, stresses, bending moments, and shears due to inertia forces only are called *inertia* stresses, moments, and shears; they are calculated as though the body were outside the field of gravitation. Stresses, moments, and shears due to balanced forces (including gravity) may be superposed thereon.

1. A slender uniform rod of weight W lb., length L in., section area A sq. in., and modulus of elasticity E lb. per sq. in. is given a motion of translation with an acceleration of a ft. per sec. per sec. parallel to its axis by a pull (push) applied at one end. The maximum tensile (compressive) stress occurs at the loaded end and is $s = Wa/32.2A$ lb. per sq. in. The elongation (shortening) due to the inertia stresses is

$$e = \frac{1}{2}\frac{W}{32.2}\frac{aL}{AE} \text{ in.}$$

2. The rod described in (1) is given a motion of translation with an acceleration of a ft. per sec. per sec. normal to its axis by forces applied at each end. The maximum inertia bending moment occurs at the middle of the bar, and is $M = \frac{1}{8}WaL/32.2$ in.-lb. The maximum inertia vertical (transverse) shear occurs at the ends and is $V = \frac{1}{2}Wa/32.2$ lb.

3. The rod described in (1) is made to rotate about an axis through one end normal to its length at a uniform angular velocity of ω rad. per second. The maximum tensile inertia stress occurs at the pinned end and is $s = \frac{1}{2}\frac{W}{386.4}\frac{L\omega^2}{A}$ lb. per sq. in. The elongation due to inertia stresses is $e = \frac{1}{3}\frac{W}{386.4}\frac{L^2\omega^2}{AE}$ in.

4. The rod described in (1) is pinned at the lower end and allowed to swing down under the action of gravity from an initially vertical position. When the rod reaches a position where it makes with the vertical the angle θ, it is subjected to a positive bending moment (owing to its weight and the inertia forces) which has its maximum value at a section distant $\frac{1}{3}L$ from the pinned end. This maximum value is $M = \frac{1}{27}WL \sin \theta$ in.-lb. The maximum positive inertia shear occurs at the pinned end and is $V = \frac{1}{4}W \sin \theta$ lb. The maximum negative inertia shear occurs at a section distant $\frac{2}{3}L$ from the pinned end, and is $V = -\frac{1}{12}W \sin \theta$ lb. (This case represents approximately the conditions existing when a chimney or other slender structure topples over, and the bending moment M explains the tendency of such a structure to break in two while falling.)

5. The rod described in (1) is pinned at the lower end and, while in the vertical position, has imposed upon its lower end a horizontal acceleration of a ft. per sec. per sec. The maximum inertia bending moment occurs at a section distant $\frac{1}{3}L$ from the lower end and is $M = \frac{1}{27}WLa/32.2$ in.-lb. The maximum inertia shear is in the direction of the acceleration, is at the lower end, and is $V = \frac{1}{4}Wa/32.2$ lb. The maximum inertia shear in the opposite direction occurs at a section distant $\frac{2}{3}L$ from the lower end and is $V = \frac{1}{12}Wa/32.2$ lb. (This case represents approximately the conditions existing when a chimney or other slender structure without anchorage is subjected to an earthquake shock.)

6. A uniform circular ring of mean radius R in., weight δ lb. per cu. in. and, having a thickness in the plane of curvature that is very small compared with R, rotates about its own axis with a uniform angular velocity of ω rad. per sec. The ring is subjected to a uniform tangential tensile inertia stress

$$s = \delta R^2\omega^2/386.4.$$

7. A solid homogeneous circular disk of uniform thickness (or a solid cylinder) of radius R in. and of density δ lb. per cu. in., rotates about its own axis with a uniform angular velocity of ω rad. per sec. At any point distant r in. from the center there is a radial tensile inertia stress

$$s_r = \frac{1}{8}\frac{\delta\omega^2}{386.4}[(3 + \nu)(R^2 - r^2)] \text{ lb. per sq. in.} \tag{1}$$

and a tangential tensile inertia stress

$$s_t = \frac{1}{8}\frac{\delta\omega^2}{386.4}[(3 + \nu)R^2 - (1 + 3\nu)r^2] \text{ lb. per sq. in.} \tag{2}$$

The maximum radial stress and maximum tangential stress are equal, both occur at the center, and are

$$\text{Max } s_r = \text{Max } s_t = \frac{1}{8}\frac{\delta\omega^2}{386.4}(3 + \nu)R^2 \tag{3}$$

8. A homogeneous circular disk of uniform thickness, of radius R in., density δ lb. per cu. in., with a central hole of radius R_0 in., rotates about its own axis with a uniform angular velocity of ω rad. per sec. At any point distant r in. from the center there is a radial tensile inertia stress

$$s_r = \frac{3+\nu}{8}\frac{\delta\omega^2}{386.4}\left(R^2 + R_0^2 - \frac{R^2R_0^2}{r^2} - r^2\right) \text{ lb. per sq. in.} \quad (4)$$

and a tangential tensile inertia stress

$$s_t = \frac{1}{8}\frac{\delta\omega^2}{386.4}\left[(3+\nu)\left(R^2 + R_0^2 + \frac{R^2R_0^2}{r^2}\right) - (1+3\nu)r^2\right] \text{ lb. per sq. in.} \quad (5)$$

The maximum radial stress occurs at $r = \sqrt{RR_0}$ and is

$$\text{Max } s_r = \frac{3+\nu}{8}\frac{\delta\omega^2}{386.4}(R - R_0)^2 \quad (6)$$

The maximum tangential stress occurs at the perimeter of the hole and is

$$\text{Max } s_t = \frac{1}{4}\frac{\delta\omega^2}{386.4}[(3+\nu)R^2 + (1-\nu)R_0^2] \quad (7)$$

If there are radial pressures or pulls distributed uniformly along either the inner or outer perimeter of the disk, such as a radial pressure from the shaft or a centrifugal pull from parts attached to the rim, the stresses due thereto can be found by the formula for thick cylinders (Table XIII) and superposed upon the inertia stresses given by the above formulas.

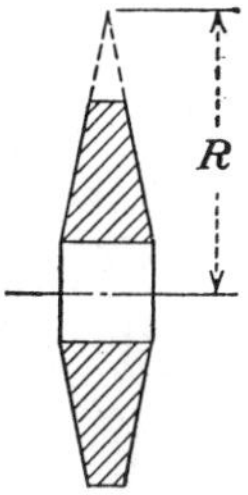

FIG. 45.

9. A homogeneous circular disk of conical section (Fig. 45), of density δ lb. per cu. in., rotates about its own axis with a uniform angular velocity of N rev. per min. At any point distant r in. from the center the tensile inertia stresses s_r and s_t are given by:

$$s_r = TK_r + Ap_1 + Bp_2 \text{ lb. per sq. in.} \quad (8)$$
$$s_t = TK_t + Aq_1 + Bq_2 \text{ lb. per sq. in.} \quad (9)$$

where $T = 0.0000282R^2N^2\delta$ (or for steel, $T = 0.000008R^2N^2$); K_r, K_t, p_1, p_2, q_1, and q_2 are given by the following table, and A and B are constants which may be found by setting s_r equal to its known or assumed values at the inner and outer perimeters and solving the resulting equations simultaneously for A and B, as in the example below. (See papers by Hodkinson and Rushing, Refs. 1 and 2, from which Eqs. 8 and 9 and the tabulated coefficients are taken.)

TABULATED VALUES OF COEFFICIENTS

$\frac{r}{R}$	K_r	K_t	p_1	q_1	p_2	q_2
0.00	0.1655	0.1655	1.435	1.435	∞	∞
0.05	0.1709	0.1695	1.497	1.475	−273.400	288.600
0.10	0.1753	0.1725	1.559	1.518	− 66.620	77.280
0.15	0.1782	0.1749	1.627	1.565	− 28.680	36.550
0.20	0.1794	0.1763	1.707	1.617	− 15.540	21.910
0.25	0.1784	0.1773	1.796	1.674	− 9.553	14.880
0.30	0.1761	0.1767	1.898	1.738	− 6.371	10.890
0.35	0.1734	0.1757	2.015	1.809	− 4.387	8.531
0.40	0.1694	0.1739	2.151	1.890	− 3.158	6.915
0.45	0.1635	0.1712	2.311	1.983	− 2.328	5.788
0.50	0.1560	0.1675	2.501	2.090	− 1.743	4.944
0.55	0.1465	0.1633	2.733	2.217	− 1.309	4.301
0.60	0.1355	0.1579	3.021	2.369	− 0.9988	3.816
0.65	0.1229	0.1525	3.390	2.556	− 0.7523	3.419
0.70	0.1094	0.1445	3.860	2.794	− 0.5670	3.102
0.75	0.0956	0.1370	4.559	3.111	− 0.4161	2.835
0.80	0.0805	0.1286	5.563	3.557	− 0.2971	2.614
0.85	0.0634	0.1193	7.263	4.276	− 0.1995	2.421
0.90	0.0442	0.1100	10.620	5.554	− 0.1203	2.263
0.95	0.0231	0.0976	20.645	8.890	− 0.0555	2.140
1.00	0.0000	0.0840	∞	∞	− 0.0000	2.051

10. A homogeneous circular disk of hyperbolic section (Fig. 46) of density δ lb. per cubic inch, rotates about its own axis with uniform angular velocity ω rad. per sec. The equation $t = cr^a$ defines the section, where if t_1 = thickness at radius r_1 and t_2 at radius r_2,

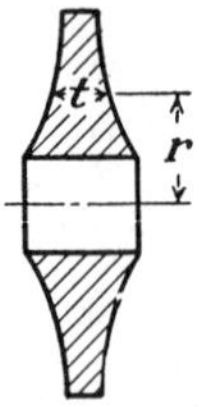

$$a = \frac{\log_e \frac{t_1}{t_2}}{\log_e \frac{r_1}{r_2}}$$

FIG. 46.

and $\log_e c = \log_e t_1 - a \log_e r_1 = \log_e t_2 - a \log_e r_2.$

(For taper toward the rim, a is negative, and for uniform t, $a = 0$.) At any point distant r in. from the center the tensile inertia stresses s_r and s_t are

$$s_r = \frac{E}{1 - \nu^2}[(3 + \nu)Fr^2 + (m_1 + \nu)Ar^{m_1-1} + (m_2 + \nu)Br^{m_2-1}]$$

lb. per sq. in. (10)

$$s_t = \frac{E}{1 - \nu^2}[(1 + 3\nu)Fr^2 + (1 + m_1\nu)Ar^{m_1-1} + (1 + m_2\nu)Br^{m_2-1}] \text{ lb. per sq. in.} \quad (11)$$

where

$$F = \frac{-(1 - \nu^2)\frac{\delta}{386.4}\omega^2}{E[8 + (3 + \nu)a]}$$

$$m_1 = -\frac{a}{2} - \sqrt{\frac{a^2}{4} - a\nu + 1}$$

$$m_2 = -\frac{a}{2} + \sqrt{\frac{a^2}{4} - a\nu + 1}$$

A and B are constants, to be found by setting s_r equal to its known or assumed values at the inner and outer perimeters and solving the two resulting equations simultaneously for A and B.

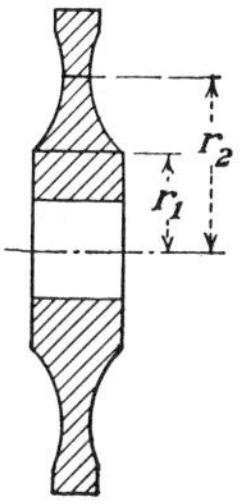

Equations 10 and 11 are taken from Stodola (Ref. 3), with some changes in notation.

Fig. 47.

11. A homogeneous circular disk with section bounded by curves and straight lines (Fig. 47) rotates about its own axis with a uniform angular velocity N r.p.m. The disk is imagined divided into annular rings of such width that each ring can be regarded as having a section with hyperbolic outline, as in (10). For each ring, a is calculated by the formulas of (10), using the inner and outer radii and the corresponding thicknesses. Then, if r_1 and r_2 represent respectively the inner and outer radii of any ring, the tangential stresses s_{t_1} and s_{t_2} at the inner and outer boundaries of the ring are related to the corresponding radial stresses s_{r_1} and s_{r_2} as follows:

$$s_{t_1} = Ar_2^2 - Bs_{r_1} + Cs_{r_2} \quad (12)$$

$$s_{t_2} = Dr_2^2 - Es_{r_1} + Fs_{r_2} \quad (13)$$

where

$$B = -\frac{m_2K^{m_1-1} - m_1K^{m_2-1}}{K^{m_2-1} - K^{m_1-1}}$$

$$K = \frac{r_1}{r_2}$$

$$E = -\frac{m_2 - m_1}{K^{m_2-1} - K^{m_1-1}}$$

$$C = \frac{E}{K^{a+2}}$$

$$F = B + a$$

$$A = -\frac{7.956(N/1000)^2}{8 + 3.3a}[1.9K^2 + 3.3(K^2B - C)]$$

$$D = -\frac{7.956(N/1000)^2}{8 + 3.3a}[1.9 + 3.3(K^2E - F)]$$

$$m_1 = -\frac{a}{2} - \sqrt{\frac{a^2}{4} - 0.3a + 1}$$

$$m_2 = -\frac{a}{2} + \sqrt{\frac{a^2}{4} - 0.3a + 1}$$

The above formulas, which are given by Loewenstein (Ref. 4) are directly applicable to steel, for which the values $\nu = 0.3$ and $\delta = 0.28$ lb. per cu. in. have been assumed.

Two values of s_r are known or can be assumed, *viz.*, the values at the inner and outer perimeters of the disk. Then by setting the tangential stress at the outer boundary of each ring equal to the tangential stress at the inner boundary of the adjacent larger ring (Eq. 13 for the smaller ring = Eq. 12 for the larger ring), one equation in s_r will be obtained for each common ring boundary. But at each such boundary there is but one unknown s_r, since the radial stresses in adjacent rings are equal at the common boundary. Therefore there are as many equations as there are unknown boundary radial stresses, and hence the radial stress at each boundary can be found. The tangential stresses can then be found by Eqs. 12 and 13, and then the stresses at any point in a ring can be found by using, in Eq. 12, the known values of s_{t_1} and s_{r_1} and substituting for s_{r_2} the unknown radial stress s_r, and for r_2 the corresponding radius r.

A fact of importance with reference to turbine disks or other rotating bodies is that geometrically similar disks of different size will be equally stressed at corresponding points when running at the same *peripheral* velocity. Furthermore, for any given peripheral velocity the axial and radial dimensions of a rotating body may be changed independently of each other, and in any ratio, without affecting the stresses at similarly situated points.

Example

The conical steel disk shown in section in Fig. 48 rotates at 2500 r.p.m. To its rim it has attached buckets the aggregate mass of which amounts to

$w = 0.75$ lb. per linear inch of rim; this mass may be considered centered 30 in. from the axis. It is desired to determine the stresses at, say, a point 7 in. from the axis.

Solution.—From the dimensions of the section, R is found to be 28 in. The values of r/R for the inner and outer perimeters and for the circumference $r = 7$ are calculated, and the corresponding coefficients K_r, K_t, etc., are determined from the table by graphical interpolation. The results are here tabulated for convenience:

	$\frac{r}{R}$	K_r	K_t	p_1	q_1	p_2	q_2
Inner rim	0.143	0.1780	0.1747	1.616	1.558	−32.5	40.5
Outer rim	0.714	0.1055	0.1425	4.056	2.883	− 0.534	3.027
$r = 7$ in.	0.25	0.1784	0.1773	1.796	1.674	− 9.553	14.88

The attached mass exerts on the rim outward inertia forces which will be assumed uniformly distributed; the amount of force per linear inch is $p = \frac{w}{g}\omega^2 r = \frac{0.75}{386.4}(261.5^2)(30) = 3980$ lb. per linear inch. Therefore at the outer rim $s_r = 7960$.

It is usual to design the shrink fit so that in operation the hub pressure is a few hundred pounds; it will be assumed to be 700 lb. per sq. in., making the radial stress at the inner rim $s_r = -700$. (For any given initial difference Δ between hub radius r_1 and shaft radius, the hub pressure or radial stress s_{r_1} can be found by the relation: $\Delta = \frac{s_{t_1} + s_{r_1}}{E} r_1$ where s_{t_1} may be taken as the tangential stress due to rotation, with $s_{r_1} = 0$, provided the actual s_{r_1} is small. This same equation may be used to determine the shrinkage Δ necessary to produce the desired hub pressure s_{r_1} during operation.)

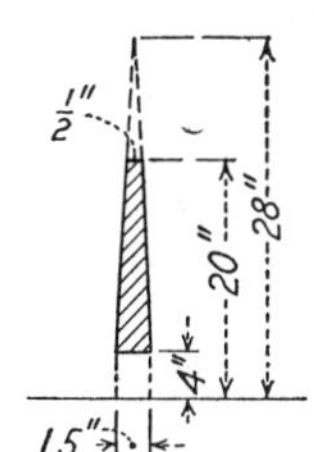

FIG. 48.

The value of $T = 0.000008(28^2)(2500^2) = 39{,}200$. Having two values of s_r, Eq. 8 can now be written

$$\text{(Inner rim)} \quad -700 = (39{,}200)(0.1780) + A(1.616) + B(-32.5)$$
$$\text{(Outer rim)} \quad 7960 = (39{,}200)(0.1055) + A(4.056) + B(-0.534)$$

Solution gives

$$A = 973; \qquad B = 285$$

The stresses at $r = 7$ are now found by Eqs. 8 and 9 to be

$$s_r = (39{,}200)(0.1784) + (973)(1.796) + (285)(-9.553) = 6020 \text{ lb. per sq. in.}$$
$$s_t = (39{,}200)(0.1773) + (973)(1.674) + (285)(14.88) = 12{,}825 \text{ lb. per sq. in.}$$

Bursting Speed.—The formulas given above for stresses in rotating disks presuppose *elastic* conditions; when the elastic limit is exceeded, plastic yielding tends to equalize the stress intensity along a diametral plane. Because of this, the average stress s_a on such a plane is perhaps a better criterion of margin of safety against bursting than is the maximum stress computed for elastic conditions.

For a solid disk of uniform thickness (Case 8),

$$s_a = 0.000863\delta\omega^2R^2$$

For a pierced disk (Case 9), $s_a = 0.000863\delta\omega^2(R^3 - R_0^3)/(R - R_0)$. Tests (Refs. 12, 13) have shown that, for some materials, rupture occurs, in both solid and pierced disks, when s_a, computed for the original dimensions, becomes equal to the ultimate tensile strength of the material as determined by a conventional test. On the other hand, some materials have failed at values of s_a as low as 61.5 per cent of the ultimate strength, and the lowest values were observed in tests of solid disks. The ratio of s_a at failure to the ultimate strength does not appear to be related in any consistent way to the ductility of the material; it seems probable that it depends rather on the form of the stress-strain diagram. In none of the tests reported did the weakening effect of a central hole prove to be nearly so great as the formulas for elastic stress would seem to indicate.

85. Impact and Sudden Loading.—When a force is suddenly applied to an elastic body, as by a blow, a wave of stress is propagated, which travels through the body with a velocity

$$V = \sqrt{\frac{386.4E}{\delta}} \tag{14}$$

where V is the velocity of the stress wave in inches per second, E is the modulus of elasticity of the material in pounds per square inch, and δ is the density of the material in pounds per cubic inch.

Bar with Free Ends.—When one end of an unsupported uniform elastic bar is subjected to longitudinal impact from a rigid body moving with velocity v in. per second, a wave of compressive stress of intensity

$$s = \left(\frac{v}{V}\right)E = v\sqrt{\frac{\delta E}{386.4}} \tag{15}$$

is propagated. The intensity of stress is seen to be independent of the mass of the moving body, but the length of the stressed zone, or volume of material simultaneously subjected to this stress, does depend on the mass of the moving body. If this mass is infinite (or very large compared with that of the bar), the wave of compression is reflected back from the free end of the bar as a wave of tension and returns to the struck end after a period $t_1 = 2L/V$ sec., where L is the length of the bar in inches. The period t_1 is the duration of contact between bar and body. If the impinging body is very large compared with the bar (so that its mass may be considered infinite) the bar, after breaking contact, moves with a velocity $2v$ in the direction of the impact and is free of stress. If the mass of the impinging body is μ times the mass of the bar, the average velocity of the bar after contact is broken is

$$\mu v \left(1 - e^{-\frac{2}{\mu}}\right)$$

and it is left vibrating with a stress of intensity $s = \left(\frac{v}{V} E\right) e^{-\beta t_1}$, where $\beta = 19.67A \sqrt{\delta E}/M$, A being the section area of the bar in square inches and M the mass of the moving body in pounds.

Bar with One End Fixed.—If one end of the bar is fixed, the wave of compressive stress resulting from impact on the free end is reflected back unchanged from the fixed end, and combines with advancing waves to produce a maximum stress very nearly equal to

$$\text{Max } s = \left(\frac{v}{V}\right) E \left(1 + \sqrt{\mu + \frac{2}{3}}\right) \tag{16}$$

where, as before, μ denotes the ratio of the mass of the moving body to the mass of the bar. The total time of contact is approximately

$$t_1 = \frac{L}{V}\left[\pi \sqrt{\mu + \frac{1}{2}} - \frac{1}{2}\right] \text{ sec.}$$

The above formulas are taken from the paper by Donnell (Ref. 5). See also Ref. 17.

Sudden Loading.—If a dead load is suddenly transferred to the free end of a bar, the other end being fixed, the resulting state of stress is characterized by waves, as in the case of impact. The space-average value of the pull exerted by the bar on the load is not, as is usually assumed, half the maximum tension, but somewhat greater than that, and therefore the maximum stress that results from sudden loading is somewhat less than twice that which results from static loading. Love (Ref. 6) shows that if μ (the ratio of the mass of the load to that of the bar) is 1, sudden loading causes 1.63 times as much stress as static loading, for $\mu = 2$ the ratio is 1.68, for $\mu = 4$ the ratio is 1.84; and it approaches 2 as a limit as μ increases. It can be seen that the ordinary assumption that sudden loading causes twice as much stress and deflection as static loading is always on the safe side.

Moving Load on Beam.—If a constant *force* moves at uniform speed across a beam with simply supported ends, the maximum deflection produced exceeds the static deflection that the same force would produce. If v represents the velocity of the force, l the span, and ω the lowest natural vibration frequency of the (unloaded) beam, then theoretically the maximum value of the ratio of dynamic to static deflection is 1.74; it occurs for $v = \omega l/1.64\pi$ and at the instant when the force has progressed a distance $0.757l$ along the span (Refs. 15, 16).

If a constant *mass* W moves across a simple beam of relatively negligible mass, then the maximum ratio of dynamic to static deflection is equal to $\left[1 + \left(\frac{v^2}{g}\right)\left(\frac{Wl}{3EI}\right)\right]$.[1] (Note that consistent units must be used in the above equations.)

Vibration.—A very important type of dynamic loading occurs when an elastic body vibrates under the influence of a periodic impulse. This occurs whenever a rotating or reciprocating mass is unbalanced, and also under certain conditions of fluid flow. The most serious situation arises when the impulse synchronizes or nearly synchronizes with the natural period of vibration, and it is of the utmost importance to guard against this condition of resonance or near resonance. There is always some resistance to vibration, natural or introduced; this is called *damping* and tends to prevent vibrations of excessive amplitude. In the absence of effective damping, the amplitude y, for near-resonance vibration, will much exceed the deflection y_s that would be produced by the same force under static conditions. The ratio y/y_s, called the *relative amplification factor*, is, in the absence of

[1] From Timoshenko's "Vibration Problems in Engineering," copyright 1955, D. Van Nostrand Company, Inc., Princeton, N.J.

Description and case number	Frequency, cycles per second
Uniform beams—lateral vibration	
1. Cantilever, end load W, own weight negligible	$\dfrac{3.13}{\sqrt{\dfrac{Wl^3}{3EI}}}$
2. Cantilever, end load W, own weight wl	$\dfrac{3.13}{\sqrt{\dfrac{(W + 0.236wl)l^3}{3EI}}}$
3. Cantilever, uniform load W	$\dfrac{3.89}{\sqrt{\dfrac{Wl^3}{8EI}}}$
4. Single span, ends supported, center load W, own weight negligible	$\dfrac{3.13}{\sqrt{\dfrac{Wl^3}{48EI}}}$
5. Single span, ends supported, center load W, own weight wl	$\dfrac{3.13}{\sqrt{\dfrac{(W + 0.486wl)l^3}{48EI}}}$
6. Single span, ends supported, uniform load W	$\dfrac{3.55}{\sqrt{\dfrac{5Wl^3}{384EI}}}$
7. Single span, ends fixed, center load W, own weight negligible	$\dfrac{3.13}{\sqrt{\dfrac{Wl^3}{192EI}}}$
8. Single span, ends fixed, center load W own weight wl	$\dfrac{3.13}{\sqrt{\dfrac{(W + 0.264wl)l^3}{192EI}}}$
9. Single span, ends fixed, uniform load W	$\dfrac{3.55}{\sqrt{\dfrac{Wl^3}{384EI}}}$
10. Free or floating beam, own weight W	$69\sqrt{\dfrac{EI}{Wl^3}}$
11. Longitudinal vibration of uniform bar or spring, end load W, own weight wl. k = tension required per in. of stretch	$3.13\sqrt{\dfrac{k}{W + \frac{1}{3}wl}}$
12. Torsional vibration of uniform shaft, length l, concentric end weight of mass moment of inertia I, mass moment of inertia of shaft = I_s, other notation as in Chap. 9	$3.13\sqrt{\dfrac{GK}{l(I + \frac{1}{3}I_s)}}$
13. Circular flat plate, thickness t, radius r, weight w per unit area, edge fixed	$9.66\sqrt{\dfrac{Et^3}{wr^4}}$
14. Same as Case 13 but plate square with sides l	$34.1\sqrt{\dfrac{Et^3}{wl^4}}$

damping, equal to $1/[1 - (f/f_n)^2]$, where f is the frequency of the forcing impulse, and f_n the natural frequency of the elastic system. Obviously, it is necessary to know at least approximately the natural period of vibration of a member in order to guard against resonance. The following table gives formulas for the natural frequency of vibration for a number of simple elastic systems (units are inches, pounds, and seconds).

86. Impact and Sudden Loading; Approximate Formulas.—If it is assumed that the stresses due to impact are distributed throughout any elastic body exactly as in the case of static loading, then it can be shown that the vertical deformation d_i and the stress s_i produced in any such body (bar, beam, truss, etc.) by the vertical impact of a body falling from a height of h in. are greater than the deformation d and stress s produced by the weight of the same body applied as a static load in the ratio

$$\frac{d_i}{d} = \frac{s_i}{s} = 1 + \sqrt{1 + 2\frac{h}{d}} \qquad (17)$$

If $h = 0$, we have the case of sudden loading, and $d_i/d = s_i/s = 2$, as usually assumed.

If the impact is horizontal instead of vertical, the impact deformation and stress are given by

$$\frac{d_i}{d} = \frac{s_i}{s} = \sqrt{\frac{v^2}{384.6d}} \qquad (18)$$

where, as before, d is the deformation the weight of the moving body would produce if applied as a static load, and v is the velocity of impact in inches per second.

Energy Losses.—The above approximate formulas are derived on the assumption that impact strains the elastic body in the same way (though not in the same degree) as static loading and that all the kinetic energy of the moving body is expended in producing this strain. Actually, in the impact, some kinetic energy is dissipated, and this loss, which can be found by equating the momentum of the entire system before and after impact, is most conveniently taken into account by multiplying the available energy (measured by h or by v^2) by a factor K, the value of which, for a number of simple cases involving members of uniform section, is as follows:

1. A moving body of mass M strikes axially one end of a bar of mass M_1, the other end of which is fixed. Then

$$K = \frac{1 + \frac{1}{3}\frac{M_1}{M}}{\left(1 + \frac{1}{2}\frac{M_1}{M}\right)^2}$$

If there is a body of mass M_2 attached to the struck end of the bar

$$K = \frac{1 + \frac{1}{3}\frac{M_1}{M} + \frac{M_2}{M}}{\left(1 + \frac{1}{2}\frac{M_1}{M} + \frac{M_2}{M}\right)^2}$$

2. A moving body of mass M strikes transversely the center of a simple beam of mass M_1. Then

$$K = \frac{1 + \frac{17}{35}\frac{M_1}{M}}{\left(1 + \frac{5}{8}\frac{M_1}{M}\right)^2}$$

If there is a body of mass M_2 attached to the beam at its center, then

$$K = \frac{1 + \frac{17}{35}\frac{M_1}{M} + \frac{M_2}{M}}{\left(1 + \frac{5}{8}\frac{M_1}{M} + \frac{M_2}{M}\right)^2}$$

3. A moving body of mass M strikes transversely the end of a cantilever beam of mass M_1. Then

$$K = \frac{1 + \frac{33}{140}\frac{M_1}{M}}{\left(1 + \frac{3}{8}\frac{M_1}{M}\right)^2}$$

If there is a body of mass M_2 attached to the beam at the struck end, then

$$K = \frac{1 + \frac{33}{140}\frac{M_1}{M} + \frac{M_2}{M}}{\left(1 + \frac{3}{8}\frac{M_1}{M} + \frac{M_2}{M}\right)^2}$$

4. A moving body of mass M strikes transversely the center of a beam with fixed ends and of mass M_1. Then

$$K = \frac{1 + \frac{13}{35}\frac{M_1}{M}}{\left(1 + \frac{1}{2}\frac{M_1}{M}\right)^2}$$

If there is a body of mass M_2 attached to the beam at the center,

$$K = \frac{1 + \frac{13}{35}\frac{M_1}{M} + \frac{M_2}{M}}{\left(1 + \frac{1}{2}\frac{M_1}{M} + \frac{M_2}{M}\right)^2}$$

87. Remarks on Stress Due to Impact.—It is improbable that in any actual case of impact the stresses can be accurately calculated by any of the methods or formulas given above. Equation 16, for instance, is supposedly very nearly precise if the conditions assumed are realized, but those conditions—perfect elasticity of the bar, rigidity of the moving body, and simultaneous contact of the moving body with all points on the end of the rod—are obviously unattainable. The dampening of the initial stress wave by elastic hysteresis in the bar and the diminution of the intensity of that stress wave by the cushioning effect of the actually nonrigid moving body, would serve to make the actual maximum stress less than the theoretical value. On the other hand, uneven contact between the moving body and the bar would tend to make the stress conditions nonuniform across the section, and probably to increase the maximum stress.

The formulas of Art. 86 are based upon an admittedly false assumption, *viz.*, that the distribution of stress and strain under impact loading is the same as under static loading. It is known, for instance, that the elastic curve of a beam under impact is different from that under static loading. Such a difference exists in any case, but it is less marked for low than for high velocities of impact, and Eqs. 17 and 18 probably give reasonably accurate values for the deformation and stress (especially the deformation) resulting from the impact of a relatively heavy body moving at low velocity. The lenitive effect of the inertia of the body struck, and of attached bodies, as expressed by K, is greatest when the masses of these parts are large compared with that of the moving body. When this is the case, impact can only be serious if the velocity is relatively high, and under such circumstances the formulas probably give but a rough indication of the actual stresses and deformations to be expected. See Ref. 18.

88. Temperature Stresses.—Whenever the expansion or contraction that would normally result from the heating or cooling of a body is prevented, stresses are developed that are called thermal or temperature stresses. It is convenient to distinguish two different sets of circumstances under which thermal stresses occur, *viz.*: (*a*) The form of the body and the temperature conditions are such that there would be no stresses except for the constraint of external forces. In any such case, the stresses may be found by determining the shape and dimensions the body would assume if unconstrained, and then calculating the stresses produced by forcing it back to its original shape and dimensions (see Example 2, Art. 26). (*b*) The form of the body and the temperature conditions are such that stresses are produced in the absence of external constraint solely because of the incompatibility of the natural expansions or contractions of the different parts of the body.

A number of representative examples of each type of thermal stress will now be considered.[1] In all instances the modulus of elasticity E and the coefficient of thermal expansion α are assumed to be constant for the temperature range involved, and the increment or difference in temperature ΔT is assumed to be positive. When ΔT is negative, the stress produced is of the opposite kind.

a. Stresses due to external constraint.

1. A uniform straight bar is subjected to a temperature change ΔT throughout while held at the ends. The resulting unit stress is $\Delta T\ \alpha E$, compression.

[1] Most of the formulas here given are taken from the papers by Goodier (Refs. 7, 14), Maulbetsch (Ref. 8), and Kent (Ref. 9).

2. A uniform flat plate is subjected to a temperature change ΔT throughout while held at the edges. The resulting unit stress is $\Delta T\ \alpha E/(1 - \nu)$, compression.
3. A solid body of any form is subjected to a temperature change ΔT throughout, while held to the same form and volume. The resulting stress is $\Delta T\ \alpha E/(1 - 2\nu)$, compression.
4. A uniform bar of rectangular section has one face at a uniform temperature T and the opposite face at a uniform temperature $T + \Delta T$, the temperature gradient between these faces being linear. The bar would normally curve in the arc of a circle of radius $d/\Delta T\ \alpha$, where d is the distance between the hot and cold faces. If the ends are fixed, the bar will be held straight by end couples $EI\Delta T\ \alpha/d$, and the maximum resulting bending stress will be $\frac{1}{2}\Delta T\ \alpha E$, compression on the hot face, tension on the cold face.
5. A flat plate of uniform thickness t and of any shape has one face at a uniform temperature T and the other face at a uniform temperature $T + \Delta T$, the temperature gradient between the faces being linear. The plate would normally assume a spherical curvature with radius $t/\Delta T\ \alpha$. If the edges are fixed, the plate will be held flat by uniform edge moments and the maximum resulting bending stress will be $\frac{1}{2}\Delta T\ \alpha E/(1 - \nu)$, compression on the hot face, tension on the cold face.
6. If the plate described in (5) is circular, no stress is produced by supporting the edges in a direction normal to the plane of the plate.
7. If the plate described in (5) has the shape of an equilateral triangle of altitude a (sides $2a/\sqrt{3}$) and the edges are rigidly supported so as to be held in a plane, the supporting reactions will consist of a uniform pressure $\frac{1}{8}\Delta T\ \alpha Et^2/a$ lb. per linear inch along each edge against the hot face, and a concentrated pressure $(\sqrt{3}/12)\Delta T\ \alpha Et^2$ lb. at each corner against the cold face. The maximum resulting bending stress is $\frac{3}{4}\Delta T\ \alpha E$ at the corners, compression on the hot face, tension on the cold face. There are also high shear stresses near the corners (Ref. 8).

8. If the plate described in (5) is square, no simple formula for the reactions necessary to hold the edges in their original plane is available. The maximum bending stress occurs near the edges, and its value approaches $\frac{1}{2}\Delta T\ \alpha E$. There are also high shear stresses near the corners (Ref. 8).

b. Stresses due to internal constraint.

9. Part or all of the surface of a solid body is suddenly subjected to a temperature change ΔT. A compressive stress $\Delta T\ \alpha E/(1 - \nu)$ is developed in the surface layer of the heated part (Ref. 7).
10. A thin circular disk at uniform temperature has the temperature changed ΔT throughout a comparatively small central circular portion of radius a. Within the heated part there are radial and tangential compressive stresses $s_r = s_t = \frac{1}{2}\Delta T\ \alpha E$. At points outside the heated part and distant r from the center of the disk the stresses are $s_r = \frac{1}{2}\Delta T\ \alpha E a^2/r^2$, compression, and $s_t = \frac{1}{2}\Delta T\ \alpha E a^2/r^2$, tension. At the edge of the heated portion there is a maximum shear stress $\frac{1}{2}\Delta T\ \alpha E$ (Ref. 7).
11. If the disk of (10) is heated uniformly throughout a small central portion of elliptical instead of circular outline, the maximum stress is the tangential stress at the ends of the ellipse, and is $s_t = \Delta T\ \alpha E/[1 + (b/a)]$, where a is the major and b the minor semiaxis of the ellipse (Ref. 7).
12. If the disk of (10) is heated symmetrically about its center and uniformly throughout its thickness, so that the temperature is a function of the distance r from the center only, the radial and tangential stresses at any point are

$$s_r = \alpha E \left(\frac{1}{R^2} \int_0^R Tr\,dr - \frac{1}{r^2} \int^r Tr\,dr \right)$$

$$s_t = \alpha E \left(-T + \frac{1}{R^2} \int_0^R Tr\,dr + \frac{1}{r^2} \int^r Tr\,dr \right)$$

where R is the radius of the disk and T is the temperature at any point distant r from the center, minus the temperature of the coldest part of the disk. In the above expressions, the negative sign denotes compressive stress (Ref. 7).

13. A rectangular plate or strip $ABCD$ (Fig. 49) is heated along a transverse line FG, uniformly throughout the thickness and across the width, so that the temperature varies only along the length with x. At FG the temperature is T_1; the minimum temperature in the plate is T_0. At any point along the edges of the strip where the temperature is T a tensile stress $s_x = E\alpha(T - T_0)$ is developed; this stress has its maximum value at F and G, where it becomes

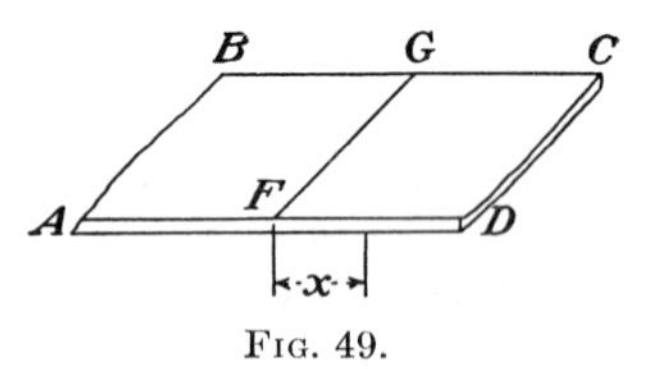

FIG. 49.

$E\alpha(T_1 - T_0)$. Halfway between F and G, a compressive stress s_y of equal intensity is developed (Ref. 7).

14. The plate of (13) is heated as there described except that the lower face of the plate is cooler than the upper, the maximum temperature there being T_2 and the temperature gradient through the thickness being linear. The maximum tensile stress at F and G is

$$s_x = \frac{1}{2} E\alpha \left[T_1 + T_2 - 2T_0 + \frac{1 - \nu}{3 + \nu}(T_1 - T_2) \right] \quad \text{(Ref. 7)}$$

15. A long hollow cylinder with thin walls has the outer surface at the uniform temperature T and the inner surface at the uniform temperature $T + \Delta T$. The temperature gradient through the thickness is linear. At points remote from the ends, the maximum circumferential stress is $\frac{1}{2}\Delta T\ \alpha E/(1 - \nu)$, compression at the inner surface, tension at the outer surface. The longitudinal stress is $\frac{1}{2}\Delta T\ \alpha E/(1 - \nu)$, compression at the inside, tension at the outside. These formulas apply to a thin tube of any cross section.

At the ends, if these are free, the maximum tensile stress in a tube of circular section is about 25 per cent greater than the value given by the formula (Ref. 7).

16. A hollow cylinder with thick walls of inner radius b, outer radius c, has the outer surface at the uniform temperature T, the inner surface at the uniform temperature $T + \Delta T$. The temperature gradient is not linear. The maximum stresses, which are circumferential and which occur at the inner and outer surfaces, are

(Outer surface) $$s_t = \frac{\Delta T\,\alpha E}{2(1-\nu)\log_e \frac{c}{b}}\left(1 - \frac{2b^2}{c^2 - b^2}\log_e \frac{c}{b}\right),$$ tension

(Inner surface) $$s_t = \frac{\Delta T\,\alpha E}{2(1-\nu)\log_e \frac{c}{b}}\left(1 - \frac{2c^2}{c^2 - b^2}\log_e \frac{c}{b}\right),$$ compression

At the inner and outer surfaces, the longitudinal stresses are equal to the tangential stresses (Ref. 7).

17. If the thick tube of (16) has the temperature of the outer surface raised at the uniform rate of m deg. per second, then after a steady state of heat flow has been reached the maximum tangential stresses are

(Outer surface) $$s_t = \frac{E\alpha m}{8A(1-\nu)}\left(3b^2 - c^2 - \frac{4b^4}{c^2 - b^2}\log_e \frac{c}{b}\right),$$ compression

(Inner surface) $$s_t = \frac{E\alpha m}{8A(1-\nu)}\left(b^2 + c^2 - \frac{4b^2c^2}{c^2 - b^2}\log_e \frac{c}{b}\right),$$ tension

where A is the coefficient of thermal diffusivity, equal to the coefficient of thermal conductivity divided by the product of the density of the material and its specific heat. (For steel, A may be taken as 0.027 sq. in. per second at moderate temperatures.)

At the inner and outer surfaces, the longitudinal stresses are equal to the tangential stresses (Ref. 9).

18. A solid rod of circular section is heated or cooled symmetrically with respect to its axis, the condition being

uniform along the length, so that the temperature is a function of r, the distance from the axis, only. The stresses are equal to those given by the formulas for (12) divided by $(1 - \nu)$ (Ref. 7).

19. If the solid rod of (18) has the temperature of its convex surface raised at the uniform rate of m deg. per sec., then after a steady state of heat flow has been reached the radial, tangential and longitudinal stresses at any point distant r from the center are

$$s_r = \frac{E\alpha m}{(1 - \nu)} \frac{c^2 - r^2}{16A}$$

$$s_t = \frac{E\alpha m}{(1 - \nu)} \frac{c^2 - 3r^2}{16A}$$

$$s_x = \frac{E\alpha m}{(1 - \nu)} \frac{c^2 - 2r^2}{8A}$$

Here A has the same meaning as in (17), and c is the radius of the shaft. A negative result indicates compression, a positive result tension (Ref. 9).

20. A solid sphere of radius c has the surface temperature increased at the uniform rate of m deg. per sec. The radial and tangential stresses produced at any point distant r from the center are

$$s_r = \frac{E\alpha m}{15A(1 - \nu)} (c^2 - r^2)$$

$$s_t = \frac{E\alpha m}{15A(1 - \nu)} (c^2 - 2r^2)$$

A negative result indicates compression, a positive result tension (Ref. 9).

21. If the sphere is hollow, with outer radius c and inner radius b, the stresses at any point are

$$s_r = \frac{E\alpha m}{15A(1 - \nu)} \left(-r^2 - \frac{5b^3}{r} + \phi - \psi\right)$$

$$s_t = \frac{E\alpha m}{15A(1 - \nu)} \left(-2r^2 - \frac{5b^3}{2r} + \phi + \frac{\psi}{2}\right)$$

where

$$\phi = \frac{c^5 + 5c^2b^3 - 6b^5}{c^3 - b^3}$$

and

$$\psi = \frac{c^5b^3 - 6c^3b^5 + 5c^2b^6}{r^3(c^3 - b^3)}$$

A negative result indicates compression, a positive result tension (Ref. 9).

Other problems involving thermal stress, the solutions of which cannot be expressed by simple formulas, are considered in the references cited above and in Refs. 3 and 10. Charts for the solution of thermal stresses in tubes are gives in Ref. 11.

References

1. HODKINSON, B.: Rotating Discs of Conical Profile, *Engineering*, Vol. 115, p. 1, 1923.
2. RUSHING, F. C.: Determination of Stresses in Rotating Disks of Conical Profile, *Trans. Am. Soc. Mech. Eng.*, Vol. 53, p. 91, 1931.
3. STODOLA, A.: "Steam and Gas Turbines," transl. 6th ed. by L. C. Loewenstein; McGraw-Hill Book Company, 1927.
4. LOEWENSTEIN, L. C.: "Marks' Mechanical Engineers' Handbook," McGraw-Hill Book Company , 1930.
5. DONNELL, L. H.: Longitudinal Wave Transmission and Impact, *Trans. Am. Soc. Mech. Eng.*, Vol. 52, No. 1, p. 153, 1930.
6. LOVE, A. E. H.: "Mathematical Theory of Elasticity," 2d ed., Cambridge University Press, 1906.
7. GOODIER, J. N.: Thermal Stress, *Am. Soc. Mech. Eng., Jour. Appl. Mech.*, Vol. 4, No. 1, March, 1937.
8. MAULBETSCH, J. L.: Thermal Stresses in Plates, *Am. Soc. Mech. Eng., Jour. Appl. Mech.*, Vol. 2, No. 4, December, 1935.
9. KENT, C. H.: Thermal Stresses in Spheres and Cylinders Produced by Temperatures Varying with Time, *Trans. Am. Soc. Mech. Eng.*, Vol. 54, No. 18, p. 185, 1932.
10. TIMOSHENKO, S.: "Theory of Elasticity," Engineering Societies Monograph, McGraw-Hill Book Company, 1934.
11. BARKER, L. H.: The Calculation of Temperature Stresses in Tubes *Engineering*, Vol. 124, p. 443, 1927.
12. ROBINSON, E. L.: Bursting Tests of Steam-turbine Disk Wheels, *Trans. Am. Soc. Mech. Eng.*, Vol. 66, No. 5, p. 373, 1944.
13. HOLMS, A. G., and J. E. JENKINS: Effect of Strength and Ductility on Burst Characteristics of Rotating Disks, *Nat. Adv. Comm. Aeron., Tech. Note* 1667, 1948.
14. GOODIER, J. N.: Thermal Stress and Deformation, *Am. Soc. Mech. Eng., Jour. Appl. Mech.*, Vol. 24, No. 3, September, 1957.
15. EICHMANN, E. S.: Note on the Maximum Effect of a Moving Force on a Simple Beam, *Am. Soc. Mech. Eng., Jour. Appl. Mech.*, Vol. 20, No. 4, December, 1953.
16. AYRE, R. S., L. S. JACOBSEN, and C. S. HSU: Transverse Vibration of 1 and 2-span Beams under Moving Mass-Load, *Proc. 1st U.S. Nat. Congr. Appl. Mech.*, 1952.

17. Burr, Arthur H.: Longitudinal and Torsional Impact in a Uniform Bar with a Rigid Body at One End, *Am. Soc. Mech. Eng., Jour. Appl. Mech.*, Vol. 17, No. 2, June, 1950.
18. Schwieger, Horst: A Simple Calculation of the Transverse Impact on Beams and Its Experimental Verification, *Jour. Soc. Exp. Mech.*, Vol. 5, No. 11, November, 1965.

MISCELLANEOUS TABLES

Factors of Stress Concentration
Values of the Rupture Factor
Properties of Materials
Allowable Stresses and Factors of Safety

Table XVII.—Factors of Stress Concentration for Elastic Stress (k), for Repeated Stress (k_f), and for Rupture (k_r)

(Here repeated stress means completely reversed stress. See Art. 8 for discussion of stress concentration)

<table>
<tr><th>Type of form irregularity or stress raiser</th><th>Stress condition</th><th>Manner of loading</th><th>Factor of stress concentration k, k_f, k_r for various dimensions</th></tr>
<tr><td rowspan="3">1. Two V notches in member of rectangular section</td><td rowspan="2">Elastic stress</td><td>Tension</td><td>
<table>
<tr><td>$\frac{r}{d}$</td><td>0.05</td><td>0.10</td><td>0.15</td><td>0.20</td><td>0.25</td><td>0.30</td><td>0.40</td><td>0.50</td></tr>
<tr><td>k</td><td>4.1</td><td>3.0</td><td>2.5</td><td>2.2</td><td>2.0</td><td>1.9</td><td>1.7</td><td>1.55</td></tr>
</table>
(Refs. 1, 4)</td></tr>
<tr><td>Bending</td><td>
<table>
<tr><td>$\frac{r}{d}$</td><td>0.025</td><td>0.05</td><td>0.10</td><td>0.15</td><td>0.20</td><td>0.25</td><td>0.30</td><td>0.40</td><td>0.50</td></tr>
<tr><td>k</td><td>3.6</td><td>2.9</td><td>2.2</td><td>1.9</td><td>1.7</td><td>1.6</td><td>1.5</td><td>1.4</td><td>1.3</td></tr>
</table>
(Ref. 1)</td></tr>
<tr><td>Static rupture</td><td>Bending</td><td>$D = 1\frac{1}{2}$, $d = 1$
<table>
<tr><td>$\frac{r}{d}$</td><td>0</td><td>0.075</td><td>0.15</td></tr>
<tr><td>Plaster</td><td>2.10</td><td>1.72</td><td>1.46</td></tr>
<tr><td>Cast iron</td><td>1.38</td><td>1.23</td><td></td></tr>
</table>
(Ref. 12)</td></tr>
<tr><td rowspan="2">2. Two U notches in member of rectangular section</td><td rowspan="2">Elastic stress</td><td>Tension</td><td>
<table>
<tr><td>$\frac{h}{r}$ \ $\frac{r}{d}$</td><td>0.05</td><td>0.095</td><td>0.15</td><td>0.225</td><td>0.30</td><td>0.40</td><td>0.52</td><td>0.75</td></tr>
<tr><td>0.5</td><td>2.25</td><td>2.10</td><td>1.95</td><td>1.85</td><td>1.70</td><td>1.60</td><td>1.50</td><td>1.35</td></tr>
<tr><td>1.0</td><td>2.57</td><td>2.34</td><td>2.16</td><td>1.96</td><td>1.81</td><td>1.65</td><td>1.51</td><td>1.36</td></tr>
<tr><td>1.5</td><td>2.72</td><td>2.50</td><td>2.26</td><td>2.00</td><td>1.84</td><td>1.65</td><td>1.51</td><td>1.36</td></tr>
<tr><td>2.0</td><td>2.90</td><td>2.64</td><td>2.32</td><td>2.03</td><td>1.85</td><td>1.65</td><td>1.51</td><td>1.36</td></tr>
<tr><td>3.0</td><td></td><td>2.80</td><td>2.40</td><td>2.05</td><td>1.86</td><td>1.65</td><td>1.51</td><td>1.36</td></tr>
<tr><td>4.0</td><td></td><td>2.94</td><td>2.43</td><td>2.06</td><td>1.86</td><td>1.65</td><td>1.51</td><td>1.36</td></tr>
</table>
When $\frac{h}{r} = 1$ (semicircular notch) $k = 2.75 - 2.75\frac{h}{D} + 0.32\left(\frac{h}{D}\right)^2 + 0.68\left(\frac{h}{D}\right)^3$ (Ref. 22)
(Ref. 6)</td></tr>
<tr><td>Bending</td><td>
<table>
<tr><td>$\frac{h}{r}$ \ $\frac{r}{d}$</td><td>0.05</td><td>0.10</td><td>0.20</td><td>0.30</td><td>0.50</td><td>0.75</td></tr>
<tr><td>0.5</td><td>1.90</td><td>1.75</td><td>1.54</td><td>1.40</td><td>1.27</td><td>1.17</td></tr>
<tr><td>1.0</td><td>2.20</td><td>1.86</td><td>1.59</td><td>1.45</td><td>1.30</td><td>1.18</td></tr>
<tr><td>1.5</td><td>....</td><td>1.91</td><td>1.60</td><td>1.45</td><td>1.30</td><td>1.18</td></tr>
<tr><td>2.0</td><td>....</td><td>1.94</td><td>1.60</td><td>1.46</td><td>1.30</td><td>1.18</td></tr>
<tr><td>3.0</td><td>....</td><td>2.00</td><td>1.61</td><td>1.47</td><td>1.30</td><td>1.18</td></tr>
<tr><td>4.0</td><td>....</td><td>2.05</td><td>1.62</td><td>1.47</td><td>1.30</td><td>1.18</td></tr>
</table>
(Ref. 6)</td></tr>
</table>

3. One V notch in member of rectangular section

Elastic stress — Tension: $k = 1 + 2\sqrt{\frac{h}{r}}$ (for h small compared with d) (Refs. 7, 8)

Elastic stress — Bending: $k = 1 + 2\sqrt{\frac{h}{r}}$ (for h small compared with d) (Refs. 7, 8)

Static rupture — Bending:

	Sharpness effect: $D = 1\frac{1}{2}''$, $h = \frac{1}{4}$ in., $r = 0$	0.03	0.15	Depth effect: $D = 1\frac{1}{2}$ in., $r = 0$, $h =$ 0.02	$\frac{1}{8}$	$\frac{1}{4}$	$\frac{1}{2}$	$\frac{3}{4}$	1	1.21	Scale effect: $\frac{D}{h} = 6$, $\frac{r}{h} = 0.1$, $D =$ $1\frac{1}{2}$	1	$\frac{3}{4}$	$\frac{1}{2}$	$\frac{3}{8}$	$\frac{3}{16}$
Plaster	2.50	2.30	1.80	1.05	1.96	2.28	2.00	1.53	1.60	1.19						
G. Cast iron	1.56	1.54	1.43	1.28	1.51	1.59	1.55	1.53	1.34	1.14	1.24		1.19		1.20	1.15
W. Cast iron	1.33	1.66	1.40	1.03	1.22	1.21	1.37	1.08	1.08							
Ni. Cast iron	1.64	....	1.43	1.13	1.45	1.57	1.58	1.47	1.30	1.13	1.43		1.31		1.22	1.18
Al 112	1.77	....	1.39	....	1.37	1.61	1.53	1.82	1.30	1.02	1.39		1.33		1.18	0.94
Al 195 — T6	1.43	....	1.24								1.24		1.01		1.04	
Al 220 — T4	1.13	....	1.07													
Mag. Alloy	....	....	1.41								1.41		1.25		1.27	
Bakelite	....	....	1.13									1.13		1.15		

(Ref. 12)

4. One U notch in member of rectangular section

Elastic stress — Bending: $\frac{r}{D} = 0.125$

$\frac{h}{r} =$	0.667	1.33	2.00	2.67	3.33	4.00	4.67	5.33	6.00	6.67	7.34
$k =$	1.96	2.04	1.96	1.92	1.84	1.76	1.65	1.56	1.46	1.35	1.06

(Ref. 12)

Static rupture — Bending: $\frac{r}{D} = 0.125$

$\frac{h}{r} =$	0.667	1.33	2.00	3.33	4.67	6.00
Plaster	1.49	1.57	1.67	1.55	1.42	1.25
Cast iron	1.28	1.37	1.42	1.30	1.17	1.10

(Ref. 12)

TABLE XVII.—FACTORS OF STRESS CONCENTRATION FOR ELASTIC STRESS (k), FOR REPEATED STRESS (k_f), AND FOR RUPTURE (k_r).—(*Continued*)

Type of form irregularity or stress raiser	Stress condition	Manner of loading	Factor of stress concentration k, k_f, k_r for various dimensions
5. Circular hole in plate or rectangular bar	Elastic stress	Tension	(*a*) Uniaxial stress, hole central $k = 3 - 3.13\frac{a}{d} + 3.76\left(\frac{a}{d}\right)^2 - 1.71\left(\frac{a}{d}\right)^3$ (empirical formula, Ref. 22) $k = \frac{3d}{a+d}$ (approximate formula, Ref. 20) (*b*) Uniaxial stress, hole near edge of wide plate $\frac{h}{a} = 0.67$ 0.77 0.91 1.07 1.29 1.56 $k = 4.37$ 3.92 3.61 3.40 3.25 3.16 (Ref. 21) (*c*) Biaxial stress, $\frac{a}{d}$ small $k = 2$ (*d*) Biaxial stress, $\frac{a}{d}$ small $k = 4$
		Bending	$k = \frac{(1+\nu)(5-\nu)}{3+\nu}$, $\frac{a}{d}$ small (Ref. 50)
	Repeated stress	Tension	$d = 1.50$, $t = 0.064$, $a = 0.0365$ to 0.20 Cold rolled hard steel strip, 1.4% ult. elongation $k = 2.15$ (Ref. 26)
		Bending	$d = \frac{1}{2}$ $t = 0.05$ $a = 0.055$ Material ... k_f 1.20 per cent C steel (normalized) ... 1.25 0.52 per cent C steel (normalized) ... 1.31 0.37 per cent C steel (normalized) ... 1.22 Chr. Ni steel (3 heat treatments) ... 1.30, 1.53, 1.76 3.5 per cent Ni steel (2 heat treatments) ... 1.31, 1.38 Armco iron (0.02 per cent C) ... 1.30 0.49 per cent C steel ... 1.12 (Ref. 17)
	Static rupture	Bending	Beams, $d = 1$ $t = 1\frac{1}{2}$ $a = \frac{1}{16}$ $a = \frac{1}{2}$ Plaster 1.33 1.43 Cast iron 1.03 1.11 Circular flat plate, dia. = 8.4, $t = 0.375$. $a = \frac{1}{4}$ $a = \frac{1}{2}$ Plaster 1.5 .... Cast iron 1.19 (Ref. 13)

6. Elliptical hole in plate 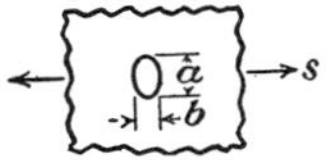	Elastic stress	Tension	$k = 1 + 2\frac{a}{b}$ (for wide plate) (Ref. 7)
7. Circular hole with bead in wide plate 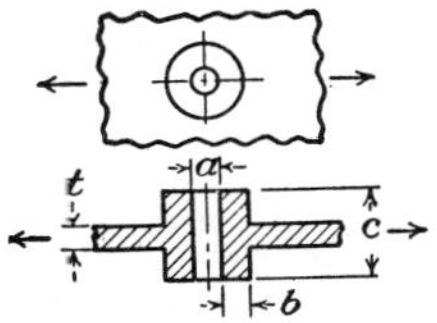	Elastic stress	Tension	(Bead area) $A_b = b(c - t)$ (Hole area) $A_h = at$ $\frac{A_b}{A_h} = 0.1 \quad 0.2 \quad 0.3 \quad 0.4 \quad 0.5$ $k = 2.53 \quad 2.17 \quad 1.90 \quad 1.69 \quad 1.53$

TABLE XVII.—FACTORS OF STRESS CONCENTRATION FOR ELASTIC STRESS (k), FOR REPEATED STRESS (k_f), AND FOR RUPTURE (k_r).—(*Continued*)

Type of form irregularity or stress raiser	Stress condition	Manner of loading	Factor of stress concentration k, k_f, k_r for various dimensions
8. Square shoulder with fillet in rectangular bar	Elastic stress	Tension	See table (a) below. (Ref. 6)
	Elastic stress	Bending	See table (b) below. (Ref. 6)
	Repeated stress	Bending	See table (c) below. (Ref. 17)

(a) Elastic stress, Tension

$\frac{h}{r}$ \ $\frac{r}{d}$	0.05	0.10	0.20	0.27	0.50	1.0
0.5	1.70	1.60	1.53	1.47	1.39	1.21
1.0	1.93	1.78	1.67	1.59	1.42	1.22
1.5		1.89	1.72	1.65	1.43	1.23
2.0		1.95	1.80	1.70	1.44	1.23
3.5		2.10	1.93	1.78	1.47	1.24

(Ref. 6)

(b) Elastic stress, Bending

$\frac{h}{r}$ \ $\frac{r}{d}$	0.05	0.10	0.20	0.27	0.50	1.0
0.5	1.61	1.49	1.39	1.34	1.22	1.07
1.0	1.91	1.70	1.48	1.38	1.22	1.08
1.5	2.00	1.73	1.50	1.39	1.23	1.08
2.0		1.74	1.52	1.39	1.23	1.09
3.5		1.76	1.54	1.40	1.23	1.10

(Ref. 6)

(c) Repeated stress, Bending

Material	k_f		
1.20 per cent C steel (normalized)	1.23		
0.52 per cent C steel (normalized)	1.23		
0.37 per cent C steel (normalized)	1.03		
Chr. Ni steel (3 Heat Treatments)	1.26	1.48	1.46
3.5 per cent Ni steel (2 Heat Treatments)	1.25	1.10	
Armco Iron (.02 per cent C)	1.08		
0.49 per cent C steel (normalized)	1.14		

(Ref. 17)

9. Square or filleted corner in tension	Elastic stress	As shown	$\frac{D}{d} = 5.5$ $\frac{r}{d} = 0.125$ 0.15 0.20 0.25 0.30 0.40 0.50 0.70 1.00 $k = 2.50$ 2.30 2.03 1.88 1.70 1.53 1.40 1.26 1.20 (Ref. 12)
	Static rupture	As shown	$D = 8\frac{1}{4}$ $d = 1\frac{1}{2}$ $\frac{r}{d} = 0$ 0.393 0.914 Plaster 2.60 1.54 1.28 Cast iron 1.56 1.02 1.00 (Ref. 12)
10. Square or filleted corner in compression	Static rupture	As shown	Reinforced concrete (d = 6 in. and 3 in.) Condition (a) sharp corner (b) fillet, $\frac{r}{d} = \frac{1}{3}$ (c) chamfered, $\frac{h}{d} = \frac{1}{3}$ $k_r =$ 1.00 1.02 1.06 (Ref. 12)

TABLE XVII.—FACTORS OF STRESS CONCENTRATION FOR ELASTIC STRESS (k), FOR REPEATED STRESS (k_f), AND FOR RUPTURE (k_r).—(*Continued*)

<table>
<tr><th>Type of form irregularity or stress raiser</th><th>Stress condition</th><th>Manner of loading</th><th>Factor of stress concentration k, k_f, k_r for various dimensions</th></tr>
<tr><td rowspan="6">11. Square shoulder with fillet in circular shaft</td><td rowspan="3">Elastic stress</td><td>Tension</td><td>Approximately same as Case 8</td></tr>
<tr><td>Bending</td><td>Approximately same as Case 8</td></tr>
<tr><td>Torsion</td><td>
<table>
<tr><th>$\frac{D}{d}$ \ $\frac{r}{d}$</th><th>0.005</th><th>0.01</th><th>0.02</th><th>0.03</th><th>0.04</th><th>0.06</th><th>0.08</th><th>0.10</th><th>0.12</th></tr>
<tr><td>2.00</td><td>....</td><td>3.0</td><td>2.25</td><td>2.00</td><td>1.82</td><td>1.65</td><td>1.51</td><td>1.44</td><td>1.39</td></tr>
<tr><td>1.33</td><td>....</td><td>2.7</td><td>2.16</td><td>1.91</td><td>1.76</td><td>1.60</td><td>1.48</td><td>1.40</td><td>1.35</td></tr>
<tr><td>1.20</td><td>3.00</td><td>2.5</td><td>2.00</td><td>1.75</td><td>1.62</td><td>1.50</td><td>1.40</td><td>1.34</td><td>1.30</td></tr>
<tr><td>1.09</td><td>2.20</td><td>1.88</td><td>1.53</td><td>1.40</td><td>1.30</td><td>1.20</td><td>1.16</td><td>1.15</td><td>1.15</td></tr>
</table>
(Refs. 2, 3)</td></tr>
<tr><td rowspan="3">Repeated stress</td><td>Tension</td><td>
<table>
<tr><th>Material</th><th>D</th><th>d</th><th>$\frac{r}{d}$</th><th>k_f</th><th>$\frac{r}{d}$</th><th>k_f</th></tr>
<tr><td>0.065% C steel.....</td><td>0.57</td><td>0.295</td><td>0</td><td>1.56</td><td>.21</td><td>1.39</td></tr>
<tr><td>0.331% C steel.....</td><td>0.57</td><td>0.295</td><td>0</td><td>1.82</td><td>.21</td><td>1.39</td></tr>
<tr><td>0.446% C steel.....</td><td>0.57</td><td>0.295</td><td>0</td><td>1.67</td><td>.21</td><td>1.41</td></tr>
<tr><td>0.645% C steel.....</td><td>0.57</td><td>0.295</td><td>0</td><td>2.08</td><td>.21</td><td>1.47</td></tr>
</table>
(Ref. 25)</td></tr>
<tr><td>Bending</td><td>
<table>
<tr><th>Material</th><th>D</th><th>d</th><th>$\frac{r}{d}$</th><th>K_f</th></tr>
<tr><td>.57% C steel (H.T.)..........</td><td>....</td><td>0.080</td><td>0.15</td><td>1.03</td></tr>
<tr><td>.57% C steel (H.T.)..........</td><td>....</td><td>0.410</td><td>0.15</td><td>1.50</td></tr>
<tr><td>.57% C steel (H.T.)..........</td><td>....</td><td>2.13</td><td>0.15</td><td>1.75</td></tr>
<tr><td>.30% C steel..................</td><td>....</td><td>0.37</td><td>0.21</td><td>1.13</td></tr>
<tr><td>.30% C steel..................</td><td>....</td><td>0.37</td><td>0.053</td><td>1.59</td></tr>
<tr><td>.49% C steel (H.T.)..........</td><td>0.40</td><td>0.275</td><td>0</td><td>2.04</td></tr>
<tr><td>.46% C steel (H.T.)..........</td><td>2.0</td><td>1.0</td><td>0.188</td><td>1.35</td></tr>
<tr><td>Alloy steel (3.5% Ni; 0.8% Cr.)</td><td>....</td><td>0.30</td><td>0.267</td><td>1.21</td></tr>
<tr><td>Alloy steel (3.5% Ni; 0.8% Cr.)</td><td>....</td><td>0.30</td><td>0.062</td><td>2.17</td></tr>
</table>
(Ref. 10)</td></tr>
<tr><td>Torsion</td><td>Approximately same as bending (Ref. 10)</td></tr>
</table>

$\frac{\ }{d} = 0.875$ and 0.50; $\frac{\ }{d} = 0$

k_r for cast iron = 1 (Ref. 12)

Static rupture

Te.ision

Bending

$\frac{D}{d}$ \ $\frac{r}{d}$	0	0.015	0.021	0.031	0.042	0.062	0.083	0.093	0.125	0.166	0.186	0.25	0.375	
Plaster... $\frac{4}{2}$	1.84	1.80		1.80		1.72		1.50	1.37		1.44	1.21	1.13	(Ref. 13)
Plaster... $\frac{4}{3}$	1.82		1.53		1.55		1.38			1.26		1.19		(Ref. 13)
Cast iron. $\frac{1}{0.5}$	1.00													(Ref. 12)

$\left(\frac{D}{d}\right.$ values represent actual dimensions$\left.\right)$

Torsion

Material	D	d \ $\frac{r}{d}$	0	0.062	0.073	
Plaster	4	2	1.30	1.13		(Ref. 13)
Plaster	1.10	0.823	0.87		0.78	(Ref. 12)
Cast iron	0.65	0.50	1.00		1.03	(Ref. 12)
Ni cast iron	0.65	0.50	0.95		0.80	(Ref. 12)
Al 112	0.475	0.331	0.91		0.76	(Ref. 12)
Al 195–T6	0.475	0.331	0.87		0.87	(Ref. 12)
Al 220–T4	0.475	0.331	0.94		0.86	(Ref. 12)

TABLE XVII.—FACTORS OF STRESS CONCENTRATION FOR ELASTIC STRESS (k), FOR REPEATED STRESS (k_f), AND FOR RUPTURE (k_r).—(*Continued*)

Type of form irregularity or stress raiser	Stress condition	Manner of loading	Factor of stress concentration k, k_f, k_r for various dimensions
12. U notch in circular shaft	Elastic stress	Tension	Approximately same as Case 2 (Ref. 1)
		Bending	Approximately same as Case 2 (Ref. 1)
		Torsion	$k = \frac{(D - d + 2r)(d + 2r)^2 + 4r^2(D - d - 2r)}{2rD(d + 4r)}$ For semicircular notch ($d = D - 2r$) $k = \frac{2D}{D + 2r}$ (Refs. 2, 3)
	Repeated stress	Bending	See table below (Refs. 14, 10)
	Static rupture	Tension	See table below (Ref. 12)

Repeated stress, bending:

Material	D	h	r	k_f	
6130 steel, 0.29 per cent C. (H.T.)	0.48	0.015	0.015	2.20	(Ref. 14)
6130 steel, 0.29 per cent C. (H.T.)	0.716	0.156	0.125	1.37	
0.10 per cent C steel	0.3	0.008	0.002	1.21	
0.10 per cent C steel	0.6	0.008	0.002	1.07	
0.62 per cent C steel	0.34	0.012	0.006	1.78	(Ref. 10)
Chr Ni steel {3.5 per cent Ni, 0.8 per cent Cr (H.T.)}	0.60	0.008	0.002	2.00	
0.2 per cent C cast steel, annealed	0.30	0.008	0.002	1.31	

Static rupture, tension:

Material	D	h	r	k_r
Cast iron	0.6	0.052	0.03	1.01
Cast iron	0.4	0.035	0.02	1.18
Nickel cast iron	0.6	0.052	0.03	1.06
Nickel cast iron	0.4	0.035	0.02	1.01
Cast magnesium	0.475	0.04	0.02	1.16
Al 112	0.35	0.035	0.02	1.24
Al 195–T6	0.35	0.035	0.02	0.81
Al 220–T4	0.35	0.035	0.02	0.76

(Ref. 12)

13. **V notch in circular shaft**

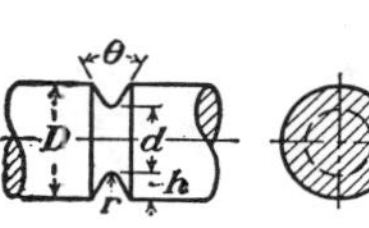

Elastic stress — Tension

$\frac{r}{d}$	0.05	0.10	0.15	0.20	0.30	0.40	0.50
k	3.4	2.5	2.1	1.9	1.62	1.5	1.4

(Refs. 1, 4)

Elastic stress — Bending

$\frac{r}{d}$	0.05	0.10	0.15	0.20	0.30	0.40	0.50
k	2.55	2.0	1.74	1.6	1.43	1.31	1.25

(Refs. 1, 4)

For $\frac{h}{d}$ small, $k = \frac{\left(1 + 2\sqrt{\frac{h}{r}}\right)}{\left(1 + \sqrt{\frac{h}{r}}\right)}$ times value given below for k in torsion (Ref. 8)

Elastic stress — Torsion

θ \ $\frac{h}{r}$	0.5	1	3	5	9
0°	1.85	2.01	2.66	3.23	4.54
60°	1.84	2.00	2.54	3.06	3.90
90°	1.81	1.95	2.40	2.64	3.12
120°	1.66	1.75	1.95	2.06	2.13

(Ref. 8)

Repeated stress — Bending

Material	θ \ $\frac{h}{r}$	1	4	7	∞		
0.33 per cent C steel	72°	1.16	1.31	1.42		(h < 0.0025) D = 0.45	(Ref. 8)
0.33 per cent C steel	63½°	1.45	1.90	2.20		(h = 0.005 to 0.045) D = 0.45	(Ref. 8)
Normalized ext. mag Al alloy	60°		1.50			(h = 0.036 to 0.040, D = 0.5)	(Ref. 14)
1050 steel (H.T.)	60°		2.37			(h = 0.036 to 0.040, D = 0.5)	(Ref. 14)
6130 (.29 per cent C) steel (H.T.)	60°		2.62			(h = 0.036 to 0.040, D = 0.5)	(Ref. 14)
25 S Al	60°		1.80			(h = 0.036 to 0.040, D = 0.5)	(Ref. 14)
Cast Al 220–T4*	72°				0.81	(h = 0.05, D = 0.40)	(Ref. 12)
Cast iron	72°				0.90	(h = 0.05, D = 0.40)	(Ref. 12)
Ext. Al 17 ST	60°	1.67					(Ref. 15)

* Tested to 100,000,000 cycles.

Static rupture — Tension

$\theta = 72°$ $\frac{h}{D} = 0.87$

Material	$\frac{h}{r}$ = ∞	1.72
Cast iron	1.10	1.10
Ni cast iron	1.05	1.04
Al 112	1.09	1.24
Al 195 − T6	0.82	0.81
Al 220 − T4	0.81	0.76
Mag − H1	1.23	1.16

(Ref. 12)

TABLE XVII.—FACTORS OF STRESS CONCENTRATION FOR ELASTIC STRESS (k), FOR REPEATED STRESS (k_f), AND FOR RUPTURE (k_r).—(*Continued*)

Type of form irregularity or stress raiser	Stress condition	Manner of loading	Factor of stress concentration k, k_f, k_r for various dimensions
14. **Radial** hole in circular shaft	Elastic stress	Tension	Approximately same as Case 5a
		Bending	Approximately same as Case 5a
		Torsion	For $\frac{a}{d}$ very small, $k = 4$
	Repeated stress	Bending	See table A below
	Static rupture	Bending	See table B below
		Torsion	See table C below

A. Repeated stress, bending

Material	$\frac{a}{d}$ \ d	0.10	0.50	1	3	0.273	2.13	0.30	0.35	
0.45 per cent C steel	0.0625		1.34	1.55	1.88					(Ref. 9)
0.45 per cent C steel	0.250	1.1	1.36	1.40	1.55					(Ref. 9)
0.57 per cent C steel (H.T.)	0.150					1.40	2.22			(Ref. 9)
Armco iron	0.183							1.38		(Refs. 17, 10)
0.49 per cent C steel (H.T.)	0.183							1.27		(Refs. 17, 10)
0.52 per cent C steel (H.T.)	0.183							1.34		(Refs. 17, 10)
Cyclops metal (annealed)	0.183							1.05		(Refs. 17, 10)
Cast iron	0.157								1.15	(Refs. 16, 10)

B. Static rupture, bending

Material	$\frac{a}{d}$ \ d	2	3	
Plaster	0.0625	1.84	1.65	
Plaster	0.125	1.50	1.70	
Plaster	0.250	1.37	1.46	(Ref. 13)

C. Static rupture, torsion

Material	$\frac{a}{d}$ \ d	2	0.82	0.5	0.331	
Plaster	0.0625	1.86				(Ref. 13)
Plaster	0.125	1.89				(Ref. 13)
Plaster	0.250	2.12				(Ref. 13)
Plaster	0.076		1.17			(Ref. 12.
Cast iron	0.125			1.22		(Ref. 12.
Ni cast iron	0.125			1.11		(Ref. 12.
Al 112	0.20				1.14	(Ref. 12.
Al 195–T6	0.20				1.06	(Ref. 12.
Al 220–T4	0.20				1.05	(Ref. 12.

D = over-all diameter h = depth of thread	Repeated stress	Tension	Material / Whitworth / U.S. Standard / Rolled 0.065 per cent C steel.... / 1.35 / / } (Ref. 25) 0.331 per cent C steel.... / 1.41 / / 0.446 per cent C steel.... / 1.51 / / 0.645 per cent C steel.... / 1.45 / / 0.300 per cent C steel.... / 1.76 / 2.84 / 2.15 } (Ref. 27) S.A.E. 2320 Ni steel H.T. / 3.32 / 3.85 /
		Bending	Material / $D = \frac{1}{4}''$, $h = 0.0232$, 28 threads to inch (Continuous thread / Single notch) / $D = \frac{3}{8}''$, $h = 0.0271$, 24 threads to inch (Continuous thread / Single notch) Tie rod steel 0.43 per cent C / 1.18 / 4.25 / 1.38 / 2.42 (Ref. 14)
16. Keyway in circular shaft	Elastic stress	Torsion	For $r = 0$, theoretical $k = \infty$. For small values of r see formula of Table IX Tests to determine elastic failure gave $k = 1.30$ (Refs. 18, 19)
Sled-runner type (a)	Repeated stress	Bending	Material / (a) / (b) Chr Ni steel (H.T.).............. / 1.35 / 1.74 Medium C steel (normalized)..... / 1.11 / 1.35 (Ref. 23)
		Torsion	Type (b), $d = 0.4$, $h = 0.036$ Material / $b = 0.109$ / $b = 0.055$ 0.65 per cent C steel............ / 1.27 / 1.27 Armco iron...................... / 1.14 / 1.14 (Ref. 18)
Profile type (b)	Static rupture	Bending	Material / Type (a) / Type (b) Plaster......................... / 1.08 / 1.28 (Ref. 13)
		Torsion	Material / Type (a) / Type (b) Plaster......................... / 1.44–1.29 / 1.68 Cast iron...................... / 1.17 / .... (Refs. 12, 13)
17. Circular thickening (assumed rigid) in wide plate	Elastic stress	Tension	For either uniaxial or biaxial (equal) stress, $k = 1.54$ (Ref. 24)

TABLE XVII.—FACTORS OF STRESS CONCENTRATION FOR ELASTIC STRESS (k), FOR REPEATED STRESS (k_f), AND FOR RUPTURE (k_r).—(*Continued*)

<table>
<tr><th>Type of form irregularity or stress raiser</th><th>Stress condition</th><th>Manner of loading</th><th>Factor of stress concentration k, k_f, k_r for various dimensions</th></tr>
<tr><td rowspan="2">(Additional data)
1. Two V notches in member of rectangular section</td><td rowspan="2">Elastic stress</td><td>Bending (normal to plane of d)</td><td>
<table>
<tr><td>$\frac{r}{d}$</td><td>0.01</td><td>0.0125</td><td>0.025</td><td>0.05</td><td>0.10</td></tr>
<tr><td>k</td><td>4.0</td><td>3.6</td><td>2.7</td><td>2</td><td>1.5</td></tr>
</table>
(Ref. 28)</td></tr>
<tr><td>Torsion</td><td>$k = 1 + 0.47 \frac{d}{r}$ (Ref. 28)</td></tr>
<tr><td rowspan="3">(Additional data)
5. Circular hole in plate or rectangular bar</td><td>Elastic stress</td><td>Tension (load applied through close-fitting pin)</td><td>
<table>
<tr><td>$\frac{a}{d}$</td><td>0.10</td><td>0.15</td><td>0.20</td><td>0.25</td><td>0.30</td><td>0.40</td><td>0.50</td><td>0.60</td><td>0.70</td></tr>
<tr><td>k</td><td>9</td><td>7</td><td>5.5</td><td>4.5</td><td>4.0</td><td>3.0</td><td>2.7</td><td>2.2</td><td>2.0</td></tr>
</table>
(approximate values, k increases with looseness of fit and with proximity of hole to end of plate) (Ref. 29)</td></tr>
<tr><td rowspan="2">Repeated stress</td><td>Tension</td><td>
<table>
<tr><th>Material</th><th>Specimen</th><th>$\frac{a}{d}$</th><th>k_f</th><th></th></tr>
<tr><td>Steel, t.s. 84,000 lb. per sq. in.</td><td>0.87 in. wide × 0.65, hole as bored</td><td>0.23</td><td>1.61</td><td rowspan="3">tension $\frac{1}{4}$s to s, 10,000,000 cycles (Ref. 30)</td></tr>
<tr><td>Same</td><td>Hole polished, edges sharp</td><td>0.23</td><td>1.49</td></tr>
<tr><td>Same</td><td>Hole polished, edges rounded</td><td>0.23</td><td>1.42</td></tr>
<tr><td>Steel, .2 per cent C, t.s. 61,800 lb. per sq. in.</td><td>8 × $\frac{3}{4}$ in. plate, two 1-in. rivet holes</td><td></td><td>2.13, 1.43</td><td rowspan="3">tension 0 to s, 2,000,000 cycles. First values comparison small polished specimens, second values comparison unpierced plate. (Ref. 31)</td></tr>
<tr><td>Silicon steel, t.s. 80,800</td><td>Same</td><td></td><td>2.33, 1.49</td></tr>
<tr><td>Nickel steel, t.s. 99,000</td><td>Same</td><td></td><td>3.03, 1.60</td></tr>
</table></td></tr>
<tr><td>Bending</td><td>
<table>
<tr><th>Material</th><th>Specimen</th><th>$\frac{a}{d}$</th><th>k_f</th></tr>
<tr><td>Alloy steel H.T., t.s. 100,000 lb. per sq. in.</td><td>0.75 in. wide, hole as bored</td><td>0.16</td><td>1.78</td></tr>
<tr><td>Same</td><td>Hole edges rounded</td><td>0.16</td><td>1.63</td></tr>
<tr><td>Same</td><td>Hole edges rounded and pressed</td><td>0.16</td><td>1.40</td></tr>
</table>
(Ref. 30)</td></tr>
</table>

Case	Stress	Loading	Material	D	d	$\frac{r}{d}$	k_f	Ref.
(*Additional data*) 11. Square shoulder with fillet in circular shaft	Elastic stress	Bending	$k = 1 + 0.375\sqrt{\frac{d}{r}}$ (approximate formula)					(Ref. 32)
		Torsion	$k = 1 + 0.188\sqrt{\frac{d}{r}}$ (approximate formula)					(Ref. 32)
	Repeated stress	Bending	Steel *A*, low alloy, t.s. 78,400 lb. per sq. in.	0.5	0.25	0.08	2.20	(Ref. 33)
			Steel *B*, low alloy, t.s. 70,800	0.5	0.25	0.08	2.08	(Ref. 33)
			Steel *C*, low alloy, t.s. 91,300	0.5	0.25	0.08	2.10	(Ref. 33)
			Steel, 1.42 per cent C, t.s. 73,800	3.5	1.60	0	2.30	(Ref. 34)
			Same	1.94	1.60	0	1.90	(Ref. 34)
			Steel 1.44 per cent C, t.s. 87,000	....	0.35	0	2.10	(Ref. 35)
		Torsion	Steel S.A.E. 1020 hot rolled, t.s. 63,300 lb. per sq. in.	0.75	0.375	0.0053	1.15	(Ref. 36)
			Steel S.A.E. 3140 hot rolled, t.s. 115,000	0.75	0.3	0.027	1.54	(Ref. 36)
			Same	0.75	0.3	0.067	1.57	(Ref. 36)
			Steel S.A.E. 3140 heat treated, t.s. 162,000	0.75	0.3	0.0087	1.51	(Ref. 36)
			Steel *N*	0.552	0.394	0.17	0.96	(Ref. 37)
			Same	0.552	0.394	0.03	0.99	(Ref. 37)
			Steel *E*	0.552	0.394	0.17	1.11	(Ref. 37)
			Same	0.552	0.394	0.03	1.66	(Ref. 37)
			Cr-Ni-W steel	0.99	0.55	0.14	1.10	(Ref. 38)
			Same	2.12	1.18	0.10	1.17	(Ref. 38)
			Same	3.19	1.77	0.11	1.03	(Ref. 38)

TABLE XVII.—FACTORS OF STRESS CONCENTRATION FOR ELASTIC STRESS (k), FOR REPEATED STRESS (k_f) AND FOR RUPTURE (k_r).—(*Continued*)

Type of form irregularity or stress raiser	Stress condition	Manner of loading	Factor of stress concentration k, k_f, k_r for various dimensions
(*Additional data*) 13. V-notch in circular shaft	Elastic stress	Bending	$k = 1 + 2\sqrt{\frac{h}{r}}$ (approximate formula, $\frac{h}{d}$ small) (Ref. 32)
		Torsion	$k = 1 + \sqrt{\frac{h}{r}}$ (approximate formula, $\frac{h}{d}$ small) (Ref. 32)
	Repeated stress	Tension	See table below (Ref. 39)
		Bending	See table below (Ref. 40, 41, 45)
		Torsion	See table below (Ref. 45)

Repeated stress, Tension: $D = 0.25$, $d = 0.200$, $r = 0.01$ (Ref. 39)

Material	θ \ $\frac{h}{r}$	2.5
Cast iron, grey, t.s. 22,000 lb. per sq. in.	60°	1.08
Cast iron, Ni. Moly., t.s. 53,400	60°	1.21
Cast iron, Ni-Cr-Cu, t.s. 46,000	60°	1.31
Cast iron, Ni-Cr-Cu, t.s. 31,600	60°	1.42

Repeated stress, Bending

Material	h	0.025	0.0035	0.0035	0.025	0.0035	0.05	0.025	
	θ \ $\frac{h}{r}$	2.5	0.45	0.83	3.2	5.83	6.4	8.33	
Steel, S.A.E. 2330 H.T., t.s. 128,700 lb. per sq. in.	60°	2.55							$D = 0.3$, $d = 0.25$, $r = 0.01$ (Ref. 40)
Steel S.A.E. 4130 normal, t.s. 76,200	60°	1.72							
Steel S.A.E. 4130 H.T., t.s. 139,500	60°	2.87							
Steel S.A.E. 4130 H.T., t.s. 199,300	60°	2.15							
Ni-Cr steel, anneal., t.s. 82,300	60°	0.83							
Ni-Cr steel, cold dr., t.s. 132,500	60°	1.40							
Alcoa 27 S.T. H.T., t.s. 60,000	60°	2.14							
Steel 0.84–0.86 per cent C, H.T. 360 Brinell	55°		1.60		2.65		2.65		$D = 0.35$ (Ref. 41)
Same	75°					2.33			
Steel 0.16 per cent C	55°				1.52				
Same	75°			1.08		1.41			
Steel 0.91 per cent C, t.s. 225,000	60°							2.22	$D = 0.25$, $d = 0.20$, $r = 0.003$ (Ref. 45)
Steel 1.04 per cent C, t.s. 237,000	60°							2.04	
Cr-Van steel t.s. 237,000	60°							3.70	
Si-Man steel t.s. 236,000	60°							3.23	
Beryllium bronze t.s. 166,000	60°							1.89	

Repeated stress, Torsion (Ref. 45)

Material	θ \ $\frac{h}{r}$	8.33	
Steel 0.91 per cent C, t.s. 225,000 lb. per sq. in.	60°	1.28	$D = 0.25$
Steel 1.04 per cent C, t.s. 237,000	60°	1.30	$d = 0.20$
Cr-Van. steel, t.s. 237,000	60°	1.75	$r = 0.003$
Si-Man steel, t.s. 263,000	60°	2.19	torsion 0 to s
Beryllium bronze, t.s. 166,000	60°	1.15	

Static rupture	Tension, compression, and torsion	Material	k_r for tension	k_r for compression	k_r for torsion	
		Cast iron *A*	0.91	0.77	0.81	$\theta = 60°$, $D = 0.625$
		Cast iron *B*	1.03	0.87	0.95	$d = 0.50$, $r = 0.01$
		Cast iron *C*	1.05	0.73	0.92	$\frac{h}{r} = 6.25$
		Cast iron *D*	0.98	0.56	0.88	
		(cast irons described under "Repeated stress, Bending," above.)				(Ref. 39)

(Additional data)

14. **Radial hole in circular shaft** — Repeated stress — Bending

Material	$\frac{a}{d}$ \ d	0.4	0.35	
Steel *A* (Described under 11 above)	0.1	2.16		(Ref. 33)
Steel *B* (Described under 11 above)	0.1	2.10		(Ref. 33)
Steel *C* (Described under 11 above)	0.1	2.06		(Ref. 33)
Steel *D* (Described under 11 above)	0.1	2.54		(Ref. 33)
Cast iron *A* (Described under 13 above)	0.1	1.12		(Ref. 39)
Cast iron *B* (Described under 13 above)	0.1	1.50		(Ref. 39)
Cast iron *C* (Described under 13 above)	0.1	1.18		(Ref. 39)
Cast iron *D* (Described under 13 above)	0.1	1.71		(Ref. 39)
Steel 0.84–0.86 per cent C (Described under 13 above)	0.134		2.07	(Ref. 41)

Torsion

Material	$\frac{a}{d}$ \ d	0.4	0.38	0.394	0.55	1.18	1.77	
Steel S.A.E. 1020, hot rolled, t.s. 63,300 lb. per sq. in.	0.1	1.31						(Ref. 36)
Same	0.175	1.43						(Ref. 36)
Same	0.250	1.62						(Ref. 36)
Steel S.A.E. 3140, hot rolled, t.s. 115,000	0.1	2.00						(Ref. 36)
Same	0.25	2.25						(Ref. 36)
Rail steel, 0.78 per cent C, t.s. 133,000	0.1	1.64						(Ref. 36)
Same	0.25	2.26						(Ref. 36)
Steel S.A.E. 3140 H.T., t.s. 162,000	0.095		1.87					(Ref. 37)
Steel *N*	0.15			1.39				(Ref. 37)
Steel *V*	0.15			1.31				(Ref. 37)
Steel *E*	0.15			1.66				(Ref. 37)
Cr-Ni-W steel	0.14				1.60			(Ref. 38)
Same	0.10					1.88		(Ref. 38)
Same	0.11						1.74	(Ref. 38)
Cast iron, alloy, t.s. 43,900	0.10	1.07						(Ref. 42)
Cast iron *A* (Described under 13 above)	0.10	1.37						(Ref. 39)
Cast iron *B* (Described under 13 above)	0.10	1.38						(Ref. 39)
Cast iron *C* (Described under 13 above)	0.10	1.20						(Ref. 39)
Cast iron *D* (Described under 13 above)	0.10	1.20						(Ref. 39)

TABLE XVII.—FACTORS OF STRESS CONCENTRATION FOR ELASTIC STRESS (k), FOR REPEATED STRESS (k_f), AND FOR RUPTURE (k_r).—(*Continued*)

Type of form irregularity or stress raiser	Stress condition	Manner of loading	Factor of stress concentration k, k_f, k_r for various dimensions
(*Additional data*) 16. Key way in circular shaft	Elastic stress	Torsion	$k = 1 + \sqrt{\frac{h}{r}}$ (approximate formula for any longitudinal groove; r = min. corner radius) (Ref. 32)
	Repeated stress	Bending	See sub-table 16 below
18. Gear tooth. 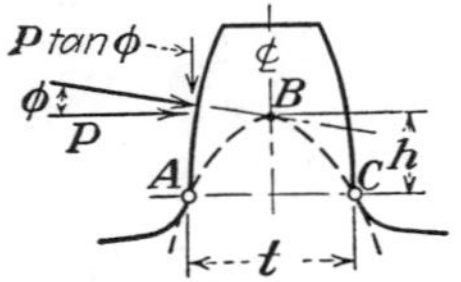 A and C are points of tangency of the inscribed parabola ABC with tooth profile, b = tooth width normal to plane of figure, r = minimum radius of tooth fillet.	Elastic stress	Bending plus some compression	For 14.5° pressure angle: $k = 0.22 + \left(\frac{t}{r}\right)^{0.2}\left(\frac{t}{h}\right)^{0.4}$ For 20° pressure angle: $k = 0.18 + \left(\frac{t}{r}\right)^{0.15}\left(\frac{t}{h}\right)^{0.45}$ k = (max s_t by photoelastic analysis) $\div$ $\left(\text{calculated max } s_t = \frac{6Ph}{bt^2} - \frac{P \tan \phi}{bt}\right)$ (Ref. 43) (Alternatively, the maximum stress can be found by the formula for a short cantilever, p. 132.)
19. Press-fitted collar on circular shaft	Repeated stress	Bending	See sub-table 19 below

Sub-table 16 (Key way in circular shaft, repeated stress, bending):

Material	Type (*a*)	Type (*b*)	
Steel 0.84–0.86 per cent, 360 Brinell		1.35	(Ref. 41)
Steel, low carbon, t.s. 60,000 lb. per sq. in.	1.25	1.71 (ends rounded as to width)	(Ref. 30)

Sub-table 19 (Press-fitted collar on circular shaft, repeated stress, bending):

Material	Shaft diameter	Collar fit or pressure	k_f (initial cracking)	k_f (break off)	
Steel 0.84–0.86 per cent C, H.T. 360 Brinell	0.25	<12,000 psi	....	1.97	(Ref. 41)
Steel S.A.E. 1045 H.T., t.s. 88,800 lb. per sq in.	2.00	0.003–0.004 in.	4.3	2.65	(Ref. 44)
Same, surface metallized	2.00	0.003–0.0073	1.64	1.64	(Ref. 44)
Same, surface flame hardened	2.00	0.003–0.0063	1.38	.....	(Ref. 44)
Steel 0.42 per cent C, t.s. 73,800	2.50	not given	....	1.50	(Ref. 34)
Same	1.60	16,000	....	2.00	(Ref. 34)
Same	1.60	90	....	1.40	(Ref. 34)
Steel 0.57 per cent C, t.s. 93,000	0.55	9,000	....	1.80	(Ref. 35)
Same	0.55	17,000	....	1.80	(Ref. 35)
Same	0.55	30,000	....	1.90	(Ref. 35)
Same, surface rolled	0.55	30,000	....	1.10	(Ref. 35)
Same, collar grooved near shaft	0.55	30,000	....	1.40	(Ref. 35)
Same, surface rolled, collar grooved	0.55	30,000	....	1.00	(Ref. 35)
Same, collar edge rounded 0.04 in. rad	0.55	30,000	....	1.80	(Ref. 35)
Same, collar edge rounded 0.12 in. rad	0.55	30,000	....	1.60	(Ref. 35)
Same, edge bearing only	0.55	30,000	....	1.70	(Ref. 35)
Cr-Ni steel H.T., t.s. 150,000	0.55	13,000	....	2.60	(Ref. 35)
Low-carbon steel, t.s. 62,000	0.55	17,000	....	1.80	(Ref. 35)
Steel 0.47 per cent C, t.s. 87,000	0.55	13,000	....	1.70	(Ref. 35)

			Material				
			Steel S.A.E. 1045 hot rolled	1.75	......	3.44 2.82 (compared 1.5 in. pol. spec.)	(Ref. 46)
			Steel S.A.E. 1045 H.T.	2.00	......	4.30 2.64 (compared 2.0 in. pol. spec.)	
			Steel S.A.E. 1045 as forged	7.00	......	1.93 1.59 (comp. 6 in. smooth turn. spec.)	
			Steel S.A.E. 1045 hot rolled, tapered from 1.89 to 1.69 on 0.75 in. rad.	1.89	......	3.67 3.00 (comp. 0.3 in. pol. spec.) 2.95 2.48 (comp. 1.5 in. pol. spec.)	
			Steel S.A.E. 1045 as forged, tapered from 7.625 to 6.8 on 2.5 in rad.	7.625	......	1.46 1.25 (comp. 6 in. smooth turn. spec.)	
			Steel S.A.E. 1045 as forged, tapered from 8.125 to 6.77 on 5 in. radius	8.125	......	1.30 1.09 (comp. 6 in. smooth turn spec.)	
			Steel S.A.E. 1045 H.T., shaft grooved next collar, groove radius 0.156 in.	2.00	......	2.44 2.06 (comp. 0.3 in. pol. spec.) 1.81 1.56 (comp. 2 in. pol. spec.)	

20. **Surface roughness**	Repeated stress	Tension	Material	Surface finish: Polished	Surface finish: Mill scale		
			Steel, 0.2 per cent C, t.s. 61,800 lb. per sq. in.	1	1.48	tension 0 to s, 2,000,000 cycles	(Ref. 31)
			Silicon steel, t.s. 80,800	1	1.56		
			Ni. steel, t.s. 99,000	1	1.89		

			Surface finish								
Bending	Material	Highly polished	Fine emery	Coarse emery	Ground	Smooth file	Coarse file	Smooth turned	Rough turned	
	Steel, 0.49 per cent C, H.T. 197 Brinell	1	1.06		1.13			1.19	1.21	(Ref. 30)
	Steel, 0.33 per cent C	1	1.02	1.06		1.08	1.24	1.14		
	Steel *A*, t.s. 55,200 lb. per sq. in.	1							1.21	(Ref. 48; see also Ref. 49)
	Steel *B*, t.s. 65,300	1							1.18	
	Steel *C*, t.s. 73,800	1							1.27	
	Steel *D*, t.s. 78,200	1							1.27	
	Steel *E*, t.s. 81,300	1							1.24	
	Steel, annealed, t.s. 60,000	1							1.19	
	Steel, annealed, t.s. 90,000	1							1.22	
	Steel, H.T., t.s. 140,000	1							1.31	

TABLE XVII.—FACTORS OF STRESS CONCENTRATION FOR ELASTIC STRESS (k), FOR REPEATED STRESS (k_f), AND FOR RUPTURE (k_r).—(*Continued*)

Type of form irregularity or stress raiser	Manner of loading	Factor of elastic stress concentration k for various dimensions (Ref. 51)								
		$\sqrt{h/r}$ \ $\sqrt{c/r}$	1	2	3	4	5	6	6.5	7.5
(*Additional data*) 1 and 2 Two notches in member of rectangular section	Tension	0.5	1.45	1.75	1.85	1.90	1.95	1.98	1.99	
		1	1.49	2.26	2.62	2.75	2.85	2.87	2.89	
		2	1.50	2.50	3.30	3.80	4.20	4.40	4.50	
		3	1.51	2.60	3.60	4.40	5.00	5.40	5.60	
		3.5	. . .	2.63	3.65	4.55	5.26	5.75	6.00	
r = notch radius, h = notch depth, c = half net width d	Bending	0.5	1.35	1.65	1.80	1.85	1.90	1.93	1.95	1.98
		1	1.37	1.80	2.26	2.60	2.70	2.80	2.83	2.85
		2	1.40	1.97	2.60	3.15	3.60	3.90	4.05	4.21
		3	1.42	1.99	2.63	3.40	3.88	4.42	4.65	5.02
		3.5	. . .	. . . .	. . . .	3.45	4.00	4.60	4.85	5.25
(*Additional data*) 3 and 4 One notch in member of rectangular section r = notch radius, h = notch depth, c = net width d	Tension	0.5	1.24	1.50	1.68	1.80	1.86	1.90	1.91	1.92
		1	1.25	1.55	1.87	2.18	2.40	2.57	2.62	2.70
		2	1.26	1.57	1.98	2.40	2.81	3.14	3.32	3.61
		3	. . . .	1.58	2.00	2.48	2.92	3.37	3.61	3.91
		3.5	. . . .	. . . .	. . . .	2.50	2.98	3.43	3.63	4.00
	Bending	0.5	1.37	1.65	1.82	1.90	1.93	1.95	1.96	1.98
		1	1.41	1.83	2.25	2.51	2.68	2.77	2.80	2.86
		2	1.45	1.91	2.50	3.05	3.50	3.80	3.91	4.11
		3	1.46	1.94	2.55	3.20	3.83	4.32	4.50	4.86
		3.5	. . . .	. . . .	2.58	3.25	3.88	4.48	4.69	5.10
(*Additional data*) 6 Elliptical hole in plate r = end radius of hole, h = half long axis a, c = distance end of hole to edge of plate	Tension	0.5	1.30	1.92	1.96	1.98				
		1	2.20	2.70	2.85	2.90				
		2	2.42	3.60	4.20	4.45				
		3	2.50	3.88	4.85	5.50				
		3.5	2.52	4.00	5.08	5.87				
	Bending	1	1.30	1.91	1.98	1.99				
		2	2.20	2.70	2.83	2.90				
		3	2.35	3.20	3.58	3.76				
		4	2.48	3.55	4.11	4.45				
		5	2.49	3.74	4.60	5.05				
		6	2.50	3.90	4.87	5.50				
		7	2.51	4.00	5.18	5.90				
(*Additional data*) 12 and 13 Circumferential notch in circular shaft r = notch radius, h = notch depth, c = half net diameter d	Tension	0.5	1.36	1.75	1.86	1.91	1.96	1.98	1.99	
		1	1.41	1.99	2.44	2.65	2.80	2.88	2.90	
		2	1.43	2.06	2.87	3.49	3.85	4.25	4.40	
		3	. . . .	2.11	3.00	3.77	4.40	5.13	5.43	
		3.5	. . . .	. . . .	3.07	3.85	4.60	5.40	5.80	
	Bending	0.5	1.35	1.68	1.80	1.87	1.91	1.95	1.98	
		1	1.40	1.80	2.20	2.48	2.62	2.76	2.80	
		2	1.42	1.86	2.40	2.91	3.30	3.80	4.05	
		3	. . . .	1.89	2.48	3.06	3.62	4.30	4.70	
		3.5	. . . .	. . . .	2.49	3.10	3.70	4.48	4.89	
	Torsion	1	1.25	1.42	1.60	1.74	1.80	1.85	1.90	
		2	1.25	1.48	1.72	1.95	2.16	2.40	2.50	
		3	. . . .	1.50	1.75	2.00	2.32	2.62	2.85	

		$\sqrt{h/r}$ →	0.5				1				2				3			
		$\sqrt{c/r}$ ↓ \ $\sqrt{b/r}$ →	1	2	4	6	1	2	4	6	1	2	4	6	1	2	4	6
21. V-notch (Case 13) in hollow circular shaft. b = distance central axis to root of notch, c = distance inner wall to root of notch, h = notch depth, r = notch radius	Tension	1	1.34	1.68	1.77	1.79	1.35	1.87	2.10	2.15	1.36	1.94	2.30	2.39	1.37	2.00	2.35	2.43
		2	1.35	1.75	1.89	1.90	1.38	2.05	2.55	2.62	1.38	2.16	3.10	3.37	1.39	2.20	3.25	3.61
		3	1.36	1.76	1.91	1.94	1.39	2.09	2.66	2.80	1.40	2.24	3.40	3.85	1.40	2.25	3.66	4.30
		4	1.36	1.77	1.94	1.97	1.40	2.11	2.68	2.86	1.40	2.25	3.52	4.04	1.42	2.28	3.86	4.68
	Bending	1	1.24	1.54	1.75	1.78	1.25	1.64	2.05	2.10	1.25	1.65	2.18	2.30	1.25	1.68	2.25	2.38
		2	1.24	1.60	1.80	1.89	1.25	1.74	2.35	2.55	1.25	1.76	2.75	3.16	1.25	1.77	2.85	3.35
		3	1.24	1.63	1.86	1.92	1.25	1.76	2.45	2.65	1.25	1.77	2.90	3.50	1.25	1.80	3.00	3.77
		4	1.25	1.65	1.90	1.94	1.25	1.80	2.48	2.70	1.25	1.80	2.95	3.60	1.25	1.81	3.10	4.00
		$\sqrt{h/r}$ →	1				2				3				4			
		$\sqrt{c/r}$ ↓ \ $\sqrt{b/r}$ →	2	4	6	7.5	2	4	6	7.5	2	4	6	7.5	2	4	6	7.5
	Torsion	1	1.25	1.30	1.35	1.37	1.25	1.31	1.36	1.38	1.25	1.31	1.37	1.39				
		2	1.34	1.52	1.55	1.58	1.35	1.70	1.72	1.74	1.35	1.70	1.73	1.76				
		3	1.35	1.73	1.77	1.79	1.40	1.83	2.00	2.06	1.42	1.90	2.08	2.13	1.42	1.91	2.09	2.14
		4	1.36	1.74	1.81	1.83	1.41	1.95	2.13	2.20	1.43	2.05	2.30	2.40	1.43	2.07	2.35	2.50
		5	1.37	1.75	1.85	1.88	1.42	2.01	2.24	2.33	1.43	2.20	2.35	2.60	1.44	2.25	2.60	2.75
		6.5	1.39	1.77	1.88	1.91	1.43	2.10	2.35	2.48	1.44	2.30	2.63	2.80	1.44	2.37	2.75	2.95
		7.5	1.40	1.78	1.89	1.92	1.43	2.15	2.42	2.55	1.44	2.35	2.70	2.85	1.44	2.45	2.82	3.04

TABLE XVII.—FACTORS OF STRESS CONCENTRATION FOR ELASTIC STRESS (k), FOR REPEATED STRESS (k_f), AND FOR RUPTURE (k_r).—(*Continued*)

Type of form irregularity or stress raiser	Stress condition	Manner of loading	Factor of stress concentration, k, k_f, k_r for various dimensions
(*Additional data*) 3. One V notch in member of rectangular section	Elastic stress	Bending	For same dimensions of specimen D, d, h, etc., change $k_u = k$ for U notch to $k_\theta = k$ for V notch according to table below. Values given by Leven and Frocht (Ref. 63) and are for single notch in rectangular bar, but probably apply without serious error to Cases 1 and 2, 12 and 13

$\theta°$															
	$k_u =$ 1.20	1.40	1.60	1.80	2.00	2.20	2.40	2.60	2.80	3.00	3.20	3.40	3.60	3.80	4.00
0	$k_\theta =$ 1.20	1.40	1.60	1.80	2.00	2.20	2.40	2.60	2.80	3.00	3.20	3.40	3.60	3.80	4.00
70	1.20	1.40	1.60	1.80	2.00	2.20	2.40	2.60	2.79	2.98	3.18	3.39	3.54	3.74	3.92
90	1.20	1.40	1.60	1.80	2.00	2.20	2.38	2.56	2.75	2.93	3.12	3.30	3.51	3.62	3.78
100	1.20	1.40	1.60	1.80	1.98	2.16	2.34	2.52	2.70	2.89	3.06	3.23	3.39	3.52	3.66
110	1.20	1.40	1.60	1.78	1.96	2.14	2.31	2.48	2.64	2.80	2.96	3.10	3.24	3.38	3.50
120	1.20	1.39	1.59	1.76	1.92	2.08	2.24	2.40	2.54	2.68	2.82	2.96	3.08	3.19	3.28
130	1.20	1.38	1.56	1.71	1.86	2.00	2.12	2.24	2.36	2.48	2.58	2.69	2.80	2.90	3.00
140	1.19	1.36	1.50	1.64	1.75	1.86	1.96	2.06	2.16	2.26	2.35	2.44	2.52	2.60	2.66
150	1.18	1.32	1.44	1.54	1.64	1.72	1.80	1.88	1.94	2.00	2.06	2.12	2.17	2.22	2.26
160	1.16	1.27	1.35	1.42	1.48	1.54	1.58	1.62	1.65	1.68	1.72	1.76	1.80	1.83	1.86
170	1.12	1.20	1.26	1.30	1.33	1.35	1.38	1.39	1.40	1.42	1.43	1.44	1.44	1.44	1.44
180	1	1	1	1	1	1	1	1	1	1	1	1	1	1	1

Type of form irregularity or stress raiser	Stress condition	Manner of loading	Factor of stress concentration, k, k_f, k_r for various dimensions
(*Additional data*) 5. Circular hole in plate or rectangular bar	Repeated stress	Tension	$a/d =$ 0.0105 0.0210 0.0400 0.0658 0.1265 0.250 0.458 $k_f =$ 1.60 1.73 1.81 1.93 1.99 1.80 1.69 0.36% C steel (Ref. 58)
(*Additional data*) 8. Square shoulder with fillet in rectangular bar	Elastic stress	Tension	see table below (Ref. 56)
		Bending	$k = 1 + \left\{\tanh^{\frac{1}{2}}\left[2\left(\frac{L}{D}+\frac{r}{d}\right)\right]\right\}\left\{\tanh\left[\frac{(D/d-1)^{\frac{1}{4}}}{1-r/d}\right]\right\}\left\{\frac{0.13+0.65(1-r/d)^4}{(r/d)^{\frac{1}{3}}}\right\}^{\frac{1}{3}}$ (Ref. 53)

D/d \ r/d	0.01	0.015	0.02	0.03	0.04	0.05	0.06
2	....	4.75	4.13	3.50	3.25	3.00	2.80
1.5	4.50	3.75	3.50	3.10	2.80	2.65	2.50

(Ref. 56)

(Additional data)

11. Square shoulder with fillet in circular shaft

Elastic stress

Tension

$\frac{D}{d}$ \ $\frac{r}{d}$	0.05	0.07	0.10	0.15	0.20	0.25	0.30
1.01	1.36	1.29	1.23	1.18	1.15	1.13	1.12
1.02	1.49	1.40	1.33	1.26	1.22	1.20	1.19
1.05	1.70	1.56	1.45	1.36	1.31	1.27	1.24
1.10	1.87	1.70	1.55	1.44	1.36	1.31	1.28
1.20	2.11	1.90	1.69	1.52	1.44	1.37	1.33
1.30	2.21	1.98	1.77	1.59	1.49	1.43	1.38
1.50	2.39	2.11	1.89	1.68	1.56	1.48	1.43
2.00	2.56	2.24	1.99	1.77	1.63	1.54	1.47

(Ref. 55)

Bending

$\frac{D}{d}$ \ $\frac{r}{d}$	0.05	0.07	0.10	0.15	0.20	0.25	0.30
1.01	1.54	1.45	1.36	1.26	1.20	1.16	1.14
1.02	1.64	1.54	1.44	1.34	1.26	1.22	1.20
1.05	1.77	1.64	1.53	1.42	1.34	1.29	1.25
1.10	1.88	1.71	1.59	1.46	1.38	1.31	1.26
1.20	1.96	1.79	1.62	1.48	1.39	1.32	1.27
1.50	2.06	1.86	1.67	1.52	1.42	1.34	1.29
2.00	2.16	1.95	1.73	1.55	1.43	1.35	1.30
6.00	2.40	2.15	1.87	1.64	1.49	1.39	1.32

(Ref. 55)

TABLE XVII.—FACTORS OF STRESS CONCENTRATION FOR ELASTIC STRESS (k), FOR REPEATED STRESS (k_f), AND FOR RUPTURE (k_r).—(*Continued*)

Type of form irregularity or stress raiser	Stress condition	Manner of loading	Factor of stress concentration, k, k_f, k_r for various dimensions
(*Additional data*) 11. Square shoulder with fillet in circular shaft	Elastic stress	Bending and torsion relative to tension	Allison (Ref. 55) determined values of k for axial loading, bending, and torsion by photoelastic methods. The values he gives are generally lower than those tabulated above and indicate an opposite influence of the D/d ratio after this reaches a value of about 1.5. Allison represents the ratios of k for bending and torsion to k for axial loading to be as tabulated below:

$\frac{r}{d}$ \ $\frac{d}{D}$	$\frac{k\ \text{bending}}{k\ \text{axial}}$ 0.4	0.6	0.8	$\frac{k\ \text{torsion}}{k\ \text{axial}}$ 0.4	0.6	0.8
0.05	0.88	0.92	0.98	0.62	0.61	0.70
0.10	0.86	0.90	0.98	0.66	0.66	0.75
0.20	0.87	0.91	0.99	0.73	0.72	0.82
0.40	0.89	0.94	0.98	0.80	0.80	0.87
0.60	0.90	0.94	0.97	0.83	0.83	0.90
1.00	0.91	0.95	0.97	0.87	0.89	0.94

Repeated stress — Bending:

Material	D	d	$\frac{r}{d}$	k_f
0.33% C steel	1.25	0.60	0.083	1.47
0.33% C steel H.T.	1.25	0.60	0.083	1.92
0.33% C steel	1.25	0.60	0.25	1.11
0.60% C steel H.T.	1.25	0.60	0.083	1.62
0.53% C steel H.T.	2.00	1.00	0.188	1.42
0.53% C steel H.T.	2.50	2.00	0.156	1.37

(Ref. 10)

(Additional data)
13. V notch in circular shaft — Repeated stress — Tension

Material	θ \ $\frac{h}{r}$	100	8	1	10	8	0.8
Mild steel (58,700) $D = 1.69$	55°	3.79	3.79	2.15			
Ni-Cr steel (141,000) $D = 0.564$	55°				8.2	2.5	5.0

(Ref. 54)

(Additional data)
14. Radial hole in circular shaft

Elastic stress — Bending

$\frac{a}{d}$	0	0.02	0.04	0.06	0.08	0.10	0.15	0.20	0.25	0.30
k	3	2.69	2.51	2.41	2.32	2.26	2.13	2.03	1.95	1.90

(Ref. 52)

Elastic stress — Torsion

$\frac{a}{d}$	0	0.02	0.04	0.06	0.08	0.10	0.15	0.20	0.25	0.30
k	2	1.90	1.83	1.75	1.70	1.65	1.57	1.50	1.46	1.42

(Ref. 52)

Repeated stress — Tension

Material	$\frac{a}{d}$ \ d	2.44	1.69	0.98	0.56	0.33	0.19
Mild steel (56,000)	0.165	2.20					
Mild steel (55,000)	0.166		2.15				
Mild steel (55,000)	0.159			1.95			
Mild steel (55,000)	0.168				1.65		
Mild steel (55,000)	0.166					1.55	
Mild steel (55,000)	0.161						1.80
Ni-Cr steel (140,000)	0.166		2.75				
Ni-Cr steel (140,000)	0.159			2.75			
Ni-Cr steel (140,000)	0.168				2.40		
Ni-Cr steel (140,000)	0.166					2.25	
Ni-Cr steel (140,000)	0.161						2.55

(Ref. 54)

TABLE XVII.—FACTORS OF STRESS CONCENTRATION FOR ELASTIC STRESS (k), FOR REPEATED STRESS (k_f), AND FOR RUPTURE (k_r).—(*Continued*)

Type of form irregularity or stress raiser	Stress condition	Manner of loading	Factor of stress concentration, k, k_f, k_r for various dimensions
22. U-shaped member	Elastic stress	As shown	k_1 is ratio of actual to nominal bending stress at point 1, and k_2 is this ratio at point 2. Nominal bending stress $= Pey/I$ at point 1 and Ply/I at point 2, where I/y = section modulus (Ref. 57)

Dimension ratios and values of k

Outer corners	$\frac{e}{r_i} = \frac{e}{w} = \frac{e}{d}$	k_1	k_2
Square	4.5 3.5 2.5 1.5	1.24 1.20 1.30 1.24	1.24 1.24 1.20 1.61
	$\frac{e}{2r_i} = \frac{e}{2w} = \frac{e}{d}$		
Square	2.5 2.0 1.5 1.0	1.50 1.52 1.53 1.46	1.29 1.33 1.22 1.75

Outer corners	Ratio	$h = \frac{3}{4}D$, k_1	$h = \frac{3}{4}D$, k_2	$h = \frac{1}{4}D$, k_1	$h = \frac{1}{4}D$, k_2
	$\frac{d}{r_i} = \frac{d}{w}$				
Square	2.0 1.5 1.25 1.0 0.75	1.50 1.34 1.29 1.24 1.21	1.29 1.10 1.23 1.24 1.10	1.53 1.37 1.33 1.30 1.24	1.22 1.40 1.41 1.20 1.22
	$\frac{r_0}{r_i} = \frac{r_0}{d} = \frac{r_0}{w}$				
Rounded to radius r_0	2.75 2.37 2.12 2.0	1.24 1.18 1.16 1.27	1.24 1.21 1.22 1.42	1.30 1.18 1.21 1.31	1.20 1.22 1.31 1.56
	$\frac{d}{r_i} = \frac{w}{r_i}$				
Square	7.0 3.0 1.67 1.0	2.29 1.72 1.49 1.24	1.93 1.59 1.37 1.24	2.38 1.76 1.41 1.30	2.38 1.62 1.52 1.20
	$\frac{d}{r_i}$ $\frac{d}{w}$				
Square	5 1.67 3 1.80 2 2.0	2.33 1.82 1.50	1.73 1.30 1.29	2.32 1.75 1.53	2.00 1.56 1.22

References for Table XVII

1. Peterson, R. E., and A. M. Wahl: Two and Three-dimensional Cases of Stress Concentration, and Comparison with Fatigue Tests, *Am. Soc. Mech. Eng., Jour. Appl. Mech.*, Vol. 3, No. 1, p. A-15, 1936.

2. Jacobsen, L. S.: Torsional Stresses in Shafts Having Grooves or Fillets, *Am. Soc. Mech. Eng., Jour. Appl. Mech.*, Vol. 2, No. 4, p. A-154, 1935.

3. Sonntag, R.: Zur Torsion von runden Wellen mit veränderlichem Durchmesser, *Zeits. angew. Math. Mech.*, Vol. 9, p. 1, 1929.

4. Neuber, H. P.: Elastische strenge Lösungen zur Kerbwirkung bei Scheiben und Umdrehungskörpern and Ein neuer Ansatz zur Lösung raumlicher Probleme der Elastizitätstheorie, *Zeits. angew. Math. Mech.*, Vol. 13, p. 439, 1933, and Vol. 14, p. 203, 1934.

5. Timoshenko, S., and W. Diet.: Stress Concentration Produced by Holes and Fillets, *Trans. Am. Soc. Mech. Eng.*, Vol. 47, p. 199, 1925.

6. Frocht, M.: Factors of Stress Concentration Photoelastically Determined, *Am. Soc. Mech. Eng., Jour. Appl. Mech.*, Vol. 2, No. 2, p. A-67, 1935.

7. Inglis, C. E.: Stresses in a Plate Due to the Presence of Cracks and Sharp Corners, *Engineering* (London), Vol. 95, p. 415, 1913.

8. Thomas, W. N.: The Effect of Scratches and Various Workshop Finishes upon the Fatigue Strength of Steel, *Engineering* (London), Vol. 116, p. 449, 1923.

9. Peterson, R. E.: Model Testing as Applied to Strength of Materials, *Am. Soc. Mech. Eng., Paper* APM 55-11, *Jour. Appl. Mech.*, Vol. 1, No. 2, 1933.

10. Peterson, R. E.: Stress Concentration Phenomena in Fatigue of Materials, *Am. Soc. Mech. Eng., Paper* APM 55-19, *Jour. Appl. Mech.*, Vol. 1, No. 4, 1933.

11. Trinks, W., and J. H. Hitchcock: Strength of Roll Necks, R. P. 55-5, *Trans. Am. Soc. Mech. Eng.*, Vol. 55, p. 67, 1933.

12. Roark, R. J., R. S. Hartenberg, and R. Z. Williams: Influence of Form and Scale on Strength, *Eng. Exp. Sta., Univ. Wis., Bull.*, 1938.

13. Private communication.

14. Moore, R. R.: Effect of Grooves, Threads and Corrosion upon the Fatigue of Metals, *Proc. Am. Soc. Testing Materials*, Vol. 26, Part II, p. 255, 1926.

15. Templin, R. L.: The Fatigue Properties of Light Metals and Alloys, *Proc. Am. Soc. Testing Materials*, Vol. 33, Part II, p. 364, 1933.

16. Moore, H. F., S. H. Lyons, and N. P. Inglis: Tests of the Fatigue Strength of Cast Iron, *Eng. Exp. Sta., Univ. Ill., Bull.* 164, 1927.

17. Moore, H. F., and T. M. Jasper: An Investigation of the Fatigue of Metals, *Eng. Exp. Sta., Univ. Ill., Bull.* 152, 1925.

18. Gough, H. J.: British Aero. Research Committee Reports, Vol. II, p. 488, 1924–1925.

19. Moore, H. F.: The Effect of Keyways on the Strength of Shafts, *Eng. Exp. Sta., Univ. Ill., Bull.* 42, 1910.

20. Coker, E. G.: Photoelastic and Strain Measurements of the Effects of Circular Holes on the Distribution of Stress in Tension Members, *Engineering* (London), Vol. 109, p. 259.

21. Jeffery, J. B.: Plane Stress and Plane Strain in Bipolar Coordinates, *Philos. Proc. Royal Soc., London,* A Vol. 221, p. 265, 1921.

22. Wahl, A. M., and R. Beeuwkes: Stress Concentration Produced by Holes and Notches, *Trans. Am. Soc. Mech. Eng.*, Vol. 56, p. 617, 1934.

23. Peterson, R. E.: Fatigue of Shafts having Keyways, *Proc. Am. Soc. Testing Materials*, Vol. 32, Part II, p. 413, 1932.

24. Palmblad, E.: Störung der gleichmässigen Spannungsverteilung in einer Scheibe durch Verdickungen, Doctor's dissertation, Darmstadt.

25. Stanton, T. E., and L. Bairstow: On the Resistance of Iron and Steel to Reversals of Direct Stress, *Inst. Civil Eng.* (British), Vol. 166, Part IV, p. 78, 1905–06.

26. Haigh, B. P.: Report of Committee on Complex Stress Distribution, Reports of British Association for Advancement of Science, 1922–1924.

27. Moore, H. F., and P. E. Henwood: The Strength of Screw Threads under Repeated Tension, *Eng. Exp. Sta., Univ. Ill., Bull.* 264, 1934.

28. Lee, G. H.: The Influence of Hyperbolic Notches on the Transverse Flexure of Elastic Plates, *Am. Soc. Mech. Eng. Paper* A-53, *Jour. Appl. Mech.*, Vol. 7, No. 2, June, 1940.

29. Frocht, M. M., and H. N. Hill: Stress Concentration Factors around a Central Circular Hole in a Plate Loaded through a Pin in Hole, *Am. Soc. Mech. Eng., Jour. Appl. Mech.*, Vol. 7, No. 1, p. A-5 March, 1940.

30. "Prevention of Fatigue of Metals," Battelle Mem. Inst., John Wiley & Sons, Inc., 1941.

31. Wilson, W. M., and F. P. Thomas: Fatigue Tests of Riveted Joints, *Eng. Exp. Sta. Univ. Ill., Bull.* 302, 1938.

32. Wilson, W. K.: "Practical Solution of Torsional Vibration Problems," 2d ed., Vol. II, John Wiley & Sons, Inc., 1941.

33. Collins, W. L. and T. J. Dolan: Physical Properties of Four Low-alloy High-strength Steels, *Proc. Am. Soc. Testing Materials*, Vol. 38, Part II, p. 157, 1938.

34. Peterson, R. E., and A. M. Wahl: Fatigue of Shafts at Fitted Members, with a Related Photoelastic Analysis, *Am. Soc. Mech. Engr.*, *Paper* A-1, *Jour. Appl. Mech.*, Vol. 2, No. 1, March, 1935.

35. Thum, A. and F. Wunderlich: Der Einfluss von Einspann und Kraffangriffsstellen auf die Dauerhaltbarkeit der Konstruktionen, *Zeit. Vereines Deutscher Ing.*, Vol. 77, No. 31, Aug. 5, 1933.

36. Dolan, T. J.: The Combined Effect of Corrosion and Stress Concentration at Holes and Fillets in Steel Specimens Subjected to Reversed Torsional Stresses, *Eng. Exp. Sta. Univ. Ill.*, *Bull.* 293, 1937.

37. Armbruster, E.: Einfluss der Oberflachenbeschaffenheit auf den Spannungsverlauf und die Schwingungsfestigkeit, Vereines Duetscher Ing. Verlag, 1931.

38. Mailander, R., and W. B. Bauersfeld: Einfluss der Probengrosse und Probenform auf die Schwingungsfestigkeit von Stahl, *Technische Mitteilungen Krupp*, Vol. 2, p. 143, December, 1934.

39. Collins, W. L., and J. O. Smith: The Notch Sensitivity of Alloyed Cast Irons Subjected to Repeated and Static Loads, *Proc. Am. Soc. Testing Materials*, Vol. 42, Part II, 1942.

40. Oberg, T. T., and J. B. Johnson: Fatigue Properties of Metals Used in Aircraft Construction at 3450 and 10600 Cycles, *Proc. Am. Soc. Testing Materials*, Vol. 37, Part II, p. 195, 1937.

41. Lea, F. C.: The Effect of Discontinuities and Surface Conditions on Failure under Repeated Stress, *Engineering*, Vol. 144, July 23, 1937.

42. Draffin, J. O., and W. L. Collins: The Mechanical Properties of a High Strength Cast Iron, *Proc. Am. Soc. Testing Materials*, Vol. 39, Part II, p. 589, 1939.

43. Dolan, T. J., and E. L. Broghamer: A Photo-elastic Study of Stresses in Gear Tooth Fillets, *Eng. Exp. Sta. Univ. Ill. Bull.* 335, 1942.

44. Horger, O. J., and T. V. Buckwalter: Fatigue Strength of 2-inch Diameter Axles with Surfaces Metal Coated and Flame Hardened, *Proc. Am. Soc. Testing Materials*, Vol. 40, Part II, p. 733, 1940.

45. Johnson, J. B.: Fatigue Characteristics of Helical Springs, *Iron Age*, Vol. 133, March 15 and 22, 1934.

46. Horger, O. J., and T. V. Buckwalter: Improving Engine Axles and Piston Rods, *Metal Progress*, Vol. 39, No. 2, Feb. 1941.

47. Horger, O. J., and H. R. Neifert: Effect of Surface Conditions on Fatigue Properties, "The Surface Treatment of Metals," *Am. Soc. of Metals*, 1940.

48. Horger, O. J.: Fatigue Strength of Members as Influenced by Surface Conditions, *Product Eng.*, November and December, 1940; January, 1941.

49. Karpov, A. V.: Fatigue Problems in Structural Design, *Metals and Alloys*, Vol. 10, November and December, 1939.

50. Dumont, C.: Stress Concentration around an Open Circular Hole in a Plate Subjected to Bending Normal to the Plane of the Plate, *Nat. Adv. Comm. Aeron., Tech. Note* 740, 1939.

51. Neuber, H.: "Theory of Notch Stresses," J. W. Edwards, 1946.

52. Peterson, R. E.: "Stress Concentration Design Factors," John Wiley & Sons, Inc., 1953.

53. Hartman, J. B., and N. M. Leven: Factors of Stress Concentration for the Bending Case of Fillets in Flat Bars and Shafts with Central Enlarged Section, *Proc. Soc. Exp. Stress Anal.*, Vol. 9, No. 1, 1951.

54. Phillips, C. E., and R. B. Heywood: Size Effect in Fatigue of Steel Specimens under Reversed Direct Stress, *Proc. Inst. Mech. Eng.*, Vol. 165, 1951.

55. Allison, I. M.: The Elastic Stress Concentration Factors in Shouldered Shafts, *Aeron. Quarterly*, May, 1961 (Tension); August, 1961 (Bending); May, 1962 (Torsion).

56. Frocht, M. M., and D. Landsberg: Factors of Stress Concentration in Bars with Deep Sharp Grooves and Fillets in Tension, *Proc. Soc. Exp. Stress Anal.*, Vol. 8, No. 2, 1951.

57. Mantle, J. B., and T. J. Dolan: A Photoelastic Study of Stresses in U-shaped Members, *Proc. Soc. Exp. Stress Anal.*, Vol. 6, No. 1, 1948.

58. Massonet, Ch.: The Effect of Size, Shape and Grain Size on the Fatigue Strength of Medium Carbon Steel, *Proc. Am. Soc. Testing Materials*, Vol. 56, 1956.

59. Mindlin, R. D.: Stress Distribution around a Hole near the Edge of a Plate under Tension, *Proc. Soc. Exp. Stress Anal.*, Vol. 5, No. 2, 1948.

60. Timoshenko, S.: "Strength of Materials, Advanced Theory and Problems," Part II, D. Van Nostrand Company, Inc., 1941.

61. Leven, M. M.: Stresses in Keyways by Photoelastic Methods and Comparison with Numerical Solution, *Proc. Soc. Exp. Stress Anal.*, Vol. 7, No. 2, 1949.

62. Lee, Geo. H.: The Influence of Hyperbolic Notches on the Transverse Flexure of Elastic Plates, *Trans. Am. Soc. Mech. Eng.*, Vol. 62, 1940.

63. LEVEN, M. M., and M. M. FROCHT: Stress Concentration Factors for a Single Notch in a Flat Bar in Pure and Central Bending, *Proc. Soc. Exp. Stress Anal.*, Vol. 11, No. 2, 1954.

64. LIPTON, CHARLES, and R. C. JUVINELL: "Handbook of Stress and Strength," The Macmillan Company, 1963.

Table XVIII.—Values of the Rupture Factor for Brittle Materials
(See Art. 9 for discussion of Rupture Factor)

Form of member and manner of loading	Rupture factor; ratio of computed max stress at rupture to ultimate tensile strength		Ratio of computed max stress at rupture to modulus of rupture in bending or torsion	
	Cast iron	Plaster	Cast iron	Plaster
1. Rectangular beam, end support, center loading $\frac{l}{d} = 8$ or more	1.70 (See Table IV)	1.60	1	1
2. Solid circular plate, edge support, uniform loading, $\frac{a}{t} = 10$ or more		1.71		1.07
3. Solid circular plate edge support, uniform loading on concentric circular area	$2.4 - 0.5\left(\frac{r_0}{a}\right)^{\frac{1}{6}}$	$2.2 - 0.5\left(\frac{r_0}{a}\right)^{\frac{1}{6}}$	$1.40 - 0.3\left(\frac{r_0}{a}\right)^{\frac{1}{6}}$	$1.4 - 0.3\left(\frac{r_0}{a}\right)^{\frac{1}{6}}$

4. Solid circular plate, edge support, loaded uniformly along concentric ring	$2.5 - 1.2\left(\frac{r_0}{a}\right)^{\frac{1}{4}}$	$2.1 - 0.8\left(\frac{r_0}{a}\right)^{\frac{1}{4}}$	$1.50 - 0.7\left(\frac{r_0}{a}\right)^{\frac{1}{4}}$	$1.3 - 0.5\left(\frac{r_0}{a}\right)^{\frac{1}{4}}$
5. Pierced circular plate, edge support, loaded uniformly along inner boundary	$5.1 - 3.4\left(\frac{b}{a}\right)^{\frac{1}{4}}$	$2.4 - 0.8\left(\frac{b}{a}\right)^{\frac{1}{3}}$	$3 - 2\left(\frac{b}{a}\right)^{\frac{1}{4}}$	$1.5 - 0.5\left(\frac{b}{a}\right)^{\frac{1}{3}}$
6. Rectangular plate, length a, width b, edge support, uniform loading, $\frac{b}{t} = 16$		1.60		1.00
7. Rectangular plate, edge support, uniform loading on small concentric circular area $r_0 > t$		1.75		1.10

TABLE XVIII.—VALUES OF THE RUPTURE FACTOR FOR BRITTLE MATERIALS.—(*Continued*)

Form of member and manner of loading	Rupture factor; ratio of computed max stress at rupture to ultimate tensile strength		Ratio of computed max stress at rupture to modulus of rupture in bending or torsion	
	Cast iron	Plaster	Cast iron	Plaster
8. Curved beam of rectangular section, $\frac{R}{c}$ from 1 to 8 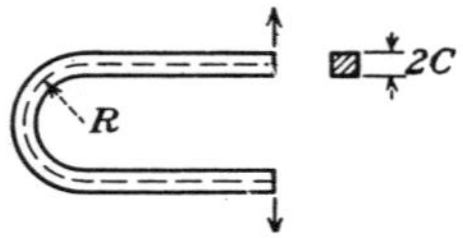	$2.7 - 0.34\left(\frac{R}{c}\right)^{\frac{1}{2}}$	$1.9 - 0.19\left(\frac{R}{c}\right)^{\frac{1}{2}}$	$1.60 - 0.2\left(\frac{R}{c}\right)^{\frac{1}{2}}$	$1.20 - 0.12\left(\frac{R}{c}\right)^{\frac{1}{2}}$
9. Circular ring of rectangular section, $\frac{R}{c}$ from 4 to 8 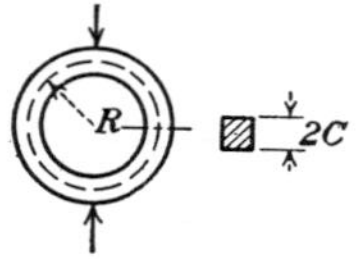	$2.7 - 0.34\left(\frac{R}{c}\right)^{\frac{1}{2}}$	$2.0 - 0.19\left(\frac{R}{c}\right)^{\frac{1}{2}}$	$1.60 - 0.2\left(\frac{R}{c}\right)^{\frac{1}{2}}$	$1.25 - 0.12\left(\frac{R}{c}\right)^{\frac{1}{2}}$
10. Bar of circular section in torsion 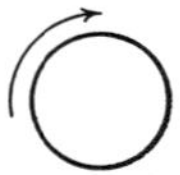	1.02 to 1.79	1.09	1	1

11. Bar of triangular section in torsion 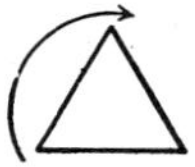	1.52	1.32	1.49	1.21
12. Bar of rectangular section in torsion 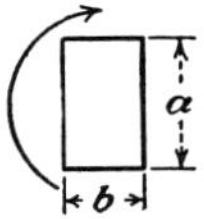	1.50	$0.6 + 0.3\left(\frac{a}{b}\right)^{\frac{1}{2}}$	1.47	$0.55 + 0.27\left(\frac{a}{b}\right)^{\frac{1}{2}}$
13 Bar of T or I section in torsion 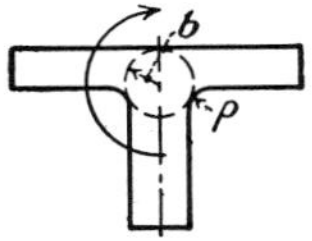		$6 - 3.8\left(\frac{\rho}{b}\right)^{\frac{1}{6}}$		$5.5 - 3.5\left(\frac{\rho}{b}\right)^{\frac{1}{6}}$

TABLE XIX.—REPRESENTATIVE PROPERTIES OF SOME IMPORTANT STRUCTURAL MATERIALS

1. Metals

Material	δ, weight, lb. per cu. in.	α, coef. of thermal exp., °F $\times 10^5$	E, million lb. per sq. in.	G, million lb. per sq. in.	Poisson's ratio	Strength properties—thousand lb. per sq. in.								
						Tensile properties			Compressive properties		Shear properties		Modulus of rupture in cross-bending	Endurance strength (Rot. beam, 10^7 cycles)
						Ultimate strength (s_u)	Elastic limit	Yield pt. or yield strength	Ultimate strength	Yield strength	Ultimate strength	Yield strength		
Aluminum, cast, pure	0.0976	1.30	9	3.7	0.36	11	5							
Aluminum, cast, 220-T4	0.093	1.36	9.5	3.55	0.33	42		22		23	30			11
Aluminum, wrought, 2014-T6	0.101	1.28	10.6	4	0.33	68		60		62	39	35		20
Aluminum, wrought, 6061-T6	0.098	1.30	10	3.75	0.3	38		35		35	24	20		17
Beryllium copper	0.297	0.93	19	7		100–200	110–150	140			100–130	70–100		40
Brass, naval	0.304	1.18	15	5.5		57–75		25–50			40–45			$0.35s_u$
Bronze, phosphor, A.S.T.M. B159	0.320	0.99	15	6.5		100–150	60–110		70–110	50–85	70–110	50–85		$0.32s_u$
Cast iron, gray, No. 20	0.251	0.60	14		0.25	20			90		32		46	10
Cast iron, gray, No. 30	0.260	0.60	15.2		0.25	30			115		44		57	14.5
Cast iron, gray, No. 40	0.260	0.60	18.3		0.25	40			130		51		66	19
Cast iron, gray, No. 60	0.270	0.60	19		0.25	60			180		72		100	24
Cast iron, malleable	0.266	0.75	26	8.8	0.25	50–65		32–45	200		49		62	32
Cast iron, nodular	0.257	0.66	23.5		0.25	60–100		45–65	200					
Magnesium, AZ80A-T5	0.065	1.60	6.5	2.4		55		38		17	24			16
Titanium, pure	0.163	0.53	15.5	5.8	0.34	65–80		55–70						$0.6s_u$
Titanium, alloy, 5 Al, 2.5 Sn	0.161	0.57	17	6.2	0.33	115		110		110	100			$0.6s_u$
Steel for bridges and buildings, A.S.T.M. A7-61T:														
All shapes	0.283	0.65	29	11.5	0.27	60–75		33		33		17		$0.5s_u$
Plates $t < 1.5$	0.283	0.65	29	11.5	0.27	60–72		33		33		17		$0.5s_u$
Plates $t > 1.5$	0.283	0.65	29	11.5	0.27	60–75		33		33		17		$0.5s_u$
High-strength low-alloy structural steel, A.S.T.M. A242-63T														
Most shapes	0.283	0.65	29	11.5	0.27	70		50		50		25		$0.5s_u$
Plates $t < 0.75$	0.283	0.65	29	11.5	0.27	70		50		50		25		$0.5s_u$
Plates $t > 0.75 < 1.5$	0.283	0.65	29	11.5	0.27	67		46		46		23		$0.5s_u$
Plates $t > 1.5 < 4$	0.283	0.65	29	11.5	0.27	63		42		42		21		$0.5s_u$
High-strength steel castings for structural purposes, A.S.T.M. A148-60 (7 grades)	0.283	0.83	29	11.5	0.27	80–175		40–145						$0.4s_u$
Steel, spring, carbon, S.A.E. 1095	0.28		30			170–220	125–170							$0.36s_u$
Steel, spring, alloy, S.A.E. 4068	0.28		30			200–270	175–240							
Steel, ball bearings, S.A.E. 52100	0.28		30			326								
Steel, stainless (0.08–0.2 C, 17 G, 7 Ni) ¼ hard	0.28	0.96	28	12.5		125		78		67				$0.35s_u$
Same, full hard	0.28	0.96	26.6	12.0		185		150		99				$0.35s_u$

TABLE XIX.—REPRESENTATIVE PROPERTIES OF SOME IMPORTANT STRUCTURAL MATERIALS.—(*Continued*)

2. Timber

Species	Weight, lb. per cu. ft.	α, coeff. thermal exp., °F.		E, lb. per sq. in.	Compressive strength			Shear strength, with grain	Bending strength	
		With grain	Across grain		With grain		Across grain, elastic limit		Modulus of rupture (rect. section)	Fiber stress at elastic limit
					Ultimate	Elastic limit				
Ash (white)	41	0.0000053		1,680,000	7,280	5,580	1,510	1,920	14,600	8,900
Birch (sweet, yellow)	44	0.0000011	0.000016	2,070,000	8,310	6,200	1,250	2,020	16,700	10,100
Elm (American)	35			1,340,000	5,520	4,030	850	1,510	11,800	7,600
Hickory (true)	51			2,180,000	8,970		2,310	2,140	19,700	10,900
Maple (sugar)	44	0.0000012		1,830,000	7,830	5,390	1,810	2,430	15,800	9,500
Oak (red)	44	0.0000019	0.00002	1,810,000	6,920	4,610	1,260	1,830	14,400	8,400
Oak (white)	48	0.0000027	0.00003	1,620,000	7,040	4,350	1,410	1,890	13,900	7,900
Fir (Douglas)	36			1,920,000	7,420	6,450	910	1,140	11,700	8,100
Hemlock (Eastern)	30			1,200,000	5,410	4,020	800	1,060	8,900	6,100
Spruce (Sitka)	26			1,570,000	5,610	4,780	710	1,150	10,200	6,700
Cypress (Southern)	32			1,440,000	6,360	4,740	900	1,000	10,600	7,200
Pine (Southern L.L.)	40	0.000003	0.000019	1,990,000	8,440	6,150	1,190	1,500	14,700	9,300

G is approximately one-sixteenth E. The endurance limit in reversed bending is approximately 28 per cent of the modulus of rupture.

Above values are taken from "Wood Handbook" and are based on tests of small specimens of select, clear, seasoned wood at 12 per cent moisture content.

TABLE XIX.—REPRESENTATIVE PROPERTIES OF SOME IMPORTANT STRUCTURAL MATERIALS.—(*Continued*)

3. Concrete and Masonry

Material	Weight, lb. per cu. ft.	α, coeff. thermal exp., °F.	E, lb. per sq. in.	ν	Ultimate strength values			
					Compression	Tension	Shear	Modulus of rupture in bending
Concrete	150	0.0000060			S_c	$\frac{1}{10}S_c$	$\frac{1}{2}S_c$	$200 + 0.09\,S_c$
1:1½:3, $\frac{w}{c} = 6.5$			3,500,000	0.15	3,500			
1:2½:3½, $\frac{w}{c} = 7.5$			3,000,000	0.13	2,500			
1:3:5, $\frac{w}{c} = 9.0$			2,500,000	0.10	1,500			
$\left(\frac{w}{c}\right.$ = water/cement ratio, gal. per sack$\left.\right)$			(at 30 days)		(at 30 days)			
Brick		0.000003			S_c			
Soft	120		1,500,000		2,000			400
Medium					3,500			600
Hard	144		3,500,000		5,000			900
Vitrified					10,000			1,800
Brick masonry	120							
1:3 Port cmt. mortar					$0.30S_c$			
1:3 lime mortar					$0.15S_c$			
(Wall or pier height = 15 × thickness)								
Granite	168	0.0000036	7,000,000	0.28	25,000			2,500
Limestone	166	0.0000028	6,000,000	0.21	8,000–16,000			700–1,500
Marble	175	0,0000038	8,000,000	0.26	12,000			1,200
Sandstone	156	0.0000052	2,500,000	0.28	6,000			600

References for Table XIX

The data in Table XIX are merely representative of a few among the almost infinite number of structural materials, and cannot even suggest the great variation introduced, in metals, by such factors as heat treatment, cold working, and temperature, and in wood and concrete by moisture, density, duration of loading, defects, etc. Far more detailed information is to be found in the following references, in the publications of the American Society for Testing and Materials, the American Society for Metals, the Portland Cement Association, the United States Forest Products Laboratory, and in various trade publications.

1. "Alcoa Structural Handbook," Aluminum Co. of America, 1960.
2. "Material Properties Handbook," Vol. 1, "Aluminum Alloys," NATO Advisory Group for Aeronautical Research and Development, 1958.
3. ANC Mil-Hdbk-5, Strength of Metal Aircraft Elements, Armed Force Supply Support Center, March, 1959.
4. Mechanical Properties of Metals and Alloys, *Nat. Bur. Standards Circ.* C447, 1943.
5. "Handbook of Metals," Vol. 1, "Properties and Selection of Metals," 8th Ed. American Society for Metals, 1961.
6. Watter, Michael, and Rush A. Lincoln: Strength of Stainless Steel Structural Members as Function of Design, Allegheny Ludlum Steel Corp., 1950.
7. American Society for Testing and Materials, Book of Standards.
8. Kinsey, H. V.: "The Mechanical and Engineering Properties of Commercially Available Titanium Alloys," NATO Advisory Group for Aeronautical Research and Development, 1957.
9. "Materials in Design Engineering" (Materials Selector Issues), Reinhold Publishing Corporation.
10. "Wood Handbook," U.S. Forest Products Laboratory, 1955.
11. ANC 18 Bulletin, Design of Wood Aircraft Structures, Munitions Board Aircraft Committee, June, 1951.
12. Withey, M. O., and Geo. W. Washa: "Materials of Construction," John Wiley & Sons, Inc., 1954.
13. Magnesium Mill Products, Dow Metal Products Co., 1961.
14. "Metallic Materials and Elements for Flight Vehicular Structures," Government Publications 19T and 20T, Catalog Nos. D 7.6/2.5/3/ and D 7.6/2.5/3/ch.1.

TABLE XX.—ILLUSTRATIVE ALLOWABLE STRESSES AND FACTORS OF SAFETY

s_w = allowable or working stress; s_u = ultimate tensile strength; s_y = tensile yield strength; s' = modulus of rupture in cross-bending of rectangular bar; s_s' = ultimate shear strength; s_c' = ultimate compressive strength; s_e = endurance limit or endurance strength for specified life; n = dividing factor applied to s_u, s_y, or s_e to obtain s_w. For allowable loads on columns see Table XI.

Application	Materials	Allowable stress s_w	Approximate factor of safety	Reference
Buildings and other structures	Structural steel	Direct tension $s_w = 0.6s_y$; $0.45s_y$ on net section at pin holes. Bending $s_w = 0.6s_y$ Shear $s_w = 0.45s_y$ on rivets, $0.40s_y$ on girder webs Bearing $s_w = 1.35s_y$ on rivets in double shear; $1s_y$ in single shear	1.70 for beams 1.85 for continuous frames	1
	Structural aluminum 6061-T6, 6062-T6 $s_u = 38{,}000$, $s_y = 35{,}000$	Direct tension $s_w = 17{,}000$ Bending structural shapes, $s_w = 17{,}000$; rectangular sections $s_w = 23{,}000$ Shear $s_w = 10{,}000$ on cold-driven rivets, 11,000 on girder webs Bearing $s_w = 30{,}000$ on rivets	1.8 for beams 2 for columns	4
	Reinforced concrete	Bending, compression in concrete, $s_w = 0.45s_c'$ Bending, tension in steel, $s_w = 0.40s_y$ Bending, tension in plain concrete footings, $s_w = 0.03s_c'$ Shear, on concrete in unreinforced web, $s_w = 0.03s_c'$ Compression in concrete column, $s_w = 0.225s_c'$		3
	Wood	Bending, $s_w = \frac{1}{6}s'$; long compression, $s_w = \frac{1}{6}s_c'$ Transverse-compression, $s_w = \frac{1}{2}$ elastic limit (400 for Douglas fir); shear parallel to grain $s_w = 120$ for Douglas fir	6 in general	7
Bridges	Structural metals and reinforced concrete	s_w about $0.9s_w$ for buildings	2.05	2, 16
	Wood	s_w same as for buildings	6	16
Machinery	Steel (shafts, etc.)	Steady tension, compression or bending, $s_w = s_y/n$ Pure shear, $s_w = s_y/2n$ Tension s_t plus shear s_s; $s_t^2 + 4s_s^2 \leqq s_y/n$ Alternating stress s_a plus mean stress s_m: point representing an alternating stress nk_fs_a and a mean stress ns_m must lie below the Goodman diagram, Fig. 1	n usually between 1.5 and 2	10, 11
	Steel (S.A.E.1095), leaf springs, thickness = t in., $t > 0 < 0.10$	Static loading, $s_w = 230{,}000 - 1{,}000{,}000t$ Variable loading, 10^7 cycles, $s_w = 200{,}000 - 800{,}000t$ Dynamic loading, 10^7 cycles, $s_w = 155{,}000 - 600{,}000t$		12, 17
	Steel (wire, A.S.T.M.-A228, helical springs)	$s_w = 100{,}000$ (for $d = 0.2$ in.; 10^7 cycles repeated stress)		
Pressure vessels (unfired)	Carbon steel	Membrane stress, $s_w = 0.211s_u$ Membrane plus discontinuity stresses, $s_w = 0.9s_y$ or $0.6s_u$	5	5, 6
	Alloy steels	Membrane stress, $s_w = 0.25s_u$ Membrane plus discontinuity stresses, $s_w = 0.95s_y$ or $0.6s_u$	4	
	Cast iron	Membrane stress, $s_w = 0.1s_u$; bending stress $s_w = 0.15s_u$	10, 6.67	
	Nonferrous metals	Same rule as alloy steels	4	
Airplanes	Aluminum alloy and steel	Ultimate strength design, Ref. 3 of Table XIX	1.5 against ultimate 1 against yield	18
	Wood	Ultimate strength design, Ref. 11 of Table XIX		

References for Table XX

Like the strength values given in Table XIX, the allowable stresses and factors of safety given in Table XX should be regarded as illustrative and tentative, rather than definitive. There are fairly explicit and widely used codes that apply to the design of conventional buildings, structures, and pressure vessels, and the values given here are consistent therewith, but the table does not purport to be a copy of any code or codes, and the designer should, of course, refer directly to the lastest edition of the applicable specification. For the designing of machinery such widely applicable codes are impracticable, because of the much greater variety of functions and conditions of service involved, and because considerations of fatigue and stress concentration are much more likely to be of governing importance. It is necessary for each design problem to be considered individually, and decisions as to allowable stresses must be based largely on judgment and experience.

1. Specification for the Design, Fabrication and Erection of Structural Steel for Buildings, American Institute of Steel Construction, 1961.
2. Specification for Steel Railway Bridges, American Railway Association, 1948.
3. Building Code Requirements for Reinforced Concrete (ACI 318.56), American Concrete Institute, 1956.
4. Suggested Specifications for Structures of Aluminum Alloys 6061-T6 and 6062-T6, *Proc. Am. Soc. Civil Eng.*, Vol. 88, ST6, *Paper* 3341, December, 1962.
5. Rules for Construction of Unfired Pressure Vessels, American Society of Mechanical Engineers, 1959.
6. Tentative Structural Design Basis for Reactor Pressure Vessels and Directly Associated Components (Pressurized Water Cooled Systems), U.S. Dept of Commerce, Office of Technical Services, 1958.
7. National Design Specifications for Stress Grade Lumber and Its Fastenings, National Lumber Manufacturers Association, 1960.
8. American Standard Building Code Requirements for Minimum Design Loads in Buildings and Other Structures, American Standards Association, 1955.
9. National Building Code of Canada, Associate Committee on the National Building Code, National Research Council, Ottawa, 1953.
10. Soderberg, R.: Working Stresses, *Am. Soc. Mech. Eng., Paper* A-106, *Jour. Appl. Mech.*, Vol. 2, No. 3, 1935.
11. Peterson, R. E.: "Stress Concentration Design Factors," John Wiley & Sons, Inc., 1953.
12. Wahl, A. M.: "Mechanical Springs," 2d ed., McGraw-Hill Book Company, 1963.
13. Wood, Lyman W.: Factor of Safety in Design of Timber Structures, *Trans. Am. Soc. Civil Eng.*, Vol. 125, *Paper* 3051, 1960.
14. Freudenthal, Alfred M.: Safety and the Probability of Structural Failure, *Trans. Am. Soc. Civil Eng.*, Vol. 121, *Paper* 2843, 1956.
15. Bergstrom, Richard N.: Overload Factors Can Cause Ultra-conservative Design, *Proc. Am. Soc. Civil Eng.*, Vol. 85, *Paper* 1941, 1959.

16. Standard Specifications for Highway Bridges, 7th ed., American Association of State Highway Officials, 1957.
17. "Manuals on Design and Application of Springs" (Leaf, SH. 7, 1962, Helical and Spiral, TR-9, 1958; Belleville, TR-63, 1955), Society of Automotive Engineers.
18. "Airplane Airworthiness, Civil Aeronautics Manual 4a," Federal Aviation Agency.

NAME INDEX

SUBJECT INDEX